T E L E - T U N E S

2 0 0 2

edition 1

COMPILED BY

MIKE PRESTON

THE REFERENCE BOOK OF

MUSIC FOR TELEVISION

COMMERCIALS, PROGRAMMES

FILMS AND SHOWS

WITHDRAWN

MIKE PRESTON MUSIC 2002

T E L E - T U N E S 2 0 0 2 / edition 1

The Reference Book Of Music For
Television Commercials, Programmes
Films and Shows

22nd Edition Completely Revised 2002

First Edition Published 1979

Compiled and Edited by Mike Preston
Contributors: Pru and Robb Preston
Cathy and Dale Wattam

Published in the UK January 2002

ISBN 0 906655 21 8

Published by
Mike Preston Music
The Glengarry
Thornton Grove
Morecambe Bay
Lancashire
LA4 5PU
England
UK

e.mail: *mikepreston@beeb.net*

Orig Copyright Regs. Stationers Hall
London England 1979, 1986, 1994, 2001
Registration Number B9 / 1187 / 37068

Printed and Bound in England by
Bookcraft CPI
Midsomer Norton BA3 4BS

C O N T E N T S 3

TELE-TUNES 2002 : THE REFERENCE BOOK OF MUSIC FOR TV
COMMERCIALS, TV PROGRAMMES, FILMS AND SHOWS

22ND COMPLETELY REVISED EDITION OF TELE-TUNES

W H A T   I S   I N   T E L E - T U N E S ?

---

*TELE-TUNES IS INTENDED AS A GUIDE TO TV AND FILM MUSIC
CURRENTLY AVAILABLE IN RETAIL MUSIC OUTLETS*

RECENT DELETIONS ARE GIVEN FOR REFERENCE ONLY, AND SOME
ITEMS MAY ONLY BE AVAILABLE FROM SPECIALIST SUPPLIERS

TV ADS, PROGRAMMES, FILMS & SHOWS *NOT LISTED* PLUS ITEMS
DELETED FROM PREVIOUS EDITIONS ARE HELD FOR REFERENCE
IN THE MIKE PRESTON MUSIC INFORMATION DATABASE, ACCESS
TO THIS INFORMATION IS AVAILABLE TO SUBSCRIBERS TO THE
FULL TELE-TUNES SUBSCRIPTION SERVICE *(see page 263)*

TELEVISION COMMERCIALS
ALPHABETICAL PRODUCT-MUSIC TITLE-(COMPOSER)-
ARTIST-LABEL-(DISTRIBUTOR)-CATALOGUE NUMBER-(FORMAT)

TELEVISION PROGRAMMES FILMS AND SHOWS (Integrated A-Z)
TV PROGRAMME TITLE-TV COMPANY-T/X DATE-MUSIC TITLE-
COMPOSER-ARTIST-LABEL (DISTRIBUTOR)-CAT.NUMBER-(FORMAT)
TV themes are cross referenced to COLLECTIONS.

FILM TITLE-YEAR-SCORE COMPOSER -S/T- OTHER INFO-LABEL
(DISTRIB)-CATALOGUE NUMBER-(FORMAT)

SHOWS TITLE-COMPOSER/LYRICIST-ORIG.CAST-YEAR-LEADING
CAST-LABEL (DIST)-CATALOGUE NUMBER-(FORMAT)

COLLECTIONS
COLLECTIONS NUMBERED 1 UP BY TITLE / ARTIST / COMPOSER
ALPHABETICALLY. COLLECTION NUMBER-TITLE-ARTIST-RECORD
LABEL-(DISTRIBUTOR)-CATALOGUE NUMBER-(FORMAT)-YEAR +
CROSS REFERENCED TITLES INCLUDED IN MAIN TEXT

DISNEY / JAMES BOND / ELVIS PRESLEY CDs -DVD- VHS
JAMES BOND AND ELVIS PRESLEY CHRONOLOGICAL FILM INDEX
WALT DISNEY CD DVD AND VIDEO INDEX

LONDON SHOWS (WEST END MUSICALS)
CURRENT MUSICALS RUNNING IN LONDON'S THEATRELAND
PREVIOUS MUSICALS REFERENCE LIST

A DIDAS 8 "Sound Of The Suburb" by MEMBERS from album
'Sound Of The Suburb' *VIRGIN (EMI): CDOVD 455 (CD)*

ADIDAS 7 "That's Entertainment" JAM 'Beat Surrender'
SPECTRUM (UNIV): 550 006-2 (CD) -4 (MC)

ADIDAS 6 "Broadway Jungle" by TOOTS (prod.by HOWIE B)
TROJAN (3MV-Pinn): JETSCD 502 (CDs) JET 502 (12"s)

ADIDAS 5 "In These Shoes" by KIRSTY MacCOLL on collect
'BEST TV ADS EVER' *VIRGIN: 7243 849420-2 (CD)*

ADIDAS 4 "Right Here Right Now" mixed by FAT BOY SLIM
from the album 'You've Come A Long Way Baby'
SKINT (3MV-Pinn): BRASSIC 11(CD)(MC)(LP)(MD)
also on 'SWITCHED ON' *TELSTAR: TTVCD 3086 (2CD)*

ADIDAS 3 (D.Beckham ad) "Step On" by HAPPY MONDAYS
from 'Pills 'n' Thrills and Bellyaches' on
FACTORY TOO (Pinn): 828 223-2 (CD)

ADIDAS 2 (Soccer Re-invented) special production by
MASSIVE ATTACK from existing uncredited MA track

ADIDAS 1 "Dive" by The PROPELLERHEADS *WALL OF SOUND*
(Vital): WALLT 034 (12"s limited edit of 5000)
also on 'SWITCHED ON' *TELSTAR: TTVCD 3086 (2CD)*

ADMIRAL SPORTSWEAR "Step On" by The HAPPY MONDAYS on
'Great.Hits' *LONDON (TEN): 556 105-2 (CD) -4 (MC)*

AIR FRANCE "Asleep From Day" by The CHEMICAL BROTHERS
from the album 'Surrender'
FREESTYLE DUST (EMI): XDUST(CD)(MC)(LP) 4

ALKA SELTZER "Who's Sorry Now" (Kalmar-Ruby-Snyder)
TV vers.unavailable. CONNIE FRANCIS version on '24
Greatest Hits' *PLATINUM (PRISM): PLATCD 3910 (CD)*

ALL GOLD (Terry's) "Will You" by HAZEL O'CONNOR feat
WESLEY MacGOOGHAN (sax) 'Live In Berlin' on
START (DISC): SRH 804 (CD)

ALLIANCE & LEICESTER "Baby Elephant Walk" (H.Mancini)
CINCINNATI POPS ORCHESTRA *TELARC: CD 80183 (CD)*

ALLIED DUNBAR "Let's Face The Music And Dance" (Irving
Berlin) NAT KING COLE on 'ULTIMATE COLLECTION'
CAPITOL-EMI: 499 575-2 (CD) -4 (MC)

ALPEN 3 "Ocean Drive" LIGHTHOUSE FAMILY 'Ocean Drive'
POLYDOR (UNIV): 523 787-2 (CD) -4 (MC)

ALPEN 2 based on "Reasons To Be Cheerful Pt.3" (Dury)
orig by IAN DURY & THE BLOCKHEADS on 'Sex Drugs
and Rock'n'Roll' *DEMON (Pinn): FIENDCD 69 (CD)*

ALPEN 1 "Sun Rising" from 'Happiness' by The BELOVED
WEA: WX 299(C)(CD) also on Coll 'NEW PURE MOODS'

ALTON TOWERS "In The Hall Of The Mountain King" from
'PEER GYNT SUITE' (GRIEG) *various recordings*

AMBRE SOLAIRE "Let The Sunshine In" from 'HAIR' *TV ver
unavailable* FILM -S/T- *RCA BMG: 07863 67812-2 (CD)*

AMBROSIA 3 "In The Navy" (based on) original by
VILLAGE PEOPLE *MUSIC CLUB (THE): MCCD 004 (CD)*

AMBROSIA 2 "Go West" original by The PET SHOP BOYS on
'Disco Vol.2' *PARLOPHONE (EMI): CDPCSD 159 (CD)*

AMBROSIA 1 (Art compet.ad) "Left Bank Two" (Vision On
Picture Gallery music) NOVELTONES on 'THIS IS THE
RETURN OF CULT FICTION' *VIRGIN EMI: VTCD 112 (CD)*

AMERICAN EXPRESS "Sleeping Beauty Ballet Music" (love
  theme) (TCHAIKOVSKY) *various recordings available*
AMERICAN EXPRESS BLUE CARD 2 "God Only Knows" (Brian
  Wilson-Tony Asher) BEACH BOYS *CAPITOL-EMI:CDEMTV 1*
AMERICAN EXPRESS BLUE CARD 1 "Blue Monday" NEW ORDER
  'Best Of' *FACTORY (UNIV): 828 580-2 (CD) -4 (MC)*
  also on 'SWITCHED ON' *TELSTAR: TTVCD 3086 (2CD)*
ANCHOR BUTTER 4 "Born Free" (John Barry-Don Black)
  TV arrangement unavailable
ANCHOR BUTTER 3 based on "My Girl" (William Robinson
  Ronald White) orig TEMPTATIONS on *MOTOWN (UNIV):*
  530015-2(CD) -4(MC) -5(DCC) OTIS REDDING 'Dock Of
  The Bay' *ATLANTIC (TEN): 9548 31708-2(CD) -4(MC)*
ANCHOR BUTTER 2 "In The Mood" (Andy Razaf-J.Garland)
  GLENN MILLER ORCH *RCA (BMG): PD 89260 (CD)*
ANCHOR BUTTER 1 "Day Trip To Bangor" (Fiddlers Dram)
  FIDDLERS DRAM *DINGLES: SID 211 (7"s)*
APPLE 3 (Power Laptop ad) "Naive Song" by MIRWAIS on
  'PRODUCTION' *NAIVE-EPIC (TEN): 498 213-2 (CD)*
APPLE 2 (Laptop) "You Turn My World Around" sung by
  BARRY WHITE *number unconfirmed*
APPLE 1 "She's A Rainbow" (M.Jagger-K.Richard)
  ROLLING STONES album 'Their Satanic Majesties
  Request' *LONDON (UNIV): 844 470-2 (CD) -4 (MC)*
APPLETISE "Tempted" performed by SQUEEZE on 'Greatest
  Hits' *A.& M. (UNIV): 397 181-2 (CD)*
ARGOS 3 "Telephone Man" (based on) orig by MERI WILSON
  on 'Sensational 70's' *CASTLE PULSE: PLSCD 314 (CD)*
ARGOS 2 "You're The First The Last My Everything" *TV*
  Vers.unavailable original by BARRY WHITE ON 'The
  Collection' *UNIVERSAL MUS: 834 790-2 (CD) -4 (MC)*
ARGOS 1 "WHATEVER YOU WANT" (Brown-Parftt) *TV Version*
  unavailable orig by STATUS QUO on 'GREATEST HITS'
  UNIVERSAL MUS: 553 507-2 (CD) -4 (MC)
ARCHERS "Querelle" by OMNIVORE from 'Feeding Frenzy'
  HYDROGEN DUKEBOX (Pinn): DUKE 45CD (CD)
ASDA 2 (main theme) composed by ROGER GREENAWAY
  and arranged by Graham Preskett *unavailable*
ASDA 1 "Perfect" (Mark E.Nevin) FAIRGROUND ATTRACTION
  'First Of A Million Kisses' *RCA:74321 13439-2 (CD)*
AUDI A2 "This Could Be Heaven" by LAMB on 'What Sound'
  MERCURY (UNIV): 586 538-2 (CD)
AUDI A4 "La Mer" (Trenet) CHARLES TRENET 'Very Best'
  EMI: CDP 794 464-2 (CD)
AUDI A8 Moon Vehicle 1 "Mooncar" (Vince POPE)
  Music Gallery *unavailable*
AUDI TT "Very Thought Of You" (Noble) ELLA FITZGERALD
  'Incomparable Ella' *POLY: 835 610-2 (CD) -4 (MC)*
AXA EQUITY & LAW "Don't Worry Be Happy" BOBBY McFERRIN
  'Walking On Sunshine' *KENWEST (THE): KNEWCD 742 CD*
  'Best Of B.M.' *BLUENOTE (EMI): CDP 853329-2 (CD)*
AXA INSURANCE "Love Theme" from 'The MISSION' by ENNIO
  MORRICONE -S/T- *VIRGIN (EMI): CDV 2402 (CD)*

B.& Q. "Walk This Land" (Banks-Hurren-Richards) by EZ
ROLLERS from 'Lock Stock and 2 Smoking Barrels"
ISLAND (UNIV): CID 8077 (CD) SHADOW 130CD1 (CDs)

B.T. 1571 "Can't Take My Eyes Off You" based on ANDY
WILLIAMS song on 'IN THE LOUNGE WITH ANDY' *COLUMBIA
(Ten) 490 618-2(CD) -4(MC) + 481 037-2(CD) -4(MC)*
also on 'SWITCHED ON' *TELSTAR: TTVCD 3086 (2CD)*

B.T. "Flying" (E.T.theme) by JOHN WILLIAMS
various recordings available

B.T.Cellnet 1 "Beat Goes On" (S.Bono) ALL SEEING I
LONDON FFFR (UNIV): FFCD 334 (CDs) FFCS 334 (MC)
also on 'SWITCHED ON' *TELSTAR: TTVCD 3086 (2CD)*

B.T.1 "CALL ME" (Tony Hatch) sung by **Chris Montez**
V.ARTS COLL 'THIS IS EASY' *VIRGIN: VTDCD 80 (2CD)*
also on IMPORT through CD ONESTOP: *DZS 056 CD)*

BACARDI 2 (Prison cell) music: VINCE POPE *unavailable*

BACARDI 1 (Casino) "Jive Samba" by JACK CONSTANZO and
GERRY WOO from Coll 'EL RITMO LATINO VOLUME 1' on
MCI (THE-Disc): MCCD 025 (CD) MCTC 025 (MC)

BAILEYS 4 (Charades) "Wrestler" by SLICK SIXTY on
'Nibs and Nabs' *MUTE RECORDS: CDSTUMM 185 (CD)*

BAILEYS 3 "One Way Or Another" by BLONDIE from the
album 'ATOMIC' *EMI: 494 996-2 (CD) -4 (MC)*
also on 'SWITCHED ON' *TELSTAR: TTVCD 3086 (2CD)*

BAILEYS 2 "Big Bamboozle" BARRY ADAMSON from 'Oedipus
Schmoedipus' *MUTE-RTM (Disc): CDSTUMM 134 (CD)*

BAILEYS 1 "Barcarolle"(Tales Of Hoffmann) (OFFENBACH)
Elizabeth Schwarzkopft-Jeanine Collard *(EMI)*

BARCLAYS BANK (ROBBIE COLTRANE ad) "Running One" by
FRANKE POTENTE from -S/T- 'RUN LOLA RUN' on
BMG: 74321 60477-2 (CD)

BARCLAY'S BANK Cashpoint "Ride On" by LITTLE AXE on
WIRED (3MV-Sony): WIRED 27 (CD) WIRED 47 (MC)

BATCHELORS CUPA SOUP (office affair) "Racetrack" by
JACKIE MITTOO *Jet Star Records*

BATCHELORS SPICY SUPER NOODLES "I'm Every Woman" (Val
Ashford-Nick Simpson) vers.by CHAKA KHAN 'CHAKA'
WARNER (TEN): 7599 25866-2 (CD) also by WHITNEY
HOUSTON from 'The BODYGUARD' *ARISTA:07822 18699-2*

BECKS BEER "Naturally" by CHRIS SMITH & SIMON STEVEN
(Final Touch Productions) *unavailable*

BEEB.COM "Habanera" from 'CARMEN' (BIZET) performed by
BBC Singers & Orchestra *unavailable*

BEECHAM FLU PLUS "I'm Still Standing"(E.John-B.Taupin)
orig by ELTON JOHN *ROCKET (Univ): 846 947-2 (2CD)*

BELLE COLOUR (Laboratoire Garnier) "Mario's Cafe" by
ST.ETIENNE on 'So Tough' *HEAVENLY (BMG): HVNLP 6CD*

BELLS WHISKY 3 "Blueberry Hill" performed by the JOOLS
HOLLAND RHYTHM AND BLUES ORCHESTRA *unavailable*

BELLS WHISKY 2 "Please Don't Go" by KC & THE SUNSHINE
BAND on 'Best Of' *EMI: CD(TC)GOLD 1021 (CD/MC)*

BELLS WHISKY 1 "Young At Heart" (Leigh-Richards) sung
by IAN McCULLOGH (Echo & Bunnymen) *unavailable*

BENDICKS MINTS 2 "Again" (L.Newman-D.Cochran) from
   'ROAD HOUSE' *TV Vers.*LANCE ELLINGTON *unavailable*
   rec.by NAT KING COLE-MEL TORME-VIC DAMONE etc.
BENDICKS MINTS (Bendicks Of Mayfair) "Missing You"
   (Romeo-Law-Mazelle) SOUL II SOUL feat KYM MAZELLE
   'New Dance Decade' *VIRGIN (EMI): DIXCD 90 (CD)*
BENYLIN "Nessun Dorma" 'Turandot' (Puccini) *TV version*
   by ANTONIO NAGORE and R.P.O. *unavailable*
BERTOLLI OLIVE OIL "Dallas" theme (Jerrold Immel)
   see TV section for recordings
BIC SOFT FEEL "Funeral March Of A Marionette" (Charles
   Gounod) on 'EUROPEAN LIGHT MUSIC CLASSICS' on
   HYPERION: CDA 66998 (CD)
BIRDS CUSTARD based on "Bloop Bleep" (Frank Loesser)
   orig DANNY KAYE *LIVING ERA (Koch): CDAJA 5270 (CD)*
BISTO "Save The Best For Last" by VANESSA WILLIAMS
   'The Comfort Zone' *POLYDOR: 511267-2 (CD) -4(MC)*
BLACK MAGIC 2 "Love Is The Sweetest Thing" (R.Noble)
   AL BOWLLY & RAY NOBLE ORCH. *EMI:CDP 794 341-2 (CD)*
BLACK MAGIC 1 (It's The Black Magic) 'Stranger Theme'
   CHRISTOPHER GUNNING *unavailable*
BLOCKBUSTER VIDEO "Sound and Vision" (Bowie) by DAVID
   BOWIE 'SINGLES COLL' *EMI: CD(TC)EM 1512 (CD/MC/LP)*
BODDINGTONS 2 'Cattle Market' ad "Back By Dope Demand"
   KING BEE on 'SWITCHED ON' *TELSTAR: TTVCD 3086 (2CD)*
BODDINGTONS 1 'Cow-Ma-Sutra' "If Loving You Is Wrong"
   FAITHLESS from 'REVERENCE' *CHEEKY: CHEKCD 500 (CD)*
BOLD AQUA "Blue Danube Waltz" (J.STRAUSS II) *various*
   recordings available
BOOTS (DESIGNER HAIR CARE AD) "Sweet Pea" SOUL HOOLIGAN
   from 'BLOW UP-A-GO-GO' *V2 (Pinn):VVR 101054-2 (CD)*
BOOTS (DOUBLE POINTS AD) "You're A Wonderful One"
   sung by MARVIN GAYE on 'Motown's Early Hits'
   MOTOWN (Univ): 552 118-2 (CD)
BOOTS New Health & Travel Cover "Kyoko's Home" from
   'MISHIMA' composed by PHILIP GLASS -S/T- originally
   NONESUCH (Warner): 7559 79113-2 (CD)
BOOTS Xmas "Make Someone Happy" sung by PAUL YOUNG
   EAST WEST (TEN): EW 148CD (CDs) EW 148C (MC) also
   JIMMY DURANTE 'SLEEPLESS IN SEATTLE' *(473 594-2)*
BOOTS NO.7 -1a "La Cumparsita" (G.Matos Rodriguez) *TV*
   vers.unavailable orig rec by XAVIER CUGAT ORCH on
   'Mundo Latino' *SONY: SONYTV2CD (CD) SONYTV2MC (MC)*
BP-MOBIL "Sing Sing Sing" (L.Prima) *TV Vers.unavailable*
   orig.BENNY GOODMAN ORCH.feat.GENE KRUPA on '16 Most
   Requested Songs' *COLUMBIA (Ten): 474 396-2 (CD) -4*
BRADFORD & BINGLEY Market Place "A Shot In The Dark" by
   HENRY MANCINI (-S/T- 'A SHOT IN THE DARK') *RCA BMG*
BRANSTON PICKLE "Left Bank 2" (Vision On TV Picture
   Gallery music) NOVELTONES on 'THIS IS THE RETURN
   OF CULT FICTION' *VIRGIN (EMI): VTCD 112 (CD)*
BREATHE.COM "Wet Stuff" by FOLK IMPLOSION based on
   "Gnossienes" (ERIK SATIE) vers.on 'KIDS' Soundtrack
   by FOLK IMPLOSION *LONDON (UNIV): 828 640-2 (CD)*

BRITA WATER "Stizzoso Mio Stizzoso" (La Serva Padrona)
(G.PERGOLESI) TERESA BERGANZA with The Royal Opera
House Orch. (A.Gibson) *DECCA UNIV: 458 217-2 (CD)*
BRITANNIC INSURANCE "Swan Lake Ballet" by TCHAIKOVSKY

BRITISH AIRWAYS 10."Something In The Air" (John Keen)
THUNDERCLAP NEWMAN on 'AND THE BEAT GOES ON VOL.2'
DEBUTANTE (Univ): 535 558-2 (2CD)
BRITISH AIRWAYS 9."Roses From The South" (J.Strauss)
on 'Vintage Themes' *EMI: CDEMS 1554 (CD)*
BRITISH AIRWAYS 8.(P.J.O'Rourke ad) "Jupiter" from
'Planets Suite' (Gustav HOLST) *various recordings*
BRITISH AIRWAYS 1-7 (1991-1997/98/99) main theme used
"Dome Epais" (Flower Duet) from 'Lakme' (DELIBES)
 7.HELEN REEVES *unavailable*
 6.LESLEY GARRETT 'Diva' *Sil.Screen: SONGCD 903 (CD)*
 5.VARD SISTERS on 'HEAVENLY' *SONY: 488 092-2 (CD)*
 4.MADY MESPLE-DANIELLE MILLET & PARIS OPERA ORCH
  'Most Famous Movie Class.2' *EMI: 568 307-2 (CD)*
 3.MALCOLM McLAREN "Aria On Air" *Virg: VTCD 28 (CD)*
  'NEW PURE MOODS' *see COLL.262,*
 2.ZBIGNIEW PREISNER "Fashion Show No.2" from
  'Three Colors Red' on *VIRGIN (EMI): VTCD 87 (CD)*
 1.YANNI (eye on the beach) "Aria" 'In The Mirror'
  PRIVATE MUSIC (BMG): 74321 47125-2 (CD)
BRITISH BEEF (Country Lunch) "Get Here" by OLETA ADAMS
from 'CIRCLE OF ONE' *FONTANA (Univ):848 740-2 (CD)*
BRITISH GAS (2001 'Electricty from British Gas' ad)
"Something Big" (Bacharach-David)BURT BACHARACH on
'Espresso' Karminsky Experience *UNIV:535 547-2(CD)*
BRITISH HEART FOUNDATION 3 "Liquidator" HARRY J.ALL
STARS on 'SKA ARCHIVE' *RIALTO (Dir): RMCD 202 (CD)*
BRITISH HEART FOUNDATION 2 "Waiting For The Miracle"
LEONARD COHEN from 'The Future' *SONY: 472 498-2*
(CD) -4 (MC) -1 (LP) -3 (MD)
BRITISH HEART FOUNDATION 1 "Stop In The Name Of Love"
(Holland-Dozier-Holland) DIANA ROSS AND SUPREMES
MOTOWN (UNIV): 530 013-2 (CD) -4 (MC)
BRITISH MEAT 3 (Lamb) "Way We Were" (Marvin Hamlisch-
Alan & Marilyn Bergman) *TV version unavailable.*
original by Barbra Streisand *(COLUMBIA)*
BRITISH MEAT 2 "I Got You Babe" by SONNY & CHER
ATLANTIC (TEN): 9548 30152-2 (CD) -4 (MC)
BRITISH MEAT 1 "Let There Be Love" (I.Grant-L.Rand)
NAT KING COLE '20 Golden Greats' *EMI:CD(TC)EMTV 9*
BRITISH NUCLEAR FUELS "Last Stand" by ALOOF from
album 'Sinking' *EAST WEST (W): 0630 17739-2 (CD)*
BROOKE BOND HOT DRINKS "Tomorrow's Just Another Day"
(Smith-Barson) MADNESS on 'Divine Madness' Coll.
VIRGIN (EMI): CDV 2692 (CD) TCV 2692 (MC)
BRYLCREEM 2 "Cissy Strut" The METERS 'Very Best of'
CHARLY (Koch): CDGR 278 (CD)
BRYLCREEM 1 (D.Beckham) "Beautiful Ones" SUEDE from
'COMING UP' *NUDE (Vit):NUDECD6(CD) NUDE 23CD(CDs)*

BT - see B.T.

BUBBALOO "Babalu" (Lecuona-Russell) XAVIER CUGAT ORCH.
  feat MIGUELITO VALDEZ 'Hit Sound Of XAVIER CUGAT'
  CHARLY (Koch): CDHO 631 (CD)
BUDWEISER 10 ("Neighbours Quality") by McHALE-BARONE
  USA PRODUCTION unavailable (sample enhanced from a
  JOAN OSBORNE track - unconfirmed)
BUDWEISER 9 (Wassuup!) "Wassuup" (Rizzo-Ireland) by
  DA MTTZ on *ETERNAL (Ten): WEA 319CD (CDs)*
BUDWEISER 8 (Crocodile) "Ooh La La" (Theo Keating) by
  WISEGUYS from album 'The Antidote' *WALL OF SOUND
  (Vital): WALL(CD)(C)020 (CD/MC) / WALLD 038X (CDs)*
  also on 'SWITCHED ON' *TELSTAR: TTVCD 3086 (2CD)*
BUDWEISER 7 (poker game) "Dirt" by DEATH IN VEGAS on
  CONCRETE (RTM/DISC): HARD 27CD (CDs)
BUDWEISER 6 (money suitcase/taxi) "Crawl" composed
  and produced by ROBERT WHITE *unavailable*
BUDWEISER 5 "St.James Infirmary Blues" (Irving Mills
  adapt.from trad.folk song) sung by SNOOKS EAGLIN
  vers.by CAB CALLOWAY *RCA (BMG): 74321 26729-2 (CD)*
BUDWEISER 4 (Ants) "Get Down Tonight" KC & SUNSHINE
  BAND 'Get Down Tonight' *EMI: 494 019-2 (CD) -4(MC)*
BUDWEISER 3 "Connection" ELASTICA *DECEPTIVE (Vital):
  BLUFF 014(CD)(MC)(LPN)*
BUDWEISER 2 "The Passenger" (Iggy Pop-Rick Gardiner)
  by MICHAEL HUTCHENCE on -S/T- 'Batman Forever' on
  ATLANTIC (TEN): 7567 82759-2 (CD) -4 (MC)
BUDWEISER 1 (Blues Train ad) "Smokestack Lightning"
  HOWLIN'WOLF "Smokestack Lightning" *INSTANT-CHARLY
  CDINS 5037 (CD) TCINS 5037 (MC) INSD 5037 (2LP)*
BURGER KING 14 "Ooh Ah Just A Little Bit" (based on)
  TV vers.unavailable ORIG by GINA G *(Eternal Rec)*
BURGER KING 13 "In The Mood" (Razaf-Garland) based on
  'Chicken' version recorded by RAY STEVENS as The
  HENHOUSE 5 + 2 *(Mercury deleted)*
BURGER KING 12 "Symphony No.5" (BEETHOVEN) *Var.rec.*
BURGER KING 11 "Nessun Dorma" from 'Turandot' PUCCINI
BURGER KING 10 "Temptation" by HEAVEN 17 feat CAROL
  KENYON. 'Best Of HEAVEN 17' *VIRGIN:VVIPD 118 (CD)*
BURGER KING 9 "I Like It" by the BLACKOUT ALLSTARS
  from FILM 'I LIKE IT LIKE THAT' (1994) -S/T-
  COLUMBIA (Ten): 477 334-2 (CD) -4 (MC)
BURGER KING 8 "Crazy" (Willie Nelson) by PATSY CLINE
  'Very Best Of' *MCA: MCD 11483 (CD) MCC 11483 (MC)*
BURGER KING 7 "Ride On Time" (Dan Hartman) BLACK BOX
  '80s Extended' *RCA CAMDEN BMG: 74321 64790-2 (CD)*
BURGER KING 6 "Hungry Like The Wolf" by DURAN DURAN
  from 'Rio' *EMI: CDPRG 1004 (CD)*
BURGER KING 5 "You Ain't Seen Nothin'Yet" (R.Bachman)
  BACHMAN TURNER OVERDRIVE 'Roll On Down Highway'
  MERCURY (UNIV): 550 421-2 (CD) -4 (MC)
BURGER KING 4 "Two Tribes" FRANKIE GOES TO HOLLYWOOD
  ZTT (Warner): 4509 93912-2 (CD) -4 (MC) -1 (LP)

BURGER KING 3 (WHOPPER) "Fire!" (Brown-Crane) CRAZY
WORLD OF ARTHUR BROWN on 'CLASSIC ROCK' *SPECTRUM
(UNIV): 550 645-2 (CD) -4(MC)* also on 'LIVE 1993'
VOICEPRINT (Pinn): VP144CD (CD)
BURGER KING 2 "Who Do Ya Love" by GEORGE THOROGOOD &
THE DESTROYERS from 'Move It On Over'
DEMON (Pinn): FIENDCD 58 (CD)
BURGER KING 1 "Double Vision" by FOREIGNER on 'Best'
ATLANTIC-E.WEST (TEN): 7567 80805-2(CD) WX 469C(MC)

C ADBURY tastes like heaven "Show Me Heaven" (M.McKee-
J.Rifkin-E.Rackin) from film 'Days Of Thunder' orig
MARIA McKEE on Coll 'Number One Movies Album' on
POLYGRAM TV: 525 962-2 (CD)
CADBURY'S JESTIVE BISCUITS "Special Brew" BAD MANNERS
'Best Of' *BLUEBEAT (UNIV): BBS(CD)(MC) 010 (CD/MC)*
CADBURY'S HIGHLIGHTS 2 "I'll Put You Together Again"
(Don Black-Geoff Stephens) by ERROL BROWN orig
HOT CHOCOLATE 'Greatest Hits' *EMI: CD(TC)EMTV 73*
CADBURY'S HIGHLIGHTS 1 "Sweet And Lovely" (G.Arnheim
-Harry Tobias-Jules Lemare) sung by AL BOWLLY on
"Very Thought Of You" *EMI CEDAR (EMI): CZ 306 (CD)*
CADBURY'S - *see also various brand names:'ROSES' etc*
CAFFREY'S ALES 4 (Storm Brewing ad) "Clubbed To Death"
from 'THE MATRIX' *MAVERICK TEN: 9362 47419-2 (CD)*
also from 'CLUBBED TO DEATH' by ROB D (DUGGAN) on
VIRGIN IMPORT: 844 062-2 (CD)
also on 'SWITCHED ON' TELSTAR: TTVCD 3086 (2CD)
CAFFREY'S ALES 3 "Brim Full Of Asha" by CORNERSHOP on
WIIIJA (Vital): WIJ 81CD (CDs) WIJ 81 (7"s)
also on 'SWITCHED ON' TELSTAR: TTVCD 3086 (2CD)
CAFFREY'S ALES 2 "Jump Around" (Muggeraud-Shrody) by
HOUSE OF PAIN on *XL (TEN): XLS 32 CD (CDs) XLT 32
(12"s) XLC 32 (MC)* + 'HOUSE OF PAIN' *XLCD(MC) 111*
also on 'SWITCHED ON' TELSTAR: TTVCD 3086 (2CD)
CAFFREY'S ALES 1 'MILLER'S CROSSING' (Carter BURWELL)
-S/T- *VARESE (Pinn): VSD 5288 (CD) deleted*
CAMPARI "Get Carter" main theme from film by ROY BUDD
-S/T- 1998 reiss: *ESSENTIAL (BMG): CINCD 001 (CD)*
Coll "Rebirth of The Budd" *SEQUEL BMG NEMCD 927 CD*
CANCER RESEARCH - see IMPERIAL CANCER RESEARCH FUND
CANDEREL "Perhaps Perhaps Perhaps" by DORIS DAY on
'LATIN FOR LOVERS' *COLUMBIA (Ten): 481 018-2 (CD)*
also on 'MUSIC TO WATCH GIRLS BY' (Collection) on
SONYMUSIC: SONYTV 67(CD)(MC) (2CDs/MC)
CARLING BLACK LABEL (beach crab) "Just The Two Of Us"
TV vers.unavailable orig by BILL WITHERS on album
'Greatest Hits' *COLUMBIA (TEN): 403 234-2 (CD)*
CARLING BLACK LABEL (alien) "I Only Have Eyes For You"
(Warren-Dubin) ART GARFUNKEL "The Very Best of Art
Garfunkel" *VIRGIN EMI: VTCD 113 (CD) VTMC 113 (MC)*
CARLING BLACK LABEL (amazing) "Much Against Everyone's
Advice" from same titled album by SOULWAX on
PLASTIC HEAD (BMG-Vital): PLASB 010CD (CD) and LP

CARLING BLACK LABEL (riveting) "Stranger On The Shore"
  (Bilk-Mellin) ACKER BILK 'Stranger On The Shore'
  PHILIPS (UNIV): 830 779-2 (CD)
CARLING PREMIER 6 Medieval ad. "Vin-Da-Loo" (K.Allen)
  FAT LES *TURTLENECK Telstar: CDSTAS 2982 (CDs)*
CARLING PREMIER 5 (high-wire cycle) "6 Underground"
  SNEAKER PIMPS *CLEAN UP (Vital): CUP 036CD (CDs)*
  also on 'SWITCHED ON' *TELSTAR: TTVCD 3086 (2CD)*
CARLING PREMIER 4 "Tonight" by SUPERGRASS from 'IN IT
  FOR THE MONEY' *PARLOPHONE (EMI): CD(TC)PCS 7388*
CARLING PREMIER 3 "Machine Gun" by The COMMODORES on
  '14 Greatest Hits' *MOTOWN (UNIV): 530 096-2 (CD)*
CARLING PREMIER 2 "California Dreamin'" (J.Phillips)
  MCA (UNI): MCSTD 48058 (CDs) also 'MAMAS & ·PAPAS
  Golden Greats' *MCA (UNI): DMCM 5001 CD*
CARLING PREMIER 1 "Cars" by GARY NUMAN 'Peel Sessions'
  STRANGE FRUIT Rio (UNIV): SFMCD 202 (CD)
CARLSBERG "Private Road" by BENT
  MINISTRY OF SOUND Records (number unconfirmed)
CARLSBERG (Copenhagen ad) "They All Laughed" (G.& I.
  Gershwin) sung by FRANK SINATRA
  WARNER: W.469CD (CDs) W.469C (MC) also on COLL:
  'COMPLETE REPRISE RECORDINGS' *9362 46013-2 (20CDs)*
CARPHONE WAREHOUSE "Connected" STEREO MC'S 'Connected'
  FOURTH & BROADWAY (Univ): BRCD(BRCA) 589 (CD/MC)
  also on 'SWITCHED ON' *TELSTAR: TTVCD 3086 (2CD)*
CARTE NOIR Kenco "Try To Remember" ('The Fantasticks')
  (H.Schmidt-T.Jones) *1998 TV version sung by* NORMAN
  GROULX *unavailable* / previous version by RICHARD
  DARBYSHIRE *VIRGIN (EMI): VSCDT(VSC) 1584 deleted*
CASTLEMAINE XXXX "Your Cheatin' Heart" (H.Williams)
  GLEN CAMPBELL 'Country Classics' collection
  MFP (EMI): CDMFP 6321 (CD) TCMFP 6321 (MC)
CATHEDRAL CITY CHEESE "Baby Now That I've Found You"
  TV version unavailable. ORIG by The FOUNDATIONS
  'ANTHOLOGY' *SEQUEL (PINN): NEECD 300 (2CD)*
CELEBRATION MARS "Celebration" by KOOL & THE GANG
  'Collection' *SPECTRUM-POLY:551 635-2 (CD) -4 (MC)*
CELEBRATION MINI-BARS "Montok Point" (WILLIAM ORBIT)
  'STRANGE CARGO Vol 4' *WEA: 4509 99295-2 (CD)*
CENTER PARCS "Don't Fence Me In" (Cole Porter) BING
  CROSBY & ANDREWS SISTERS on 'TAKE A BREAK' on
  COLUMBIA (TEN): 494 464-2 (CD) & 'AS TIME GOES BY'
  CHARLY (Koch): CPCD 8105-2 (2CD) -4 (2MC)
CGU INSURANCE 2 "Impossible" The CHARLATANS (album 'Us
  and Only Us') *MCA (Univ): MCSTD 40231 (CDsingle)*
CGU INSURANCE 1 "Heroes" comp.& perform.by DAVID BOWIE
  from 'HEROES' *EMI PREMIER: CDP 797 720-2 (CD)*
CHANEL ALLURE "Spiritual High" (Anderson-Vangelis) by
  MOODSWINGS featuring CHRISSIE HYNDE on 'Moodfood'
  ARISTA-BMG: 74321 11170-2 (CD) -4 (MC) -1(LP)
CHANEL "L'EGOISTE" "Dance Of The Knights" from Act.1
  'Romeo & Juliet' Op.64 PROKOFIEV *many recordings*

CHANNEL 4 FILMS INSPIRING TV trailer "Sparks Are Gonna Fly" CATHERINE WHEEL 'Wishville' **CHRYS: 526 776-2**

CHAT MAGAZINE "Girls Just Want To Have Fun" (R.Hazard) *TV version unavailable.* original by CYNDI LAUPER on '12 Deadly Cyns' *EPIC: 477 363 (CD) -4 (MC) -8 (md)*

CHELTENHAM & GLOUCESTER B.SOC. ('diver' ad) by ADIEMUS "Cantus Song Of Tears" (K.Jenkins) KARL JENKINS and LONDON PHILHARMONIC ORCH with MIRIAM STOCKLEY on 'BEST OF ADIEMUS' *VIRGIN: (CD)(TC)(MD) 946* also on 'NEW PURE MOODS' *VIRGIN (EMI): VTDCD 158 (2CD)*

CHICKEN TONIGHT "Leave Rasta" by HORACE ANDY from 'In The Light'(DUB) *BLOOD & FIRE (Vital): BAFCD 6 (CD)*

CHILD IMMUNISATION - see HEALTH EDUCATION AUTHORITY

CHRISTIAN AID 3 "Summer Song" by CHAD and JEREMY from -S/T- 'RUSHMORE' *LONDON (Univ): 556 074-2 (CD)*

CHRISTIAN AID 2 "Get A Life" SOUL II SOUL feat CARON WHEELER *TEN-VIRGIN: CDV 2724 (CD) + DISCD 90 (CD)*

CHRISTIAN AID 1 "First Time Ever I Saw Your Face" (Ewan MacColl) ROBERTA FLACK on 'Best Of Roberta Flack' *ATLANTIC (TEN): 250840 (CD) 450840 (MC)*

CHRISTIE'S AGAINST CANCER APPEAL "Angels" performed by ROBBIE WILLIAMS *CHRYSALIS: CD(TC)CHS 5072 (CDs/MC)*

CHURCHILL INSURANCE "Car Wash" (Whitfield) *TV Version unavailable* original by ROSE ROYCE -S/T- *(MCA)*

CITIZEN WATCHES "Kyrie" from 'Misa Criolla' Mass (A. RAMIREZ) sung by JOSE CARRERAS with A.Ramirez, Laredo Choral Salve and Bilbao Choral Society on *PHILIPS (UNIV): 420 955-2PH (CD) 420 955-4PH (MC)*

CITROEN C5 "Oxygene" JEAN MICHEL JARRE *DISQUES DREFUS POLYDOR (UNIV): 487 364-2 (CD) and 486 984-2 (CD)*

CITROEN SAXO "Counter Clockwise Circle Dance" Ly-O-Lay Ale-Loya from 'SACRED SPIRIT' Collection on *VIRGIN EMI: CDV 2753 (CD) TCV 2753 (MC)*

CITROEN XSARA (Polystyrene bits and Claudia ad) "L'Air Des Clochettes" (DELIBES)

CITROEN XSARA (PICASSO) (Robots ad) "Sympathique" by PINK MARTINI *DISCOVERY IMPORT: Y 225078 (CD)*

CITROEN XSARA (CLAUDIA SCHIFFA strip ad) "Rise" by CRAIG ARMSTRONG from 'The Space Between Us' on *MELANKOLIC-VIRGIN (EMI):CDSAD 3 (CD) SADD 3 (CDs)*

CLASSIC CAT FOOD "House That Jack Built" by ARETHA FRANKLIN 'Gr.Hits' *GLOBAL TV BMG: RADCD 110 (CD)*

CLINIQUE "I Want To Be Happy" (Youmans-Caesar-Harbach) from show 'No No Nanette') ELLA FITZGERALD on 'The Platinum Collection' *PC 605 (2CD)*

CLINTON CARDS "Stop The Cavalry" JONA LEWIE on 'Heart Skips Beat' *STIFF-DISKY (THE): STIFFCD 09 (CD)*

CLOVER MARGARINE "Love Is In The Air (H.Vanda-G.Young) *TV vers:* BOB SAKER *unavailable /* original by JOHN PAUL YOUNG *LASERLIGHT (Target-BMG): 1221-2 (CD)*

CLUB MED "There'll Be Some Changes Made" (Higgins) DINAH WASHINGTON from 'Complete Dinah Washington on Mercury Volume 4' *MERCURY IMPORT*

COCA-COLA 8 soccer match ad "3PM" by AMBER MUSIC PROD

COCA-COLA 7 "They Don't Know" by SO SOLID CREW
RELENTLESS (TEN): (-)
COCA-COLA 6 Soccer ad 1 "Dedicated To The One I Love"
MAMAS & PAPAS *MCA (UNI): DMCM 5001 (CD)*
COCA-COLA 5 Soccer ad 2 "Atomic" by BLONDIE
CHRYSALIS (EMI): CCD 1817 (CD) ZCHR 1817 (MC)
COCA COLA 4 (boys cricket) "Mustt Mustt" NUSRAT FATEH
ALI KHAN on 'Mustt Mustt' *REAL WORLD-VIRGIN (EMI):
CDRW 15 (CD) RWMC 15 (MC)*
COCA COLA 3 (olympics 96) "Temple Head" by TRANSGLOBAL
EXPRESS from 'Dream Of A Hundred Nations' *Nation
RTM (Disc): NR 021CD (CD) NR 021C (MC) NR 021L(LP)*
COCA COLA 2 "Eat My Goal" by COLLAPSED LUNG
Deceptive (Vital): BLUFF 029CD (CDs) also on Coll
'The Beautiful Game' *RCA (BMG): 74321 38208-2 (CD)*
COCA COLA 1 "The First Time" (Spencer-Anthony-Boyle)
ROBIN BECK *Mercury: MER(X) 270 (7"/12")* deleted
COCA COLA early commercials collection (65 COCA-COLA
ads) *inc* SEEKERS-TOM JONES-ARETHA FRANKLIN-PETULA
CLARK-RAY CHARLES-SUPREMES-BEE GEES-DRIFTERS-JAN &
DEAN-MOODY BLUES *EAST ANGLIA PRODUCT: CC1 (CD)*
COCA COLA - see also DIET COKE
COMFORT EASY IRON "T'ain't What You Do" by BANANARAMA
& FUN BOY THREE *POLYGRAM: 828B 146-2 (CD)*
COMFORT SILK "Feeling Good" (Leslie Bricusse-Anthony
Newley) sung by NINA SIMONE on 'Feeling Good - The
Very Best Of' *VERVE (UNIV): 522 669-2 (CD)*
COMFORT CONDITIONER (2) "Words Of Love" (Buddy Holly)
TV ver.by Lisa Millett unavailable orig BUDDY HOLLY
'20 G.Greats' *MCA (UNI): MCLD(MCLC) 19220(CD/MC)*
COMFORT CONDITIONER (1) "Air That I Breathe" (Hammond-
Hazlewood) by The HOLLIES on 'TOTALLY COMMERCIALS'
EMI (EMI): 495 475-2 (CD) EMI: CDP 746 238-2 (CD)
COMPAQ COMPUTERS cartoon "Bang On" by PROPELLERHEADS
from album 'DECKSANDRUMSANMDROCKANDROLL' *WALL OF
SOUND (Vital): WALL(CD)(C) 015 or WALLD 039 (CDs)*
CONTINENTAL TYRES "La La Means I Love You" (Bell-Hart)
The DELFONICS *ARISTA (BMG): 07822 18979-2 (CD)*
CO-OP BANK "Lid Of The Stars" by GANGER from 'Hammock
Style' *DOMINO (Vital): WIGCD 047 (CD) WIGLP 047(LP)*
COW AND GATE Baby Foods "Who Wouldn't Love You"
(Carey-Fischer) INK SPOTS *currently unavailable*
CROWN PAINTS (2) Breatheasy ad "Pelle De Luna" PIERO
UMILIANI on compilation 'Easy Tempo Volume 9' on
EASY TEMPO (Timework/BMG):ET 932CD (CD)
CROWN PAINTS "What A Difference A Day Made" (M.Grever-
S.Adams) *TV vers.sung by* AMANDA WHITE *unavailable*
orig DINAH WASHINGTON *CHARLY (Koch):CPCD 8008 (CD)*
CRUNCHIE (Cadbury) "I'm So Excited" (Pointer-Lawrence)
ORIG (82) POINTER SISTERS on 'Break Out'
PLANET-RCA (BMG): FD 89450 (CD) FK 89450 (MC)
CSL FURNITURE "Sweets For My Sweet" (Pomus-Shuman) *TV
Vers.unavailable* SEARCHERS *CASTLE: CCSCD 303 (CD)*

D AEWOO 3 "Enter The Monk" by MONK & CANATELLA on
  'SWITCHED ON' *TELSTAR: TTVCD 3086 (2CD)*
DAEWOO 2 "Purple" by CRUSTATION with BRONAGH SLEVIN on
  also on 'SWITCHED ON' *TELSTAR: TTVCD 3086 (2CD)*
DAEWOO CAR INSURANCE "Adagietto" from 'Symphony No.5'
  (MAHLER) version on 'CINEMA CLASSICS 1'
  NAXOS (Select): 8551151 (CD)
DAEWOO MATIZ "Gloria in D.Minor" by VIVALDI
DAIRY LEA - see KRAFT DAIRY LEA
DAZ AUTOMATIC "Bod" by DEREK GRIFFITHS *unavailable*
DE BEERS - *see under* 'DIAMONDS'
DEL MONTE 2 "Happiness" *original version* by PIZZAMAN
  COWBOY (Pinn)
DEL MONTE 1 "Humming Chorus" from 'Madame Butterfly'
  (PUCCINI) *many recordings available*
DELTA AIRLINES "Adiemus" (Karl Jenkins) by ADIEMUS *feat*
  MIRIAM STOCKLEY & LONDON PHILHARMONIC *VIRGIN (EMI):*
  CD(TC)VE 925 (CD/MC) and VEND 4 (CDs) VENC 4 (MCs)
  also 'NEW PURE MOODS' *VIRGIN EMI: VTDCD 158 (2CD)*
DERBYSHIRE BUILD.SOC. "Everybody's Free (To Feel Good)"
  by ROZALLA *PULSE (BMG): PULSEMC 11 (MC)*
DFS 3 "Money That's What I Want" (B.Gordy-J.Bradford)
  FLYING LIZARDS on 'Best Punk Album In The World'
  VIRGIN EMI: VTDCD 42 (2CD)
DFS 2 "Look Of Love" by ABC on 'ABSOLUTELY ABC' on
  NEUTRON-UNIVERSAL: 842 967-2 (CD)
DFS 1 "More More More" (Greg Diamond) *TV Version*
  unavailable. Original by ANDREA TRUE CONNECTION on
  RCA CAMDEN (BMG): 74321 55848-2 (CD)
DIAMONDS (A Diamond Is Forever) (De Beers) "Palladio"
  (Karl Jenkins) LONDON PHILHARMONIC ORCH (K.Jenkins)
  on 'Palladio' *SONY CLASSICAL: SK(ST) 62276 (CD/MC)*
DIET COKE 4 "Love To Love You Baby" (P.Bellotte-G.
  Moroder-D.Summer) *TV VERSION by* HONEYZ *unavailable*
  orig by DONNA SUMMER on 'Endless Summer'(Best of)
  CASABLANCA (UNIV): 526 217-2 (CD)
DIET COKE 3 "I Just Wanna Make Love To You" (Dixon)
  PATTI D'ARCY JONES *unavailable*
DIET COKE 2 "I Put A Spell On You" (Hawkins) sung by
  NINA SIMONE on Coll 'Feeling Good-The Very Best'
  VERVE (UNIV): 522 669-2 (CD) -4 (MC)
DIET COKE 1 "I Just Wanna Make Love To You" (Dixon)
  ETTA JAMES *MCA (UNI): MCSTD(MCSC) 48003 (CDs/MC)*
  also on COLL 'V.Best Of Blues Brother-Soul Sister'
  DINO (Pinn): DINCD(MC) 115 (CD/MC)
DIRECT DEBIT 2 "I Wasn't Built To Get Up" SUPERNATURALS
  on 'A Tune A Day' *FOOD (EMI): 499 576-2 (CD) -4(MC)*
DIRECT DEBIT 1 "Hit" by The WANNADIES from 'Bagsy Me"
  INDOLENT (Vital): DIECD 008 (CD)
DIXONS - The Link "Speakeasy" by SHED SEVEN from album
  'CHANGE GIVER' *POLYDOR (Univ): 523 615-2 (CD)*
DOCKERS LEVI 2 "Tu Vuo Fa L'Americano" (Nisa-Carosone)
  TV vers.arranged by JOHN ALTMAN *unavailable*
  original version by RENATO CAROSONE (1959) *deleted*

DOCKERS LEVI 1 "I'm Sitting On Top Of The World" BOBBY
    DARIN on 'Totally Commercials' *EMI: 495 475-2 (CD)*
DORITOS "Walk This Way" original by RUN DMC & AEROSMITH
    'Greatest Hits' *PROFILE (Pinn): FILECD 474 (CD)*
DUBAI INT.AIRPORT "In The Depths Of The Temple" (The
    'Pearl Fishers Duet') (BIZET) *many vers.available*
DULUX (Petals/Pastel shades) "Dulux Theme" composed
    by KEVIN SARGENT *unavailable*
DULUX ONCE "Sexy Girls" by GERT WILDEN (Germany) on
    CRIPPLED DICK/HOT WAX (Greyhound-SRD): (-) (CD)
DULUX ONCE "The Moldau" from 'Ma Vlast' (My Country)
    SMETANA *ver* 'CLASSIC ADS' *EMI CLASS: 7243 568116-2*
DUNLOP TYRES 3 "Moonage Daydream" (Bowie) *TV version*
    unavailable orig on -S/T- 'ZIGGY STARDUST T.MOTION
    PICTURE' by DAVID BOWIE - *EMI: CDP 780411-2 (CD)*
DUNLOP TYRES 2 "21st Century Schizoid Man" (R.Fripp)
    by KING CRIMSON 'In The Court Of The Crimson King'
    EG-VIRGIN (EMI): EGCD 1 (CD) EGMC 1 (MC)
DUNLOP TYRES 1 "Venus In Furs" (Lou Reed) VELVET
    UNDERGROUND 'Velvet Underground With Nico' *POLYDOR
    (UNIV): 823 290-2 (CD) 823 290-4 or SPEMC 20 (MC)*

E AGLE STAR INS.2 "You Spin Me Round (Like a Record)"
    DEAD OR ALIVE 'Youthquake' *EPIC: 477 853-2 (CD)*
EAGLE STAR INS.1 "Driving In My Car" by MADNESS from
    'Divine Madness' *VIRGIN (EMI): (CD)(TC)(V) 2692*
EGG.COM Credit Card "USSR NATIONAL ANTHEM" composed by
    (A.Aleksandrov) *CONIFER (BMG): TQ 306 (CD)*
EGYPT HOLIDAYS "Triumphal March" from 'AIDA' (VERDI)
    special arrangement-not available
ELIZABETH SHAW CHOCOLATES "Crazy" by WILLIE NELSON
    'Very Best Of' *MFP (EMI): CD(TC)MFP 6110 (CD/MC)*
ELVIVE (L'OREAL) - see L'OREAL ELVIVE
EMPORIO (ARMANI) "Angel" by MASSIVE ATTACK 'Mezzanine'
    WILD BUNCH-VIRGIN (EMI): WBRCD 4 (CD)
EUROMILK "The Clog Dance" from ballet 'LA FILLE MAL
    GARDEE' (HEROLD) *EMI EMINENCE: CDEMX 2268 (CD)*
EUROSTAR "Sway" (Ruiz-Gimbel) DEAN MARTIN 'Very Best'
    EMI-CAPITOL: 496 721-2 (CD) -4 (MC)
EUROTUNNEL (Le Shuttle) "Bean Fields" (Simon Jeffes)
    The PENGUIN CAFE ORCHESTRA on 'Signs Of Life' *EG
    (UNIV): EEGCD 50 (CD) EGEDC 50 (MC)*
EVIAN Spring Water "Bye Bye Baby" (Robin-Styne) from
    'GENTLEMEN PREFER BLONDES' with MARILYN MONROE on
    'Kiss' *CAMEO (BMG): CD 3555 (CD)*
F CUK (French Connection UK) (a) "Mr.Benn theme" (Don
    Warren) (b) "The Kiss" (Jan Cyrka-T.Brichenko)
    (a) deleted (b) unavailable
FEBREZE (2) "Barrelhouse Rag" (Messien-Tone) from CD
    'SOUNDS OF LIFE' *CONNECT LIBRARY 122 (CD)*
       (1) "Funky Rio" by RICHARD MYHILL *unavailable*
FELIX CAT FOOD 3 "I Wanna Know" sung by JOHN E.PAUL
    on compilation 'Out On The Floor Tonight" on
    GOLDMINE (Vital): GSCD 107 (CD)

FELIX CAT FOOD 2 (RASCALS REWARD) "You've Been Away"
by RUBIN on compilation 'WIGAN CASINO STORY'
GOLDMINE (Vital): GSCD 103 (CD)

FELIX CAT FOOD 1 "Mambo No.5" (P.Prado) PEREZ PRADO
'King Of Mambo' *RCA (BMG): ND 90424 (CD)* also on
'OUR MAN IN HAVANA' *RCA (BMG): 74321 58810-2 (CD)*

FERRERO ROCHER "The Ambassador's Party" dance version
ROBERT FERRERA *KRUNCHIE (Pinn): KCD1(CDs) KT1(12")*
deleted. orig music (Graham De Wilde) *unavailable*

FIAT BRAVA TROFEO "Rubber Biscuit" by CHIPS from 'Cry
Baby' *MCA (UNIV): MCLD 19260 (CD)*

FIAT BRAVO 2 / BRAVA "2:1" (Matthews) by ELASTICA
'Elastica' *DECEPTIVE (Vital): BLUFF 014(CD(MC)(LP)*

FIAT CINQUENCENTO "But I Do" (Paul Gayten-R.Guidry)
CLARENCE FROGMAN HENRY *MCA (UNI): MCSTD(MCSC) 1797*
(CDs/MC) 'But I Do' *CHESS (Charly): CDRED 13 (CD)*

FIAT PUNTO 3 "Wink and a Smile" (SLEEPLESS IN SEATTLE)
by HARRY CONNICK JR *COL (Ten): 473 598-2 (CD) -4*

FIAT PUNTO 2 "Music To Watch Girls By" (Velona-Ramin)
sung by ANDY WILLIAMS on 'MUSIC TO WATCH GIRLS BY'
SONYMUSIC (Ten): SONYTV 67(CD)(MC) (2CDs/MC)
also 'BEST OF': *481 037-2 (CD) -4 (MC) 667 132-2*

FIAT PUNTO 1 "Amami Se Voui" sung by TANZIN DALLEY
TV vers.unavailable. Coll (1) 'ITALY AFTER DARK'
vers.by MARISA FIORDALISA *EMI: CDP 780023-2 (CD)*
TCEMS 1458 (MC) / Coll (2) 'FESTIVAL DE SAN REMO
VOL.1' vers. TONINA TORRIELLI *Butterfly Mus (Imp)*

FIAT SEICENTO "Cum on Feel The Noize" (Holder-Lea) by
SLADE 'Very Best' *POLYDOR: 537 105-2 (CD) -4(MC)*

FINDUS Various "I Feel Good" (J.Brown) JAMES BROWN
'Very Best of James Brown' *Poly: 845 828-2 (CD)*

FIRST DIRECT (Bob Mortimer ads) "Gurney Slade theme"
MAX HARRIS (1960) on Collect. 'NO.1 JAZZ ALBUM'
POLYGRAM TV: 553 937-2 (2CD)

FISHERMAN'S FRIEND "I Want You" by the UTAH SAINTS
FFFR-LONDON (UNIV): FCD 213 (CDs) 828 379-2 (CD)

FLORA 3 "Everybody Needs Somebody To Love (S.Burke-B.
Berns-J.Wexler) from 'The BLUES BROTHERS' *TV vers.*
unavailable (BLUES BROS. -S/T-) *(TEN) K.250715 CD*

FLORA 2 "You Make Me Feel So Young" (M.Gordon-Joseph
Myrow) *TV version by* TERESA JAMES *unavailable*

FLORA 1 "If I Love Ya Then I Need Ya" (Bob Merrill)
EARTHA KITT on 'BEST OF EARTHA KITT' on *MCA (UNI):*
MCLD 19120 (CD) MCLC 19120 (MC)

FORD (2001 Demands A Closer Look campaign) Specially
comp.by VINCE POPE *note: similiar to* 'CHAN CHAN'
from 'BUENA VISTA SOCIAL CLUB' -S/T- *WCD 050 (CD)*

FORD (1999 global campaign) "Just Wave Hello" sung by
CHARLOTTE CHURCH from 'CHARLOTTE CHURCH' album
SONY CLASS: SK 64356 (CD) also *668 531-2 (CDs)*

FORD (1999 feature models) "Song Of Ancient Mariner"
by VANGELIS from -S/T- '1492 Conquest Of Paradise'
EAST WEST (War): 4509 91014-2 (CD) WX 497C (MC)

FORD ESCORT 2 "Jeepers Creepers" *TV vers.unavailable*
LOUIS ARMSTRONG version on 'JEEPERS CREEPERS' on
MILAN (BMG): CDCH 602 (CD)

FORD ESCORT 1 "Lovely Day" (B.Withers) BILL WITHERS
COLUMBIA: 491 961-2 (CD) -8 (md) 'Best Of'

FORD FIESTA 3 "I'll Take You There" (Isbell) *TV vers.
unavailable / Original* by The STAPLE SINGERS on
'Best Of' *STAX 9Pinn): CDSXK 125 (CD)*

FORD FIESTA 2 "Roadrunner" by The ANIMALS on
EMI: 498 936-2 (CD)

FORD FIESTA 1 "My Favourite Game" by The CARDIGANS
'GRAN TURISMO' *STOCKHOLM (UNIV): 559 081-2 (CD)
559 081-4 (MC) 567 991-2 (CDs)*

FORD FOCUS 2 "It's A Man's Man's Man's World" sung by
JAMES BROWN 'Very Best Of' *POLYDOR: 845 828-2 (CD)*

FORD FOCUS 1 "You Gotta Be" sung by DES'REE
SONY S2: 666 893-2 (CDs) -4 (MC) also on 'I Ain't
Movin' *SONY: 475 843-2 (CD) -4 (MC) -8 (md)*

FORD GALAXY 2 "Flower Duet" from 'Lakme' (DELIBES)
TV instrumental version unavailable

FORD GALAXY "Light and Shadow" VANGELIS '1492 CONQUEST
OF PARADISE' *WARNER: 4509 91014-2 (CD) WX 497C (MC)*

FORD KA 2 "Orignal" from 'Leftism' LEFTFIELD *COLUMBIA
SONY: HANDCD 2 (CD) HANDMC 2 (MC) HANDLP 2 (LP)*

FORD KA 1 "Bright Red" (Anderson) *TV vers.unavailable*
original LAURIE ANDERSON version on "Bright Red"
WB (TEN): 9362 45534-2 (CD) -4 (MC)

FORD MONDEO 3 (Built To Lead ad) "World Looking In" by
MORCHEEBA 'Fragments Of Freedom' *CHINA-CHRYSALIS:
8573 83602-2 (CD) -4 (MC) also EW 225CD1 (CDs)*

FORD MONDEO 2 'Zetec' "Casta Diva" from opera 'NORMA'
(BELLINI) by MARIA CALLAS *EMI: CDC 557 050-2 (CD)*

FORD MONDEO 1 "Speaking Of Happiness"(Radcliffe-Scott)
by GLORIA LYNNE *ISLAND (UNIV):CID(CIS) 659 (CDs/MC)*
also on -S/T- 'SEVEN' *EDEL (Vital) 0022432CIN (CD)*

FORD PROBE 2 "Fly Me To The Moon" (Bart Howard) by
JULIE LONDON 'Best Of Liberty Years' *Liberty (EMI)
EMI CZ 150 (CD)* also on Coll 'THIS IS THE RETURN
OF CULT FICTION' *VIRGIN (EMI): VTCD 112 (CD)* and on
'TOTALLY COMMERCIALS' *EMI (EMI): 495 475-2 (CD)*

FORD PROBE 1 "You Can Go Your Own Way" (Chris Rea)
sung by CHRIS REA on 'Best Of Chris Rea' *EAST-WEST
(TEN): 4509 98040-2 (CD) -4 (MC)*

FORD PUMA "Bullitt" score from 1968 -S/T- LALO SCHIFRIN
W.BROS (Fra.imp)(TEN/Discovery): 9362 45008-2 (CD)
Black Dog remix *WEA: WESP 002(CD=CDs)(C=MC)(T=12s)*
also on 'SWITCHED ON' *TELSTAR: TTVCD 3086 (2CD)*

FORD TRANSIT "Coz I Luv You" (N.Holder-J.Lea) by SLADE
'Very Best Of' *POLYDOR: 537 105-2 (CD) -4 (MC)*

FORTE (TRUSTHOUSE) "Le Lac De Come" (Galas) *(TV version
unavailable)* vers.on 'Classics' by FRANCK POURCEL &
HIS ORCHESTRA on *EMI: CZ 22(CD) TCEMS 1263 (MC)*

FOSTERS "Exploration" The KARMINSKY EXPERIENCE on
'Blow Up A-Go-Go' *VVR (Pinn): 101 054-2 (CD)*

FOX'S BISCUITS "Gonna Be A Stranger" sung by SELAH
   unavailable
FREESERVE "Plink Plank Plunk" by LEROY ANDERSON on
   'The Typewriter' *RCA (BMG): 09026 68048-2 (CD)*
FREESERVE NET "L'Amour D'Escargot" (Bruno COULAIS)
   MARIE KOBAYASHI (mezzo-sop) -S/T- 'MICROSOSMOS'
   AUVIDIS (Harmonia Mundi): KT 1028 (CD)
FRENCH CONNECTION - see FCUK
FRIEND'S PROVIDENT "Chi Mai" (also 'LIFE & TIMES OF
   DAVID LLOYD GEORGE' BBC) by ENNIO MORRICONE on
   'PURE MOODS' VIRGIN (EMI): VTCD 28 (CD)
FRUIT-TELLA 2 "Let's Talk About Sex" by SALT'n' PEPA
   feat PSYCHOTROPIC on 'Greatest Hits' *FFFR LONDON
   (UNIV): 828 291-2 (CD) 828 291-4 (MC)*
FRUIT-TELLA 1 "I'm Too Sexy" (Fred/Richard Fairbrass
   Rob Manzoli) RIGHT SAID FRED *TUG (BMG): CDSNOG 1
   (CDs) CASNOG 1 (MC) 12SNOG 1 (12"s) SNOG 1 (7"s)*
FRUITOPIA music (Robin Guthrie-Simon Raymonde) by The
   COCTEAU TWINS *specially recorded and not available*
FUJI FILMS "Gorecki" by LAMB from 'LAMB' on
   FONTANA (UNIV): 532 968-2 (CD) -4 (MC)
G **ALAXY** (2) "The Sky Is Broken" by MOBY from 'PLAY'
   MUTE (Vital): (CD)(CS)(MD)STUMM 172 (CD/MC/md)
GALAXY (1) "Summertime" (Porgy and Bess) (Gershwin)
   BILLIE HOLIDAY 'Essential Billie Holiday' on
   COLUMBIA (Ten): 467 149-2 (CD) -4 (MC)
GALAXY ICE CREAM "What Becomes of The Broken Hearted"
   TV Vers unavailable / ORIG by JIMMY RUFFIN *MOTOWN*
GALAXY RIPPLE "Guns Of Navarone" The SKATALITES (1967)
   Col 'OLD SKOOL SKA' *SNAPPER (Pinn): SMDCD 139 (CD)*
GAP 18 (CAROLE KING ad)1."So Far Away" from 'Tapestry'
   ODE TEN: 480 422-2 (CD) / 2."Love Makes The World"
   from 'Love Makes The World' *ROCKINGALE (Koch): (-)*
GAP 17 (girl with guitar) "Back in Black" by AC/DC
   on 'Back in Black' *EMI: 495 153-2 (CD)*
GAP 16 (robots girl dance) "Digital Love" by DAFT PUNK
   from album 'Discovery' *VIRGIN (EMI):CDVX 2940 (CD)
   and VSCDT 1810 (CDs)*
GAP 15 (Kiss) "The Shining" (D.Gough) BADLY DRAWN BOY
   TWISTED NERVE (Vital): TNXLCD 133 (CD)
GAP 14 (lightbulb) "Boys Better" by The DANDY WARHOLS
   on 'Come Down' *PARLOPHONE-EMI: 836 505-2 (CD)*
GAP 13 (snowflake) "All Mixed Up" by RED HOUSE PAINTERS
   on 'Songs For A Blue Guitar' *4AD (Vital) (-) (CD)*
GAP 12 (slow down) "Little Drummer Boy" by LOW on CD
   'Christmas' *TUGBOAT (Vital): TUGCD 014 (CD)*
GAP 11 Kids "You Really Got Me" (Ray Davies) *TV Vers.
   unavailable.* KINKS *POLYDOR: 516 465-2 (CD) -4(MC)*
   10/9/8 (Dance Routines WEST SIDE STORY) *TV Session
   Recordings unavailable* 'AMERICA'/'DANCE AT THE GYM'
   'THE RUMBLE' *FILM -S/T- (1961) SONY: 467 606-2 (CD)*
GAP 7 "Just Can't Get Enough" *TV version unavailable*
   orig DEPECHE MODE *MUTE (Vital): CDSTUMM 101 (CD)*

GAP 6 "Mellow Yellow" *TV version unavailable.* orig by
  DONOVAN *SEE FOR MILES (Pinn): SEECD 300 (CD)*

GAP 5 "Dress You Up" *TV version unavailable.* orig by
  MADONNA *SIRE (Warner): WX 20C (MC)*

GAP 4 Khaki-A-Go-Go "BLOW UP A-GO-GO"(Wild Elephants)
  by JAMES CLARKE *V2 (Pinn): VVR 5009523 (CDs) and
  VVR 5010073 (2CDs) VVR 5009525 (MC)*
  'EXCLUSIVE BLEND VOL.2' *BLOWUP (SRD): BU 011CD*
  also on 'SWITCHED ON' *TELSTAR: TTVCD 3086 (2CD)*

GAP 3 Khaki Country "Crazy Little Thing Called Love"
  (F.Mercury) by DWIGHT YOAKAM *REPRISE: W497CD (CDs)*

GAP 2 Khaki Soul "Lovely Day" by BILL WITHERS 'Best
  Of' *COLUMBIA (Ten): 491 161-2 (CD) -8 (md)* / ALSO
  "I Hear Music On The Streets" by UNLIMITED TOUCH
  'ESSENTIAL UNDERGROUND DANCEFLOOR CLASSICS VOL.2'
  DEEP BEATS (BMG): DGPCD 705 (CD)

GAP 1 (Khaki Swing) "Jump Jive & Wail" by LOUIS PRIMA
  CAPITOL (EMI): CDP 794 072-2 (CD)

GAS - *see under heading BRITISH GAS*

GEORGE AT ASDA 4 "Simply Irrestible" (R.Palmer) by
  ROBERT PALMER on 'Essential Collection'
  EMI GOLD: 528 560-2 (CD)

GEORGE AT ASDA 3 "Would You" by TOUCH AND GO
  V2 (3M-Pinn): VVR 500 308-2 (CDs) -4 (MC) -6 (12"s)

GEORGE AT ASDA 2 "Ready To Go" by REPUBLICA from
  1997 album 'Republica' *DE CONSTRUCTION (BMG):
  74321 41052-2 (CD) -4 (MC)*

GEORGE AT ASDA 1 "Get Ready For This" by 2 UNLIMITED
  'Get Ready' *PWL (TEN): HFCD 47 (CD) HFC 47 (MC)*

GIFTAID "Sunny Afternoon" (Ray Davies) The KINKS
  POLYDOR TV: 516 465-2 (CD) -4 (MC)

GILLETTE / GILLETTE CONTOUR PLUS "Looking Sharp" (Jake
  Holmes) and "The Best A Man Can Do" *unavailable*

GOING PLACES (2000 holiday ad) "Go Now" (Larry Banks-
  Milton Bennett) *TV Vers.unavailable* orig versions
  by BESSIE BANKS *(deleted)* and MOODY BLUES *(Univ)*

GOLF (VW) - see under **VOLKSWAGEN GOLF**

GOODYEAR TYRES "Pre 63" by GROOVE ARMADA from 'Vertigo'
  PEPPER (Pinn): 053 033-2 (CD) -4 (MC) -0 (2LP)

GRATTAN'S CATALOGUE "I Get The Sweetest Feeling"
  (V.McCoy-A.Evelyn) JACKIE WILSON on 'Very Best'
  ACE (Pinn): CDCHK 913 (CD)

GREEN GIANT NIBLETS "The More I See You" sung by
  CHRIS MONTEZ on compilation 'And The Beat Goes On'
  POLYGRAM: 535 693-2 (CD)

GROLSCH "I'm Bored" by IGGY POP on 'PoP Music' on
  RCA CAMDEN (BMG): 74321 41503-2 (CD)

GUARDIAN "Dick Tracy" by SKATALITES on 'FOUNDATION SKA'
  HEARTBEAT (Greensleeves/Jetstar): CDHB 185/6 (2CD)
  also by DEAN FRASER on 'BIG UP' *IJCD 4003 (CD)*

GUINNESS 14 "Summer Samba (So Nice)" WALTER WANDERLEY
  on 'Rain Forest' *VERVE (UNIV): 825 533-2 (CD)*

GUINNESS 13 cartoon "City" by PETER LAWLOR *unavailable*

GUINNESS 12 (Draft) dance "It's A Burke's Law" (Cornell Campbell) performed by PRINCE BUSTER *unavailable*

GUINNESS 11 (Snail race) "Barbarabatiri" (Perez Prado) *new mix ver.*(Todd Terry & Masters at Work) GYPSYMEN *SOUND DESIGN (3MV-TEN): SDES 09CDS (CDs) 09T (12"s) orig* PEREZ PRADO on 'MAMBOS' *RCA BMG:CD 62051 (CD)*

GUINNESS 10 (Surfer) "Phatt Planet" by LEFTFIELD *HARD HANDS-HIGHER GROUND (Ten): HAND 057CD1 (CD1) HAND 057CD2 (CD2) HAND 057T (12"s) from the album* 'RHYTHM & STEALTH' *(Ten): HANDCD 4 (CD)*

GUINNESS 9 "Hear The Drummer Get Wicked" CHAD JACKSON *BIG WAVE: BWR 36 (7"s) deleted*

GUINNESS 8 Swimmer "Mambo No.5" *TV vers.unavailable* original by PEREZ PRADO ORCH on 'OUR MAN IN HAVANA' *RCA (BMG): 74321 58810-2 (CD) also RCA: ND 90424 CD*

GUINNESS 7 (Strange But Untrue) "First Big Weekend' by ARAB STRAP *CHEMICAL UNDERGROUND (SRD):CHEM 007 (7")*

GUINNESS 6 (St.Patrick's Day) "I'm Sitting On Top Of The World'" (Young-Henderson-Lewis) by AL JOLSON *PRESIDENT (BMG): PLCD 542 (CD)*

GUINNESS 5 (old man) "Story Of My Life" (B.Bacharach-Hal David) sung by MICHAEL HOLLIDAY 'EP COLLECTION' SEE FOR MILES (Pinn): SEECD 311 (CD)

GUINNESS 4 (bicycle) "I'm Gonna Wash That Man Right Out Of My Hair" (R.Rodgers-O.Hammerstein II) sung by MITZI GAYNOR from -S/T- of 'South Pacific' *RCA (BMG): ND 83681 (CD) NK 83681 (MC)*

GUINNESS 3 (zoom) "We Have All The Time In The World" (John Barry-Hal David) LOUIS ARMSTRONG from the JAMES BOND -S/T- 'ON HER MAJESTY'S SECRET SERVICE' *EMI-LIBERTY (EMI): CZ 549 (CD) also on CDEMTV 89*

GUINNESS 2a "Laudate Dominum" / 'Vesperae Solennes De Confessore' (K.339) (Mozart) *vers:* KIRI TE KANAWA-ST.PAUL'S CATHEDRAL CHOIR *PHILIPS (UNIV): 412 629-2 (CD)* (2b)"Party Time" (L.Smith-Gerry Th omas-Dave Gibson) FATBACK BAND on "Raising Hell' on *ACE-SOUTHBOUND (Pin): CDSEWM 028(CD) SEWC 028(MC)*

GUINNESS 1 mambo dance "Guaglione" PEREZ PRADO ORCH. 'King Of Mambo' *RCA (BMG): ND 90424 (CD) also on* 'OUR MAN IN HAVANA' *RCA: 74321 58810-2 (CD)*

H AAGEN-DAZS ICE CREAM "Make Yourself Comfortable" (B. Merrill) sung by SARAH VAUGHAN on 'Golden Hits' *Mercury (UNIV): (CD/MC)*

HALIFAX 13 (singing bank manager) based on "Livin La Vida Loca" orig by RICKY MARTIN on 'RICKY MARTIN' on *COLUMBIA (TEN): 494 406-2 (CD) -4 (MC)*

HALIFAX 12 (singing bank manager) based on "Sexbomb" originally by TOM JONES & MOUSSE T. on *GUT (Pinn-Vital): CDGUT 033 (CDs)*

HALIFAX 11 (Intel.Finance) "Right Here Right Now" by FATBOY SLIM on 'You've Come A Long Way' *SKINT (3MV-Pinn) BRASSIC 11(CD)(MC(LP)(MD) ALSO COLLECTION* 'SWITCHED ON' *TELSTAR (CD)* see page 52

HALIFAX 10 "Help" (J.Lennon-P.McCartney) *TV Version unavailable / original by* THE BEATLES *(EMI)*

HALIFAX 9 "I and I Survive" by BURNING SPEAR 'Chant Down Babylon' *ISLAND (UNIV): 524 190-2 (2CD set)*

HALIFAX 8 "Consider Yourself" from 'Oliver' (Lionel Bart) *TV vers.unavailable* / see also under 'OLIVER'

HALIFAX 7 (Kaleidoscope) "Surfin'" by ERNEST RANGLIN from 'Below The Bassline' *ISLAND (UNIV): IJCD4002 (CD) IJMC 4002 (MC) IJLP 4002 (LP) also CDsingle*

HALIFAX 6 Week In The Life "The Gift" (Wisternoff-Warren-MacColl) by WAY OUT WEST and JOANNA LAW *De CONSTRUCTION (BMG):74321 40191-2(CD) -4(MC) -1(12")*

HALIFAX 5 Financial Services (figures skating ad) "Clock" by DAVID A.STEWART *unavailable*

HALIFAX 4 Financial Services "Moon River" (H.Mancini Johnny Mercer) *TV vers.unavailable* / HENRY MANCINI Coll 'IN THE PINK' on *RCA (BMG): 74321 24283-2 (CD)*

HALIFAX 3 Financial Services "Sentinel" (M.Oldfield) from 'Tubular Bells II' MIKE OLDFIELD on *WEA (TEN) 4509 90618-2 (CD) -5 (DCC) WX 2002(C) (LP/MC)*

HALIFAX 2 "Let's Do It (Let's Fall In Love)"(Porter) EARTHA KITT 'Best Of' *MCA (UNI): MCLD(MCLC 19120*

HALIFAX 1 "Our House" (Jenkins-Nash) CROSBY STILLS NASH & YOUNG on 'Deja Vu' *ATLANTIC: K.250001 (CD)*

HALL'S MENTHOLYPTUS "Air That I Breathe" (A.Hammond-Lee Hazlewood) The HOLLIES *EMI: CDP 746238-2 (CD)*

HALL'S SOOTHERS "Addicted To Love" by ROBERT PALMER on 'Addictions' *ISLAND: CID(ICT) 9944 (CD/MC) 4 (MC)*

HARVEY'S BRISTOL CREAM "The Clog Dance" from 'La Fille Mal Gardee' (Louis HEROLD) ROYAL OPERA HOUSE ORCH. (John Lanchbery) *DECCA (UNIV): 436 658-2 (CD)*

HAVEN HOLIDAYS "Heaven Is A Place On Earth" (Nowells-Shipley) *TV vers.unavailable.* BELINDA CARLISLE on 'Heaven On Earth' *VIRGIN (EMI): CDV 2496 (CD)*

HAVING BABIES MAGAZINE "Canon in D" PACHELBEL *version* 'CLASSIC ADS' *EMI: 7243 568116-2 (CD)*

HEALTH EDUCATION : CHILD IMMUNISATION CAMPAIGN "Sanvean: I Am Your Shadow" (Gerrard-Claxton) LISA GERRARD from album 'The Mirror Pool' *4AD-B.Banquet (RTM-DISC): CAD 5009CD (CD) CADC 5009 (MC)*

HEINEKEN Paul & Debbie "Close To You" (Bacharach-David) *TV vers.unavailable* / orig.by CARPENTERS *(A.& M)*

HEINZ "Big Noise From Winnetka" (Crosby-Rodin) by the BOB CROSBY ORCHESTRA on '22 ORIGINAL RECORDINGS' *HINDSIGHT (Target-BMG-Jazz Music): HCD 409 (CD)*

HEINZ (Baked Beans/Tomato Soup etc) "Inkanyezi Nezazi" (J.Shambalala) THE LADYSMITH BLACK MAMBAZO 'Best Of LADYSMITH BLACK MAMBAZO' *POLYG 565 298-2 (CD)*

HEINZ WEIGHT WATCHERS 2 "What A Beautiful Day" by The LEVELLERS from the album 'Mouth To Mouth' *CHINA (TEN): 0630 19856-2 (CD)*

HEINZ WEIGHT WATCHERS 1 "Leaving Rome" by JO JO BENNETT USA Collection 'BLOW MR.HORNSMAN' *(not on UK copy) TROJAN (USA IMPT.through CD1STOP): TJN 2572 (CD)*

HIGHLIGHTS - *see under* 'CADBURY'S HIGHLIGHTS'
HOLLAND & BARRETT (Sale ad) "I'm Alive" (Ballard) The
   HOLLIES *EMI: CDEMTC 74 (CD)* 'Greatest Hits'
HOME OFFICE REGISTRATION FOR LOCAL ELECTIONS
   "Piano Concerto NO.21 in C.Major K.467" (MOZART)
HONDA ACCORD 2 "Mystical Machine Gun" by KULA SHAKER
   COLUMBIA: KULA 22(CD)(CDX)(MC) taken from album
   'PEASANTS PIGS & ASTRONAUTS'*SHAKER 2(CD)(MC)(LP)*
HONDA ACCORD 1 "We've Gotta Get Out Of This Place"
   (Mann-Weil) *TV version by* SPACE *unavailable*
   orig by The ANIMALS *(EMI): CZ 10 (CD)*
HONDA CIVIC "Made For Lovin' You" by ANASTASIA on
   'Not That Kind' *EPIC (TEN): 497 412-2 (CD)*
   671 717-2 (CDs)
HONDA SOLAR POWERED CAR "Stabat Mater Dolorosa" by
   PERGOLESI *TV version unavailable*
HOTPOINT "Dreams" sung by GABRIELLE on 'FIND YOUR WAY'
   GO BEAT! (Univ): 828 441-2 (CD)
HOVIS BREAD "Largo" from Symphony No.9 in E.Min Op.95
   by DVORAK *many recordings available*
HP SAUCE 2 (HP Makes A Bacon Sandwich) "Soul Singer"
   unavailable library track
HP SAUCE 1 "That's The Way I Like It" (Casey-Finch)
   KC & SUNSHINE BAND *EMI: 494 019-2 (CD) -4 (MC)*
HSBC 3 (Chicken) "Einstein A-Go-Go" orig by LANDSCAPE
   coll 'INTO THE 80s' *GLOBALTV (BMG): RADCD 09 (2CD)*
HSBC 2 (Parrot) "Hotel Dyonisos" LOUIS FELIPE AUCLAIR
   from 'Au Coeur De Tricatel' *MUTE: 304 924-2 (CD)*
HSBC 1 (MIDLAND BANK) "She's A Star" JAMES 'Whiplash'
   FONTANA (UNIV): 534 354-2 (CD) JIMCD 16 (CDs)
HUGO BOSS (Bar model) "What It Means" by BARRY ADAMSON
   'As Above So Below' *MUTE (Vital): CDSTUMM 161 (CD)*
HULA HOOPS "Cry Baby" (Stallings) by APHROHEAD
   CREDENCE (EMI) number to be confirmed (CDs)
HYUNDAI 2 "Ready To Go" by REPUBLICA from 'Republica'
   DE CONSTRUCTION (BMG): 74321 41052-2 (CD) -4 (MC)
HYUNDAI 1 "Adagietto" from 'Symphony No.5' (G.MAHLER)
   vers 'CINEMA CLASS.1' *NAXOS (Select):8.551151 (CD)*
I CELAND 5 "1812 Overture" (TCHAIKOVSKY) *var.records*
ICELAND 4 "Young At Heart" (Leigh-Richards) *TV version*
   unavailable. original by FRANK SINATRA *CAPITOL EMI*
ICELAND 3 (Buy One Get One Free) "At The Ball That's
   All" (Commence To Dancing) by The AVALON BOYS from
   LAUREL & HARDY 'Way Out West' *EMI; 522 816-2 (CD)*
ICELAND 2 "It Must Be Love" (Labi Siffre) by MADNESS
   on 'Divine Madness' *VIRGIN: CDV(TCV) 2692 (CD/MC)*
ICELAND 1 "Driving Home For Christmas" (Rea) CHRIS REA
   'BEST OF CHRIS REA' *MAGNET (TEN): 243841-2 (CD)*
IKEA "Walk Away" by The CAST from 'All Change'
   POLYDOR (Univ): 529 312-2 (CD)
iMAC APPLE "Sunburn" by MUSE from album 'Showbiz' on
   MUSHROOM (Pinn): MUSH 59CD (CD) / MUSH 68CDS (CDs)
IMPERIAL CANCER RESEARCH 3 "What A Wonderful World" by
   LOUIS ARMSTRONG 'Pure Genius' *EMI: CDEMTV 89 (CD)*

IMPERIAL CANCER RESEARCH 2 "Wind" CAT STEVENS on
'TEASER & THE FIRECAT' *ISLAND (Univ): IMCD 104 (CD)*
IMPERIAL CANCER RESEARCH 1 "United We Stand" orig by
BROTHERHOOD OF MAN *DERAM (UNIV): 820 632-2 (CD)*
IMPERIAL LEATHER SHOWER GEL "Disco Inferno" (orig.by
TRAMMPS from 'SATURDAY NIGHT FEVER') *POLYDOR -S/T-*
IMPULSE 5 (Free Your Arms) "Dada Struttin'" (Jim Burke)
SGT.ROCK -S/T- 'BRING IT ON' *cat.no.unconfirmed*
IMPULSE 4 ('Bar' ad) "Sugar Is Sweeter" (Bolland)
C.J.BOLLAND *FFFR (UNIV): 828 909-2 (CD) -4 (MC)*
also on 'SWITCHED ON' *TELSTAR: TTVCD 3086 (2CD)*
IMPULSE 3 "Female Of The Species" by SPACE 'Spiders'
GUT (BMG): GUTCD 1 (CD) GUTMC 1 (MC) GUTLP 1 (LP)
IMPULSE 2 (art class) "Pressure Drop" by The MAYTALS
ISLAND Records (UNIV): number unconfirmed
IMPULSE 1 "Fever" (Cooley-Davenport) by PEGGY LEE on
Coll 'TOTALLY COMMERCIALS' *EMI: 495-475-2 (CD)*
INDIGO SQUARE.COM 'La Gazza Ladra' ("Thieving Magpie")
by ROSSINI *various recordings available*
INTEL PENTIUM III 4 "O Mio Babbino Caro" from Opera
'GIANNNI SCHICCHI' *(PUCCINI) various recordings*
INTEL PENTIUM 3 "Song 2" by BLUR (Damon Albarn)
EMI: FOOD(CD)(MC)(LP) 19
INTEL PENTIUM 2 "Shake Your Groove Thing" by PEACHES
& HERB *ELEVATE (3MV-SONY): CDELV 05 (CD)*
INTEL PENTIUM 1 "Play That Funky Music" WILD CHERRY
on 'Night Fever' *GLOBAL TV (Pinn): RADCD 24 (2CD)*
IONICA "Something In The Air" (John Keene) *TV Version:*
OCEAN COLOUR SCENE *unavailable.(orig.by* THUNDERCLAP
NEWMAN) 'And The Beat Goes On Vol.2' *535 558-2 (CD)*
IRELAND (TOURISM) ('Live A Different Life' ad) "Dream"
by The CRANBERRIES from 'Everyone Else Is Doing It
So Why Can't We' *ISLAND (UNIV): CID(ICT)(ILPS) 8003*
ITS INVESTMENT TRUST (S'Wonderful ad) "Via Con Mi" by
PAOLO CONTI 'Best' *EAST WEST (Ten): 7559 79512-2 CD*
also on -S/T- 'FRENCH KISS' *MERCURY: 528 321-2 (CD)*
J ACOBS CRACKERS "Train To Skaville" The ETHIOPIANS on
'Anthology 1966-75' *TROJAN (Proper):CDTRD 457 (2CD)*
'Orig.Reggae Hitsound' *TROJAN (Proper): CDTRL 228*
JAGUAR X TYPE new "Wicked Game" CHRIS ISAAK from -S/T-
'WILD AT HEART' *SPECTRUM (UNIV): 551 318-2 (CD)*
JAGUAR S.TYPE (STING) "Desert Rose" from album 'Brand
New Day' *A.& M.(Univ): 490 425-2 (CD) -4 (MC)*
JAGUAR S.TYPE "History Repeating" The PROPELLERHEADS
and SHIRLEY BASSEY *WALL OF SOUND (Vital):*
WALLD 036 (CDs) WALLCS 036 (MC) WALLT 036 (12"s)
also on 'SWITCHED ON' *TELSTAR: TTVCD 3086 (2CD)*
JEAN PAUL GAULTIER mus.from "Norma" (BELLINI) complete
work on *EMI: CMS 763000-2 (3CD set)*
JJB SPORTS 2 "At The Sign Of The Swingin' Cymbal" by
BRIAN FAHEY (Alan Freeman Pick Of The Pops Theme)
'WORLD OF SOUND' *BBC W.WIDE (Koch): 33635-2 (CD)*
JJB SPORTS 1 "Everyone's A Winner" (Errol Brown) orig
HOT CHOCOLATE 'Greatest Hits' *EMI: CD(TC)EMTV 73*

JOHN SMITH'S BITTER (Ladybirds ad) "Je T'aime Moi Non
Plus" (S.Gainsbourg) JANE BIRKIN-SERGE GAINSBOURG
(69) on 'Amoreuse' *PICKWICK (ABM): PWKS 539 (CD)*

JOHN SMITH'S EXTRA STRONG (Penguins) "Help Yourself"
(Gli Occhi Miel)(C.Donida-J.Fishman) *TV vers.not
available* TOM JONES *DERAM (UNIV): 820 559-2 (CD)*

JOHNSON'S PLEDGE "Humming Chorus" ('Madam Butterfly')
(PUCCINI) *TV version unavailable*

JUNGLE.COM "The Lion Sleeps Tonight" PAUL DA VINCI &
The JUNGLE RUMBLE BAND *JAMMIN' MUSIC (-) (CDs)*

K ELLOGG'S **'Help Yourself' ad** "Keep Young & Beautiful"
(Dubin-Warren) *TV vers unavailable* / HARRY ROY &
HIS ORCHESTRA on *MFP (EMI): CDMFP 6361 (CD)*

KELLOGG'S Selction "Dry Bones" ('Dem Bones!')(Trad.)
version: FRED WARING & HIS PENNSYLVANIANS on CD
'SINGING DETECTIVE' (TV -S/T-) *POTTCD 200 (2CD)*

KELLOGG'S BRAN FLAKES "Spirit In The Sky" (Greenbaum)
orig by NORMAN GREENBAUM on 'Spirit In The Sky-Back
Home Again' *EDSEL-DEMON (Pinn): ECDC 470 (CD) also*

KELLOGG'S CEREALS "Please Sir" by SAM FONTEYN *deleted*

KELLOGG'S CORN FLAKES "Brideshead Revisited" (theme)
GEOFFREY BURGON *SILVA SCREEN (Koch): FILMCD 117 CD)*

KELLOGG'S CRUNCHIE NUT CORN FLAKES "Stay" (M.Williams)
MAURICE WILLIAMS & THE ZODIACS on 'The Best Of'
AIM (ADA/Jazz Music): AIM 2016CD (CD)

KELLOGG'S FRUIT 'N FIBRE "Banana Boat Song" (Day-O) *TV
version unavailable* orig by HARRY BELAFONTE *(BMG)
comedy version* by STAN FREBERG *(Capitol-EMI)*

KELLOGG'S FRUIT 'N FIBRE "I Yi Yi Yi Yi Like You Very
Much" *TV Version unavailable* ORIG from 'THAT NIGHT
IN RIO' by CARMEN MIRANDA on 'Brazilian Bombshell'
ASV LIVING ERA (Select): CDAJA 5242 (CD)

KELLOGG'S FROSTIES "Born Free" (Barry-Black) MATT MONRO
'COMPLETE HEARTBREAKERS' *EMI: CDEM 1600 (2CD)*

KELLOGG'S NUTRI-GRAIN Overture to 'The Thieving Magpie'
(La Gazza Ladra)(ROSSINI)*many recordings available*

KELLOGG'S RICE CRISPIES CHOCOLATE SQUARES "Buttons"
(Thompson-Jarvis) MCCASSO PRODUCTIONS *unavailable*

KELLOGG'S SPECIAL K "Turning Ground" CAROLINE LAVELLE
from 'Spirit' *WEA (TEN): 4509 98137-2(CD) -4(MC)*

KENCO CARTE NOIR "Try To Remember" fr.'The Fantasticks'
(H.Schmidt-T.Jones) *1998 TV version sung by* NORMAN
GROULX *unavailable* / previous version by RICHARD
DARBYSHIRE *VIRGIN (EMI): VSCDT(VSC) 1584 deleted*

KENCO RAPPOR 2 "Little Green Bag" by the GEORGE BAKER
SELECTION *LASERLIGHT (BMG): CD 16029 (CD) also on
'RESERVOIR DOGS' -S/T- MCA: MCD 10793 (CD)*

KENCO RAPPOR 1 "She Sells Sanctuary" by The CULT on
'Pure Cult' *BEGGARS BANQUET (TEN): BEGA 130CD (CD)
also on* 'SWITCHED ON' *TELSTAR: TTVCD 3086 (2CD)*

KENWOOD BREAD MAKER "Three Steps To Heaven" sung by
EDDIE COCHRAN *SEE FOR MILES (Pinn): SEECD 271 (CD)*

KFC 11 (Honey Barbecue Tower Burger) "Sledgehammer" by
PETER GABRIEL on 'SO' *CHARISMA-VIRGIN: PGCD 5 (CD)*

KFC 9 ""Life Of Riley" (I.Broudie) LIGHTNING SEEDS on
'Sense' *VIRGIN (EMI): CDV 2690 (CD) TCV 2690 (MC)*
KFC 8 "Disco Inferno" by The TRAMMPS *see KFC 2*

KFC 7 "Twist" (Ballard) HANK BALLARD & MIDNITERS on
'20 Hits' *KING USA (Koch): KCD 5003 (CD)*
KFC 6 "Easy" (L.Richie) The COMMODORES on 'Very Best'
MOTOWN (Univ): 530 457-2 (CD)
KFC 5 "That Sound!" by MICHAEL MOOG *Warner Music
(Ten): FCD 374 (CDs) FCS 374 (MC) FX 374 (12"s)*
KFC 4 "We Are Family" *originally by* SISTER SLEDGE on
'Very Best' *ATLANTIC-WEA: 9548 31813-2 (CD) -4(MC)*
KFC 3 "She's Not There" (R.Argent) *orig* The ZOMBIES &
COLIN BLUNSTONE *SEE FOR MILES (Pinn): SEECD 30 (CD)*
KFC 2 (Fire Station) "Disco Inferno" from) 'SATURDAY
NIGHT FEVER' by TRAMMPS -S/T- *POLY: 825 389-2 (CD)*
KFC 1 "Canteloupe (Island)" (Herbie Hancock) version
US3 on Collection 'Jazz Moods' *TELSTAR (BMG): TCD
2722 (CD) STAC 2722 (MC) ALSO by* HERBIE HANCOCK on
'Best Of H.Hancock' *BLUENOTE (EMI): BNZ 143 (CD)*
KILKENNY IRISH BEER 2 "She Moves Through The Fair"
by SHANE McGOWAN *TV version unavailable. other
recordings inc.* FEARGAL SHARKEY on 'CELTIC MOODS'
KILKENNY IRISH BEER 1 "Need Your Love So Bad" (Green)
FLEETWOOD MAC on 'Greatest Hits' *SONY Nice Price
Collection: R.460704-2 (CD) -4 (MC)*
KISS 100 "25 Miles 2001" by The THREE AMIGOS
WONDERBOY (UNIV): WBOYD 25 (CDs) WBOYC 25 (MCs)
KISS 100 "Mucho Mambo" by SHAFT (based on 'Sway')
*WONDERBOY-UNIVERSAL: WBOYD 015 (CDs) WBOYC 015 (MC)
also on 'SWITCHED ON' TELSTAR: TTVCD 3086 (2CD)*
KIT-KAT 3 (Parking ticket ad) "5 Contredanses" 1st
movement K.609 (MOZART) *version by* VIENNA MOZART
ENSEMBLE (W.Boskovsky) *DECCA CLASS: 433 323-2 (CD)*
KIT-KAT 2 (Daleks ad) "Romance No.2 in F op.50 violin &
orch" (BEETHOVEN) *version UNIV: 425 851-2 (CD)*
KIT KAT 1 "Have Yourself A Merry Little Christmas" (H.
Martin-R.Blane) sung by JUDY GARLAND on 'Very Best
Of Judy Garland *PLATINUM (PRISM) PLATCD 513 (CD)*
KLEENEX Double Velvet "Blue Velvet" (Wayne-Morris)
TV version unavailable / orig BOBBY VINTON "16 MOST
REQUESTED SONGS' *COLUMBIA (Ten): 469 091-2 (CD)*
KNORR (various) "Perpetuum Mobile" by The PENGUIN CAFE
ORCHESTRA on 'Preludes Airs and Yodels' *AMBIENT-
VIRGIN (EMI): AMBT 15 (CD)*
KOLOR AT SUPERDDRUG "Popcorn" (G.Kingsley) HOT BUTTER
on 'It's The Seventies' *MCI (Pinn): MCCD 300 (CD)*
KP LOWER FAT CRISPS "It Started With A Kiss" (E.Brown)
HOT CHOCOLATE *RAK (EMI): CDP 746375-2 (CD)*
KRAFT "Mellow Yellow" DONOVAN on 'TOTALLY COMMERCIALS'
EMI (EMI): 495 475-2 (CD)
KRAFT DAIRY LEA "You Were Made For Me" (Mitch Murray)
FREDDIE & THE DREAMERS on 'Very Best Of' on
MFP EMI: CDMFP 6382 (CD)

KRONENBOURG 3 "Slip Into Something More Comfortable"
KINOBE 'Soundphiles' *PEPPER (Pinn): 923 027-2 (CD)*
also on 923 026-2 (CDs)
KRONENBOURG 2 "She" sung by CHARLES AZNAVOUR
ENGLISH VERSION *EMI PREMIER: PRMTVCD 4 (CD)*
FRENCH VERSION *EMI: CDEMC 3716 (CD) deleted*
KRONENBOURG 1 (French rap) "A La Claire Fontaine" by
MC SOLAAR on 'Prose Combat' *POLY: 521 289-2 (CD)*
KWIK-FIT song based on "The Thing" (Grean) original by
PHIL HARRIS *LIVING ERA-ASV (Koch): CDAJA 5191 (CD)*
L'EGOISTE AFTERSHAVE Chanel "Dance Of The Knights"
from Act.1 of 'Romeo And Juliet' Op.64 (PROKOFIEV)
L'OREAL ELVIVE "Encore Une Fois" by SASH and RODRIGUEZ
from album 'It's My Life' *BYTE BLUE (Arabesque/*
Amati): SRCD 5424-2 (CD) and MULTIPLY: MULTYCD 1
also on 'SWITCHED ON' *TELSTAR: TTVCD 3086 (2CD)*
LADYBIRD COLL 2 Woolworths "Into Each Life Some Rain
Must Fall" (Roberts-Fisher) by The INK SPOTS
CONNOISSEUR (Pinn): XPOTTCD 201 (CD)
LADYBIRD COLL 1 Woolworths "Q5 Theme"/"Ning Nang
Nong" (Spike Milligan) SPIKE MILLIGAN 'A Collect
ion Of Spikes' *EMI: CDECC 11 (CD) ECC 11 (MC)*
LANCOME PERFUME - *see 'OUI'*
LAND ROVER DISCOVERY "Mad Alice Lane (A Ghost Story)"
(Peter Lawlor) by LAWLOR *WATER (3MV-Sony) WAT 1CD*
(CDs) WAT 1MC(MC) see COLL 'SPIRITS OF NATURE'
LANSON CHAMPAGNE "Tipitina" PROFESSOR LONGHAIR 'Big Chi
ef' *TOMATO/PLAY IT AGAIN SAM (Vital):598109320 (CD)*
LEE JEANS 3 (Hard To Be Parted From ad) music by
JOHN ALTMAN *Jeff Wayne Productions unavailable*
LEE JEANS 2 "Legends" by SACRED SPIRIT *VIRGIN (EMI):*
VSCDT 1598 (CDs) VSC 1598 (MC) from album 'SACRED
SPIRIT 2' *VIRGIN (EMI): CDV(TCV) 2827 (CD/MC)*
LEE JEANS 1 "Baby Lee" (J.L.Hooker) JOHN LEE HOOKER
with ROBERT CRAY on 'The Healer' *SILVERTONE (Pinn)*
ORE(CD)(MC) 508 (CD/MC) / ORE(CD)(C) 81 (CDs/MC)
LEMSIP 3 "Always Care For Me" (Mike Connaris for
MCASSO Productions) *unavailable*
LEMSIP 2 "Moon River" (Henry Mancini-Johnny Mercer)
HENRY MANCINI *see 'Henry Mancini' Collections*
LEMSIP 1 "Goodnight Sweetheart Well It's Time To Go"
(Calvin Carter-James Hudson) by The SPANIELS on
'Play It Cool' *CHARLY R&B: CDCHARLY 222 (CD)*
LEVI 36 (Twisted) "Before You Leave" by PEPE DeLUXE
INCREDIBLE (TEN) 671 239-2 (CDs) + 'SUPER SOUND'
CATSKILLS (Pinn): RIDC 002 (CD)
LEVI 35 (Twisted Jeans) "Itchy and Scratchy" BOSS HOGG
from 'Whiteout' *CITY SLANG (Vital): 201 502-2 (CD)*
LEVI 34 (Twisted Jeans) "Second Line" CLINIC
DOMINO (Vital): RUG 116CD (CDs) from 'Internal
Wrangler' album *DOMINO (Vital): WIGCD 078 (CD)*
LEVI 33 (Twisted Jeans) "You Make Me Feel" by ARCHIVE
'Take My Head' *INDEPENDIENTE (TEN):ISOM 10CD (CD)*

LEVI 32 (Twisted Jeans) "Dirge" by DEATH IN VEGAS on
CONCRETE/ARISTA (BMG): 74321 75544-2 (CDs) from
'Contino Sessions' *CONCRETE (BMG)*: HARD 41CD (CD)
LEVI 31 (Sta-Prest) 'Guitar' based on "The Bass Walks"
(Kaempfert) *orig* BERT KAEMPFERT ORCH *POLYDOR (-)*
LEVI 30 (Sta-Prest) "Flat Beat" from 'Analogue Worms
Attack" (Quentin Dupieux) MR.OIZO *F.COMM (Vital)*
F.104CD (CDs) also on 'SWITCHED ON' *TELSTAR:
TTVCD 3086 (2CD)* / *note: Country song insert*
"What's Happened To Me" by DON GIBSON *Hickory USA*
LEVI 1-29 *see previous TELE-TUNES books*
LEVI DOCKERS "Tu Vuo Fa L'Americano" (Nisa-Carosone)
vers arr.by JOHN ALTMAN (JEFF WAYNE M) *unavailable*
orig version by RENATO CAROSONE (1959) *deleted*
LEXUS - *see under* TOYOTA LEXUS
LILT "Come Dig It" (Machel Montano) by MACHEL *LONDON
(UNIV)*: LONCD 386 (CDs) LONCS 386(MC) *deleted*
LINDT CHOCOLATE "Wild Is The Wind" (Tiomkin-Washington)
sung by NINA SIMONE on Coll 'TOTALLY COMMERCIALS'
EMI (EMI): 495 475-2 (CD)
LINK The (Mobile Phones) track based on SHED SEVEN song
"Speakeasy" from 'Change Giver' *UNIV:523 615-2 (CD)*
LISTERINE MOUTHWASH "Kiss" (Prince) TOM JONES with Art
Of Noise on 'At This Moment' *JIVE (BMG)*: TOMCD 1
(CD) TOMTC 1 (MC) TOMTV 1 (LP)
LITTLEWOODS (Berkertex Fashion Range) "Perdido" (Juan
Tizol-H.Lenk-E.Drake) DUKE ELLINGTON ORCHESTRA on
COLUMBIA (Ten): 476 719-2 (CD) -4 (MC)
LLOYDS TSB.COM INSURANCE "Call Mr Irresponsible" (Cahn-
Van Huesen) *TV Vers.unavailable* based on JACK JONES
recording *EMPORIO*: EMPRCD 630 (CD) 'LIVE RECORDING'
LLOYDS TSB 2 "What Can I Do" 'Talk On Corners' The
CORRS *LAVA-ATLANTIC (TEN)*: 7567 83051-2(CD) -4(MC)
LLOYDS TSB 1 "Let's Work Together" by CANNED HEAT
LIBERTY (EMI): CZ 226 (CD) TCGO 2026 (MC) 'Best Of'
LLOYDS BANK (Black Horse ad 2) music prod.by JOE & CO
based on Symph.No.1 (BRAHMS) *TV version unavailable*
LLOYDS BANK (Black Horse ad 1) "Zion Hears The Watchmen
Singing" ('Wachet Auf,Ruft Uns Die Stimme')
"Cantata No.BWV 140" (J.S.BACH) *various recordings*
LOCAL ELECTIONS - **see under HOME OFFICE**
LOCKETS "After The Storm" from 'Pastoral Symphony'
Number 9 (BEETHOVEN) *many recordings available*
LUCOZADE 5 "Firestarter" by PRODIGY from 'Fat Of The
Land' *XL (Vital)*: XLCD 121 (CD) XLMC 121 (MC)
LUCOZADE 4 "Lara Croft Goes To The Dogs" by ANTHONY
PARTOS *unavailable*
LUCOZADE 3 'Quadrophenia' "Louie Louie" by KINGSMEN
on 'SON OF CULT FICTION' *VIRGIN*: VTCD 114 (CD)
also on *CHARLY (Koch)*: CPCD 8160 (CD)
LUCOZADE 2 (NRG) "Leave You Far Behind" LUNATIC CALM
MCA (UNI): MCSTD 40131 (CDs) *deleted*
LUCOZADE 1 "EVA" (Prilly-Perrault-Badale)JEAN JACQUES
PERREY *MOOG INDIGO BGP-ACE (Pinn)*: CDBGPM 103 (CD)

LUNN POLY "There She Goes" by The LA's on
  GO DISCS (UNIV): 828 202-2 (CD)
LUNN POLY (THOMSON AT) "Love Is Just Around The Corner"
  (Robin-Gensler) played by LEO ADDEO & HIS ORCH
  RCA (BMG): 07863 66647-2 (CD)
LURPAK 2 "Flight Of The Bumblebee" (RIMSKY-KORSAKOV)
  and part of "Requiem" (FAURE) *many recordings*
LURPAK 1 "Spread A Little Happiness" from the Musical
  'Mr.Cinders' (V.Ellis-R.Myers-G.Newman) - STING on
  A.& M.: AMS 8242 (7"s) see also 'Mr.Cinders' SHOWS
LYCOS.CO.UK "Puppy Love" (P.Anka) *TV VERS.unavailable*
  DONNY OSMOND on *POLYDOR (Univ): 527 072-2 (CD)*
LYNX (5) (Toe-nail seduction ad) "Chewy Chewy" by The
  OHIO EXPRESS *REPERTOIRE: REP 4017 (CD)*
LYNX 4 (Pied-Piper ad) "Bentley's Gonna Sort You Out"
  BENTLEY RHYTHM ACE from 1997 self titled album
  PARLOPHONE EMI: (CD)(TC)PCS 7391 & PCS 7391 (2LP)
  also on 'SWITCHED ON' *TELSTAR: TTVCD 3086 (2CD)*
LYNX 3 (caveman) "Mini-Skirt" (D.J.Esquivel) ESQUIVEL
  on 'LOUNGECORE' *RCA (BMG): 74321 57815-2 (CD)* and
  'Cabaret Manana' *RCA (BMG): 07863 66657-2 (CD)*
LYNX 2 (elevator) original music produced by NOVA
  PRODUCTIONS (Paris, France) *unavailable*
LYNX 1 "Boom Shack-A-Lak" by APACHE INDIAN
  from 'Make Way For The Indian' on *ISLAND (UNIV):*
  CID 8016 (CD) ICT 8016 (MC) ILPSD 8016 (2LP)

M.& M.'s 2 "Nocturne in E.Flat" (CHOPIN)
  various recordings available
M.& M.'s 1 (fun pack) "Trip Your Trigger" by
  Stephen Williams *unavailable*
McCAINS HOME FRIES 2 "O Mio Babbino Caro" from PUCCINI
  opera 'Gianni Schicchi' MONSERRAT CABBALE and LSO
  EMI: CDC 747 841-2 (CD) also avilable by
  LESLEY GARRETT on 'Diva' *S.SCREEN: SONGCD 903 (CD)*
McCAINS HOME FRIES 1 "I'm A Believer" (N.Diamond) The
  MONKEES on 'Greatest Hits' *WEA: 0630 12171-2 (CD)*
McCAINS MICRO CHIPS "Yakety Yak" (Leiber-Stoller) *orig*
  COASTERS 'G.Hits' *ATLANTIC (TEN): 7567 90386-2 (CD)*
McDONALDS 4 'Hot Dog' "Hot Diggity" (Hoffman-Manning)
  TV version unavailable based on PERRY COMO version
  'VERY BEST OF' *RCA (BMG): 07863 67968-2 (CD)*
McDONALDS 3 'Euro 2000'ad "If The Kids Are United" by
  SHAM 69 'Best Of' *ESSENTIAL (Pinn): ESMCD 512 (CD)*
McDONALDS 2 'Baby ad'"Baby Sittin' Boogie" (J.Parker)
  TV VERSION based on RALPH BENDIX recording *deleted*
  BUZZ CLIFFORD version on 'TEEN IDOLS' collection
  COLLECTORS CHOICE (Silver Sounds): CCM 5800-2 (CD)
McDONALDS 1 'Bacon Roll ad' "AYLA" MINISTRY OF SOUND
  compilation 'TRANCE NATION 2' on *CDTIV 117 (CDs)*
  MINISTRY OF SOUND (3MV-TEN): TN(CD)(MC) 2 (CD/MC)
McEWANS LAGER ('Trainspotting' montage) "Do What You
  Wanna Do" EDDIE & THE HOT RODS on 'Best Of Eddie
  and The Hot Rods *ISLAND (UNIV): IMCD 156 (CD)*

McVITIES BN "Mah Na Ma Nah" (Piero Umiliani) orig.by
The MUPPETS / PIERO UMILIANI *both versions deleted*
MACLEANS TOOTHPASTE "Cold As Ice" by MOP from album
'Warriorz' *LOUD-EPIC (TEN): 498 277-2 (CD)*
MAGNUM CARAMEL & NUTS BAR "True" by SPANDAU BALLET on
'GOLD' *CHRYSALIS (EMI): 526 700-2 (CD) -4 (MC)*
MALTESERS "Tease Me" by CHAKA DEMUS & PLIERS on 'Tease
Me" *MANGO-ISLAND (UNIV): CIDMX(MCTX) 1102 (CD/MC)*
MARTINI "Enchant Me" by AMALGAMATION OF SOUNDZ on
FILTER (Pinn): FILT 041CD (CD) FILT 036CD (CDs)
MARTINI V2 2 (Italian Job ad) "Return Of The Carboot
Techodisco Roadshow" from 'BRA' BENTLEY RHYTHM ACE
PARLOPHONE-EMI: CD(PCS)7391 (CD/MC) PCS 7391 (2LP)
MARTINI V2 1 "Oceana" (Matt Fowler) by MUMBLES (USA)
'AUDIO ALCHEMY' *UBIQUITY (Timewarp): URCD 020 (CD)*
MASTERCARD 4 "Body Groove" by The ARCHITECHS feat NANA
GO BEAT (Univ): GOBCD 33 (CDs) GOBX 33 (12"s)
MASTERCARD 3 "Have A Go Hero" by URBAN DK from album on
CRITICAL MASS (Amato-Vital): CRIT 9001 (CD)
also on 'SWITCHED ON' *TELSTAR: TTVCD 3086 (2CD)*
MASTERCARD 2 "Angelina" (Allan Roberts-Doris Fisher-
Paolo Citarella-L.Prima) perf.by LOUIS PRIMA ORCH
*CAPITOL (EMI): CZ 423 (CDP 794072-2) (CD) also on
CO11 'TOTALLY COMMERCIALS' EMI: 495 475-2 (CD)*
MASTERCARD 1 Football "I Believe" by EMF from 'Schubert
Dip' *EMI-PARLOPHONE: CD(TC)PCS 7353 (CD/MC)*
MATALAN STORES "I Get The Sweetest Feeling" (Van McCoy
Alicia Evelyn) *TV VERS.unavailable* / JACKIE WILSON
'Very Best Of J.Wilson' *ACE (Pinn): CDCHK 913 (CD)*
MAX FACTOR (Madonna) "Ray Of Light" by MADONNA from RAY
OF LIGHT *MAVERICK (TEN): 9362 46847-2 (CD) -4 (MC)*
MAXWELL HOUSE 3 "Honey Honey" composed and sung by MOBY
from album 'Play' *MUTE (Vital): CDSTUMM 172 (CD)
CSTUMM 172 (MC) MDSTUMM 172 (MD)*
MAXWELL HOUSE 2 "Going Home" (M.Knopfler) from film
'Local Hero' -S/T- *VERTIGO (UNIV): 811 038-2 (CD)*
MAXWELL HOUSE 1 "The Mission" (Ennio Morricone) from
film -S/T- of the 1986 Robert De Niro-Jeremy Irons
movie *VIRGIN (UNIV): CDV 2402 (CD) TCV 2402 (MC)*
MAYNARDS JUST FRUITS based on "Gimme Dat Ding" (Mike Ha
zlewood-Albert Hammond) orig The PIPKINS (1970)
MAYNARDS WINE GUMS 2 "Goodies" *TV version unavailable*
orig theme (B.Oddie-M.Gibbs) 'BEST OF THE GOODIES'
CASTLE PIE (Pinn): PIESD 243 (CD)
MAYNARDS WINE GUMS 1 "Hoots Mon" LORD ROCKINGHAM'S XI
(1959) Coll 'AND THE BEAT GOES ON VOLUME 4'
DEBUTANTE (UNIV): 555 000-2
MAZDA CARS "Silver Machine" (R.Calvert-S.McManus) by
HAWKWIND (originally 1972 from 'SILVER MACHINE')
SPECTRUM-UNIVERSAL: 550 764-2 (CD)
MERCEDES 4 "I Can Help" (Swan) by BILLY SWAN on 'Best
of Billy Swan' *MONUMENT (TEN): 491 449-2 (CD)*
MERCEDES 3 "If Everybody Looked The Same" GROOVE ARMADA
'Vertigo' *PEPPER (Pinn): 053 033-2 (CD) -4 (MC)*

MERCEDES 2 (A Class) "Fun Lovin' Criminal" by FUN
LOVIN' CRIMINALS from 'Come Find Yourself' on
CHRYSALIS (EMI): CD(TC)CHR 6113 (CD/MC/LP)
also on 'SWITCHED ON' *TELSTAR: TTVCD 3086 (2CD)*

MERCEDES 1 "Mercedes Benz" (Oh Lord Why Won't You Buy
Me A MERCEDES BENZ) by JANIS JOPLIN from 'Pearl'
COLUMBIA (Ten): CD 480 415-2 (CD)

MICHELOB LAGER 2 "Possente-Possente" (Act 1 'AIDA')
VERDI *(TV vers.unavailable)* also on Coll 'Relaxing
Opera' *CFP (EMI): CD(TC)CFP 4664 (CD/MC)*

MICHELOB LAGER 1 "Put A Little Love In Your Heart" (J
De Shannon-Holiday-Myers) *by* JACKIE DE SHANNON
'Definitive Collect' *EMI LIBERTY: 829 786-2 (CD)*
also on 'TOTALLY COMMERCIALS' *EMI: 495 475-2 (CD)*

MICROSOFT XP "Ray Of Light" by MADONNA on album 'RAY
OF LIGHT' *MAVERICK (TEN):9362 46847-2 (CD) -4 (MC)*

MICROSOFT PRODUCTS "Heroes" (D.Bowie) by DAVID BOWIE
EMI: CDP 797720-2 (CD)

MICROSOFT WINDOWS 95 "Start Me Up" (Jagger-Richard)
ROLLING STONES 'Tattoo You' *VIRGIN: CDV 2732 (CD)*

MILK 2 Dancing Bottles "Grasshopper's Dance" (Ernest
BUCALSSI) PALM COURT THEATRE ORCH. 'Picnic Party'
CHANDOS: CHAN 8437 (CD) LBT 002 (MC)

MILK 1 "Clog Dance" from ballet 'LA FILLE MAL GARDEE'
(Louis HEROLD) *EMI EMINENCE: CDEMX 2268 (CD)*

MILK TRAY (Cadbury's) (orig)"The Night Rider" (Chris
Adams) by ALAN HAWKSHAW on Coll 'SOUND GALLERY' on
EMI STUDIO TWO: CD(TC)TWO 2001 (CD/MC) also on
'TOTALLY COMMERCIALS' *EMI (EMI): 495 475-2 (CD)*

MILLER (Lite/Genuine Draft ads)

MILLER 9 "Loco" by the FUN LOVIN'CRIMINALS
CHRYSALIS (EMI): CDCHS 5121 (CDs) TCCHS 5121 (MC)
'LOCO' album *CHRYSALIS (EMI): 531 471-2 (CD)*

MILLER 8 (Rock The House ad) "What I Like About You"
LOOP DA LOOP (Nick Dresti) on coll 'SWITCHED ON'
TELSTAR: TTVCD 3986 (2CD)

MILLER 7 (Beer Breath) "Multi Family Garage Sale" by
LAND OF LOOPS *POP (Cargo-Greyhound): UP 011 (7"s)*

MILLER 6 (Honk Bobo) "900 NUMBER" (Jones) by 45 KING
TUFF CITY (Cargo): TUFFEP 3001 (12"s)

MILLER 5 (Opera) "Je Veux Vivre" from ROMEO & JULIET
(GOUNOD) *version by* INESSA GALANTI (debut album)
*CAMPION: RRCD 1335 (CD) / also available complete
version EMI: CDS5 56123-2 (CD)*

MILLER 4 (Rob) "Girl At The Bus Stop" by MY DRUG HELL
VOLTONE (Shellshock-Pinn-DISC): VTONECD 001X (CD)

MILLER 3 "Town Without Pity" (D.Tiomkin-N.Washington)
sung by EDDI READER on *BLANCO Y NEGRO
(TEN): NEG 90CD (CDs) NEG 90MC (MC)*

MILLER 2 Lite "Somewhere Down The Crazy River" ROBBIE
ROBERTSON *GEFFEN-MCA (UNI): GFLD 19294 (CD)*

MILLER 1 Lite "He Ain't Heavy He's My Brother" by The
HOLLIES *EMI: CDP 746238-2 (CD)*

MINUMUM WAGE "Fine Time" by The CAST from 'All Change'
POLYDOR: 529 312-2 (CD)
MITSUBISHI CARISMA "Zip-A-Dee-Doo-Dah"(Gilbert-Wrubel)
(Disney's 'Song Of The South') *orig* 'DISNEY'S HIT
SINGLES' *WALT DISNEY (UNIV): WD 11563-2 (CD)*
MORE! Magazine "Give It Up" KING ARTHUR *WONDERBOY Univ*
MORE THAN.(Royal & Sun Alliance) "Old Shep" (Red Foley)
TV vers.unavailable / ELVIS PRESLEY on Collection
'ELVIS RE-MASTERED' *RCA (BMG): 07863 67736-2 (CD)*
MORGAN STANLEY DEAN WITTER credit card (2) "Five" by
LAMB 'Fear Of Fours' *FONTANA (UNIV): 558 821-2 (CD)*
MORGAN STANLEY DEAN WITTER credit card (1) "Heat Miser"
by MASSIVE ATTACK from 'Protection' album' on
WILD BUNCH-VIRGIN (EMI): WBRCD 2 (CD)
MOTOROLA 2 "Come On Baby" by the PSYCHO COWBOYS on
WALL OF SOUND (Prime-Vital): WALLD 055 (CDs)
MOTOROLA 1 (Wings)"You Can't Always Get What You Want"
(Jagger-Richards) The ROLLING STONES from 'Let It
Bleed' *DECCA (UNIV): 820 052-2 (CD)*
MULLERICE 2 "The Saint" by ORBITAL -S/T- 'THE SAINT'
VIRGIN: CDVUS 126 (CD)
MULLERICE 1 "(This Is The) Captain Of Your Ship" orig.
REPARATA & DELRONS *RCA BMG: 74321 44923-2 (CD Coll*
N.H.S.DIRECT "Sanvean I Am Your Shadow" LISA GERRARD
from album 'The Mirror Pool' *4AD-B.Banquet
(RTM-DISC): CAD 5009CD (CD) CADC 5009 (MC)*
N.S.P.C.C. "Pie Jesu" (Andrew LLoyd Webber) sung by
CHARLOTTE CHURCH on Coll 'Voice Of An Angel'
SONY CLASSICAL: SK 60957 (CD)
N.T.L. "On Every Street" (Mark Knopfler-Nick Amore)
originally DIRE STRAITS album 'On Every Street'
TV Version unavailable
NAT.WEST 4 (trendy wine bar ad) "Gambling Joint"
(Kurt WEILL) *DeWOLFE-HUDSON unavailable*
NAT.WEST 3 "Rodney Yates" by DAVID HOLMES from 'Let's
Get Killed' *GO BEAT (UNIV): 539 100-2 (CD)*
also on 'SWITCHED ON' *TELSTAR: TTVCD 3086 (2CD)*
NAT.WEST 2 ('Nat West.Com') "Hang Up Your Hang-Ups" by
HERBIE HANCOCK on 'VSOP' *SONY JAZZ: 486 569-2 (CD)*
NAT.WEST 1 (Air Miles) "Maybe Tomorrow" by TERRY BUSH
from TV series 'The Littlest Hobo' *unavailable*
version by 'SCOOT' on collect 'BEST TV ADS...EVER'
VIRGIN (EMI): VTDCDX 306 (2CD) VTDMC 306 (MC)
NATREL PLUS Flower Girl "Read My Lips (Saturday Night
Party)" (A.Party) ALEX PARTY *CLEVELAND CITY BLUE
(3MV Sony): CCICD 17000 (CDs) CCI 17000 (12"s)*
NATREL PLUS (Willow ad) "Sex Sleep Eat And Drink" by
KING CRIMSON *DISCIPLINE-VIRGIN (EMI):KCCDY1 (CDs)*
NEW ZEALAND TOURIST BOARD "Don't Dream It's Over" by
CROWDED HOUSE on *CAPITOL (EMI): CDESTU 2016 (CD)*
NIGHT NURSE "Night Nurse" *TV VERS.arranged by MCASSO*
SLY & ROBBIE, SIMPLY RED on 'Friends' *(EAST WEST)*
original by GREGORY ISAACS on 'Night Nurse' album
REGGAE REFRESHERS (Univ): RRCD 9 (CD)

NIKE 7 (Euro 2000) "Know How" YOUNG MC on 'Stone Cold
   Rhymin' *4TH & BROADWAY-ISL (Univ): IMCD 122 (CD)*
NIKE 6 "Easy Listening Superstar" LE HAMMOND INFERNO
   'SWITCHED ON' *TELSTAR: TTVCD 3086 (2CD)*
NIKE 5 TIGER WOODS ad "Straight Down The Middle"
   (Burke-Van Huesen) BING CROSBY on 'Quintessential'
   CASTLE (BMG): CTVMC 211 (MC)
NIKE 4 Roll on 2002, World Cup ad "You're Nobody Now"
   EMBRACE from 'Good Will Out' *HUT-VIRGIN (EMI)*
   CDHUT 46 (CD) HUTMC 46 (MC) MDHUT 46 (MD)
NIKE 3 (Brazil Football.airport ad) "Mas Que Nada"
   (a) TAMBA TRIO from 'NOVA BOSSA RED HOT AND VERVE'
   VERVE (UNIV): 535 884-2 (CD) and TLCD 34 (CDs)
   (b) SERGIO MENDEZ on 'MUNDO LATINO' *VERVE (UNIV):*
                         841 396-2 (CD) -4(MC)
   (c) RENALDO'S REVENGE (Re-mixed version) *(AM:PM)*
   (d) ECHOBEATZ (dance v) *ETERNAL: WEA176(CD)(T)(C)*
NIKE 2 Brazil Football.beach ad "Soul Bossa Nova" by
   QUINCY JONES 'MUNDO LATINO' *SONY:SONYTV2(CD)(MC)*
   also 'AUSTIN POWERS' -S/T- *POLYD: 162 112-2 (CD)*
NIKE 1 (Eric Cantona ad) "Parklife" by BLUR
   FOOD (EMI): FOOD(CD)(MC)(LP) 10
NIMBLE BREAD (60's ad) "I Can't Let Maggie Go" (Pete
   Dello) The HONEYBUS on 'At Their Best' on
   See For Miles (Pinn): SEECD 264 (CD)
· **NISSAN** (theme) "Astrea" by JOHN HARLE on 'SILENCIUM'
   ARGO-DECCA (UNIV): 458 356-02 (CD)
NISSAN: (321 Committ:MICRA/ALMERA/PRIMERA) "Sugar Baby
   Love" (Bickerton-Waddington) RUBETTES 'Best Of'
   POLYDOR: 843 896-2 (CD) also 'It's The Sensation
   al Seventies' *MCI (THE-DISC): MCD 051 (CD)*
NISSAN ALMERA 3 "Find My Baby" by MOBY from 'PLAY'
   MUTE (Vital): (CD)(CS)(MD)STUMM 172 (CD/MC/md)
NISSAN ALMERA 2 "The Sweeney" theme by HARRY SOUTH
   see COLL.2,6,109,110,270,360,390,
NISSAN ALMERA 1 "The Professionals" (Laurie Johnson)
   see COLL.6,149,215,217,360,363,
NISSAN MICRA 3 "The Glory Of Love" (B.Hill) *version*
   JIMMY DURANTE *WB (TEN): 9362 45456-2 (CD)*
NISSAN MICRA 2 ('Hollywood') (Stuntman) "Beach Samba"
   ASTRUD GILBERTO on 'Beach Samba' *VERVE-POLYDOR*
   (UNIV.): 519 801-2 (CD)
NISSAN MICRA 1 "You Don't Love Me (No No No)" (Dawn
   Penn) DAWN PENN
NISSAN PRIMERA 3 "Aquarium" 'Carnival Of The Animals'
   (SAINT-SAENS) I MUSICI DE MONTREAL (Turovsky)
   CHANDOS: CHAN 9246 (CD)
NISSAN PRIMERA 2 "Wild Thing" (Chip Taylor) TROGGS
   'Greatest Hits' *POLYGRAM: 522 739-2 (CD)*
NISSAN PRIMERA 1 New Primera 1996 "Lifted" sung by
   LIGHTHOUSE FAMILY from album 'Ocean Drive'
   POLDOR: 523 787-2(CD) -4(MC) / 851 669-2 CD s
NO.7 - see BOOTS NO.7

NOA by Cacherel "Song To The Siren" performed by
THIS MORTAL COIL on album 'It'll End In Tears'
4AD (Vital): CAD 411 (CD) CADC 411 (MC)

NOKIA "Gran Vals" (Francisco TARREGA) *version on COLL*
'19th Century Guitar Fav.'played by NORBERT KRAFT
NAXOS (Select): 8.553007 (CD)

NORWICH UNION "Part Of The Union" (Hudson-Ford)
by the STRAWBS on 'Halcyon Days (Very Best Of)'
A.& M. (UNIV): 540 662-2 (2CD)

NOUVELLE "Alla Hornpipe" from 'Water Music' (HANDEL)
many recorded versions available

NTL "On Every Street" (Mark Knopfler-Nick Amore)
originally DIRE STRAITS album 'On Every Street'
TV Version unavailable

NUROFEN FOR CHILDREN "Yeah Yeah" The RIOTS from 'The
TROJAN Story Vol.1' *TROJAN (Proper):CDTAL100 (2CD)*

O **LD SPICE** 2 "I Feel Good" (Brown) JAMES BROWN 'Very
Best of James Brown' *Poly: 845 828-2(CD) -4(MC)*

OLD SPICE 1 "Prima Vere" (Carmina Burana) (Carl ORFF)
various recordings available

ON DIGITAL CHAMPIONS LEAGUE "Gritty Shaker" by DAVID
HOLMES from 'Let's Get Killed' *UNIV: 539 100-2 (CD)*

ONE 2 ONE 2 (Gary Oldman ad) "Lovely Head" by GOLDFRAPP
on 'FELT MOUNTAIN' *MUTE (Vital): CDSTUMM 188 (CD)*
also CDMUTE 267 (CDs)

ONE 2 ONE 1 "Telephone and Rubber Band" (Simon
Jeffes) PENGUIN CAFE ORCHESTRA on 'Penguin Cafe Orc
hestra' *EG-VIRGIN (EMI): EEGCD 11(CD) OVEDC 429(MC)*

ONKEN BIOPOT "I Feel Good" by JAMES BROWN 'Very Best of
James Brown' *POLYDOR (UNIV): 845 828-2 (CD) -4 (MC)*

OPEN UNIVERSITY "Lily Was Here" by DAVE STEWART and
CANDY DULFER on compilation 'New Pure Moods'
VIRGIN VTDCD 158 (2CD)

ORANGE 6 "Sunday 8pm" (Rollo Armstrong-Sister Bliss) by
FAITHLESS *CHEEKY (BMG): 74321 81165-2 (2CD)*

ORANGE 5 "Loose Fit" by The HAPPY MONDAYS on 'GREATEST
HITS' *LONDON (Univ): 556 105-2 (CD) -4 (MC)*
also on 'SWITCHED ON' TELSTAR: TTVCD 3086 (2CD)

ORANGE 4 (dog ad) produced by HUM MUSIC PRODUCTIONS
French vocal by CHRISTIAN MARTEC *unavailable*

ORANGE 3 "I Loves You Porgy" (Gershwin) from 'Porgy
and Bess) by NINA SIMONE on 'TOTALLY COMMERCIALS'
EMI (EMI): 495 475-2 (CD) also 'Blue For You-Very
Best Of NINA SIMONE' *GLOBAL TV (BMG): RADCD 84*

ORANGE 2 "To Cure A Weakling Child" by The
APHEX TWIN from the album 'Richard D.James LP' on
WARP (RTM-Disc):WARP(CD)(MC)43

ORANGE 1 "Blow The Wind Southerly" arranged by
JOCELYN POOK and featuring KATHLEEN FERRIER on
VIRGIN (EMI): VTDCD 158 (2CD) 'New Pure Moods'
orig= KATHLEEN FERRIER solo on 'World Of Kathleen
Ferrier' *DECCA (UNIV): 430 096-2 (CD) -4 (MC)*

ORANGINA "Pida Me La" (Michel Berger) THE GYPSY KINGS
"Greatest Hits" *COLUMBIA: 477242-2 (CD) -4 (MC)*

ORGANICS 3 "Can't Take My Eyes Off You" sung by ANDY WILLIAMS 'IN THE LOUNGE WITH ANDY' *COLUMBIA (Ten): 490 618-2(CD) -4(MC) + 481 037-2(CD) -4(MC) also on* 'SWITCHED ON' *TELSTAR: TTVCD 3086 (2CD)*

ORGANICS 2 "There She Goes" by The LA's on *GO DISCS (UNIV): 828 202-2 (CD)*

ORGANICS 1 "You Sexy Thing" (Errol Brown-T.Wilson) HOT CHOCOLATE 'Greatest Hits' *EMI: CDEMTV 73 (CD)*

OUI Perfume (Lancome) "Everything's Gonna Be Alright" SWEETBOX *RCA (BMG): 74321 60684-2 (CDs) deleted*

OVALTINEYS (orig radio ads) "We Are The Ovaltineys Little Girls & Boys" (Ovaltineys Song) OVALTINEYS *EVERGREEN MUSIC (CD/MC)*

P.& O.STENA LINE "Riptide" (Gus Kahn-W.Donaldson) ROBERT PALMER 'Riptide' *ISLAND UNIV: IMCD 25(CD)*

P.& O.FERRIES "Stompin'At The Savoy" (Benny Goodman-A.Razaf-E.Sampson-C.Webb) BENNY GOODMAN on Coll: 'TOTALLY COMMERCIALS' *EMI (EMI): 495 475-2 (CD)*

PANTENE 4 "Higher and Higher" sung by JACKIE WILSON on 'Very Best Of J.Wilson' *ACE (Pinn):CDCHK 913 (CD)*

PANTENE 3 "All I Wanna Do" by SHERYL CROW on 'Tuesday Night Music Club' *A.& M. (Univ): 540 126-2 (CD)*

PANTENE 2 "You and Me Song" by the WANNADIES from CD 'Be A Girl' *INDOLENT-3MV (BMG):74321 32546-2 (CD)*

PANTENE 1 "Une Very Stylish Fille" DIMITRI FROM PARIS on 'Sacre Bleu' *EAST WEST (TEN) 0630 17832-2 (CD)*

PEDIGREE PUPPY "The Puppy Song" (Harry Nilsson) *orig by* NILSSON on 'Everybody's Talkin' (Very Best Of Harry Nilsson) *RCA BMG: 74321 47677-2 (CD)*

PEDIGREE SENIOR "Do The Dog" by RUFUS THOMAS on 'STAX REVUE' *STAX (Pinn): CDSXD 040 (CD)*

PEDIGREE PAL "I Love My Dog" by CAT STEVENS 'Ultimate Collect' *ISLAND (UNIV): CID 8079 (CD) ICT 8079(MC)*

PEDIGREE PAL ('Dog Head' ad) "Jesus" music by the TIGER LILLIES *recording unconfirmed*

PENTIUM 4 music by The BLUE MEN GROUP *unavailable*

PENTIUM 2 "Song 2" by BLUR *EMI: FOOD(CD)(MC)(LP) 19*

PEPSI 6 MAX "Thank Heaven For Little Girls" (GIGI) by LUSCIOUS JACKSON *USA Studio session unavailable*

PEPSI 5 NEXT GENERERATION "Step To Me" SPICE GIRLS *PEPSI promotions only*

PEPSI 4 "Rhythm Of My Heart" by ROD STEWART *W.BROS (TEN): W0017(7")(T=12")(MC)(CD)*

PEPSI 3 "Seal Our Fate" (G.Estefan) GLORIA ESTEFAN *EPIC (TEN): 656773-7(7") -6(12") -4(MC) -2(CDs)*

PEPSI 2 "The Best" (Knight-Chapman)- TINA TURNER 'Foreign Affair' *CAPITOL (EMI): CD(TC)ESTU 2103*

PEPSI 1 "It Takes Two" (W.Stevenson-S.Moy) ROD STEWART & TINA TURNER *W.BROS.(TEN) ROD 1(T)(C)(CD) / orig* MARVIN GAYE & KIM WESTON *MOTOWN UNIV:ZD 72397 (CD)*

PERRIER "Crossroads Blues" (Robert Johnson) on Collect 'King Of The Delta Blues Singers' *COLUMBIA (Ten): 4844102 (CD) + 'Complete Rec.'Sony: 46222-2 (CD) +* 'CROSSROADS' The BRIDGE *ILC (Ten): ILC 1CDS (CDs)*

PERSIL "Que Sera Sera" (Livingston-Evans) orig from
film 'Man Who Knew Too Much' with DORIS DAY on Coll
'Magic Of The Movies' *SONY (TEN): SONYTV 79 (2CD)*
PERSIL Capsules "Telstar" (J.Meek) *TV Vers unavailable*
TORNADOS *SEE FOR MILES: SEECD 445 (CD)*
PERSIL (Revive) music based on "Jesu Joy Of Man's
Desiring" (J.S.BACH) in style of Swingle Singers
PEUGEOT 106 2 KEY WEST/KEY LARGO "Open Your Heart" by
MADONNA from 'True Blue' (86) *SIRE (TEN):52*
925 442-2 (CD) WX 54C (MC) WX 54 (LP) & on single
PEUGEOT 106 1 "(We Want)The Same Thing" (R.Howells-E.
Shipley) BELINDA CARLISLE 'Best Of Belinda Vol.1'
VIRGIN (EMI): BELCD(MC)(MD)1 (CD/MC/md)
PEUGEOT 206 3 "Simply Beautiful" by AL GREEN on 'Im
Still In Love With You' *HI (UNIV): HILO 153 (CD)*
PEUGEOT 206 2 "Song 2" by BLUR (Damon Albarn)
EMI: FOOD(CD)(MC)(LP) 19
PEUGEOT 206 1 "Fly Away" by LENNY KRAVITZ from '5' on
*VIRGIN (EMI): CDVUS 140 (CD) VUCMC 140 (MC) MDVUS
40 (md)* also on *VUSCD 141 (CDsingle) VUSC 141 (MC)*
PEUGEOT 306 3 "Memories Are Made Of This" sung by
DEAN MARTIN *EMI-CAPITOL: 496 721-2 (CD) -4 (MC)*
PEUGEOT 306 2 "I Want Two Lips" by APRIL STEVENS on
'TEACH ME TIGER' *MARGINAL: MAR 086 (CD) deleted*
PEUGEOT 306 1 "Can't Take My Eyes Off You" sung by
ANDY WILLIAMS 'IN THE LOUNGE WITH ANDY' *COLUMBIA
(Ten): 490 618-2(CD) -4(MC) + 481 037-2(CD) -4(MC)*
also on 'SWITCHED ON' *TELSTAR: TTVCD 3086 (2CD)*
PEUGEOT 307 "Something Inside So Strong" LABI SIFFRE
on 'So Strong' *CHINA (TEN): 4509 96208-2 (CD)*
PEUGEOT 405 "Take My Breath Away" (Moroder-T.Whitlock)
BERLIN from -S/T- 'Top Gun' *COLUMBIA (Ten)*
PEUGEOT 406 "Proud" by HEATHER SMALL (album 'Proud')
ARISTA (BMG): 74321 76548-2 (CD)
PEUGEOT 406 3 "True Colors" sung by DOMINIQUE MOORE
unavailable (orig by CYNDI LAUPER)
PEUGEOT 406 2 (Kim Basinger) "Dream A Little Dream Of
Me" (Kahn-Schwandt-Andre) orig MAMAS AND PAPAS on
'20 GOLDEN GREATS' *MCA (UNI): MCLD 19125 (CD)*
PEUGEOT 406 1 "Search For The Hero" (Mike Pickering)
M.PEOPLE from 'Bizarre Fruit II' *De CONSTRUCTION
(BMG): 74321 32817-2 (CD) -4 (MC)*
PEUGEOT 607 "Blue Danube Waltz" (J.Strauss II) *Various*
PHILIPS PHILISHAVE FOR MEN "The Man Inside" by JOHN
SILVERMAN *unavailable*
PHILIPS STEREOS (TEST IT ON YOUR NEIGHBOURS) MOTORBASS
from 'PANSOUL' *DIFFERENT (Vital): DIF 001CD (CDs)*
PHILIPS WIDESCREEN "Getting Better" (Lennon-McCartney)
by GOMEZ on 'Abandoned Shopping Trolley Hotline'
HUT (EMI): CDHUTX 64 (CD)
PHOSTROGEN (Dancing Hedgehogs) "Ma Belle Marguerita"
from 'Bless The Bride' (V.Ellis-AP.Herbert)sung by
GEORGES GUETARY *DRG (New Note-Pinn): CDXP 605 (CD)*
ROSSENDALE MALE VOICE CHOIR *CHANDOS: CHAN 6604 CD*

PHYSIO SPORTS 4 "Love Boat Theme" (C.Fox-P.Williams)
TV Vers.unavailable. Orig JACK JONES on 'TVs GREAT
HITS VOL.3'*CINERAMA-EDEL (Vital): 002272-2 (CD)*
PHYSIO SPORTS 3 "Together We Are Beautiful" (K.Leray)
FERN KINNEY on 'ALL TIME GREATEST LOVE SONGS'
SONY TV: SONYTV 34CD (2CD) SONYTV 34MC (2MC)
PHYSIO SPORTS 2 "Sound Of Da Police" by KRS 1
also on 'SWITCHED ON' *TELSTAR: TTVCD 3086 (2CD)*
PHYSIO SPORTS 1 "Hersham Boys" by SHAM 69 'Best Of'
ESSENTIAL (BMG): ESMCD 512 (CD) also on 'First The
Best And The Last *POLYGRAM: 513 429-2 (CD)*
PILLSBURY THOMAS TOASTERS based on"Choo Choo Ch'Boogie"
TV vers unavailable orig recorded by LOUIS JORDAN &
TYMPANI 5 '5 Guys Name MOE' *MCA: MCLD 19048 (CD)*
PIRELLI TYRES 3 (Running Girl) "Elektrobank" CHEMICAL
BROTHERS *FREESTYLE DUST-VIRGIN (EMI):CHEMSD 6 CDs*
PIRELLI TYRES 2 "Riders On The Storm" (Densmore-Krieg
er-Morrison-Manzarek) THE DOORS on 'L.A.Woman'
ELEKTRA (WAR): K2-42090 (CD) K4 (MC)
PIRELLI TYRES 1 "Vesti La Giubba"'On With The Motley'
from 'Pagliacci' (LEONCAVALLO) vers.inc: FRANCO
CORELLI *EMI:CDC 747851-2(CD)* JOSE CARRERAS *HMV: EX
290811-3 (2LP) EX 290811-5 (2MC)* LUCIANO PAVAROTTI
DECCA:414590-2(2CD) JUSSI BJORLING *EMI:CDC 749503-2*
PIZZA HUT 2 'ITALIAN' "That's Amore" (Brooks-Warren)
DEAN MARTIN 'Very Best' *EMI: 496 721-2 (CD) -4(MC)*
PIZZA HUT 1 "Hot Hot Hot" by ARROW on 'Sound Of Soul'
BLATANT (Castle): BLATCD 11 (CD)
PLAYTEX "Cloud In The Sky" by ARCHIVE from album 'TAKE
MY HEAD' *INDEPENDIENTE (TEN): ISOM 10(CD)(MC)(LP)*
POLO SMOOTHIES "Ebben Ne Andro Lotana" Aria from act 1
of 'La Wally' by CATALINI *version by* RENATA TEBALDI
DECCA JUBILEE (Univ): 415 205-2 (CD)
POST OFFICE - see under ROYAL MAIL
PPP HEALTHCARE 2 "Boum!" CHARLES TRENET on 'PARIS..
CAFE CONCERT' *FLAPPER (Pavilion-Pinn): PASTCD 9797*
also 'Extraordinary Garden Best Of CHARLES TRENET'
EMI: CDP 794 464-2 (CD) / *also available on* 'Boum'
MUSIDISQUE (Target-BMG): MDF 10264 (CD)
PPP HEALTHCARE 1 "Someone To Watch Over Me" (George &
I.Gershwin) *TV ver* DUSTY SPRINGFIELD *unavailable*
PRINGLES RIGHT based on "Mambo No.5" (Perez Prado) by
LOU BEGA "A Little Bit Of..." (Mambo No.5)
RCA (BMG): 74321 65801-2 (CDs)
PROMISE CO.UK "Stuck In The Middle With You" (Rafferty
-Egan) sung by STEALERS WHEEL from 'RESERVOIR DOGS'
-S/T- *MCA (UNI): MCD 10793 (CD)*
Q UALITY STREET 2 "On The Street Where You Live" (A.J.
Lerner-F.Loewe) NAT KING COLE '20 Golden Greats'
CAPITOL (EMI): CDEMTV 9 (CD)
QUALITY STREET 1 "Magic Moments" (Bacharach-David)
TV Version by NEIL INNES *unavailable*
QUENCHERS "Oddbod" (Geoff Hunnett) KENT DAVISON from
'Teapot Lane' *MD MUSIC (Ind): MDC 81443-4 (MC)*

QUITLINE (Anti-Smoking Campaign) "Ain't Go No - I Got Life" (Ragni-Rado-McDermott from 'Hair') sung by NINA SIMONE on "Feeling Good" *POLY: 522669-2 (CD)*

R ADIO ONE (BBC) "Groove Jet (If This Ain't Love)" by SPILLER *POSITIVA (EMI): CDTIV 137 (CDs) 12TIV 137*

RADIO TIMES "Oriental Shuffle" by DJANGO REINHARDT and STEPHANE GRAPELLI Quintet Of Hot Club Of France *FLAPPER (Pav/Pinn): PASTCD 9738 (CD)*

RAGU PASTA SAUCE "Funiculi-Funicula" (DENZA) version: JOSE CARRERAS *POLY:400015-2 (CD)* LUCIANO PAVAROTTI *DECCA: 410015-2 (CD) and 417011-2 (CD)*

RALPH (Ralph Lauren perfume) "I Need Love" SAM PHILLIPS -S/T- 'DOWN TO YOU' *EPIC (TEN): 497 613-2 (CD)*

RED CROSS (British Red Cross appeal) "Light and Shadow" VANGELIS from '1492 CONQUEST OF PARADISE' *WARNER: 4509 91014-2 (CD) WX 497C (MC)*

RED MAGAZINE "Fun For Me" MOLOKO 'Ladykillers Vol.1' *POLYGRAM TV: 535 536-2 (CD)*

REEBOK 2 "Are You Experienced" JIMI HENDRIX EXPERIENCE *MCA (UNI): MCD 11608 (CD) MCC 116908 (MC)*

REEBOK 1 (Raindrops ad) 2nd m/m Symphony No.7 in A.Maj (BEETHOVEN) *TV ver: special arr.unavailable*

RENAULT CLIO (Nicole/Papa) "Johnny and Mary" (Robert Palmer) MARTIN TAYLOR on 'ONLY JAZZ ALBUM YOU'LL EVER NEED' *RCA (BMG): 74321 66895-2 (2CD) -4(2MC)*

RENAULT CLIO NEW (size matters) "Organ Grinder's Swing" (Hudson-Parish-Mills) by JIMMY SMITH 'Jazz Masters' *VERVE (UNIV): 521 855-2 (CD)*
also on 'SWITCHED ON' *TELSTAR: TTVCD 3086 (2CD)*

RENAULT KANGOO 'Frisbee' "Run On" by MOBY from 'Play' *MUTE (Pinn): (CD)(CS)(MD)STUMM 172 (CD/MC/md)*
also on 'SWITCHED ON' *TELSTAR: TTVCD 3086 (2CD)*

RENAULT MARQUE "Apres Time" by ETIENNE DE CRECY *currently unavailable* / 'TEMPOVISION' album on *XL RECORDS (Vital) XLCD 141 (CD)*

RENAULT MEGANE SCENIC "Marvellous" The LIGHTNING SEEDS 'JOLLIFICATION' *SONY: 477 237-2 (CD) -4(MC) -8(MD)*

RENAULT SCENIC 2 medley: "Summer Holiday"/"Bohemian Rhapsody"/"Hi Ho Silver Lining"/"Teenage Dirt Bag" *Session studio mix unavailable*

RENAULT SCENIC 1 based on "Unsquare Dance" originally composed and performed by DAVE BRUBECK *(CBS, 1962)* *SONY JAZZ (TEN): CK 64668 (CD)*

REVLON "Man I Feel Like A Woman" sung by SHANIA TWAIN 'Come On Over' *MERCURY (Univ): 170 081-2 (CD) -4MC*

RIBENA 3 'Robbie G' ad "I Feel Good" by JAMES BROWN *POLYDOR: 848 845-2 (CD)*

RIBENA 2 'Smoothie' (1) "Norbert's Working" (2)"Bada Bada Schwing" by FREDDIE FRESH & mixed by FATBOY SLIM from CD 'Last True Family Man' on *EYE Q (Vital): EYEUKCD 017 (CD) EYEUK 040CD (CDs)*

RIBENA 1 "Absurd" FLUKE *CIRCA-VIRGIN (EMI): YRCD 126 (CDs) YRT 126 (12"s)*

RIMMEL LIPSTICK "Running Free" PLAYPEN from 'Downtime'
  POPPY (Pinn): OPIUMCD 3 (CD)
RIMMEL (COSMETICS) 2 "Girl Like You" by EDWYN COLLINS
  'Gorgeous George'*SETANTA Vital: SET(CD)(MC) 014*
RIMMEL (COSMETICS) 1 "Allright" by SUPERGRASS from
  'I Should Coco' *EMI PARLOPHONE: CD(TC)PCS 7373*
RIPPLE - see GALAXY RIPPLE
ROAD SAFETY (Don't Look Now) "Mysteries Of Love"
  JULEE CRUISE *WB (TEN): 925 859-2 (CD) -4 (MC)*
ROBERTSON'S GOLDEN SHRED "Jumping Bean" (R.Farnon)
  'British Light Music Classics' NEW LONDON ORCH
  HYPERION: CDA 66868 (CD)
ROBINSONS FRUIT DRINKS "Music Box Dancer" (Mills)
  FRANK MILLS *CHERRY RED (Pinn): MONDEM 23CD (CD)*
ROCKY BAR (Fox's) based on "Rockin'Robin" *original by*
  BOBBY DAY (58) 'Rockin'Robin' *ACE: CDCH 200 (CD)*
  MICHAEL JACKSON (72) 'Best Of M.J.' *MOTOWN (BMG)*
ROLLING ROCK 3 "La Frecuencia Del Amour" by TITAN from
  'ELEVATOR' *VIRGIN (EMI): CDVIR(LPVIR) 104 (CD/LP)*
ROLLING ROCK 2 "Drinking In L.A." by BRAN VAN 3000
  CAPITOL-EMI: CDCL 811 (CDs) and TCCL 811 (MC)
  from 'GLEE' *PARLOPHONE-EMI: 823 604-2 (CD) -4(MC)*
  also on 'SWITCHED ON' *TELSTAR: TTVCD 3086 (2CD)*
ROLLING ROCK 1 "Drifting Away" by FAITHLESS from
  'Reverence' *CHEEKY (3MV-BMG):CHEKCD 500 (CD)*
  also on 'SWITCHED ON' *TELSTAR: TTVCD 3086 (2CD)*
ROLO "Main theme from Adventures of Robinson Crusoe"
  (R.Mellin-G.P.Reverberi) FRANCO-LONDON ORCHESTRA
  SILVA SCREEN (Koch): FILMCD 705 (CD)
ROLO COOKIES "Skippy The Bush Kangaroo" (Eric Jupp) on
  coll 'TELEVISION'S GREATEST HITS VOLUME 5'
  EDEL-CINERAMA (Vital) 002 274-2CIN (CD)
ROMANCE (Ralph Lauren perfume) "My Romance" sung by
  CARLY SIMON 'MY ROMANCE' *ARISTA (BMG): 262019 (CD)*
ROVER 25 "Life in Mono" by MONO from 'Formica Blues'
  ECHO (EMI-Pinn): ECHCD 017 (CD) ECHMC 017 (MC)
ROVER 45 "Goin'Out Of My Head" by FAT BOY SLIM
  'Better Living Through Chemistry' *SKINT (3MV-Vit)*
  BRASSIC 2CD (CD) BRASSIC 2LP(2LP) BRASSIC 2MC(MC)
  also on 'SWITCHED ON' *TELSTAR: TTVCD 3086 (2CD)*
ROVER 75 "Proverb" by the STEVE REICH ENSEMBLE from
  'City Life' *NONESUCH-WARNER: 7559 79376-2 (CD)*
ROVER 200 3 "Downtown" (Hatch) sung by PETULA CLARK
  CASTLE (BMG): SELCD 508 (CD) SELMC 597 (MC)
ROVER 200 2 "This Town Ain't Big Enough For The Both
  Of Us" (Ron Mael) by SPARKS on 'Mael Intuition'
  ISLAND (UNIV): IMCD 88 (CD)
ROVER 200 1 "Englishman In New York" (Sting) by STING
  'Fields of Gold' *A.& M.(UNIV): 540307-2(CD) -4(MC)*
ROVER 400 4 "Ever Fallen In Love With Someone You
  Shouldn't 'ave" (P.Shelley) by The BUZZCOCKS on
  'SINGLES GOING STEADY' *EMI Fame: CDFA 3241 (CD)*
ROVER 400 3 "Donald, Where's Your Troosers" sung by
  ANDY STEWART *MFP (EMI): CDMFP 5700 (CD)*

ROVER 400 2 "Virginia Plain" (B.Ferry) ROXY MUSIC on
'Thrill Of It All' *EG-VIRGIN (EMI): CDBOX 5 (CDx4)*
ROVER 400 1 "Rupert Bear" from 'The ENGLISH PATIENT'
by GABRIEL YARED *FANTASY (Pinn): FCD 16001 (CD)*
ROVER 800 "Lullaby In Ragtime" (H.Nilsson) NILSSON
RCA (BMG): ND 90582 (CD) NK 83761 (MC)
ROYAL AIR FORCE 2 "Keep Hope Alive" performed by
CRYSTAL METHOD *SONY MUSIC: Sony CM3CD (CDs)*
ROYAL AIR FORCE 1 (Boredom) "Adagietto" from Symphony
No.5 (G.MAHLER) *various recordings available*
ROYAL & SUN ALLIANCE 2 "Duo Seraphim"'L'Coronazione Di
Poppea' (The Coronation Of Poppea) (MONTEVERDI) by
JENNIFER LARMORE *HARM.MUNDI: HMC 901330-32 (3CDs)*
ROYAL & SUN ALLIANCE 1 - see **'MORE THAN'**
ROYAL BANK OF SCOTLAND mus.based on "Caravan Of Love"
by HOUSEMARTINS *TV version unavailable. Or.Vers.*
by HOUSEMARTINS *GO DISCS! (UNIV): 828 344-2 (CD)*
ROYAL LIVER ASSURANCE "Lean On Me" *TV vers unavailable*
BILL WITHERS *SONY: 491 961-2 (CD) -8(md)* 'BEST OF'
ROYAL MAIL "I Want Love" (E.John) sung by ELTON JOHN
ROCKET (UNIV): 588 706-2 (CDs)
ROYAL MAIL "Patricia" (Prado) *original by* PEREZ PRADO
ORCH on 'KING OF MAMBO' *RCA (BMG): ND 90424 (CD)*
and on 'OUR MAN IN HAVANA' *RCA: 74321 58810-2 (CD)*
S ADOLIN WOOD PRESERVE "Air That I Breathe" (Hazlewood)
TV version sung by CARRIE RYAN CARTER *unavailable*
SAFEWAY MILLENNIUM PARTY "I'm In The Mood For Dancing"
(Mike Myers-Ben Findon-R.Puzey) sung by The NOLANS
EPIC (Ten): 484 044-2 (CD)
SAINSBURY'S 10 (Gran on bike) "What's New Pussycat"
sung by TOM JONES *DECCA (UNIV): 820 523-2 (CD)*
SAINSBURY'S 9 (Zoo Trip) "It's Caper Time" from 'The
ITALIAN JOB' Soundtrack *MCA (UNIV) MCD 60074 (CD)*
SAINSBURY'S 8 (Ice Desert) "More I See You" sung by
CHRIS MONTEZ on compilation 'And The Beat Goes On'
POLYGRAM: 535 693-2 (CD)
SAINSBURY'S 7 (Kids) "Special Brew" BAD MANNERS 'Viva
La Ska Revolution *SNAPPER (Pinn): SMDCD 140 (2CD)*
SAINSBURY'S 6 (Fry up) "Dancing In The Moonlight" by
TOPLOADER on *S2 (TEN): 669985-2 (CDs) -4 (MC)*
SAINSBURY'S 5 (Xmas ads 2000) "Sound The Trumpet"
BOB MARLEY & WAILERS *STUDIO ONE/ISLAND (UNIV) (-)*
SAINSBURYS 4 (Jamie Oliver 3) "Got Myself A Good Man"
(Whitfield-Strong) PANCHO & LATIN SOUL BROTHERS
FANTASY (USA Imprt)
SAINSBURYS 3 (Jamie Oliver 2) "Message To You Rudy"
(Thompson) The SPECIALS on 'Best Of The Specials'
CHRYSALIS (EMI): CCD 5010 (CD)
SAINSBURYS 2 (Jamie Oliver 1) "All Day and All Of The
Night" (Ray Davies) KINKS 'Definitive Collection'
UNIVERSAL: 516 465-2 (CD) -4 (MC)
SAINSBURYS 1 (memories of..ad) "The Norville Suite"
film 'HUDSUCKER PROXY' composed by CARTER BURWELL
-S/T- *(VARESE Import): VSD 5477 (CD)*

SARSONS VINEGAR "Coronation Scott" (VIVIAN ELLIS)
see *COLL.147,*
SCHWEPPES MALVERN WATER "Symphony No.1" (4th movement)
(ELGAR) *many recordings available*
SCOTTISH TOURIST BOARD 2 "Happiness" BLUE NILE feat:
PAUL BUCHANAN from the album 'PEACE AT LAST'
WARNER: 9362 45848-2 (CD) -4 (MC)
SCOTTISH TOURIST BOARD 1 "Wild Mountain Thyme" trad.
performed by THE SILENCERS on 'NEW PURE MOODS' on
VIRGIN (EMI): VTDCD 158 (2CD)
SCOTTISH WIDOWS "Looking Good" (Tony & Gaynor SADLER)
p.Logorythm Music *unavailable*
SCRUMPY JACK CIDER "The Moldau" 'Ma Vlast'(My Country)
Smetana *vers.*'CLASSIC ADS' *EMI: 7243 568116-2 (CD)*
SEAFISH INDUSTRIES (Fish The Dish ad) "Accentuate The
Positive" (H.Arlen-J.Mercer) sung by JOHNNY MERCER
'More Of The Best' *LASERLIGH6T (BMG): 12618 (CD)*
SEVEN SEAS "Let's Twist Again" (Mann-Appell) *TV vers.*
unavailable / ORIGINAL *by* CHUBBY CHECKER
SHAPE YOGHURT - *see under* ST.IVEL
SHELL "Going Home" from 'Local Hero' by MARK KNOPFLER
-S/T- *VERTIGO (Univ): 811 038-2 (CD)*
SHIPPAMS "Here You Come Again" (B.Mann-Cynthia Weil)
sung by DOLLY PARTON on 'Essential D.P.Volume 2'
RCA (BMG): 07863 66933-2 (CD)
SHREDDED WHEAT 3 (HONEY NUT) "Two Little Boys" by
ROLF HARRIS on Coll 'Best Of Rolf Harris'
SILVER SOUNDS-DISKY (THE): SI 85633-2 (CD) -4(MC)
SHREDDED WHEAT 1 "Walking On Sunshine" (Rew) *orig.by*
KATRINA & T.WAVES 'Best Of' *EMI: CDEMC 3766 (CD)*
SHU UEMURA LIPSTICK "Ain't That A Kick In The Head"
(Sammy Cahn) sung by DEAN MARTIN on 'Very Best Of'
EMI-CAPITOL: 496 721-2 (CD) -4 (MC)
SIDEKICK (superman ad) "Eyes In The Back Of Your Head"
The ADICTS *Captain OI (Plastic Head): AHOYCD 088*
SIEMENS 2 (SL10) "The Devil's Trill" (TARTINI) played
by VANESSA MAE *EMI: 498 082-2 (CD) -4 (MC)*
SIEMENS 1 (S10) "Canon In D." (PACHELBEL)
'CLASSIC ADS' *EMI: 7243 568116-2 (CD)*
SILVIKRIN HAIR PRODUCTS "Saltibanco" (Rene Dupere) by
CIRQUE DU SOLEIL 'Il Sogno Du Volare' *RCA (BMG):*
74321 25707-2 (CD) -4 (MC)
SKI YOGHURT "Pennies From Heaven" (Johnston-Burke) The
CLOVERS 'VERY BEST' *RHINO (TEN): 8122 72971-2 (CD)*
SKODA OCTAVIA "Steppin' Out With My Baby" (Irv.Berlin)
from 'Easter Parade' *TV version unavailable*
FRED ASTAIRE -S/T- 'EASTER PARADE' *EMI: CDODEON 4*
SKY 1 "Happy People" by STATIC REVENGER on 'Clubbers
Guide To Ibiza' *MINISTRY OF SOUND: MOSCD 18 (2CD)*
SKY DIGITAL "Express Yourself" by CHARLES WRIGHT &
103RD STREET RHYTHM BAND on Coll 'Ultimate Funk'
BEECHWOOD (Pinn): ULTIMCD 2 (2CD)
SKY FOOTBALL Sean Bean ad "Strings For Yasmin" by TIN
TIN OUT *VIRGIN (EMI): VCRD 20 (CDs) VCRT 20 (12")*

SKYTOURS "We Are Family" (Rodgers-Edwards) orig SISTER SLEDGE *ATLANTIC (TEN): 9548 31813-2 (CD) -4 (MC)*
SMA PROGRESS (Babyfood) "Take Good Care Of My Baby" (Goffin-King) *TV Version unavailable.* original by BOBBY VEE 'Very Best' *MFP (EMI): CDMFP 6386 (CD)*
SMILE ON LINE "Smile" by The SUPERNATURALS on 'It Doesn't Matter' *FOOD (EMI): FOODCD 21 (CD)*
also on 'SWITCHED ON' *TELSTAR: TTVCD 3086 (2CD)*
SMIRNOFF 4 (1999 ad) "Tame" by THE PIXIES 'DOOLITTLE' *4AD (Vital): GAD905CD (CD) GADC 905 (MC)*
also on 'SWITCHED ON' *TELSTAR: TTVCD 3086 (2CD)*
SMIRNOFF 3 (GIRL IN GREEN ad) "Naked And Ashamed" DYLAN RHYMES on 'Attack Of The Killer DJ's' on *JUNIOR BOYS OWN (RTM/DISC): JBOCD 6 (CD)*
SMIRNOFF 2 (BLACK) "Conquest Of Paradise" -S/T- '1492 CONQUEST OF PARADISE' by VANGELIS *EAST WEST (TEN): 4509 91014-2 (CD) WX 497C (MC)*
SMIRNOFF 1 (Reflections Bottle) "Midnight The Stars & You" *TV version not available*
orig: RAY NOBLE ORCHESTRA featuring AL BOWLLY
SMOKE ALARMS "Down To The Valley To Pray" AIR-EDEL *vers.available by* MOLLIE & TIM O'BRIEN from 'Take Me Back' *SUGAR HILL (Proper): SHCD 3766 (CD)*
SONY CAMERAS Cyber Shot "Tape Loop" by MORCHEEBA from 'Who Can You Trust'*INDOCHINA TEN:0630 14373-2 (CD)*
SONY MINI-DISC 3 "Rude Boy Rock" (Robertson) LIONROCK *CONCRETE-DeCONSTRUCTION (BMG): HARD 31CD (CDs)*
on 'CITY DELERIOUS' *(BMG): HARD 32LPCD (CD)*
also on 'SWITCHED ON' *TELSTAR: TTVCD 3086 (2CD)*
SONY PLAYSTATION 'DOUBLE LIFE: MUSIC FOR PLAYSTATION' incl.JAMIROQUAI "Canned Heat" CHEMICAL BROTHERS "Hey Boy Hey Girl" APOLLO 440 "Carrera Rapida" CHUMBAWUMBA "Tubthumping" RIDGE RACER etc. *SONY TV: SONYTV 65CD (2CD)*
SPAR SUPERMARKET "Gentle On My Mind" (John Hartford) *TV vers.based on* DEAN MARTIN on Coll 'VERY BEST OF DEAN MARTIN VOL.1' *CAPITOL (EMI): 496 721-2 (CD)*
SPECSAVERS OPTICIANS "Aquarium" ('Carnival Of The Animals') (SAINT-SAENS) *CHANDOS CHAN 9246 (CD)*
STANDARD LIFE "Ring Telephone Ring" (Ram-Tinurin) sung by The INK SPOTS on album 'Bless You' *PRESIDENT (BMG): PLCD 535 (CD)*
STAKIS HOTELS "Time To Say Goodbye" sung by ANDREA BOCELLI and SARAH BRIGHTMAN from 'ROMANZA' on *PHILIPS (UNIV): 456 456-2 (CD) -4 (MC)*
STELLA ARTOIS 'Jean De Florette'/'Manon Des Sources' (JEAN CLAUDE PETIT) TOOTS THIELMANS *from FILMS*
STENA LINE (Ireland) "Dream" by the CRANBERRIES on from 'Everyone Else Is Doing It So Why Can't We' *ISLAND (UNIV): CID(ICT)(ILPS) 8003*
STENA LINE (P.& O.) "Riptide" (Gus Kahn-W.Donaldson) by ROBERT PALMER taken from the album 'Riptide' *ISLAND (UNIV): IMCD 25 (CD)*

STORK MARGARINE "Big Rock Candy Mountain"
(McClintock) ROBERT TEX MORTON on collection
'Yodelling Crazy' *EMI: CDP 798 656-2 (CD)*
STREPSILS 2 "Shout" (R.& O.Isley) by LULU 'Something
To Shout About' *DERAM (Univ): 820 618-2 (CD)*
STREPSILS (Sword Swallow) "Waltz In Black" STRANGLERS
on 'Meninblack' *FAME (EMI): CDFA 3208 (CD)*
STRONGBOW CIDER 2 "Toccata & Fugue in D.Min" BWV 538
(BACH) *version* PETER HURFORD 'Great Organ Works'
DECCA (UNIV): 436 225-2 (CD)
STRONGBOW CIDER 1 "Smoke On The Water" (R.Blackmore-
Ian Gillan-Roger Glover) by DEEP PURPLE 'Machine
Head' *FAME-MFP (EMI): CDFA 3158(CD) TCFA 3158(MC)*
SUNKIST Solar Power "Krupa"(Noko-Gray-Gray) APOLLO 440
from album 'ELECTRO GLIDE IN BLUE' *STEALTH SONIC
(Ten): SSX 2440CDR (CD) SSX2440CR (MC)*
SUNNY DELIGHT 2 "How'd I Do Dat" by BENTLEY RHYTHM ACE
from the album 'FOR YOUR EARS ONLY' on
PARLOPHONE (EMI): 525 732-2 (CD) -1 (2LP)
SUNNY DELIGHT 1 "Jacques Your Body" by LES RHYTHMES
DIGITALES 'DARKDANCER' *WALL OF SOUND (Vit) WALLCD
021 also* 'SWITCHED ON' *TELSTAR: TTVCD 3086 (2CD)*
SUPERDRUG "Y'a D'La Joie" (Trenet) by CHARLES TRENET
on 'Very Best Of Charles Trenet' *EMI: CZ 314 (CD)*
SURE SENSIVE "Jeepers Creepers" (Harry Warren-Johnny
Mercer) LOUIS ARMSTRONG from film 'Going Places'
on 'Jeepers Creepers' *MILAN: CDCH 602 (CD) deleted*
SURE ULTRA DRY "Ultra Stimulation" by FINLAY QUAYE on
'Maverick A Strike' *EPIC:488 758-2(CD)-4(MC)-8(md)*
SWATCH 2 "Snow On The Sahara" by ANGGUN
EPIC (Ten): 6678762 (CDs) 6678765 (2CD)
SWATCH 1 "Breathe" by MIDGE URE from 'Breathe'
ARISTA (BMG): 74321 34629-2 (CD) -4 (MC)
SYNTEGRA SYSTEMS "You Sexy Thing" (E.Brown-T.Wilson)
HOT CHOCOLATE 'Greatest Hits' *EMI: CDEMTV 73 (CD)*

T AKE A BREAK MAGAZINE "Don't Stop Moving" LIVIN'JOY
on *MCA (UNI): MCD 60023 (CD) MCC 60023 (MC)*
TANGO BLACKCURRANT "Don't You Want Me" (Fexix-Ware-Wash
ington-Richardson-Jenkins) sung by FELIX *(96 Remix)*
DeCONSTRUCTION (BMG): 74321 41814-2 (CDs) -4 (MCs)
also on 'SWITCHED ON' *TELSTAR: TTVCD 3086 (2CD)*
TATE & LYLE (Gary Rhodes ad) "Won't You Get Off It,
Please" by FATS WALLER on collect 'You Rascal You'
ASV (Koch): CDAJA 5040 (CD) ZCAJA 5040 (MC)
TCP (Gargling Horse ad) "White Horses" (Carr-Nisbet)
TV ver.unavailable / original by JACKY on 'THIS IS
THE RETURN OF CULT FICTION' *VIRGIN: VTCD 112 (CD)*
TEACHER'S HIGHLAND CREAM WHISKY "Cement Mixer" (Slim
Gaillard-L.Ricks) SLIM GAILLARD'Legendary McVouty'
HEP-N.NOTE (Pinn):HEPCD 6 (CD) + 'CEMENT MIXER
PUTTI PUTTI' *PRESIDENT-DELTA (BMG): PLCD 558 (CD)*
TEFAL Thermospot "Don't Mess With My Man" IRMA THOMAS
'Roots Of Northern Soul'*GOLDMINE (Vit):GSCD 083CD*

TENNENTS 2 (feminist ad) "The More I See You" (Warren-Gordon) sung by CHRIS MONTEZ on Coll 'And The Beat Goes On' (Vol.1) *DEBUTANTE (UNIV): 535 693-2 (2CD)*

TENNENTS 1 Romeo & Juliet "Can't Take My Eyes Off You" ANDY WILLIAMS *COLUMBIA (Ten): 477 591-2(CD)*

TERRY'S - *see under brand* 'ALL GOLD' etc.

TETLEY BITTER (dog on beach) "Moanin'" CHARLES MINGUS *TV version unavailable. orig* CHARLES MINGUS *vers.* 'Blues & Roots' *ATLANTIC (TEN): 81227 52205-2 (CD)*

TETLEY TEA 3 (Soft Pack) "Bend It" (Howard-Blaikley) *TV vers.n/a* orig: DAVE DEE-DOZY BEAKY MICK & TICH on 'Best Of' Coll *SPECTRUM (UNIV): 551 823-2 (CD)*

TETLEY TEA 2 (Draw String Bags) "The Stripper" (Rose) DAVID ROSE ORCH *EMPORIO (THE-DISC):EMPRCD 501 (CD)* and 'TOTALLY COMMERCIALS' *EMI (EMI):495 475-2 (CD)*

TETLEY TEA 1 "Lovely Day" (Bill Withers) BILL WITHERS *COLUMBIA (Ten) 491 961-2 (CD) -8 (md)* 'Best Of'

THEAKSTON Cool Cask "Fool's Gold" by STONE ROSES on *SILVERTONE (Pinn) ORECD 535 (CD)* Complete Stone R.

THOMPSON HOLIDAYS "SOAP" (theme from) (Geo.A.Tipton) 'TV's G.Hits Vol.6' *EDEL (Vital) 0022752-CIN (CD)*

THOMSON LOCAL DIRECTORY "You Showed Me" by LIGHTNING SEEDS *EPIC: 489 034-2 (CD) -4(MC) 884 328-2 (CDs)*

THORNTONS ('Chocolate Home' ad) "Everloving" by MOBY on 'PLAY' *MUTE (Vital): (CD)(CS)(MD)STUMM 172*

TIC-TAC "27 WOMEN" (Malcolm DOCHERTY) by LA HONDA on *MORPHEUS (Pinn): MORPH9CDAMS1 (CDs)*

TIMES NEWSPAPER "Adagio For Strings" (Samuel Barber) by WILLIAM ORBIT from 'Pieces in a Modern Style' *WEA (TEN): 3984 28957-2 (CD) -4 (MC)*

TOFFEE CRISP "If I Were With Her Now" by SPIRITUALIZED from 'Laser Guided Melodies' *DEDICATED (Vital): DEDCD 004 (CD) DEDMC 004 (MC)*

TOPJOBS.CO.UK "Banana Bunch Theme" (Tra-La-La)(R.Adams-M.Barkan) *original deleted TELSTAR: TCD 2874 (CD)*

TOYOTA AVENSIS 2 "Voodoo Chile (Slight Return)" from 'Electric Ladyland' by JIMI HENDRIX *MCA-UNIVERSAL (BMG): MCD 11600 (CD) MCC 11600 (MC)*

TOYOTA AVENSIS 1 "The Passenger" (I.Pop-R.Gardiner) IGGY POP on 'Lust For Life' *VIRGIN: CDOVD 278 (CD)*

TOYOTA LEXUS 3 "Laudate Dominum" (Vesperae Solennes De Confessore) K.339 (MOZART) *TV Version unavailable* version by KIRI TE KANAWA & LONDON SYMPH ORCHESTRA *PHILIPS (Univ): 446 239-2 (CD)*

TOYOTA LEXUS 2 "Pure Morning" PLACEBO 'Without You...' *ELEVATOR (Vital): CDFLOOR 8 (CD) FLOORMC 8 (MC)*

TOYOTA LEXUS 1 "Ending (Ascent)" BRIAN ENO 'Apollo' *EG-Virgin (EMI): EGCD 53 (CD)*

TOYOTA PICNIC "Cape Fear" (BERNARD HERRMANN) CITY OF PRAGUE P.ORCH *SILVA SCREEN (Koch): FILMCD 162 (CD)*

TOYOTA RAV "Madness" by PRINCE BUSTER on 'Orig Golden Oldies Vol.1' *PRINCE BUSTER (Jetstar): PBCD 9 (CD)*

TOYOTA YARIS "Wondrous Place" (Giant-Lewis) sung by BILLY FURY *DECCA-LONDON: 882 267-2 (CDs) -4 (MC)*

TRAFFORD CENTRE "Don't Stop Me Now" by QUEEN *(EMI)*
TRAVEL INN "Lazybones" (Hoagy Carmichael) *solo piano*
TUNES (Hunchback ad) "I Feel Pretty" (West Side Story)
    (Bernstein-Sondheim) *sung by* ROB BERT *unavailable*
TWEED PERFUME "Pastoral" from 'Symphony No.6 in F.Maj
    Op.68' (BEETHOVEN) *many recordings available*
TWIX 2 (Norman's car) "Beat Boutique" ALAN HAWSHAW
    and KEITH MANSFIELD on 'GIRL IN A SPORTS CAR' on
    Coliseum (TEN): 0630 18071-2 (CD) or HF 53CD
TWIX 1 "I Want It All" composed & performed by QUEEN
    'Greatest Hits 2' *EMI: CDP 797971-2 (CD) -4 (MC)*
TYPHOO TEA "Fresh" (J.Taylor) orig by KOOL AND THE GANG
    'Collect' *SPECTRUM (UNIV): 551 635-2 (CD) -4(MC)*
U NCLE BEN'S EXPRESS RICE "Dearest Darling" (P.Gayten)
    ROSEBUDS 'George Goldner Presents The Gee Story'
    WESTSIDE (UNIV): WESD 223 (2CD)
UNITED FRIENDLY INSURANCE "All Together Now" originally
    by The FARM on *PRODUCE (Vital): CDMILK 103 (MC)*
UNITED NATIONS (For Refugees) "Where Have All The
    Flowers Gone" (Pete Seeger) by MARLENE DIETRICH
    'Essential Marlene Dietrich' *EMI: CDEMS 1399 (CD)*
V ASELINE BODY LOTION "In The Hall Of T.Mountain King"
    from the 'PEER GYNT SUITE' (GRIEG) *Var.versions*
VASELINE INTENSIVE CARE "Button Up Your Overcoat" (DeSy
    lva-Brown-Henderson) sung by RUTH ETTING on 'Love
    Me Or Leave Me' *FLAPPER (Pinn): PASTCD 7061 (CD)*
VAUXHALL "Papa Don't Preach" (Madonna) LEFTFIELD mix.
    Strings sample by PROGRESS titled 'EVERYBODY' on
    MANIFESTO (Univ): FESCD 65 (CDs) FESMC 65 (MC)
VAUXHALL ASTRA string part of The VERVE's "Bitter Sweet
    Symphony" (Ashcroft) from 'URBAN HYMNS' The VERVE
    HUT-VIRGIN (EMI): CDHUT 45 (CD) HUTMC 45 (MC)
VAUXHALL ASTRA CONVERTIBLE "Daydream" (John Sebastian)
    TV vers.based on LOVIN' SPOONFUL original 1968 hit
    on 'Very Best Of' *CAMDEN (BMG): 74321 55849-2 (CD)*
VAUXHALL ASTRA SRI "Tiger Rag" MILLS BROTHERS 'Best of
    The MILLS BROTHERS' *HALF MOON (UNIV) HMNCD 021 (CD)*
VAUXHALL CORSAIR "Original" by LEFTFIELD from 'Leftism'
    also on 'SWITCHED ON' *TELSTAR: TTVCD 3086 (2CD)*
VAUXHALL SINTRA "Pure" by The LIGHTNING SEEDS from
    'Cloudcuckooland' *VIRGIN (EMI): CDOVD(OVDC) 436*
VAUXHALL TIGRA "Fiesta" POGUES from 'If I Should Fall
    From Grace With God' *WEA TEN: 244493-2 (CD)*
VAUXHALL VECTRA 3 "Say What You Want" TEXAS on 'White
    On Blonde' *MERCURY (UNIV): 534 315-2 (CD) -4 (MC)*
VAUXHALL VECTRA 2 "Peter Gunn theme" (Henry Mancini)
    TV version unavailable / HENRY MANCINI vers: 'Best
    Of HENRY MANCINI' *RCA (BMG): 74321 47676-2 (CD)*
VAUXHALL VECTRA 1 "The Next Millenium" (Arnold) DAVID
    ARNOLD on 'Senses' *POLYGRAM: 516 627-2 (CD)* / *voc.
    vers* BJORK on 'NEW PURE MOODS' *VIRGIN see COLLECT*
VAUXHALL ZAFIRA GSI TURBO "Daddy Cool" (Farian-Reyham)
    TV version unavailable orig by BONEY M on 'BEST OF
    BONEY M' *RCA CAMDEN (BMG): 74321 47681-2 (CD)*

VENUS (Gillette) "Venus" (Robert Van Leeuwen) *TV Vers unavailable / ORIG by* SHOCKING BLUE *RRTCD 70 (2CD)*

VICKS VAPO RUB "The Air That I Breath" (A.Hammond-Lee Hazlewood) sung by The HOLLIES *EMI: 746 238-2 (CD)*

VIRGIN 1 (Finance) "L'Heure Exquise" (Reynaldo Hahn) by MISCHA MAISKY-DARIO HOVARA on 'Apres Un Reve' *DG (UNIV): 457 657-2 (CD)*

VIRGIN ATLANTIC AIRWAYS 2 "Crazy Horses" The OSMONDS on 'Very Best' *POLYDOR: CURCD 065 (CD)*

VIRGIN ATLANTIC AIRWAYS 1 "Sleep Walk" SANTO & JOHNNY Coll 'Rock'n'Roll' *ACE (Pinn): CDCHD 600 (CD)*

VIRGIN RADIO (1) "Beautiful Day" U2 *(ISLAND: CID 766)* (2) "Going Underground" JAM *(537 423-2)* (3) "Rock The Casbah" CLASH *(495 353-2) (CD)*

VIRGIN TRAINS "Charlie Brown theme" by VINCE GUARALDI VINCE GUARALDI TRIO 'A Boy Named Charlie Brown' on *FANTASY (Complete): FCD 8430-2 (CD)*

VODAPHONE (a) "Bohemian Like You" The DANDY WARHOLS *CAPITOL EMI: 857 787-2 (CD) / CDCLS 823 (CDs)*

VOLKSWAGEN BEETLE "Made To Last" by SEMISONIC from the album 'Feeling Strangely Fine' on *MCA (Univ): MCCD 11733 (CD) MCC 11733 (MC)*

VOLKSWAGEN GOLF 3 "Love Theme from Romeo and Juliet" (Nino ROTA) *vers:* ANDRE RIEU on 'The Collection' *PHILIPS (UNIV): 589 015-2 (CD) / also* 'FILM MUSIC' *CHANDOS: CHAN 9771 (CD) and* 'CINEMA CENTURY 2000' *SILVA SCREEN (Koch): FILMXCD 318 (2CD)*

VOLKSWAGEN GOLF 2 "Gassenhauer" from 'SCHULWERK' (CARL ORFF-G.KEETMAN) 'BEST OF CARL ORFF' on *RCA (BMG): 75605 51357-2 (CD) -4 (MC)*

VOLKSWAGEN GOLF 1 "Left Bank Two" (Vision On Picture Gallery music) NOVELTONES on 'THIS IS THE RETURN OF CULT FICTION' *VIRGIN (EMI): VTCD 112 (CD) also on* 'A-Z OF BRIT.TV THEMES 2' *(KOCH): PLAY 006 (CD)*

VOLKSWAGEN LUPO "'6/8/ WAR' by LEFTFIELD from 'RHYTHM & STEALTH' *HARD HANDS-HIGHERGROUND (EMI): HANDCD 4 CD*

VOLKSWAGEN POLO "Born To Be With You" by The CHORDETTES *ACE (Pinn): CDCHD 934 (CD Collection) VARESE (Pinn): VSD 6097 (CD Collection)*

VOLVO C70 "Can't Stand It" by WILCO from 'Summerteeth' *WB (TEN): 9362 47282-2 (CD) -4 (MC)*

VOLVO S40 "One To One Religion" (White Knuckle Remix) by BOMB THE BASE (orig track on 'Clear') *FOURTH & BROADWAY-ISL.(UNIV): BRCD 611 (CD) BRCA 611 (MC)*

VOLVO V40 2 "When Somebody Thinks You're Wonderful" sung by FATS WALLER on 'Ultimate Collection' *PULSE-RCA (BMG): PDSCD 550 (2CD) PDSMC 550 (2MC)*

VOLVO V40 1 "Butterfly 747" by MOLOKO from 'Do You Like My Tight Sweater' *ECHO (Pinn): ECH(CD)(LP) 7*

W ALES "Design For Life" by MANIC STREET PREACHERS *EPIC (Ten): 483 930-2 (CD) -4 (MC) -1(LP) -8(md)*

WALL'S CALIPPO "My Generation" (Pete Townshend) WHO 'The Singles' *POLYDOR: 815 965-2(CD) WHOHC 17(MC) 854 637-2 (CDs) 863 918-4 (MC) -7 (7"s)*

WALKERS CHEESE & OWEN "Instant Karma" (J.Lennon) sung
by JOHN LENNON *EMI: 821 954-2 (CD) -4 (MC) -1 (LP)*
WALKERS DORITOS "Walk This Way" by RUN DMC & AEROSMITH
'Greatest Hits' *PROFILE (Pinn): FILECD 474 (CD)*
WALKERS RED HOT MAX "Sing Sing Sing" (Louis Prima) by
BENNY GOODMAN ORCH *COLUMBIA (TEN): 474 396-2 (CD)*
WEETABIX (Horses) "Galloping Home" (Denis King) from
'Adventures of Black Beaty' on themes collection
PLAY IT AGAIN (Koch): PLAY 006 (CD)
WEETABIX (Tidal Wave) 'Wipeout' SURFARIS 1963 orig on
REPERTOIRE (Greyh): REP 4118 (CD)
WEETABIX based on "Tragedy" BEE GEES *POLY: 847 339-2CD*
WEIGHT WATCHERS *see under* **HEINZ WEIGHT WATCHERS**
WH SMITH 'Regression ad' "Tiger Feet" (Chinn-Chapmqan)
MUD 'Gold Collection' *EMI: CD(TC) 1003 (CD/MC)*
WHICH MAGAZINE "Money" (Gordy-Bradford) sung by FLYING
LIZARDS *VIRGIN (EMI):VTDCD 42 (2CD) VTDMC 42 (2MC)*
WHISKAS 6 (Snow Cat) "Let It Snow" (J.Styne-S.Cahn)
sung by ANDY WILLIAMS *COLUMBIA (TEN)*
WHISKAS 5 SINGLES "Lazybones" (H.Carmichael-J.Mercer)
sung by HOAGY CARMICHAEL on 'Mr.Music Master'
FLAPPER-PAVILION (Pinn): PASTCD 7004 (CD) also on
'Sometimes I Wonder' *LIVING ERA: CDAJA 5345 (CD)*
WHISKAS 4 "On The Rebound" comp/perf.by FLOYD CRAMER
on Collection 'THE ESSENTIAL FLOYD CRAMER' on
RCA (BMG): 74321 66591-2 (CD) -4 (MC)
WHISKAS 3 "Hold Tight (I Want Some Sea Food Mama)" by
FATS WALLER *CLASSICS (Discov): CLASSICS 943 (CD)*
WHISKAS 2 Kittens "Onions" (Bechet) *TV ver.unavailable*
HUMPHREY LYTTLETON BAND *DOORMOUSE: DM21CD deleted*
WHISKAS 1 "Teach Me Tiger" sung by APRIL STEVENS on
'TOTALLY COMMERCIALS' *EMI: 495 475-2 (CD)* also on
'Cocktail Capers-Ult.Lounge 8' *EMI:CDEMS 1595 (CD)*
WOODPECKER CIDER car in puddle "Mr.Vain" CULTURE BEAT
'Serenity' *EPIC (TEN) 474 101-2 (CD)-4 (MC) -8(MD)*
WRANGLER JEANS "We're Off To See The Wizard" from the
'WIZARD OF OZ' (H.Arlen-E.Y.Harburg) SOUNDTRACK
MGM (EMI): CDODEON 7 (CD)
WRIGLEY'S SPEARMINT "Give Her A Great Big Kiss" by the
NEW YORK DOLLS *ESSENTIAL (Pinn): ESMCD 734 (CD)*
originally "Give HIM A Great Big Kiss" by the
SHANGRI-LAS *RED BIRD (Universal): 552 764-2 (CD)*
WRIGLEY'S SPEARMINT "All Right Now" (Andy Fraser-Paul
Rodgers) by FREE on 'All Right Now' *ISLAND CITV 2
(CD) CID 486 (CDsingle) CIS 486 (MC single)*
X FM RADIO "Naive Song" by MIRWAIS from 'Production'
NAIVE-EPIC (TEN): 498 213-2 (CD) -4 (MC)
Y ELL.COM "Mad Dog" by ELASTICA from 'The MENACE' on
DECEPTIVE (Vital): BLUFF 075CD (CD) + 077CD1 (CDs)
YELLOW PAGES 4 "You're More Than A Number In My
Little Red Book" (T.Macaulay-R.Greenway) orig by
DRIFTERS *RCA (BMG): 74321 44674-2 (CD) -4 (MC)*
YELLOW PAGES 3 "Baby I Love You" (Spector-Greenwich-
Barry) The RAMONES *SIRE (TEN): 7599 27429-2 (CD)*

YELLOW PAGES 2 "Days" (Ray Davies) by The KINKS on 'Best of Ballads' *ARISTA (BMG): 74321 13687-2 (CD)*
YELLOW PAGES 1 (J.R.Hartley book ad) (piano piece) composed and played by DICK WALTER *unavailable*
YOUNGS SEAFOODS "When The Boat Comes In" (Dance Ti Thi Daddy)(trad) vers: ALEX GLASGOW on 'A-Z OF BRITISH TV THEMES V.3' *PLAY IT AGAIN (Koch): PLAY 010 (CD)*
Z URICH INVESTMENT INSURANCE "JUPITER" from 'PLANETS' SUITE (HOLST) *Various recordings available*

T. V. A D C O L L E C T I O N S

BEST TV ADS...EVER - Various Artists
   VIRGIN (EMI): VTDCDX 306 (2CD) VTDMC 306 (MC) 2000
   C1 1.INKANYEZI NEZAZI Ladysmith Black Mambazo *HEINZ*
   2.I HEARD IT THROUGH THE GRAPEVINE Marvin Gaye *LEVI*
   3.YOU GOTTA BE Des'ree *FORD FOCUS* 4.SERACH FOR THE
   HERO M People *PEUGEOT 406* 5.I JUST WANNA MAKE LOVE
   TO YOU Etta James *DIET COKE* 6.LET'S FACE THE MUSIC
   & DANCE Nat King Cole *ALLIED DUNBAR* 7.MEMORIES ARE
   MADE OF THIS Dean Martin *PEUG.306* 8.MUSIC TO WATCH
   GIRLS BY Andy Williams *FIAT PUNTO* 9.GUAGLIONE Perez
   Prado *GUINNESS* 10.BULLITT Lalo Schifrin *FORD PUMA*
   11.BLOW UP A-GO-GO James Clark *GAP* 12.MAS QUE NADA
   Sergio Mendes *NIKE* 13.FLY ME TO THE MOON Julie
   London *FORD PROBE* 14.WONDROUS PLACE Billy Fury *TOY.*
   YARIS 15.MELLOW YELLOW Donovan *GAP* 16.I CAN'T LET
   MAGGIE GO Honeybus *NIMBLE* 17.GOOD VIBRATIONS Beach
   Boys *BT* 18.PART OF THE UNION Strawbs *NORWICH UNION*
   19.WILD THING Troggs *B.KING* 20.WE GOTTA GET OUT OF
   THIS PLACE Animals *HONDA* 21.HE AIN'T HEAVY Hollies
   MILLER LITE 22.YOUR CHEATIN' HEART Glen Campbell
   CASTLEMAINE XXXX 23.THAT'S AMORE Dean Martin *PIZZA
   HUT* 24.STAND BY ME Ben E.King *LEVI* 25.WHEN A MAN
   LOVES A WOMAN Percy Sledge *LEVI* 26.MERCEDES BENZ
   Janis Joplin *MERCEDES BENZ* CD2 1.FIND MY BABY Moby
   NISSAN ALMERA 2.THE UNIVERSAL Blur *BRITISH GAS* 3.
   SHE'S THE ONE Robbie Williams *SEGA DREACAST* 4.SMILE
   Supernaturals *SMILE INTERNET* 5.PASSENGER Iggy Pop
   TOYOTA AVENSIS 6.HEROES David Bowie *CGU* 7.INSIDE
   Stiltskin *LEVI* 8.DO YOU WANT ME Felix *TANGO* 9.FLAT
   BEAT Mr.Oizo *LEVI* 10.DRINKING IN L.A.Bran Van 3000
   ROLLING ROCK 11.TURN ON TUNE IN COPOUT Freakpower
   LEVI 12.SPACEMAN Babylon Zoo *LEVI* 13.BOOMBASTIC
   Shaggy *LEVI* 14.JUMP AROUND House of Pain *CAFFREYS*
   15.OOH LA LA Wiseguys *BUDWEISER* 16.CARS Gary Numan
   CARLING 17.ONE WAY OR ANOTHER Blondie *CAFFREYS* 18.
   THAT'S THE WAY I LIKE IT KC & Sunshine Band *KFC* 19.
   IN THESE SHOES? Kirsty MacColl *ADIDAS SPORTWEAR* 20.
   MAYBE TOMORROW (LITTLEST HOBO THEME) Scooch *(not
   the orginal Terry Bush version) NAT.WEST*

COMMERCIAL BREAK: Old Tunes from The New Ads - Var
ASV *(Select): AJA 5281 (CD)* *1998*
1.JEEPERS CREEPERS *(SURE SENSIVE)* Louis Armstong 2.
HAPPY FEET *(CLARK'S SHOES)* Jack Hylton Orchestra 3.
BOTTLENECK BLUES 4.JUNGLE JAMBOREE Duke Ellington
4.SWEET AND LOVELY *(CADBURY HIGH LIGHTS)* Al Bowlly
5.WON'T YOU GET OFF IT PLEASE *(TATE & LYLE)* Fats
Waller 6.EGYPTIAN ELLA *(TERRY'S PYRAMINTS)*Ted Lewis
7.SUN HAS GOT HIS HAT ON *(BRITISH GAS)* Sam Browne 8
LOVE IS THE SWEETEST THING *(BLACK MAGIC)* Al Bowlly
9.TEDDY BEAR'S PICNIC *(PERSIL/SONY CAMCORDER)* Henry
Hall Orch 10.LET'S FACE THE MUSIC AND DANCE *(ALLIED
DUNBAR)* Fred Astaire 11.STOMPIN'AT THE SAVOY *(P.& O
FERRIES)* Benny Goodman Orch 12.VERY THOUGHT OF YOU
PRETTY POLLY)* Al Bowlly 13.PENNIES FROM HEAVEN*(BT)*
Frances Langford, Bing Crosby & Louis Armstrong 14.
ORIENTAL SHUFFLE *(RADIO TIMES)* Stephane Grappelli &
Django Reinhardt 15.BOUM *(PPP HEALTHCARE)* Charles
Trenet 16.IN THE MOOD *(RADION/ANCHOR BUTT/DORITOS)*
Glenn Miller Or 17.LA CUMPARSITA *(No. 7)* Dinah Shore
18.WHEN YHOU WISH UPON A STAR *(DISNEYLAND)* Cliff
Edwards 19.GRASSHOPPERS DANCE *(MILK)*Alfredo Campoli
20.YES SIR THAT'S MY BABY *(JOHNSON'S BABY)* Eddie
Cantor 21.TICO TICO *(WHISKAS)* Andrews Sisters 22.
SENTIMENTAL JOURNEY *(CADBURY'S INSPIRATIONS)* Doris
Day 23.ZIP-A-DEE-DOO-DAH *(MITSUBISHI CARISMA)* 24.
AS TIME GOES BY *(NPI PENSIONS)* Dooley Wilson
COMMERCIAL BREAKS COLLECTION - Various Artists
EMI HMV: 533 842-2 (CD) *2001*
1.YOUR CHEATIN' HEART Glen Campbell *CASTLMAINE XXXX*
2.YOU WERE MADE FOR ME Freddie & Dreamers *DAIRYLEA*
3.ROADRUNNER Animals *FORD FIESTA* 4.AIR THAT I
BREATHE Hollies *COMFORT CONDITIONER* 5.I'LL PUT YOU
TOGETHER AGAIN Hot Chocolate *CADBURY'S HIGHLIGHTS* 6
MELLOW YELLOW Donovan *KRAFT MELLO* 7.TEACH ME TIGER
April Stevens *WHISKAS* 8.WHEN YOU'RE SMILING Louis
Prima *FINCHES ORANGE* 9.WILD IS THE WIND Nuna Simone
LINDT CHOCOLATE 10.NIGHT RIDER Alan Hawkshaw *MILK
TRAY orig* 11.THOSE MAGNIFICENT MEN IN THEIR FLYING
MACHINES Ron Goodwin *RED BULL* 12.IN THE MOOD Joe
Loss *ANCHOR BUTTER* 13.I'M SITTING ON TOP OF T.WORLD
Bobby Darin *LEVI DOCKERS* 14.ANGELENA Louis Prima
MASTERCARD 15.STOMPIN' AT THE SAVOY Benny Goodman
P.& O.Ferries 16.GOPHER TANGO Perez Prado *ADDICTION*
17.PUT A LITTLE LOVE IN YOUR HEART Jackie DeShannon
MICHELOB 18.CALL ME IRRESPONSIBLE Dinah Washington
VW 19.I LOVE YOU PORGY Nina Simone *ORANGE* 20.FLY ME
TO THE MOON Julie London *FORD PROBE* 21.STORY OF MY
LIFE Michael Holliday *GUINNESS* 22.CRAZY Willie
Nelson *ELIZABETH SHAW CHOCOLATES*

COMMERCIAL BREAKS: COOLER SIDE OF TV ADVERTISING
COMMERCIAL BREAKS: COMBCD 001 (2CD) *2001*
1.WOMAN IN BLUE Pepe De Luxe *LEVI* 2.ORIGINAL

COMMERCIAL BREAKS: COOLER SIDE OF TV ADVERTISING

COMMERCIAL BREAKS: COMBCD 001 (2CD)   *2001*
1.WOMAN IN BLUE Pepe De Luxe *LEVI* 2.ORIGINAL
Leftfield *GUINNESS* 3.UNDERWATER LOVE SmokeCity *LEVI*
4.ITCHY & SCRATCHY Boss Hogg *LEVIS* 5.SLIP INTO
SOMETHING MORE COMFORTABLE Kinobe *KRONENBERG* 6.
DEATH IN VEGAS Dirge *LEVI* 7.RUN ON Moby *RENAULT* 8.
THE CHILD *ALEX GOPHER* 9.NOVELTY WAVES Biosphere
LEVI 10.HISTORY REPEATING ITSELF Propellerheads
JAGUAR 11.CLUBBED TO DEATH Rob D *CAFFREYS* 12.SIX
UNDERGROUND Sneaker Pimps *CARLING* 13.BLINDFOLD
Mocheeba 14.IF EVERYBODY LOOKED THE SAME Groove
Armada *MERCEDES* 15.EVA Jean Jacques Perrey *LUCOZADE*
16.CARS Gary Numan *A.EXPRESS* 17.SECOND LINE Clinic
LEVI 18.HEATMISER/ANGEL Massive Attack *MORGAN
STANLEY* 19.LIFE IN MONO Mono *ROVER 25* 20.ADAGIO FOR
STRINGS William Orbit *TIMES* 21.PURE MORNING Placebo
LEXUS 22.IN THE MEANTIME Spacehog *MERCURY ONE-2-ONE*
23.SUNBURN Muse *IMAC* 24.PLAY DEAD Bjork *VAUXHALL*

OFF YER BOX - Various Original Artists (TV ADS MUSIC)

WRASSE (UNIV): WRASS 039 (CD)   *2001*
1.GUAGLIONE Perez Prado 2.CHEWY CHEWY Ohio Express
3.GIMME DAT DING Pipkins 4.HOT DIGGITY Perry Como
5.ISRAELITES Desmond Dekker 6.WIPEOUT Surfaris
7.MINISKIRT Esquivel Orc.8.BABY ELEPHANT WALK Henry
Mancini 9.BARBARABATIRI Benny More 10.BOUM Charles
Trenet 11.INCIDENTALLY ROBERT Tot Taylor 12.VA BA
BOOM Edmundo Ross 13.SOUL BOSSA NOVA Quincy Jones
14.FOX Hugo Montenegro 15.DICK TRACY Dean Fraser
16.GREEN BOSSA Tot Taylor 17.SURFIN' Ernest Ranglin
18.DA DA DA Trio 19.HOOTS MON Lord Rockingham's XI
20.RUBBER BISCUIT Chips 21.BANANA BOAT SONG (DAY-O)
Harry Belafonte 22.FOLLOW THE YELLOW BRICK ROAD
Victor Young Orchestra

SPIRITS OF NATURE - Various Original Artists

VIRGIN (EMI): VTCD 87 (CD) VTMC 87 (MC)   *1996*
1.YE-HA NO-HA (WISHES OF HAPPINESS AND PROSPERITY)
Sacred Spirit 2.SWEET LULLABY Deep Forest 3.LITTLE
FLUFFY CLOUDS The Orb 4.THE SUN RISING The Beloved
5.X-FILES (DJ DADO PARANORMAL ACTIVITY MIX) DJ Dado
6.RETURN TO INNOCENCE Enigma 7.STARS (MOTHER DUB)
Dubstar 8.THE WAY IT IS Chameleon 9.PLAY DEAD Bjork
& David Arnold 10.ARIA ON AIR *BRITISH AIRWAYS AD*
Malcolm McLaren 11.ADIEMUS *DELTA AIRWAYS AD* Adiemus
12.ONLY YOU *FIAT TEMPRA* Praise 13.FALLING*TWIN PEAKS*
Julee Cruise 14.MAD ALICE LANE: A GHOST STORY *LAND
ROVER DISCOVERY* Peter Lawlor 15.SENTINEL Mike Oldfi
eld 16.THEME FROM THE MISSION Ennio Morricone 17.
THE HEART ASKS PLEASURE FIRST/THE PROMISE from THE
PIANO Michael Nyman 18.FASHION SHOW II from THREE
COLOURS RED Zbigbniew Preisner 19.CHARIOTS OF FIRE

SWITCHED ON: THE COOL SOUND OF TV ADVERTISING *2000*

TELSTAR RECORDS: TTVCD 3086 (2CD) TTVMC 3086 (2MC)
CD1 1.SMILE Supernaturals *SMILE* 2.WHAT I LIKE ABOUT

YOU Loop Da Loop *MILLER* 3.DRIFTING AWAY Faithless
ROLLING ROCK 4.DRINKING IN LA Bran Van 3000 *R.ROCK*
5.ORIGINAL Leftfield *VAUXHALL* 6.AND THE BEAT GOES
ON All Seeing Eye *BT CELLNET* 7.RIGHT HERE RIGHT NOW
Fatboy Slim *ADIDAS* 8.PURPLE Crustation with Bronagh
Slevin *DAEWOO* 9.LOOSE FIT Happy Mondays *ORANGE* 10.
RUDE BOY ROCK Lion Rock *SONY MD* 11.MUCHO MAMBO SWAY
Shaft *KISS* 12.SOUND OF DA POLICE KRS One *PHYSIO*
SPORTS 13.SUGAR IS SWEETER CJ Bolland *IMPULSE* 14.
ORGAN GRINDER'S SWING Jimmy Smith *RENAULT CLIO* 15.
JUMP AROUND House Of Pain *CAFFREYS* 16.ENTER THE
MONK Monk & Canatella *DAEWOO* 17.CAN'T TAKE MY EYES
OFF YOU Andy Williams *PEUGEOT 306* 18.HISTORY REPEAT
ING Propellerheads-Shirley Bassey *JAGUAR* 19.BULLITT
Lalo Shifrin *-S/T- BULLITT* 20.6 UNDERGROUND Sneaker
Pimps *CARLING* 21.FLAT BEAT Mr.Oizo *LEVI* CD2: 1.DIVE
Propellerheads *ADIDAS* 2.CLUBBED TO DEATH Rob D *THE*
MATRIX/CAFFREYS 3.EASY LEASING SUPERSTAR Le Hammond
Inferno *NIKE* 4.BACK BY DOPE DEMAND King Bee *BODDING*
TONS 5.CONNECTED Stereo MCs *CARPHONE WAREHOUSE* 6.
RUN ON Moby *RENAULT KANGOO* 7.BLUE MONDAY '88 New
Order *AMERICAN EXPRESS* 8.RODNEY YATES David Holmes
NAT.WEST 9.BENTLEY'S GONNA SORT YOU OUT Bentley
Rhythm Ace *LYNX* 10.TURN ON TUNE IN COP...Freakpower
LEVI 11.BLOW UP A GO-GO James Clarke *GAP* 12.DON'T
YOU WANT ME Felix *TANGO* 13.ENCORE UNE FOIS Sash!
L'OREAL 14.GOING OUT OF MY HEAD Fatboy Slim *ROVER45*
15.BRIMFUL OF ASHA Cornershop *CAFFREYS* 16.HAVE A GO
HERO Urban DK *MASTERCARD* 17.JACQUES YOUR BODY (MAKE
ME SWEAT) Les Rhythmes Digitales *SUNNY DELIGHT* 18.
TAME Pixies *SMIRNOFF RED LAB.*19.SHE SELLS SANCTUARY
Cult *KENCO* 20.ONE WAY OR ANOTHER Blondie *BAILEYS*
21.OOH LA LA Wiseguys *BUDWEISER* 22.FUN LOVIN'
CRIMINAL Fun Lovin' Criminals *MERCEDES*

TAKE A BREAK! - Various Artists

COLUMBIA (Ten): 494 464-2 (CD) -4 (MC)   1999
1.MUSIC TO WATCH GIRLS BY Andy Williams *FIAT PUNTO*
2.PUT YOU TOGETHER AGAIN Hot Chocolate *CADBURY'S HC*
3.DOWNTOWN Petula Clark *ROVER* 4.ON THE STREET WHERE
YOU LIVE Nat King Cole *QUALITY STREET* 5.WHAT A DIFF
ERENCE A DAY MADE Dinah Washington *CROWN PAINTS* 6.
PERHAPS PERHAPS PERHAPS Doris Day *CANDEREL* 7.I CAN
HELP Billy Swan *BT* 8.CALL ME Chris Montez *BT* 9.IF I
HAD A HAMMER Trini Lopez*BARCLAYCARD* 10.SHE'S A LADY
Tom Jones *WEETABIX* 11.JUMP JIVE & WAIL Louis Prima
GAP 12.DON'T FENCE ME IN Bing Crosby & Andrews Sist
ers *CENTERPARCS* 13.YOU DO SOMETHING TO ME Alma Cogan
GALAXY 14.CAN'T SMILE WITHOUT YOU Lena Fiagbe *BT* 15
SHE'S NOT THERE Santana *KFC* 16.WALK LIKE AN EGYPTIAN
Bangles *KINDER EGGS* 17.WALKING ON SUNSHINE Katrina
& The Waves *SHREDDED WHEAT* 18.THAT LADY Isley Bros.
KFC 19.LOLA Kinks *WEETABIX* 20.DON'T STOP MOVIN'
Livin' Joy *TAKE A BREAK*

TURN ON! TUNE IN! - Various Artists

JAZZ FM/BEECHWOOD (BMG): JAZZFMCD 15 (2CD)   *1999*
1.ON THE STREET WHERE YOU LIVE Nat King Cole *TV AD: QUALITY STREET* 2.WE HAVE ALL THE TIME IN THE WORLD Louis Armstrong *GUINNESS* 3.I JUST WANNA MAKE LOVE TO YOU Etta James *DIET COKE* 4.FEELING GOOD Nina Simone *VW GOLF/COMFORT* 5.MAD ABOUT THE BOY Dinah Washington *LEVI* 6.SPEAKING OF HAPPINESS Gloria Lynn *FORD MONDEO* 7.LEFT BANK2 Noveltones *VW GOLF/AMBROSIA* 8.LET'S FACE THE MUSIC & DANCE Nat King Cole *ALLIED DUNBAR* 9.MY SHIP HAS SAILED Sarah Vaughan *GALAXY* 10 I PUT A SPELL ON YOU Nina Simone *DIET COKE/PERRIER* 11.I WANT TWO LIPS April Stevens *PEUGEOT 306* 12. WHEN A A MAN LOVES A WOMAN Percy Sledge *LEVI* 13.I'M SITTING ON TOP OF THE WORLD Al Jolson *GUINNESS/RENN IES* 14.STAND BY ME Ben E.King *LEVI* 15.MY BABY JUST CARES FOR ME Nina Simone *CHANEL NO.5* 16.SMOKESTACK LIGHTNING John Lee Hooker *BUDWEISER* 17.CAN'T SMILE WITHOUT YOU Lena Fiagby *BT* 18.OCEAN DRIVE The Lighthouse Family *ALPEN* 19.FLY ME TO THE MOON Julie London *FORD PROBE* 20.DREAM A LITTLE DREAM Mamas and Papas *PEUGEOT 406* 21.CALL ME Chris Montez *BT* 22. TURN ON TUNE IN COP OUT Freakpower *LEVI* 23. CANTELOUPE ISLAND Us 3 *KFC* 24.SOUL BOSSA NOVA Quincy Jones *NIKE* 25.MAS QUE NADA Tamba Trio *NIKE* 26.GUAGLIONE Perez Prado *GUINNESS* 27.BIG BAMBOOZLE Barry Adamson *BAILEY'S IRISH CREAM* 28.JUMP JIVE AND WAIL Brian Setzer *GAP JEANS* 29.EVA Jean Jacques Perrey *LUCOZADE* 30.MOVE ON UP Curtis Mayfield *CITROEN XSARA* 31.GET DOWN TONIGHT KC & Sunshine Band *BUDWEISER* 32.PATRICIA Perez Prado *ROYAL MAIL*

2.4 CHILDREN (BBC1 3/9/91-2000) series theme music by HOWARD GOODALL *unavailable*

7 *see under* **SEVEN**

8MM (1999) Music score by MYCHAEL DANNA -S/T- on *SILVA SCREEN (Koch): FILMCD 313 (CD)*

8½ (1963) Music score b NINO ROTA -S/T- on *CAM IMPT.(HOT): 493 091-2 (CD)*

9 songs by Maury Yeston ORIG LONDON CONCERT CAST 1992 *with:* JONATHAN PRYCE ELAINE PAIGE *TER (Koch): CDTER2 1193 (2CD)*

9 TO 5 Theme DOLLY PARTON *(BMG) ND 84830 (CD)*

9TH GATE The (1999) Music sco: WOJCIEK KILAR perf.by CITY OF PRAGUE PHILH. & CHORUS with SUMI JO (sopr) *SILVA SCREEN (Koch): FILMCD 321 (CD)*

9½ WEEKS (1986) Music score: JACK NITZSCHE -S/T- reiss *CAPITOL (EMI): CDP 746722-2 (CD)*

10 COMMANDMENTS The (1956) Music sco: ELMER BERNSTEIN -S/T- *TSUNAMI Imp (Sil.Screen): TSU 0123 (CD) and* -S/T- *MCA USA (Silva Screen): MCAD 42320 (CD)*

10 THINGS I HATE ABOUT YOU (1998) Music: RICHARD GIBBS -S/T- *HOLLYWOOD-EDEL (Vital) 010254-2HWR (CD)*

10TH KINGDOM (2000) Music score by ANNE DUDLEY -S/T- *VARESE (Pinn): VSD 6115 (CD)*

13 GHOSTS (2001) Music score by JOHN FRIZZELL -S/T- on *VARESE (Pinn): VSD 6298 (CD)*

13TH FLOOR The (1999) Music score: HARALD KLOSER -S/T- *MILAN (BMG): 74321 69216-2 (CD)*

13TH WARRIOR The (1999) Music score by JERRY GOLDSMITH -S/T- *VARESE (Pinn): VSD 6038 (CD)*

15 MINUTES (2000) Music sco: ANTHONY MARINELLI-J.PETER ROBINSON -S/T- *MILAN-BMG IMP: 74321 84668-2 (CD)*

20TH CENTURY FOX (Fanfare) (ALFRED NEWMAN) *see COLL.1*

21 JUMP STREET USA m: LIAM STERNBERG *see COLL.14,248,*

24/7 (1997) Music sc: BOO HEWERDINE-NEIL MacCOLL -S/T- *INDEPENDIENTE (TEN): ISOM 6CD (CD) ISOM 6MC (MC)*

28 DAYS (2000) Music score by RICHARD GIBBS -S/T- on *VARESE (Pinn): VSD 6151 (CD)*

30 IS A DANGEROUS AGE CYNTHIA (1967) Music score by DUDLEY MOORE performed by The DUDLEY MOORE TRIO -S/T- *HARKIT (Koch/Silva Screen): HRKCD 8011 (CD)*

42nd STREET (1933 MUSICAL) DICK POWELL-RUBY KEELER- WARNER BAXTER-BEBE DANIELS *inc.*'SKY'S THE LIMIT' 'DUBARRY WAS A LADY' *TARGET (BMG):CD 60010 (CD) + SOUNDTRACK FACTORY (Discov): SFCD 33516 (CD)*

42nd STREET (MUSICAL 1980) Songs AL DUBIN-HARRY WARREN O.Broadway Rev.Cast *feat* JERRY ORBACH-TAMMY GRIMES LEE ROY REAMES-WANDA RICHERT-CAROLE COOK & Company *RCA Victor (BMG): BD 83891 (CD)*

49TH PARALLEL (1941) mus: VAUGHN WILLIAM *see COLL.49,*

70s MANIA (ITV 16/6/2001) 1970s V.ARTISTS COMPILATION *BMG: 74321 85219-2 (CD)*

77 SUNSET STRIP (USA) *see COLL.242, +BMG 74321 59154-2*

80s MANIA (ITV 2001) 1980s VARIOUS ARTISTS COMPILATION *BMG: 74321 85257-2 (CD)*

100 RIFLES (1968) Music score: JERRY GOLDSMITH *LTD ED.*
RETROGRADE (S.Screen/MFTM): FSMCD Vol.2 No.1 (CD)
also on TARAN (Silver Sounds): W.9101 (CD)
101 DALMATIONS (1996) Music score: MICHAEL KAMEN -S/T-
DISNEY-EDEL (Vit) WD 69940-2 (CD) see DISNEY p.341
101 REYKJAVIK (2001) Music score by DAMON ALBARN -S/T-
EMI SOUNDTRACKS: 532 989-2 (CD)
102 DALMATIONS (2000) Music Score by DAVID NEWMAN
-S/T- HOLLYWOOD-EDEL (Vital): 012 219-2DNY (CD)
110 IN THE SHADE (MUSICAL) songs by HARVEY SCHMIDT and
TOM JONES. *NEW RECORDING* JOHN OWEN EDWARDS (cond)
TER (KOCH): CDTER2 1255 (2CD)
187 (1997) VARIOUS ARTISTS -S/T- on
ATLANTIC (TEN): 7567 92760-2 (CD) -4 (MC)
200 MOTELS (1971) music by FRANK ZAPPA and The MOTHERS
OF INVENTION and ROYAL PHILHARMONIC ORCH.& CHORUS
-S/T- *reiss with additional items RYKODISC (Vital)*
RCD 10513/14 (2CD) RAC 10513/14 (2MC)
633 SQUADRON (1964) Music score by RON GOODWIN
see COLL.94,116,123,265,
999 / 999 INT / 999 LIFESAVERS (BBC1 25/06/1992-2001)
theme music by ROGER BOLTON *unavailable*
1492 CONQUEST OF PARADISE (1992) Music score: VANGELIS
S/T- EAST WEST (TEN): 4509 91014-2(CD) WX 497C(MC)
see COLL.62,263,264,
1914-18 (BBC2 10/11/96) Music sco: MASON DARING -S/T-
'The Great War and The Shaping Of T.20th Century'
DARING (Direct Dist): DARINGCD 3029 (CD)
1941 (1979) Music score: JOHN WILLIAMS -S/T- *reissue*
VARESE (Pinn): VSD 5832 (CD)
1969 (1988) Music score: MICHAEL SMALL -S/T- reissue
POLY (IMS-Poly): AA 837 362-2 (CD)
1984 (1984) Mus.comp/perform by EURYTHMICS -S/T- *reiss*
VIRGIN-MFP (EMI): CDVIP 135 (CD) TCVIP 135 (MC)
2000 THOUSAND YEARS (ITV 18/04/1999) title music by
ROBERT HARTSHORNE -S/T- *feat Various Classics on*
CONIFER CLASSICS (BMG): 75605 51353-2 (2CD)
2001-A SPACE ODYSSEY (1968) Classical -S/T- featuring
"Blue Danube"(J.STRAUSS) "Also Sprach Zarathustra"
(R.STRAUSS) etc. -S/T- *EMI ODEON: CDODEON 28 (CD)*
see COLL.88,218,232,237,
2001-A SPACE ODYSSEY (REJECTED SCORE by ALEX NORTH)
National Philharmonic Orchestra (JERRY GOLDSMITH)
VARESE (Pinn): VSD 5400 (CD)
20,000 LEAGUES UNDER THE SEA (1996 TV Mini-Series)
Music score: JOHN SCOTT.recording by UTAH STUDIO
SYMPHONY ORCHESTRA on *PROMETHEUS: PCD 143 (CD)*
Orig -S/T- *JOS RECORDS (S.Screen): JSCD 122 (CD)*
A.I.(2001) Music score by JOHN WILLIAMS
-S/T- *WEA (TEN): 9362 48096-2 (CD)*
A.TEAM The (USA) ITV from 29/7/83) theme by MIKE POST
PETE CARPENTER *SIL.SCREEN (Koch):SILVAD 3509 (CD)*
see COLL.14,77,244,

ABERDEEN (2000) Music score by ZBIGNIEW PREISNER -S/T-
   SILVA SCREEN (Koch): SILKD 6028 (CD)
ABBOTT & COSTELLO SHOW The (USA TV) *see COLL.245,*
   also available 'WHO'S ON FIRST' (comedy routine)
   ON THE AIR-DELTA (Target-BMG): OTA 101913 (CD)
ABOUT LAST NIGHT (1986) Music sc: MILES GOODMAN -S/T-
   EMI AMER (EMI): CDP 746 560-2 (CD)
ABOVE THE RIM (1993) Music score: MARCUS MILLER -S/T-
   V.ARTISTS *DEATH ROW (RMG/UNIV): DROW 102 (CD) also*
   INTERSCOPE (UNI):IND 92359 + WEA:6544-92359-2 (CD)
ABSOLUTE BEGINNERS (Film Musical 86) Score: GIL EVANS
   -S/T- *VIP (EMI): CDVIP 112 (CD) TCVIP 112 (MC)*
   also Highlights on *VIRGIN: CDV 2386 (CD)*
ABSOLUTE POWER (1996) Music score: LENNIE NIEHAUS with
   CLINT EASTWOOD -S/T- *VARESE (Pinn): VSD 5808 (CD)*
ABSOLUTE TRUTH (BBC2 27/9/1998) Music: DEBBIE WISEMAN
   BBC Worldwide (Pinn-Koch): WMSF 60002 (CD)
ABSOLUTELY FABULOUS (BBC2 12/11/92) theme song "This
   Wheel's On Fire" (Dylan-Danko) ABSOLUTELY FABULOUS
   (PET SHOP BOYS) *on COLL.260,*'TV2000'*SONY TV82CD*
ABYSS The (Film 89) Music score: ALAN SILVESTRI -S/T-
   VARESE (Pinn): VSD 5235 (CD)
ACROSS 110TH STREET (1972)Mus: JJ JOHNSON-BOBBY WOMACK
   -S/T- *RYKODISC (Vital): RCD 10706 (CD) / see also*
   BOBBY WOMACK on *CHARLY (Charly): CPCD 8340 (CD)*
   DAGORED (Koch): RED 123 (LP)
ACT The (1978) ORIG BROADWAY CAST *feat:* LIZA MINNELLI
   ORIG CAST RECORDING *DRG (Pinn): CDDRG 6101 (CD)*
ADAM 12 (USA TV) *see COLL.242,*
ADDAMS FAMILY The (USA 64) Music from orig TV ser.by
   VIC MIZZY *RCA IMP (S.Screen): 61057-2(CD) -4 (MC)*
   see COLL.38,82,84,242,
ADDAMS FAMILY The (1991) Music sco: MARC SHAIMAN -S/T-
   CAPITOL (EMI): CDESTU 2161 (CD) TCESTU 2161 (MC)
ADDAMS FAMILY VALUES (1993) Music score: MARC SHAIMAN
   SCORE -S/T- *VARESE (Pinn): VSD 5465 (CD)*
ADIEMUS - *see COLL.10,*
ADVENTURES IN PARADISE (USA TV) *see COLL.245,*
ADVENTURES OF AGGIE (ITV) theme music "High Stepper"
   RONALD BINGE *MARCO POLO (Sel): 8223515 (CD)*
ADVENTURES OF BLACK BEAUTY The (LWT 23/9/72 & C4 1986)
   theme "Galloping Home" (DENIS KING) London String
   Chorale *see COLL.3,*
ADVENTURES OF DON JUAN (1948) MAX STEINER *see COLL.239,*
ADVENTURES OF MARCO POLO (1937) Music: HUGO FRIEDHOFER
   Suite on Col1 "HUGO FRIEDHOFER" *with* 'THE LODGER'/
   'RAINS OF RANCHIPUR'/'SEVEN CITIES OF GOLD' perf.
   by The MOSCOW SYPHONY ORCH (cond: W.T.Stromberg)
   MARCO POLO (Select): 8.223857 (CD)
ADVENTURES OF MARK TWAIN (1944) Music sc: MAX STEINER
   score perf.by BRANDENBURG PHILHARMONIC ORCHEST
   (William T.Stromberg) *with* 'PRINCE AND THE PAUPER'
   (KORNGOLD) *RCA BMG 09026 62660-2(CD) see COLL.239,*
ADVENTURES OF NICHOLAS NICKLEBY *see COLL.5,*

ADVENTURES OF OZZIE AND HARRIET (USA TV) see *COLL.245,*

ADVENTURES OF PRISCILLA QUEEN OF THE DESERT (1994) Mus sco: GUY CROSS -S/T- *MOTHER (Univ): 516 937-2 (CD)*

ADVENTURES OF ROBIN HOOD The (ITV 17/2/56-1960) theme mus (Carl Sigman) DICK JAMES *EMI:TCEM 1307 (MC) CDS 791255-2 (CD)* GARRY MILLER see *COLL.243,*

ADVENTURES OF ROBIN HOOD The (1938) Mus sco: ERICH WOLFGANG KORNGOLD -S/T- *TER (Koch): CDTER 1066 + VARESE: VSD 47177 (CD)* see *COLL.45,69,92,160,240,*

ADVENTURES OF ROBINSON CRUSOE The (BBC1 12/10/65) Mus score: ROBERT MELLIN-GIAN PIERO REVERBERI Original TV S/TRACK *reissued w.ADDITIONAL unreleased music S.SCREEN (Koch): FILMCD 705 (CD)* see *COLL.83,*

ADVENTURES OF SUPERMAN (USATV) Music by SHIRLEY WALKER -S/T- on *VARESE (Pinn): VSD 6093 (CD)*

AFFLICTION (1997) Music score by MICHAEL BROOK -S/T- *CITADEL (Hot): STC 77121 (CD)*

AFRICAN FOOTPRINT (MUSICAL SHOW 2000) VARIOUS ARTISTS *FIRST NIGHT (Pinn): CASTCD 77 (CD) CASTC 77 (MC)*

AFRICAN SANCTUS 1 (BBC2 29/7/95) Music: DAVID FANSHAWE *new digital rec.feat:* WILHELMENIA FERNANDEZ and KATAMANTO + BOURNEMOUTH SYPH.CHORUS +CHORISTERS OF ST.GEORGE'S CHAPEL WINDSOR. *SILVA SCREEN (Koch): SILKD 6003 (CD) SILKC 6003(MC)* see also MISSA LUBA

AFRICAN SANCTUS 2 (BBC1 1978) Mass For Love and Peace DAVID FANSHAWE *PHILIPS: 426 055-2 (CD) -4(MC) also available* Allmanna Sangen cond.by ROBERT SUND *PROPRIUS Records: PR(C)(CD) 9984 (LP/MC/CD)*

AFTER THE FOX (1966) Music score: BURT BACHARACH -S/T- *RYKODISC (Vital): CD 10716 (CD)*

AGAINST ALL ODDS (1984) Music sco: MICHEL COLOMBIER -S/T- *VIRGIN (MFP-EMI): CDVIP 112 (CD)*

AGATHA CHRISTIE'S POIROT (LWT from 8/1/89) Theme music by CHRISTOPHER GUNNING see *COLL.4,*

AGE OF INNOCENCE (1992) see *COLL.40,68,*

AGIA NAPIA: FANTASY ISLAND (C4 07/01/2000) Mus.tracks mixed by DJ SPOONY on V.Arts Coll: 'AGIA NAPIA' on *TELSTAR: TTVCD 3115 (2CD)* / ALSO 'AGIA NAPIA 2000' *SMART (Univ): SMARTCD 009 (CD)*

AGNES BROWNE (1999) Music score by PADDY MOLONEY -S/T- *DECCA-LONDON (UNIV): 466 939-2 (CD)*

AGONY AND THE ECSTASY The (1965) Music sco: ALEX NORTH *with* 'PRIDE & THE PASSION' (George Antheil) 75mins *CLOUD NINE (Import, S.Screen): CNS 5001 (CD)* **New Record** *VARESE (Pinn): VSD 5901 (CD, 10.1998)*

AIDA (1999) Musical songs by TIM RICE and ELTON JOHN ORIGINAL BROADWAY CAST *DISNEY: DSN 860 671-2 (CD)* ANIMATED FILM V.ARTISTS *UNIVERSAL: 524 651-2 (CD)*

AIN'T MISBEHAVIN' (ORIG LONDON CAST 1995) *FIRST NIGHT (Pinn): ORCD 6053 (CD)*

AIN'T MISBEHAVIN' (O.BROADWAY CAST 1979) Music: FATS WALLER with Andre de Shields-Nell Carter-Ken Page *RCA Imp. (S.Screen): 2965-2 (2CD) CBK2 2965 (MC)*

AIR FORCE ONE (1997) Music score: JERRY GOLDSMITH with
additional music by JOEL McNEELY -S/T- on
VARESE (Pinn): VSD 5825 (CD)
AIRPORT (1970) Music score: ALFRED NEWMAN -S/T- reiss
VARESE (Pinn): VSD 5436 (CD)
AIRPORT (BBC1 2/4/96-2000) series title music composed
and performed by HAL LINDES *unavailable*
AIRWOLF (USA 1984) theme by SYLVESTER LEVAY 'AIRWOLF
THEMES' arr.by MARK J.CAIRNS-SYLVESTER LEVAY
MCA (Univ): GERCD 3 (2CD) also see COLL.14,38,247,
ALADDIN (1993) Mus.& songs: ALAN MENKEN-HOWARD ASHMAN
TIM RICE -S/T- *feat* "A Whole New World" sung by
PEABO BRYSON-REGINA BELLE -S/T- *DISNEY (B.Vista):*
WD 74260-2 (CD) WD 74260-4 (MC) also available
'BEST OF ALADDIN' *WD 69080-2 see also* DISNEY p.341
ALAMO The (1960) Music sco: DIMITRI TIOMKIN title song
"Green Leaves Of Summer" (Tiomkin-Webster) sung by
BROTHERS FOUR -S/T- *COLUMBIA (S.Scr) CB 66138 (CD)*
ORCHESTRAL SUITE on 'HIGH NOON' (D.TIOMKIN Coll)
(BMG): 09026 62658-2 (CD) see COLL.63,146,258,279,
ALEGRIA (Royal Albert Hall 01/1998) SHOW featuring the
Circus Troupe CIRQUE DU SOLEIL Music: RENE DUPERE
-S/T- *RCA (BMG): 09026 62701-2 (CD)*
ALEXANDER NEVSKY (1938 Eisenstein) Mus sc: S.PROKOFIEV
1.*SOUNDTRACK FACTORY (Discovery): SFCD 33550 (CD)*
2.ST.PETERSBURG PHILH.ORCH *RCA: 09026 61926-2 (CD)*
3.SCOTTISH NAT.ORCH. *CHANDOS: CHAN 8584 (CD)*
ALEXANDER THE GREAT (1956) Music sco: MARIO NASCIMBENE
WITH 'BARABBAS' *DRG (Pinn): DRGCD 32964 (CD)*
ALFIE (1966) Music sco: SONNY ROLLINS -S/T- *reissue*
IMPULSE-GRP-New Note (Pinn): IMP 12242 (CD)
"Alfie" (Bacharach-David) *by* CHER *see COLL.186,*
ALFRED HITCHCOCK PRESENTS (USA 55) / ITV 60's) Theme
"Funeral March Of A Marionette" (GOUNOD)
see COLL.83,142,144,219,242,
ALI (2001) Music by LISA GERRARD and other artists
-S/T- *POLYDOR (UNIV): 493 173-2 (CD)*
ALIAS SMITH AND JONES (USA 71/rpt.BBC2 1997/98 title
theme music by BILLY GOLDENBERG *deleted*
ALICE IN WONDERLAND (1950) -S/T- *DISNEY-EDEL (Vital)*
019 607-2DNY (CD) see WALT DISNEY INDEX p.341
ALICE IN WONDERLAND (2000)(C4 23/04/2000) Music score:
RICHARD HARTLEY orch.by ARTHUR KEMPEL-JOHN BELL
VARESE (Pinn): VSD 6021 (CD)
ALICE'S RESTAURANT (1969) Music: GARRY SHERMAN Songs
by ARLO GUTHRIE feat PETE SEEGER -S/T- *REPRISE*
(TEN):K244045 (CD) RYKODISC (Vit): RCD 10737 (CD)
30TH ANNIVERSARY EDITION *KOCH: 37959-2 (CD)*
ALIEN (1979) Music sco: JERRY GOLDSMITH -S/T *deleted*
see COLL.83,114,138,218,232,
ALIEN (2) ALIENS (1986) Music sco: JAMES HORNER -S/T-
VARESE USA (Pinn): VCD 47263 (CD)
ALIEN 3 (92) Music score: ELLIOT GOLDENTHAL -S/T- on
MCA (UNI): MCD 10629 (CD)

ALIEN TRILOGY - Royal Scottish National Orch (New Rec)
VARESE (Pinn): VSD 6241 / VSD 5753 (CD) Music by
JERRY GOLDSMITH-JAMES HORNER-ELLIOT GOLDENTHAL
ALIEN 4 (97) Music score: JOHN FRIZZELL -S/T-
RCA (BMG): 09026 68955-2 (CD)
ALIEN NATION (1988) Mus score: JOE HARNELL
see COLL.220,248,
ALIEN NATION (SKY1 13/6/94) m: STEVE DORFF-LARRY HERBS
TRITT-DAVID KURTZ -S/T- *GNP (ZYX) GNPD 8024 (CD)*
ALL ABOUT EVE (1950) Music score by ALFRED NEWMAN
-S/T- with 'LEAVE HER TO HEAVEN' (A.Newman, 1945)
FSM CLASSICS (USA Ltd Ed.): FSMCD Vol 2.No.8 (CD)
new rec: MOSCOW S.O.& CHORUS (William Stromberg) +
'BEAU GESTE' 1939; 'HUNCHBACK OF NOTRE DAME' 1939
MARCO POLO (Select): 8.223750 (CD) see.COLL.1,
ALL ABOUT MY MOTHER (1999) Music sco: ALBERTO IGLESIAS
-S/T- *UNIVERSAL MUSIC: 676 208-2 (CD)*
ALL CREATURES GREAT AND SMALL (BBC1 8/1/1978) Theme &
incidental music: JOHNNY PEARSON *see COLL.3,*
ALL QUIET ON THE PRESTON FRONT (BBC1 4/1/94) theme mus
"Here I Stand" by The MILLTOWN BROTHERS   'Slinky'
A.& M. (Univ): 395 346-2 (CD) 395 346-4 (MC)
ALL THAT JAZZ (1979) Mus sc: RALPH BURNS "On Broadway"
GEORGE BENSON -S/T- *SPECTRUM (Univ):551 269-2 (CD)*
ALL THAT MONEY CAN BUY aka 'Devil And Daniel Webster'
(1941) Music score: BERNARD HERRMANN   Film Suite
UNICORN-KANCHANA (Harmonia Mundi): UKCD 2065 (CD)
ALL THE BROTHERS WERE VALIANT (1953) Music sco: MIKLOS
ROSZA *PROMETHEUS (Silva Screen): PCD 131 (CD)*
ALL THE KINGS MEN (BBC1 14/11/1999) Music score by
ADRIAN JOHNSTON and perf.by BBC CONCERT ORCHESTRA
-S/T- *BBC WORLDWIDE (Pinn): WMSF 6017-2 (CD)*
ALL THE PRETTY HORSES (2000) Music by MARTY STEWART-
KRISTIN WILKINSON-LARRY PAXTON
-S/T- *SONY CLASSICS (TEN): SK 89465 (CD)*
ALONG CAME A SPIDER (2001) Music score JERRY GOLDSMITH
-S/T- *VARESE (Pinn): VSD 6238 (CD)*
ALLY McBEAL (C4 03/6/1998) theme "Searchin' My Soul"
sung by VONDA SHEPARD -S/T- *SONY: 491 124-2(CD) -4
(MC) theme: 666 633-2 (CDs)*
'ALLY McBEAL: FOR ONCE IN MY LIFE'   VONDA SHEPARD
EPIC (TEN): 500 577-2 (CD) -4 (MC)
'HEART & SOUL OF ALLY McBEAL' *feat VONDA SHEPARD*
EPIC (TEN): 495 091-2 (CD) -4 (MC)
'ALLY McBEAL THE CHRISTMAS ALBUM'   feat V.ARTISTS
EPIC (TEN): 501 017-2 (CD) -4 (MC)
theme also on Coll.260, 'TV 2000' SONYTV82CD (CD)
ALMANAC (USA MUSICAL) Songs by JOHN MURRAY ANDERSON
ORIG USA CAST *DRG (N.Note-Pinn): DRGCD 19009 (CD)*
ALMOST FAMOUS (2000) Music: DANNY BRAMSON-NANCY WILSON
-S/T- VARIOUS ARTISTS *UNIVERSAL: 450 279-2 (CD)*
AMADEUS (1984) Music (MOZART) Academy Of St.Martin-In
The Fields -S/T- *LONDON (TEN): 825 126-2 (CD)*
LONDON 511 126-2 (CD Boxed Set) see COLL.64,

AMAHL AND THE NIGHT VISITORS (CHRISTMAS OPERA) Music & Libretto (Gian Carlo MENOTTI) R.Opera House Orch.& Chorus (David Syrus) with JAMES RAINBIRD as Amahl *TER (Koch) CDTER 1124 (CD)*

AMANDA (1996) Music score by BASIL POLEDOURIS -S/T- on *PROMETHEUS USA IMPORT: PCR 508 (CD)*

AMARCORD (1973) Music score b NINO ROTA -S/T- on *CAM IMPT.(HOT): 493 093-2 (CD)*

AMAZING STORIES (STEVEN SPIELBERG) (BBC119/4/1992) Mus JOHN WILLIAMS. ROYAL SCOTTISH NAT.ORCH.+ music by GEORGES DELERUE *VARESE (Pinn): VSD 5941 (CD)*

AMELIE FROM MONTMARTRE (2001) Music score: YANN TIERSEN -S/T- *VIRGIN (EMI): 7243 810790-2*

AMERICA'S SWEETHEARTS (2001) Music: JAMES NEWTON HOWARD -S/T- (V.ARTISTS) *ATLANTIC (TEN): 7567 83495-2 (CD)*

AMERICAN BANDSTAND (USA TV) *see COLL.244,*

AMERICAN BEAUTY (1999) Music sco: THOMAS NEWMAN -S/T- *DREAMWORKS (Univ): E450 233-2 (CD) + 450 210-2(CD)*

AMERICAN GIGOLO (1980) Music sc: GIORGIO MORODER -S/T- with V/Arts *reiss SPECTRUM (Univ) 551 103-2 (CD)*

AMERICAN GRAFFITI (1973) Music by VARIOUS ORIG ARTISTS *MCA (UNI): MCLDD 19150 (CDx2)*

AMERICAN HISTORY X (1998) Music score by ANNE DUDLEY -S/T- *EMI CLASSICS: CDQ 556 781-2 (CD)*

AMERICAN IN PARIS (1951) Songs: GEORGE & I.GERSHWIN
1.-S/T- *EMI-Soundtrack: CDODEON 20 (2CD) DELETED*
2.import score with -S/T- of 'SINGIN' IN THE RAIN' *BLUE MOON (Discovery): BMCD 7008 (CD)*
3.new recording on *VIRGIN (EMI): VM 561247-2 (CD)*

AMERICAN OUTLAWS (2001) Music by TREVOR RABIN -S/T- *VARESE (Pinn): VSD 6276 (CD)*

AMERICAN PIE (1999) Music score by DAVID LAWRENCE -S/T- *UNIVERSAL MUSIC: UND 53269 (CD)*

AMERICAN PIE 2 (2001) VARIOUS ARTISTS SOUNDTRACK on *ISLAND (UNIV): 014 494-2 (CD) or 16348-2 (CD)*

AMERICAN PSYCHO (1998) Music score by DANNY ELFMAN -S/T- *KOCH INT: KOCCD 8077 (CD)*

AMERICAN TWISTORY A HYSTERICAL LOOK AT AMERICA (SHOW) Songs: KEVIN KAUFMAN-JOHN EVEREST / ORIG.CAST REC *DUCY LEE (Silver Sounds): DLR 900106 (CD)*

AMERICAN VISIONS (BBC2 03/11/1996) *see COLL.104,*

AMISTAD (1998) Music score: JOHN WILLIAMS -S/T- on *DREAMWORKS (BMG): DRD 50035 see COLL.3,*

AMITYVILLE DOLLHOUSE (1996) Music score by RAY COLCORD -S/T- *CITADEL (HOT): STC 77125 (CD)*

AMONGST WOMEN (1999) Music by NIALL BYRNE -S/T- on *CLADDAGH (Proper/Highlander): SPINCD 1003 (CD)*

AMORES PERROS (2000) VARIOUS ARTISTS SOUNDTRACK on *UNIVERSAL MUSIC-IMS (UNIV): E.524 933-2 (CD)*

AN AMERICAN RHAPSODY (2001) Music score: CLIFF EIDELMAN -S/T- *IMPORT MILAN USA: MILAN 35955 (CD)*

AN AMERICAN WEREWOLF IN LONDON (1981) Music sco: ELMER BERNSTEIN / "Blue Moon" (Rodgers-Hart) songs by MARCELS/BOBBY VINTON/SAM COOKE *-S/T- unavailable*

AN AMERICAN WEREWOLF IN PARIS (1996) Music sc: WILBERT
HIRSCH -S/T- *EDEL-HOLLYW.(Vital) 012131-2HWR (CD)*
AN ANGEL AT MY TABLE (1990) Music score: DON McGLASHAN
-S/T- *DRG USA (Pinn): CDSBL 12603 (CD)*
AN AWFULLY BIG ADVENTURE (1994) Music: RICHARD HARTLEY
-S/T- *FILMTRACKS (S.Screen): TRAXCD 2001 (CD)*
AN EVENING WITH ALAN JAY LERNER (O.LONDON CAST 1987)
LIZ ROBERTSON-MARTI WEBB-PLACINDO DOMINGO-ELAINE
PAIGE & others *FIRST NIGHT (Pinn): OCRCD 6012 (CD)*
AN EVERLASTING PIECE (2000) Music score by HANS ZIMMER
-S/T- *VARESE (Pinn): VSD 6202 (CD)*
AN IDEAL HUSBAND (1999) Music score: CHARLIE MOLE
-S/T- *BMG SOUNDTRACKS: 74321 66992-2 (CD)*
AN OFFICER AND A GENTLEMAN (1982) Music: JACK NITZSCHE
-S/T- *ISLAND Univ: IMCD 77 (CD) ICM 2041 (MC)*
see COLL.73,
ANACONDA (1997) Music score: RANDY EDELMAN
-S/T- *EDEL (Vital) 002281-2CIN (CD)*
ANALYZE THIS (1998) Music score by HOWARD SHORE -S/T-
VARESE (Pinn): VSD 6016 (CD)
ANASTASIA (1997) Music score: DAVID NEWMAN
-S/T- *ATLANTIC (TEN): 7567 80753-2 (CD) -4 (MC)*
ANASTASIA: THE MYSTERY OF ANNA (1986) Music score by
LAURENCE ROSENTHAL with MUNICH SYMPHONY ORCHESTRA
SOUTHERN CROSS (HOT): SCCD 1015 (CD)
ANCHORS AWEIGH (1945 MUSICAL) *w:* FRANK SINATRA-GRACE
KELLY-KATHRYN GRAYSON *TARGET (BMG): CD 60003 (CD)*
also abailable -S/T- Import with 'ON THE TOWN'
BLUE MOON (Discovery): BMCD 7007 (CD)
AND DO THEY DO Music: MICHAEL NYMAN with MICHAEL NYMAN
BAND *TER (Koch): CDTER 1123 (CD)*
AND THE BAND PLAYED ON (1993) Music sc: CARTER BURWELL
-S/T- *VARESE (Pinn): VSD 5449 (CD)*
ANDES TO AMAZON (BBC1 06/11/2000) Music score by
NICHOLAS HOOPER -S/T- *BBC (Pinn): WMSF 6034-2 (CD)*
ANGEL (USA)(C4 15/09/2000) title theme music performed
by DARLING VIOLETTA / TV score by CHRISTOPHE BECK-
ROBERT J.KRAL *currently unavailable*
ANGEL & THE SOLDIER BOY The (1989) BBC1 27/12/89
-S/T- *reissue BMG Kidz (BMG): 74321 25081-2 (CD)*
ANGEL HEART (1987) Music score: TREVOR JONES -S/T- on
ISLAND (Univ) IMCD 76 (CD)
ANGELA'S ASHES (1999) Music score by JOHN WILLIAMS
-S/T- score *SONY CLASSICS (TEN): SK 89009 (CD)*
-S/T- songs *SPECTRUM (Univ): 466 761-2 (CD) -4(MC)*
ANGELS (BBC1 1976-80) theme music "Motivation" by ALAN
PARKER *see COLL.3,172,*
ANGELS AND INSECTS (1994) Mus sco: ALEX BALANESCU perf
BALANESCU QUART.-S/T- *MUTE-RTM (Disc) CDSTUMM 147*
ANGELS EYES (2001) Music score by MARCO BELTRAMI -S/T-
CURB / UNIVERSAL MUSIC: CURCD 104 (CD)
ANGELS OF THE UNIVERSE (2000) Mus HILMAR ORN HILMARSSON
-SIGUR ROS -S/T- *FATCAT (Vital) FATOSTCD 001 (CD)*

ANGIE (1993) Music sco: JERRY GOLDSMITH -S/T-
VARESE (Pinn): VSD 5469 (CD)
ANIMAL ATTRACTION (2001) Music score: ROLFE KENT -S/T-
COLOSSEUM (Pinn/Vital): CST 8085 (CD)
ANIMAL FARM (1998) Music score by RICHARD HARVEY
VARESE (Pinn): VSD 6082 (CD)
ANIMAL HOSPITAL (BBC1 5/1/1995-2001) theme music
composed & arranged by RONALD DE JONG *unavailable*
ANIMAL MAGIC (BBC1 to 84) "Las Vegas" LAURIE JOHNSON
see COLL.3,119,
ANNA (FRENCH TV SERIES 1967) Music: SERGE GAINSBOURG
MERCURY (Univ): 558 837-2 (CD)
ANNA AND THE KING (1999) Music score by GEORGE FENTON
-S/T- *BMG IMPORTS (BMG): 73008 26075-2 (CD)*
ANNA AND THE KING OF SIAM (1946) Mus: BERNARD HERRMANN
new rec: VARESE (Pinn): VSD 6091 (CD) see COLL.1,
ANNA KARENINA (1997) TCHAIKOVSKY-RACHMANINOV-PROKOFIEV
-S/T- *LONDON (Univ): 455 360-2 (CD) 455 360-4 (MC)*
ANNA OF THE FIVE TOWNS (BBC2 9/1/85) title music by
NIGEL HESS London Film Orch *see COLL.137,*
ANNE OF A THOUSAND DAYS (1969) Music: GEORGES DELERUE
-S/T- with 'MARY QUEEN OF SCOTS' (1971 JOHN BARRY)
ARTEMIS (Hot): ARTF 005 (CD)
ANNIE - songs by Charles Strouse and Martin Charnin
1.STUDIO RECORDING 1997 *feat:* KIM CRISWELL-RUTHIE
HENSHALL-RON RAINES-SARAH FRENCH and Company
TER-Music Theatre Hour (Koch): CDTEH 6001 (CD)
2.FILM MUSICAL 1982 *feat* ALBERT FINNEY-AILEEN QUINN
CAROL BURNETT -S/T- *Sony: 467 608-2 (CD) -4 (MC)*
3.ORIG BROADWAY CAST 1977 *feat:* ANDREA McARDLE-REID
SHELTON-DOROTHY LOUDEN-SANDY FAISON-ROBERT FITCH
COLUMBIA (Ten): SK 60723 (CD) see COLL.88,,
ANNIE GET YOUR GUN songs: Irving Berlin-Dorothy Fields
1.FILM S/TRACK 1950 *feat* BETTY HUTTON & HOWARD KEEL
RHINO RECORDS (USA) cat.number to be confirmed
2.1998 REVIVAL CAST STUDIO RECORDING *featuring:*
BERNADETTE PETERS and The NEW BROADWAY CAST
ANGEL (EMI): CDQ 556 812-2 (CD)
3.LINCOLN CENTER EDIT.FIRST COMPLETE RECORDING *w:*
JUDY KAYE-BARRY BOSTWICK *TER (Koch): CDTER2 1229*
4.CARLTON SHOWS COLLECTION 1995 *feat:* GEMMA CRAVEN-
with EDMUND HOCKRIDGE-STEVE BUTLER-ALISON COX
CARLTON Shows Collect: 30362 0012-2 (CD) -4 (MC)
5.NEW LONDON CAST 1986 *feat:* SUZI QUATRO & Company
FIRST NIGHT (Pinn): OCRCD 6024 (CD)
6.ORIG LONDON CAST 1947 *feat* DOLORES GRAY-BILL JOHNS
ON-HAL BRYAN-IRVING DAVIES-WENDY TOYE-PADDY STONE
LASERLIGHT (Target-BMG): 12 449 (CD)
7.ORIG BROADWAY CAST 1946 *w:* ETHEL MERMAN-BRUCE YARN
ELL-BENAY VENUTA-JERRY ORBACH *BMG: RD 81124 (CD)*
8.STUDIO 1990 *feat* KIM CRISWELL-THOMAS HAMPSON-JASON
GRAAE-REBECCA LUKER-Ambrosian Chor-London Sinfonia
(J.McGlinn) *EMI: CDANNIE 1 (CD) TCANNIE 1 (MC)*

ANNIVERSARY PARTY The (2000) Music score: MICHAEL PENN
 VAR.ARTISTS -S/T- *BMG IMPORTS: 09026 63818-2 (CD)*
ANOTHER DAWN (1937) Music sco: ERICH WOLFGANG KORNGOLD
 new version: MOSCOW S.ORCH (Stromberg) also feat:
 "Ballet Fantasy" from 'ESCAPE ME NEVER' on
 MARCO POLO (Select): 8.223871 (CD)
ANTARCTICA (1983) Music score: VANGELIS -S/T-
 POLYDOR (Univ) E.539 269-2 (CD) / 815 732-2 (CD)
ANTHOLOGY - THE BEATLES (ITV 26/11/95) music and songs
 TV S/T *EMI: CD(PC)PCSP 727 (2CD/2MC/3LPs)*
ANTIQUES ROAD SHOW (BBC1 18/2/79-2001)
 1989-2001 series theme: PAUL READE *unavailable*
 1985-1989 series theme: ROGER LIMB *unavailable*
ANTONIA'S LINE (1995) Music score: ILONA SEKACZ -S/T-
 SILVA SCREEN (Koch): FILMCD 183 (CD)
ANTONIO CARLUCCI'S ITALIAN FEAST (BBC2 17/9/96) music:
 CROCODILE MUSIC *see COLL.241,*
ANTONY AND CLEOPATRA (1972) Music score by JOHN SCOTT
 Royal Philharmonic Orch (Scott) Symphonic score on
 JOHN SCOTT Records (Silva Screen): JSCDC 114 (CD)
ANTZ (1998) Music score: HARRY GREGSON WILLIAMS & JOHN
 POWELL -S/T- *EMI: CDANTZ 001 (CD)*
ANY GIVEN SUNDAY (2000) VARIOUS ARTISTS SOUNDTRACK on
 ATLANTIC (TEN): 7567 83272-2 (CD) -4 (MC)
ANYTHING GOES - songs by Cole Porter
 1.FILM 1936 *feat:* BING CROSBY-ETHEL MERMAN etc
 recording also incl.extracts from 'PANAMA HATTIE'
 SANDY HOOK (Silver Sounds): CDSH 2043 (CD)
 2.ORIG LONDON CAST 1989 *feat:* ELAINE PAIGE-HOWARD
 McGILLIN-BERNARD CRIBBINS and Comp *FIRST NIGHT
 (Pinn): OCRCD 6038 (CD)*
 3.STUDIO RECORDING 1989 *feat* FREDERICA VON STADE-KIM
 CRISWELL-CRIS GROENENDAAL-JACK GILFORD and the LSO
 EMI: CDC 749848-2 (CD) EL 749848-4 (MC)
ANYWHERE BUT HERE (1999) Music score by DANNY ELFMAN
 -S/T- (V.Arts) *ATLANTIC (TEN): 7567 83234-2 (CD)*
APARTMENT The (1960) *see COLL.75,*
APE-MAN (BBC1 22/02/2000) Series music composed by
 PAUL LAWLER *unavailable*
APOCALYPSE NOW (1979) Music: CARMINE & FRANCIS COPPOLA
 + 'Die Walkure' (WAGNER) + V.Artists -S/T- *reissue
 WEA (TEN): 7559 79644-2 (CD) + 7559 60689-2 (2CD)
 also see COLL.123,197,*
APOLLO 13 (1994) Music score by JAMES HORNER -S/T- on
 MCA (UNI): MCD 11241 (CD) see COLL.61,148,149,232,
APPLAUSE (MUSICAL) songs: CHARLES STRAUSS-LEE ADAMS
 ORIGINAL BROADWAY CAST with LAUREN BACALL & Comp.
 UNIVERSAL (IMS): AA 12159404-2 (CD)
APPOINTMENT The (1968) Music: JOHN BARRY *see COLL.26,*
AQUA MARINA (ATV 60's) theme music by BARRY GRAY with
 vocal by GARRY MILLER *see COLL.118,250,*
ARABESQUE (1966) Music sco: HENRY MANCINI -S/T- with
 score from 'BREAKFAST AT TIFFANYS' (1961)
 RCA CAMDEN (BMG): 74321 69878-2 (CD)

ARABIAN NIGHTS (BBC1 30/04/2000) Music score compos.by
RICHARD HARVEY -S/T- *VARESE (Pinn): VSD 6141 (CD)*
ARCTIC BLUE (1993) Music score: PETER MELNICK -S/T-
NARADA (New Note-Pinn): ND 63030 (CD)
ARE YOU LONESOME TONIGHT (ORIG LONDON CAST 1985)
PRESLEY songs sung by MARTIN SHAW-SIMON BOWMAN
FIRST NIGHT (Pinn): OCRCD 6027
ARENA (BBC2) Theme "Another Green World" by BRIAN ENO
EG (Univ): EGMC 21 (MC) EGCD 21 (CD) see COLL.188,
ARISTOCATS The (1970) Songs: RICHARD & ROBERT SHERMAN
-S/T- *DISNEY (B.Vista): WD 74250-2 (CD) -4 (MC)*
see WALT DISNEY INDEX p.341
ARISTOCRATS The (BBC 1999) Music score: MARK THOMAS
BBC (Pinn): WMSF 6011-2 (CD)
ARLINGTON ROAD (1998) Music score: ANGELO BADALAMENTI
-S/T- (V.ARTISTS) *RCA (BMG): 74321 65152-2 (CD)*
ARMADILLO (BBC1 16/09/2001) Mus.score: RICHARD HARTLEY
theme "Yiriyaro" by BAABA MAAL from 'NOMAD SOUL'
PALM PICTURES (3MV-TEN): PALMCD 2002 9CD)
ARMAGEDDON (1997) Music score: TREVOR RABIN
-S/T- *COLUMBIA (Ten): 491 384-2 (CD) -4 (MC)*
also available 'MUSIC INSPIRED BY THE FILM' (Coll)
BGRM (Silver Sounds): 1096 34011-2 (CD)
ARMY OF DARKNESS (1992) Music sco: JOSEPH LoDUCA -S/T-
VARESE (Pinn): VSD 5411 (CD) VSC 5411 (MC)
AROUND THE WORLD IN 80 DAYS (1956) *see COLL.284,*
AROUND THE WORLD IN 80 RAVES (C4 18/05/2001) "Music in
You" by MONOBOY *PERFECTO (Pinn): PERF 18CDS (CDs)*
PERF 18T (12"s)
ARRIVAL The (1996) Mus: ARTHUR KEMPEL feat NORTHWEST
SINFONIA *SILVA SCREEN (Koch): FILMCD 182 (CD)*
ARTHUR (1980) Theme 'Best That You Can Do' sung by
CHRISTOPHER CROSS *see COLL.11,*
ARTHUR C.CLARKE'S MYSTERIOUS UNIVERSE (USA)/Discovery)
Music score by ALAN HAWKSHAW -S/T- music on
HUNGRY HAWK (Grapevine/Polygram): HHCD 101 (CD)
AS IF (E4 01/2001) -S/T- (Various) *VIRGIN TV (EMI)*
VTDCD 366 (2CD) theme "Would You" by TOUCH AND GO
-S/T- 'AS IF' on *VIRGIN (EMI): VTDCD 366 (2CD)*
AS THOUSANDS CHEER (SHOW with songs by IRVING BERLIN)
ORIG CAST STUDIO on *VARESE (Pinn): VSD 5999 (CD)*
AS TIME GOES BY (BBC1 12/1/92-2000) theme song "As Time
Goes By" (Hupfeld) by JOE FAGIN on Coll 'Best Of on
Westmoor (BMG): CDWM 107 (CD) see also 'CASABLANCA'
AS YOU LIKE IT (1936) Music sc: WILLIAM WALTON select.
'Walton Film Music' LONDON PHILHARMONIC ORCHESTRA
conduct: CARL DAVIS *EMI: CDM 565585-2 (CD) also*
ACADEMY of ST.MARTIN-IN-THE-FIELDS (N.Marriner)
and 'HAMLET' *CHANDOS: CHAN 8842 (CD)*
ASK THE FAMILY (BBC2) *see COLL.5,*
ASPECTS OF LOVE -songs by Andrew Lloyd Webber-Charles
Hart and Don Black
1.ORIG LONDON CAST 1989 *feat:* MICHAEL BALL-ANN CRUMB
DIANA MORRISON-KEVIN COLSON *POLY: 841 126-2 / -4*

2. SHOWS COLLECTION Studio 1993 *feat:* PAUL JONES with
   STEPHANIE LAWRENCE-DAVE WILLETTS-FIONA HENDLEY-
   CARL WAYNE-WEST END CONCERT OR.+ *music of* 'PHANTOM
   OF THE OPERA' *CARLTON: PWKS(PWKMC) 4164 (CD(MC)*
3. ROYAL PHILH.ORCH *PLAY SUITES from* Aspects Of Love
   Cats/Joseph and The Amazing Technicolor Dreamcoat
   Carlton: PWKS(PWKMC) 4115 (CD(MC)
4. Classic Musicals series *feat:* JOHN BARROWMAN-JANIS
   KELLY-SHONA LINDSAY-JOHN DIEDRICH + 'JESUS CHRIST
   SUPERSTAR' *KOCH INT: 34083-2 (CD)*

ASSASSIN The: Point Of No Return (1992) Music score by
HANS ZIMMER includes songs by NINA SIMONE -S/T-
MILAN (BMG): 14302-2 (CD)

ASSASSINATION BUREAU The (1968) *see COLL.6,*

ASSASSINS (ORIG USA CAST 1991) Songs: STEPHEN SONDHEIM
William Parry-Terence Mann *(BMG): RD 60737 (CD)*

ASSAULT ON PRECINCT 13 (1976) Music sc: JOHN CARPENTER
see COLL.83,

ASSAULT The (1986) - *see under* 'CRY IN THE DARK'

ASTERIX (1999) Music by JEAN JACQUES GOLDMANN & ROLAND
ROMANELLI -S/T- *COLUMBIA (TEN): 494 402-2 (CD)*

ASTERIX IN BRITAIN (1986) Music: VLADIMIR COSMA -S/T-
inc 'CAESAR'S GIFT' *POMME (Discov): 95129-2 (CD)*

ASTRO BOY (USA TV) *see COLL.221,245,*

ASTRONAUT'S WIFE The (1998) Music sc: GEORGE S.CLINTON
-S/T- *SIRE (USA Impt): SIRE 31084 (CD)*

AT FIRST SIGHT (1998) Music score: MARK ISHAM -S/T-
MILAN (BMG: 74321 65510-2 (CD)

AT HOME WITH THE BRAITHWAITES (ITV 20/01/2000) t.music
composed & performed by THE EGG / incidental music
by RUPERT GREGSON WILLIAMS *unavailable*

AT THE DROP OF A HAT (Musical Revue 1958 Fortune)
featuring MICHAEL FLANDERS and DONALD SWANN on
EMI: CDP 797465-2(CD) / AT THE DROP OF ANOTHER HAT
(Musical Revue 1960 Haymarket) MICHAEL FLANDERS-
-DONALD SWANN *EMI: CDP 797466-2 (CD) ECC (2MC)*

ATHLETICS (BBC 70s-2001) "World Series" KEITH MANSFIELD
+"Fanfare For T.Common Man"(A.COPLAND)*see COLL.122,*

ATLANTIC REALM (BBC1 8/1/89) Music comp.& performed by
CLANNAD -S/T- *reis: RCA (BMG): 74321 31867-2 (CD)*

ATLANTIS THE LOST EMPIRE (2001) Mus:JAMES NEWTON HOWARD
-DIANE WARREN -S/T- *DISNEY-WEA (TEN) 092742333-2 CD*

ATOM ANT SHOW (USA TV) *see COLL.221,246,*

ATOMIC CAFE The (1982) PRO-NUCLEAR FILM DOCUMENTARY
-S/T- *FUTURE (Timewarp): FR 996 (CD)*

ATTACK ON THE IRON COAST 1967 Music: GERARD SCHURMANN
'Coastal Command' *S.SCREEN (Koch): FILMCD 072*

AU REVOIR LES ENFANTS 1987 *NAXOS: 8551158 (CD)*

AUF WIEDERSEHEN PET (C4 11/3/95 orig ITV 11/11/83)
"That's Livin' Alright"/"Breakin'Away" (David Mac
Kay-Ian La Frenais) JOE FAGIN 'BEST OF AUF W.PET'
PRESTIGE-NOVA (Pinn): CDSGP 0201 (CD)
+ *WESTMOOR: CDWM 107(CD) also see COLL.3,5,7,20,*

AUGUST (1995) Music sco: ANTHONY HOPKINS arr/orch and
   conducted by GEORGE FENTON *featur: ANTHONY HOPKINS
   (piano) -S/T- DEBONAIR (Pinn): CDDEB 1003 (CD)*
AUSTIN POWERS:INTERNATIONAL MAN OF MYSTERY (1997)
   -S/T- VAR.ARTISTS *BMG IMPORTS: 09026 63735-2 (CD)*
AUSTIN POWERS 2: THE SPY WHO SHAGGED ME (1999) V.ARTS
   -S/T-(1) *MAVERICK-WB (TEN):9362 47348-2 (CD)*
   -S/T-(2) *MAVERICK-WB (TEN):9362 47538-2 (CD)*
AUTUMN IN NEW YORK (2000) Music score by GABRIEL YARED
   -S/T- *HOLLYWOOD-EDEL (Vital): 0122 802-2HWR (CD)*
AUTUMN SONATA (1978) m: CHOPIN *NAXOS: 8551160 (CD)*
AVENGERS The (1998) Music sco: JOEL McNEELY -S/T- *incl*
   -S/T- (songs) *WB: 7567 83118-2 (CD) -4 (MC)*
   -S/T- (score) *SILVA SCREEN (Koch): FILMCD 304 (CD)*
AVENGERS The (ABCTV 65-69) music by LAURIE JOHNSON
   see COLL.2,24,38,74,77,83,124,157,158,243,
                                   250,253,261,
AVENUE X (MUSICAL SHOW) with music by RAY LESLEE and
   lyrics by JOHN JILER / ORIG USA CAST RECORDING on
   RCA VICTOR (BMG): 09026 63208-2 (CD)
B ABE 2: PIG IN THE CITY (1998) Music score:
   -S/T- *GEFFEN (BMG): GED 25310 (CD) see COLL.65,*
BABES IN ARMS (1999) ORIGINAL NEW YORK CAST RECORDING
   featuring The Cast and The COFFEE CLUB ORCHESTRA
   DRG USA (New Note-Pinn): DRGCD 94769 (CD)
BABES IN ARMS (1939) Songs RICHARD RODGERS-LORENZ HART
   -S/T- *with* JUDY GARLANDO-MICKEY ROONEY *NEW WORLD
   (Harmonia Mundi): NW 386-2 (CD) NW 386-4 (MC)*
BABES IN TOYLAND (1937) Music score by VICTOR HERBERT
   SOUND TRACK FACTORY (Discov): SFCD 33546 (CD)
BABY (ORIG BROADWAY CAST 1983) Mus: DAVID SHIRE Lyrics
   RICHARD MALTBY JR *feat:* LIZ CALLAWAY-BETH FOWLER-
   JAMES CONGDON & Co. *JAY-TER (SSD): CDJAY 1325 (CD)*
BABY BOY (2001) Music score by DAVID ARNOLD
   -S/T- score *VARESE (PINN): VSD 6280 (CD)*
   -S/T- songs *UNIVERSAL: 014 276-2 (CD)*
BABY IT'S YOU (C4 25/5/94) theme music "Spiritu" by
   JOHN HARLE on 'Silencium' *see COLL.130,*
BABY OF MACON The (1993) Classical music by MONTEVERDI
   CORELLI-TALLIS-BACH-CLAMER-FRESCOBALDI etc. -S/T-
   KOCH International (Koch): 34014-2 (CD)
BABYLON 5 (C4 1994-99) Music by CHRISTOPHER FRANKE
   *SONIC IMAGES (Greyhound-Cargo-Silver Sounds) CD's
   SI 8403-2 (VOLUME 1) SI 8502-2 (VOLUME 2)
   SI 8602-2 (VOLUME 3) (MESSAGES FROM EARTH)
   SI 0312 (DELIVERY FROM AVALON) SI 0318 (WALKABOUT)
   SI 0513 (RAGGED EDGE)   SI 0310 (SEVERED DREAMS)
   SI 0321 (SHADOW DANCING) SI 0222 (FALL OF NIGHT)
   SI 0417 (FACE OF T.NIGHT) SI 0406 (INTO THE FIRE)
   SI 0315 (INTERLUDES AND EXAMINATIONS)
   SI 0415 (NO SURRENDER NO RETREAT)
   SI 0516 (CD) (DARKNESS ASCENDING)
   SI 0404 (CD) (FALLING TOWARDS..)
   SI 8900 (CD) (THIRDSPACE)* also *see COLL.83,218,*

BACHELOR The (2000) Music score by DAVID A.HUGHES and
JOHN MURPHY -S/T- *including* MADNESS/JACKIW WILSON/
LOUIS PRIMA/LEAPY LEE/DAVID BYRNE/BARRY WHITE etc.
RCA (BMG): 09026 63583-2 (CD)

BACK TO THE FUTURE (Trilogy) Music from all 3 movies
conducted by JOHN DEBNEY / music by ALAN SILVESTRI
VARESE (Pinn): VSD 5950 (CD)

BACK TO THE FUTURE (1985) Music score: ALAN SILVESTRI
-S/T- *MCA (UNI): MCLD 19151 (CD)*

BACK TO THE FUTURE 3 (1990) Mus: ALAN SILVESTRI -S/T-
VARESE (Pinn): VSD 5272 (CD)

BACKBEAT (1994) Beatles Early Years -S/T- songs:
VIRGIN (EMI): CD(TC)V 2729 (CD/MC/LP) -S/T-
score: (DON WAS) *Virgin CDV(TCV)2740 (CD/MC)*

BAD BOYS (1995) Music score: MARK MANCINA -S/T- on
COLUMBIA (Ten): 480 453-2 (CD)

BAD CHANNELS (1992) Music by BLUE OYSTER CULT -S/T-
ANGEL AIR (Direct): SJPCD 046 (CD)

BAD GIRLS (ITV 01/06/1999) mus: NINA HUMPHREYS (ser.1)
KATH GOTTS-MICHAEL WALTON (series 2) *unavailable*

BAD INFLUENCE (1990) Music score: TREVOR JONES -S/T- +
V.Arts *reissued SPECTRUM (Univ): 551 102-2 (CD)*

BAD MOON (1996) Music score: DANIEL LICHT -S/T- on
SILVA AMERICA (Koch): SSD 1068 (CD)

BAD TASTE (1988) Music by various artists -S/T- on
NORMAL (Topic/Proj/Dir): QDKCD 002 (CD)

BADGER (BBC1 11/07/1999) music by NIGEL HESS on
'NIGEL HESS TV THEMES' *CHANDOS: CHAN 9750 (CD)*
see COLL.137,

BADLANDS (1973) music inc. "Gassenhauer" ('SCHULWERK')
(CARL ORFF-G.KEETMAN) on 'THE BEST OF CARL ORFF'
RCA (BMG): 75605 51357-2 (CD) -4 (MC)

BAGDAD CAFE (1988) M: (Telson-Adlon-Ebner-Bruehr-Bach)
Theme "Calling You" sung by JEVETTA STEELE
-S/T- *ISLAND: IMCD 102 (CD) ICM 2005 (MC)*

BAGPUSS (BBC1 12/02/1974) music & songs by SANDRA KERR
& JOHN FAULKNER *SMALLFOLK (Dir): SMF 1 (CD)*

BALLYKISSANGEL (BBC1 11/2/1996-2001) theme SHAUN DAVEY
1996/1997 series incidental music by SHAUN DAVEY
-S/T- *VIRGIN (EMI): VTCD 17 (CD) VTMC 17 (MC)*
1998-2000 series music by DOMINIC CRAWFORD COLLINS

BAMBI (1942) Songs (Frank Churchill-Edw.Plumb) -S/T-
DISNEY-EDEL (Vital) 010 880-2DNY (CD)
see WALT DISNEY INDEX p.341

BAMBOOZLED (2000) Music score: TERENCE BLANCHARD -S/T-
(VAR.ARTISTS) *UNIVERSAL: AA 121 53291-2 (CD)*

BANACEK (USA TV) theme: BILLY GOLDEBERG *see COLL.124,*

BANANA SPLITS (aka BANANA BUNCH) (USA68) theme "Tra La
La Song" (Adams-Barkan) *see COLL.246,259,*

BAND OF ANGELS (1957) Music score by MAX STEINER -S/T-
LABEL X (Hot): LXCD 3 (CD)

BAND OF BROTHERS (2001) Music score by MICHAEL KAMEN
-S/T- *SONY CLASSICS (TEN): SK 89719 (CD)*

BAND OF GOLD (ITV 12/3/95) theme and music score by HAL LINDES *unavailable* song "LOVE HURTS" (Bryant) by BARBARA DICKSON from 'Dark End Of The Street' *TRANSATLANTIC-CASTLE (Pinn): TRACD 117 (CD)*

BANDIT QUEEN (1993) Music score: NUSRAT FATEH ALI KHAN -S/T- *MILAN (BMG IMPORTS): 74321 77745-2 (CD) also on OSA (Hot): CDSR 254 (CD)*

BANDITS (2001) Music score by CHRISTOPHER YOUNG -S/T- VAR.ARTISTS songs *COLUMBIA (TEN): 505 233-2 (CD)*

BANZAI (C4 19/06/2001) VARIOUS ARTISTS SOUNDTRACK *CHANNEL 4 MUSIC (UNIV): C4M 0013-2 (CD)*

BAR WARS (C4 14/09/2001) theme music: CHRISTIAN HENSON *TRACK SELECTION AND THEME MUSIC on 'BAR WARS' COLL INCredible SONY (TEN): 504 525-2 (2CD)*

BARABBAS (1962) Mus: MARIO NASCIMBENE + 'ALEXANDER THE GREAT' *DRG (Pinn): DRGCD 32964 (CD)*

BARAKA (1993) Music score: MICHAEL STERNS -S/T- on *MILAN (BMG): 15306-2 (CD) 15306-4 (MC)*

BARBARA COOK SINGS MOSTLY SONDHEIM (LYRIC THEATRE 2001) 'BARBARA COOK SINGS MOSTLY SONDHEIM' (CARNEGIE HALL ALBUM 2000) *DRG USA (Pinn): DRGCD 91464 (2CD)*

BARBARELLA (1967) Music score: CHARLES FOX-BOB CREWE -S/T- *reissue DYNOVOICE (Greyhound): DY 31908 (LP)*

BARBER OF SIBERIA The (1999) Music sc: EDWARD ARTEMYEV -S/T- *SONY CLASSICS (TEN): SK 61802 (CD)*

BAREFACED CHIC (1999) MUSICAL SHOW *f:* FASCINATING ADA *FIRST NIGHT (Pinn): SCENECD 25 (CD)*

BAREFOOT CONTESSA The (1954) Mus sco: MARIO NASCIMBENE -S/T- inc.scor: *'ROOM AT THE TOP'/'QUIET AMERICAN' DRG (Pinn): DRGCD 32961 (CD) see also COLL*

BARETTA (USA) *see COLL.244,*

BARMY AUNTY BOOMERANG (BBC Scotland 16/09/1999) series music GREGOR PHILP vocal TOYAH WILLCOX *unavailable*

BARNABY JONES (USA) *see COLL.14,244,*

BARNEY MILLER (USA) *see COLL.244,*

BARON The - *see COLL.250,*

BARRIO Neighbourhood (1998) m: HECHOS CONTRA EL DECORO -S/T- *KARONTE (Silver Sounds-Discovery): EQ 137CD*

BARRY LYNDON (1975) MD: LEONARD ROSENMAN *feat.Classics* -S/T- *reiss: WB (TEN): 7599 25984-2 (CD) SONY Fra. (Disc): SK(ST) 61684 (CD/MC) see COLL.88,*

BARTON FINK (1991) Music: CARTER BURWELL *with* 'FARGO' -S/T- *SNAPPER (Pinn): SMCCD 614 (CD)*

BASIC INSTINCT (1992) Music sco: JERRY GOLDSMITH -S/T- *VARESE (Pinn): VSD(VSC) 5360 (CD/MC)*

BASQUIAT (1996) Music score by JOHN CALE -S/T- on *ISLAND (Univ.): 524 260-2 (CD) 524 260-4 (MC)*

BAT BOY: THE MUSICAL (ORIG USA CAST RECORDING 2000) Songs by LAURENCE O'KEEFE / featuring DEVEN MAY *BMG IMPORTS: 09026 63800-2 (CD)*

BAT MASTERSON (USA TV) *see COLL.243,*

BATHING BEAUTY (1944 MUSICAL) *feat* ESTHER WILLIAMS and RED SKELTON *incl.songs from* 'HERE COMES THE WAVES' + 'THIS GUN FOR HIRE' *TARGET (BMG): CD 60001 (CD)*

BATMAN (USATV 1966) Theme & incid music: NEAL HEFTI
TV -S/T- 'BATMAN THEME AND 11 HEFTI BAT SONGS' on
RCA (BMG): 74321 78172-2 (CD) also issued on
RAZOR & TIE (Koch): RE 2153 (CD)
see COLL.38,75,83,84,221,242,253,
BATMAN (FILM 1989) *Songs* comp & sung by PRINCE -S/T-
W.BROS (TEN): K.7599 25936-2 (CD) WX 281C (MC)
Score: DANNY ELFMAN *WEA 925977-2 CD deleted*
BATMAN BEYOND (Animated) Music score: SHIRLEY WALKER
RHINO (USA): RHINO 75925 (CD)
BATMAN FOREVER (1994) Music: ELLIOT GOLDENTHAL -S/T-
<u>score</u>: *ATLANTIC (TEN): 7567 82776-2 (CD) deleted*
<u>songs</u>: *ATLANTIC: 7567 82759-2*
BATMAN RETURNS (1992) Mus: DANNY ELFMAN *see COLL.221,*
BATMAN TRILOGY / JOEL McNEELY & ROYAL SCOTTISH N.ORCH
VARESE (Pinn): VSD 5766 (CD) 1997
music from 'BATMAN'/'BATMAN RETURNS'*(DANNY ELFMAN)*
'BATMAN FOREVER'/'BATMAN AND ROBIN' *(E.GOLDENTHAL)*
'BATMAN' TV THEME *(NEAL HEFTI/NELSON RIDDLE)* and
BATTERSEA DOGS HOME (BBC1 07/12/1998-2000) theme mus.
based on "Perfect Day" (Lou Reed) & "Always Look
On The Bright Side Of Life" (Eric Idle)
Doggy arrangements by JANE ELLER *unavailable*
BATTLE OF BRITAIN (1969) Music score by RON GOODWIN.
"Air Battle Sequence" WILLIAM WALTON -S/T- reissue
*RYKODISC (Vital): RCD 10747 (CD) / also selection
of WILLIAM WALTON mus EMI: CDM 565585-2 (CD) also*
Academy of St.Martin-in-the-Fields (N.Marriner) +
'Escape Me Never'/'3 Sisters'/'Spitfire Prelude
& Fugue'/'Wartime Sketchbook' *CHANDOS:CHAN 8870*
see COLL.123,
BATTLE OF NERETVA (1969) Music score: BERNARD HERRMANN
LONDON PHILHARMONIC ORCH on *SOUTHERN CROSS (Hot):*
SCCD 903 & 5005 (CD) also on 'BERNARD HERRMANN AT
THE MOVIES' *inc* 'SISTERS' (73) 'NIGHT DIGGER' (71)
LABEL X (Hot): ATMCD 2003 (CD)
BATTLE OF THE BULGE (1965) Music sco: BENJAMIN FRANKEL
NEW RECORDING OF THE COMPLETE SCORE (PREMIER) by
QUEENSLAND SYMPHONY ORCH.cond: WERNER A.ALBERT
CPO (Select): 999 696-2 (CD)
BATTLEFIELD EARTH (2000) Music score: ELIA CMIRAL
-S/T- *VARESE (Pinn): VSD 6144 (CD)*
BATTLESHIP POTEMKIN 1925 Mus.sco: EDMUND MEISAL
SOUND TRACK FACTORY (Discov): SFCD 335347 (CD)
BATTLESTAR GALACTICA (USA 78/ITV) Music score by STU
PHILLIPS. New Recording by ROYAL SCOTTISH NAT.ORCH
VARESE: VSD 5949 (CD) see COLL.14,84,218,233,
BAYWATCH (USA/ITV from 1990)
-S/T- *BMG IMPT (Pinn): 72392 75445-2 (CD)*
Theme 95 "I'm Always Here" JIM JAMISON *unavailable*
Theme 93 "Current Of Love" DAVID HASSELHOFF *Arista*
Theme 90 "Save Me" PETER CETERA *TEN: WX161(C)(CD)*
see COLL.14,

BBC Learning Zone "Rundadinella" from 'Schulwerk'
on 'BEST OF CARL ORFF' *RCA BMG: 75605 51357-2 (CD)*
also a 6 CD set *RCA (BMG): 09026 68031-2 (6CDs)*
also used "That's Life" sung by SHIRLEY BASSEY *EMI*

BBC PROMS 2000/1999 (BBC1/2/RADIO 2) 'BBC PROMS 99'
V.ARTS.*(2CD SELECTION) TELDEC: 9548 37591-2 (2CD)*
also available 'BEST PROMS ALBUM IN THE WORLD EVER'
VIRGIN (EMI): VTDCD 323 (2CD)

BBC SPORTS PERSONALITY OF THE YEAR "The Challenge" by
CHARLES WILLIAMS *see COLL.122,*

BEACH The (1999) Music score by ANGELO BADALAMENTI
-S/T- songs: *LONDON (TEN): 431 079-2 (CD) -4 (MC)*
-S/T- score: *LONDON (TEN): 431 136-2 (CD)*

BEACHES (1989) feat BETTE MIDLER (songs: Cole Porter-
Randy Newman and others) -S/T- *ATLANTIC (TEN):*
K.781933-2 (CD) -4 (MC) see COLL.87,

BEAN (1997) Music sc: HOWARD GOODALL -S/T- with V.Arts
MERCURY-POLYGRAM TV: 553 774-2 (CD) -4 (MC)

BEAST The (USA TV mini-series) Music score: DON DAVIS
-S/T- *VARESE (Pinn): VSD 5731 (CD)*

BEAST WITH FIVE FINGERS The (1947) Music: MAX STEINER
new rec: MOSCOW S.O.(Stromberg)+ 'VIRGINIA CITY'
/'LOST PATROL' *MARCO POLO (Select): 8.223870 (CD)*

BEAT GIRL (1960) Music sco: JOHN BARRY feat Adam Faith
-S/T- *PLAY IT AGAIN (Koch): PLAY 001 (CD)*

BEATLES - see 'ANTHOLOGY'

BEATRIX POTTER TV animated see 'WORLD OF PETER RABBIT'
AND FRIENDS' *and* 'TALES OF BEATRIX POTTER'

BEAU GESTE (1939) Music score: ALFRED NEWMAN. Suite by
MOSCOW SYMPH.ORCH.& CHORUS (William T.Stromberg)
'HUNCHBACK OF NOTRE DAME'(1939) 'ALL ABOUT EVE'
MARCO POLO (Select): 8.223750 (CD)

BEAUTIFUL GAME The (2000) Music by ANDREW LLOYD WEBBER
Lyrics BEN ELTON "Our Kind Of Love" sung by HANNAH
ORIG CAST RECORDING *TELSTAR (BMG): TCD 3160 (CD)*

BEAUTIFUL PEOPLE (1999) Music score by GARRY BELL and
GHOSTLAND plus -S/T- Various Artists
COLOSSEUM (Pinn): CST 348081 (CD)

BEAUTIFUL THING (1997) Music score: JOHN ALTMAN with
songs sung by MAMA CASS and The MAMAS & The PAPAS
-S/T- *MCA (UNI): MCD 60013 (CD)*

BEAUTY AND THE BEAST
Songs: Alan Menken-Howard Ashman-Tim Rice
1.FILM 1992 -S/T- *WALT DISNEY (B.Vista): WD 71360-2*
(CD) -4(MC) see also DISNEY FILM INDEX p.341
2.ORIGINAL BROADWAY CAST 1994
EDEL-DISNEY (Vital) 010861-2DNY (CD) -4(MC)

BEAUTY AND THE BEAST (Belle Et La Bette, La) (1946) M.
score: GEORGES AURIC *new record:* MOSCOW SYMPHONY
ORCH.(Adriano) *MARCO POLO (Select): 8.223765 (CD)*
see COLL.26,88,117,

BEAVIS AND BUTTHEAD (USA/C4 13/1/95)'Beavis & Butthead
Experience' -S/T- *GEFFEN-MCA (UNI): GED 24613 (CD)*

BEAVIS AND BUTTHEAD DO AMERICA (1996) M: JOHN FRIZZELL
   -S/T- songs: *GEFFEN (BMG): GED(GEC) 25002 (CD/MC)*
   -S/T- score: *MILAN (BMG): 74321 47536-2 (CD)*
BECOMING COLLETTE (1991) Music score by JOHN SCOTT
   JOHN SCOTT RECORDS (Silva Screen): JSCD 115 (CD)
BEDAZZLED (1967) Music by DUDLEY MOORE including songs
   by PETER COOK -S/T- *HARKIT: HRKCD 8001 (CD)*
BEDKNOBS AND BROOMSTICKS see WALT DISNEY INDEX p.341
BEDLAM (1946) - see 'CAT PEOPLE' see COLL.275,
BEETLEJUICE (1988) Music score: DANNY ELFMAN -S/T- +
   HARRY BELAFONTE *GEFFEN-MCA (UNI):GFLD 19284 (CD)*
   see COLL.84,219,
BEFORE NIGHT FALLS (2000) Music score: CARTER BURWELL
   LOU REED-LAURIE ANDERSON -S/T- VARIOUS ARTISTS on
   BLUE THUMB (UNIV): 549 672-2 (CD)
BEGGAR'S OPERA The (LIGHT OPERA by John Gay) *featur:*
   WARREN MITCHELL-MICHAEL HORDERN-JOAN SUTHERLAND-
   KIRI TE KANAWA-ANGELA LANSBURY-STAFFORD DEAN-
   ALFRED MARKS-JAMES MORRIS-REGINA RESNIK & National
   Phil.Orch (Richard Bonynge) *DECCA:430 066-2 (2CDs)*
BEIDERBECKE AFFAIR The (C4 4/93 o.1985) music of BIX
   BEIDERBECKE performed by FRANK RICOTTI ALL-STARS
   & KENNY BAKER -S/T- *DOORMOUSE (C.Wellard): DM20CD*
   also *'Collection' CASTLE (Pinn): CCSCD 350 (CD)*
BEIDERBECKE CONNECTION see COLL.4,
BEING JOHN MALKOVICH (1999) Music sco: CARTER BURWELL
   -S/T- *SOURCE-VIRGIN (EMI): CDSOUR 004 (CD)* also on
   -S/T- *ASW (USA Import): ASW 48768 (CD)*
BELFRY WITCHES The (BBC1 29/09/1999-2000) series music
   by KIRSTEN MORRISON with title theme performed by
   ATOMIC KITTEN *unavailable*
BELIEVER The (2001) Music score by JOEL DIAMOND -S/T-
   USA IMPORT MILAN USA: MILAN 35964 (CD)
BELLE ET LA BETTE, LA - see 'BEAUTY AND THE BEAST'

BELLE OF NEW YORK The (1952) FRED ASTAIRE-VERA ELLEN
   BLUE MOON (Discov):BMCD 7011 (CD) inc 'BAND WAGON'
BELLE OF THE NINETIES (1934) VARIOUS ART.SOUNDTRACK
   SOUNDTRACK FACTORY (Discov): SFCD 33552 (CD)
BELLS ARE RINGING The (SHOW 1956) ORIG BROADWAY CAST
   with JUDY HOLLIDAY-SYDNEY CHAPLIN-JEAN STAPLETON
   SONY CLASSICS: SMK 89545 (CD)
BELLY VARIOUS HIP-HOP ARTISTS
   DEF JAM (Univ): 558 952-2 (CD) -1 (2LP)
BELOVED (1998) Music score: RACHEL PORTMAN -S/T- feat
   V.Arts. on *EPIC (Ten): 492 679-2 (CD)* see COLL.3,
BEN CASEY USA(C4 4/1/97) m: DAVID RAKSIN see COLL.243,
BEN-HUR (silent 1925) Contemporary score by CARL DAVIS
   see *Collections* 'The SILENTS'
BEN-HUR (1959) Music score: MIKLOS ROSZA / digitally
   re-mastered 75m.CD *EMI ODEON: CDODEON 18 (CD)*
   also available: 'MIKLOS ROZSA FILM MUSIC VOL.1'
   PROMETHEUS (S.Scr): PCD 122 (CD)
   see COLL.15,85,117,213,214,215,266,

BENEATH THE 12 MILE REEF see *COLL.1,*
BENEATH THE VALLEY OF THE ULTRA VIXENS 1979 RUSS MEYER
   includes music from Russ Meyer Films "UP" & "Mega
   Vixens" *NORMAL-QDK (Pinn): QDK(CD)(LP) 009 (CD/LP)*
BENNY AND JOON - see *COLL.202,*
BENNY HILL SHOW see *COLL.247,*
BENSON (USA TV) see *COLL.247,*
BERGERAC (BBC1 from 18/10/1981) theme by GEORGE FENTON
   see *COLL.3,20,42,77,*
BERTHA (BBC TV) see *COLL.132,*
BESIEGED (1998) Music score by ALESSIO VLAD -S/T- on
   ARISTA (BMG): 74321 64027-2 (CD)
BEST (2000) Music score by MARK STEVENS -S/T- (V.Arts)
   RECOGNITION (Univ): CDREC 508 (CD)
BEST FOOT FORWARD (ORIG OFF-BROADWAY CAST 1963) Songs
   (Hugh Martin-Ralph Blane) *f:* LIZA MINNELLI-RONALD
   CHRISTOPHER WALKEN *DRG USA (Pinn) CD15003 (CD)*
BEST IN FOOTBALL (TV) m: TONY HATCH see *COLL.131,200,*

BEST LAID PLANS (1999) Music score: CRAIG ARMSTRONG
   -S/T- *VIRGIN (EMI): CDVUS 157 (CD)*
BEST OF BOTH WORLDS (BBC1 18/02/2001) theme music by
   CHRYSSIE HYNDE "Don't Get Me Wrong" by PRETENDERS
   WEA (TEN): 8573 84607-2 (CD) -4 (MC) -8 (MD)
BEST OF EVERYTHING see *COLL.1,*

BEST YEARS OF OUR LIVES The (1946) Music score by
   HUGO FRIEDHOFER *LABEL X (HOT): LXCD 14 (CD)*
BETTER THAN SEX (2000) Music score: DAVID HIRCHFELDER
   -S/T- *feat* KYLIE MINOGUE-SNEAK-THE CRUEL SEA *etc.*
   MILAN (BMG IMPORTS): 74321 80251-2 (CD)
BETTY BLUE (1986) Music score: GABRIEL YARED -S/T- on
   VIRGIN: CDV 2396 (CD)
BEVERLY HILLBILLIES The (USA 62) Theme "The Ballad Of
   Jed Clampett" sung by LESTER FLATT & EARL SCRUGGS
   see *COLL.242,*
BEVERLY HILLS COP (1985) Music Sco: HAROLD FALTERMEYER
   -S/T- *MCA (UNI): MCLD 19087 (CD)*
BEVERLY HILLS 90210 (ITV 12/1/91) theme: JEFFREY Skunk
   BAXTER & STACY WIDELITZ -S/T- + theme: JOHN DAVIS
   'Vol.1'*GIANT (BMG):74321 14798-2(CD)* / Volume 2 on
   74321 20303-2(CD) see *COLL.14,248,*
BEWITCHED (USA 60's) theme music by JACK KELLER and
   HOWARD GREENFIELD see *COLL.243,*
BEYOND The (1981 It.Horror) Music: FABIO FRIZZI -S/T-
   DAGORED (Cargo/Koch) RED 133-2 (CD) RED 133-1 (LP)
BEYOND THE CLOUDS (C4 28/2/94) music: GEORGE FENTON
   -S/T- *WESTMOOR (Targ/BMG): CDWM(CWM) 109 (CD/MC)*
   see *COLL.20,* 'AS SEEN ON TV'
BEYOND THE FRINGE (The Complete) *REVUE 1961 Fortune
   London) feat* PETER COOK-DUDLEY MOORE-ALAN BENN
   ETT-JONATHAN MILLER-PAXTON WHITEHEAD *and also ORIG
   BROADWAY CAST 1962) feat:* PETER COOK-DUDLEY MOORE-
   ALAN BENNETT-JONATHAN MILLER *EMI: CDBTF 61 (3CDs)*

BEYOND THE VALLEY OF THE DOLLS (1970) m: STU PHILLIPS
-S/T- (V.Arts) *reissued with* 'GROUPIE GIRL' (1970)
SCREEN GOLD (Greyhound): SGLDCD 0010 (CD)

BICENTENNIAL MAN The (1999) Music score: JAMES HORNER
song "Then You Look At Me" sung by CELINE DION
-S/T- *SONY CLASS (TEN): SK 89038 (CD) ST 89038(MC)*

BIG (SHOW USA 1996) Songs RICHARD MALTBY JR-DAVID SHIRE
Orig Cast *UNIVERSAL IMS (UNIV): AA.12153009-2 (CD)*

BIG BAD WORLD (ITV 20/06/1999) Music by HAL LINDES
SONGS INSPIRED BY AND FROM SERIES *INC.THEME MUSIC
VIRGIN (EMI): VTDCD 257 (2CD) VTDMC 257 (2MC)*

BIG BLUE The (1988) Music sco: ERIC SERRA -S/T- *VIRGIN
CDV 2541 (CD) MDV 2541 (MiniD)*

BIG BREAK (BBC1 30/4/91) theme "The Snooker Song"
(Mike Batt) sung by CAPTAIN SENSIBLE *deleted*

BIG BROTHER (C4 18/07/2000) theme music composed by
PAUL OAKENFOLD & ANDY GRAY performed by ELEMENT 4
theme on CHANNEL 4 MUSIC (Univ): C4M 0007-2 (CDs)
'BIG BROTHER' THE ORIGINAL SOUNDTRACK *featuring*
PRODIGY/LEFTFIELD/FATBOY SLIM/UNDERWORLD & others
CHANNEL FOUR MUSIC (Univ): C4M 0006-2 (CD)

BIG CHILL (1984) -S/T- MARVIN GAYE-TEMPTATIONS-4TOPS
*MOTOWN UNIV: 530 017-2 (CD) 530 953-2 (CD) also
636 062-2 (CD)* 'MORE SONGS FROM BC' *636 094-2 (CD)*

BIG COUNTRY The (1958) Music score: JEROME MOROSS New
Digital R: PHILHARMONIA ORCHESTRA (Tony Bremner)
SILVA SCREEN (Koch): FILMCD 724 (CD)
see COLL.277,279,

BIG DADDY (1999) -S/T- *feat:* SHERYL CROW-GARBAGE-BIG
AUDIO DYNAMITE-MEL C-SHAWN MULLINS-YVONNE ELLIMAN
COLUMBIA: 494 395-2 (CD)

BIG DEAL (BBC1 14/10/84) title song composed/sung by
BOBBY G. see COLL.5,

BIG EASY The (1987) Music score: BRAD FIEDEL + V.Arts
-S/T- *re-issue SPECTRUM (Univ): 551 159-2 (CD)*

BIG GUNDOWN The (1966) Music sco ENNIO MORRICONE *Imp
with* 'FACE TO FACE' *Mask (S.Screen): MK 701 (CD)*

BIG KAHUNA The (2000) Music score: CHRISTOPHER YOUNG
-S/T- *VARESE (Pinn): VSD 6140 (CD)*

BIG LEBOWSKI The (1998) Music score: CARTER BURWELL
-S/T- *MERCURY (Univ): 536 903-2 (CD) see COLL.65,*

BIG MATCH The (ITV) Themes include "Aztec Gold" ROD
ARGENT-PETER VAN HOOKE *see also COLL.5,122,231,*

BIG MOMMAS HOUSE (2000) Music score by RICHARD GIBBS
-S/T- *COLUMBIA (TEN): 498 757-2 (CD)*

BIG PARADE (1926) Contemp.sc.(CARL DAVIS) *see COLL.85,*

BIG SWAP The (1996) Mus: JASON FLINTER & CRAIG JOHNSON
-S/T- *OCEAN DEEP (Univ): OCD 011 (CD)*

BIG SQUEEZE The (2000) Music score: MARK MOTHERSBAUGH
-S/T- *CITADEL (Pinn-Hot): STC 77109 (CD)*

BIG TEASE The (1999) Music score by MARK THOMAS -S/T-
VIRGIN (EMI): CDVUS 165 (CD)

BIG VALLEY (USA) see COLL.246,

BILITIS (1977) Music score by FRANCIS LAI -S/T- *reiss:*
MILAN (BMG): 74321 64881-2 (CD) on 'FRANCIS LAI-A
MAN AND A WOMAN' *see COLL.60,97,162,*

BILL The (Thames 16/10/84-2001) theme "Overkill"
ANDY PASK-CHARLIE MORGAN *see COLL.42,77,*

BILL AND BEN - *see COLL.285*

BILL AND TED'S BOGUS JOURNEY (1991) Mus: DAVID NEWMAN
-S/T- *f:* STEVE VAI-MEGADETH-SLAUGHTER-KISS-WINGER
PRIMUS *reiss: INTERSCOPE-MCA (UNI):IND 91725 (CD)*

BILLY (O.LONDON CAST 1974) Songs:JOHN BARRY-DON BLACK
feat: MICHAEL CRAWFORD-ELAINE PAIGE-AVIS BUNNAGE-
BILLY BOYLE and Company *SONY: 472818-2(CD)*

BILLY BUNTER OF GREYFRIARS SCHOOL (BBC 1950's) theme
"Sea Songs" (VAUGHAN WILLIAMS) *see COLL.119,*

BILLY CONNOLLY'S WORLD TOUR OF AUSTRALIA (BBC/Sleepy
Dumpling/BBC1 28/10/96) end theme song "Dreamtime"
(Ralph McTell) sung by BILLY CONNOLLY *unavailable*
other music by GRAHAM PRESKETT and RALPH McTELL

BILLY CONNOLLY'S WORLD TOUR OF SCOTLAND (BBC/Sleepy
Dumpling/BBC1 12/7/94) end theme "Irish Heartbeat"
sung by BILLY CONNOLLY 'Musical Tour Of Scotland'
POLYGRAM TV: 529 816-2 (CD) -4(MC) also by
VAN MORRISON *POLYDOR (Univ):839 604-2 (CD) -4(MC)*

BILLY ELLIOTT (2000) Music score by STEPHEN WARBECK
VAR.ARTISTS -S/T- *inc:* STEPHEN GATELY-EAGLE EYE
CHERRY-JAM-T.REX-ORANGE JUICE-STYLE COUNCIL-CLASH
POLYDOR (UNIV): 549 360-2 (CD 09/2000)
POLYDOR (UNIV) 549 813-2 (CD 04/2001)

BIOGRAPH GIRL The (O.LONDON CAST 1980) Songs: David
Heneker-Warner Brown *feat* SHEILA WHITE-BRUCE BARRY
KATE REVILL-GUY SINER *TER (Koch): CDTER 1003 (CD)*

BIONIC WOMAN (USA TV) *see COLL.221,246,*

BIRD OF PREY (BBC1 22/4/82) theme mus: DAVE GREENSLADE
see COLL.5,

BIRD WITH THE CRYSTAL PLUMAGE (1969) Music sco: ENNIO
MORRICONE -S/T- inc 'FOUR FLIES ON GREY VELVET'
'CAT O'NINE TAILS' *DRG (Pinn): DRGCD 32911 (CD)*

BIRDMAN (BBC 14/05/1999) Music by SIAN JAMES -S/T-
BBC WORLDWIDE MUSIC (Pinn): WMSF 6007-2 (CD)

BIRDS OF A FEATHER (BBC1 16/10/1989-1998) Theme song
"What'll I Do" (Irving Berlin) *TV vers.by* PAULINE
QUIRKE-LINDA ROBSON *unavailable see COLL.199,*

BIRDY (1985) Music score: PETER GABRIEL -S/T-
CHARISMA VIRGIN (EMI): CASCD 1167 (CD)

BIRTH OF A NATION (1915 D.W.GRIFFITHS) Contemporary
recording based on orig JOSEPH CARL BRIEL score
performed by The NEW ZEALAND S.O.(John Lanchberry
Allen Clyde) *CD Imp: LABEL X (Hot): LXCD 701 (CD)*

BITTER SWEET (Musical Show 1988) Songs: NOEL COWARD
New Sadlers Wells Opera VALERIE MASTERSON
TER (Koch): Highlights CDTEO 1001 (CD)

BLACK AND WHITE (2000) Music score by
-S/T- *EPIC-LOUD (TEN): 497 692-2 (CD)*

BLACK BEAUTY *(TV) see COLL.3,*

BLACK CAESAR (1973) Mus: JAMES BROWN inc.LYNN COLLINS
  POLYDOR (Univ): 517 135-2 (CD) -1 (LP)
BLACK CAULDRON (1985) ELMER BERNSTEIN *see COLL.40,*
BLACK HOLE The (1979) Music score by JOHN BARRY *this
  recording inc.* 'HOWARD THE DUCK' (JOHN BARRY,1986)
  MASK (USA Imp): MK 703 (CD) see COLL.26,218,232,
BLACK KNIGHT The (2001) Music score by RANDY EDELMAN
  -S/T- *VARESE (Pinn): VSD 6307 (CD)*
BLACK MASK (1999) VARIOUS ARTISTS -S/T-
  TOMMY BOY (Pinn): TBCD 1343 (CD)
BLACK ROBE (1991) Music score: GEORGES DELERUE -S/T-
  VARESE (Pinn): VSD 5349 (CD)
BLACK SHIELD OF FALWORTH (1954) Mus: Hans J.Salter +
  mus.'HITLER' (61) 'INCREDIBLE SHRINKING MAN' (57)
  INTRADA (Koch): MAF 7054CD (CD)
BLACK WINDMILL The (1974) Music score: ROY BUDD -S/T-
  CINEPHILE-CASTLE (Pinn): CINCD(LP) 004 (CD/LP)
BLACKADDER (BBC2 5/9/1984) music by HOWARD GOODALL
  BBC Radio Collection: ZBBC 2227 (6 AUDIO CASS)
BLACKOUT The (1998) Music: SCHOOLLY D and JOE DELIA
  -S/T- *POLYDOR (Univ): 537 854-2 (CD) -4 (MC)*
BLACULA (1972) Music score by GENE PAGE -S/T-
  RAZOR & TIE (Koch): RE 82179-2 (CD)
BLADE (1998) Music score by MARK ISHAM
  -S/T- (score) *VARESE (Pinn): VSD 5976 (CD)*
  -S/T- (songs) *EPIC (Ten): 492 884-2 (CD)*
BLADE RUNNER (1982) Music score: VANGELIS origin -S/T-
  EAST WEST (TEN): 4509 96574-2 (CD) -4 (MC)
  see COLL.83,97,218,250,263,264,
BLAIR WITCH PROJECT The (1999) -S/T- includes music by
  PUBLIC IMAGE LTD/BAUHAUS/LYDIA LUNCH/SKINNY PUPPY/
  CREATURES etc.*GOLD CIRCLE (Direct): GC 0120-2 (CD)*
BLAIR WITCH 2:BOOK OF SHADOWS (2000) m: CARTER BURWELL
  -S/T- (score) *MILAN (BMG): 74321 80372-2 (CD)*
  -S/T- (songs) *PRIORITY (EMI): CDPTY 209 (CD)*
BLAKE'S 7 (BBC1 02/01/1978) Theme music DUDLEY SIMPSON
  see COLL.4,38,83,237,
BLESS THE CHILD (2000) Music score: CHRISTOPHER YOUNG
  -S/T- *GNP USA (ZYX): GNPD 8066-2 (CD)*
BLIND DATE (LWT 30/11/85-2002) theme: LAURIE HOLLOWAY
  unavailable
BLISS (1997) Music score: JAN A.P.KACZMAREK -S/T- on
  VARESE (Pinn): VSD 5836 (CD)
BLONDEL - songs: Stephen Oliver and Tim Rice
  ORIG CAST 1983 *feat:* PAUL NICHOLAS-SHARON LEE HILL
  reissue: MCA (UNI): MCD 11486 (CD)
BLOOD AND SAND (1941) music score: ALFRED NEWMAN -S/T-
  extracts including music from 'PANAMA HATTIE' on
  GREAT MOVIE THEMES (BMG): CD 60047 (CD)
BLOOD BROTHERS - songs by Willy Russell
  1.ORIG LONDON CAST 1995 *feat:* STEPHANIE LAWRENCE
  FIRST NIGHT (Pinn): CASTCD 49 (CD) CASTC 49 (MC)
  2.INTERNATIONAL CAST 1995 PETULA CLARK-DAVID & SHAUN
  CASSIDY & Co *FIRST NIGHT (Pinn): CASTCD 50 (CD)*

3.ORIG LONDON CAST 1988 *feat:* KIKI DEE and Comapny
FIRST NIGHT (Pinn): CASTCD 17 (CD)
4.ORIG LONDON CAST 1983 *feat:* BARBARA DICKSON & Comp
CASTLE MUSIC (Pinn): ESMCD 825 (CD)

BLOOD IS STRONG The (C4/Grampian 1/9/88) music comp.&
performed: CAPERCAILLE with KAREN MATHESON -S/T-
SURVIVAL (Pinn): SURCD 014 (CD) SURMC 014 (MC)

BLOOMFIELD (1969) Music score by JOHNNY HARRIS -S/T-
CINEPHILE-CASTLE (Pinn): CINCD 031 (CD)

BLOTT ON THE LANDSCAPE (BBC2 6/2/85) mus: DAVE MACKAY
performed by VIV FISHER *see COLL.4,20,*

BLOW (2001) Music score by GRAEME REVELL -S/T- feat
VARIOUS ARTISTS on *VIRGIN (EMI): CDVUS 195 (CD)*

BLOW-UP (1966) Music score: HERBIE HANCOCK / Songs by
YARDBIRDS/TOMORROW -S/T- *EMI GOLD:CDODEON 15 (CD)*
also available 'EXTRA SESSIONS' (Herbie Hancock)
VINTAGE CLASSICS (Timewarp): VCS 005 (CD)

BLUE (1993) Music score: SIMON FISHER TURNER + V.Arts
-S/T- *MUTE (Pinn): CDSTUMM 49 (CD)*

BLUE ANGEL The (1930) *featuring* MARLENE DIETRICH on
DEFINITIVE (Discovery): SFCD 33507 (CD)

BLUE COLLAR (1978) Music score: JACK NITZSCHE -S/T-
EDSEL-DEMON (Pinn): EDCD 435 (CD)

BLUE HAWAII (1961) feat: ELVIS PRESLEY remast. -S/T-
(BMG): 07863 67459-2 (ltd CD) 07863 66959-2 (CD)
also CASTLE MUSIC (Pinn): ELVIS 107 (LP)
see also ELVIS PRESLEY FILM INDEX p.348

BLUE LAGOON The (1980) Music score: BASIL POLEDOURIS
-S/T- *SOUTHERN CROSS (HOT): SCCD 1018 (CD)*

BLUE PETER (BBC1 27/10/58-2001) Theme "Barnacle Bill"
(Hornpipe) 95-98 theme YES/NO PEOPLE *unavailable*
Orig SIDNEY ORCH ORCH *EMI* MIKE OLDFIELD *VIRGIN
EMI CDMOC 1 (2CD) original theme on COLL 132,*

BLUE PLANET (BBC 2001) Music by GEORGE FENTON -S/T-
BBC WORLDWIDE 9Pinn): WMSF 6043-2 (CD)

BLUE SKIES (1946) VARIOUS -S/T- SELECTIONS on
GREAT MOVIE THEMES: (Targ-BMG): CD 60025 (CD)

BLUE STREAK (1999) VARIOUS ARTISTS -S/T-
COLUMBIA (Ten): 495 491-2 (CD) -4 (MC) -1 (LP)

BLUE VELVET (1987) Music sco: ANGELO BADALEMENTI -S/T-
VARESE (Pinn): VCD 47277 (CD) see COLL.95,185,

BLUES ARE RUNNING The / KING MACKEREL (USA MUSICALS)
SUGAR HILL USA (Koch): SHCD 8503 (CD) SH 8503(MC)

BLUES BROTHERS (1980) *Featur:* RAY CHARLES-JAMES BROWN
ARETHA FRANKLIN-CAB CALLOWAY-BLUES BROTHERS -S/T-
WEA: K4 50715 (MC) K2 50715 (CD) 756781471-5 (DCC)

BLUES BROTHERS 2000 V.ARTS inc: PAUL BUTTERFIELD-BLUES
BAND-MATT MURPHY-JOHN POPPER-DAN AYKROYD-LONNIE
BROOKS-JUNIOR WELLS *UNIVERSAL (BMG): UND 53116 (CD)*

BLUES IN THE NIGHT (O.DONMAR WAREHOUSE THEATRE 1987)
DEBBY BISHOP-MARIA FRIEDMAN-CLARKE PETERS-CAROL
WOODS & Co. *FIRST NIGHT (Pinn): OCRCD 6029 (CD)*

BOAT The (DAS BOOT) (BBC2 17/9/89 orig 21/10/84) music
KLAUS DOLDINGER *see COLL.265,*

BOB AND ROSE (ITV1 10/09/2001) theme mus: MARTIN PHIPPS
  -S/T- V.Arts album on *ALMIGHTY (BMG):ALMYCD 38 (CD)*
BOB MARTIN (ITV 02/04/2000) Music by GRAHAM JARVIS
  closing theme "Rhapsody in Blue" (G.Gershwin)
BOB THE BUILDER (BBC1 11/10/1999) Music: PAUL K.JOYCE
  "Bob The Builder" (theme) sung by NEIL MORRISSEY
  ALBUM *BBC WORLDWIDE Pinn WMSF 6047-2 (CD) -4 (MC)*
  SINGLE "Bob The Builder" *WMSS 6037-2 (CDs) -4 (MC)*
  SINGLE "Mambo No.5" *BBC WMSF 6044-S (CDs) -4 (MC)*
  see COLL.285,
BODY The (1970) Mus: ROGER WATERS-RON GEESIN -S/T-
  EMI Premier (EMI): CZ 178 (CD)
BODY BAGS (1993) Music score: JOHN CARPENTER-JIM LANG
  -S/T- *VARESE (Pinn): VSD 5448 (CD)*
BODY CHEMISTRY (BBC2 01/02/2000) theme mus "Bentley's
  Gonna Sort You Out" by BENTLEY RHYTHM ACE on
  EMI-PARLOPHONE: CDPCS 7391 (CD) TCPSC 7391 (MC)
BODY HEAT (1981) Music score: JOHN BARRY.new recording
  VARESE Pinn: VSD 5951 (CD) see COLL.26,30,32,83,
BODY SHOTS (1999) Music score by MARK ISHAM -S/T- on
  MILAN (BMG): 74321 35898-2 (CD)
BODY SNATCHER The (1945) m: ROY WEBB *see COLL.275,*
BODYGUARD (1992) *Songs* WHITNEY HOUSTON-LISA STANSFIELD
  JOE COCKER-SASS JORDAN-CURTIS STIGERS-KENNY G-
  AARON NEVILLE -S/T- *ARISTA (BMG): 07822 18699-2 CD*
BODYWORK LIGHT OPERA MUSICAL 1988) Mus/Lyrics: RICHARD
  STILGOE featuring *The National Youth Music Theatre*
  with LONNIE DONEGAN-CHAS & DAVE and JAKE THACKRAY
  FIRST NIGHT (Pinn): CASTCD 15 (CD) CASTC 15 (MC)
BONANZA (USA 59) theme by Jay Livingston-Ray Evans and
  played by DAVID ROSE ORCHESTRA *see COLL.242,*
BONE COLLECTOR The (1999) Music score: CRAIG ARMSTRONG
  -S/T- *DECCA (Univ): 466 804-2 (CD)*
BONES (2001) VARIOUS ARTISTS SOUNDTRACK on
  VIRGIN (EMI): CDPTY 223 (CD)
BOOGIE NIGHTS (1998 SHOW) 70's music ORIG CAST RECORD.
  BEECHWOOD MUSIC (BMG): BOOGIE(CD)(MC) 1 (2CD/2MC)
BOOGIE NIGHTS (1997 FILM) Music score: MICHAEL PENN
  Vol.1 *EMI PREMIER: 855 631-2 (CD)* Vol.2 *deleted*
BOOK OF LIFE The (1998) VARIOUS ARTISTS SOUNDTRACK on
  ECHO (Pinn/Cargo/Greyhound): ECHO 0108 (CD)
BOON (Central 14/1/86-1992) theme "Hi Ho Silver" by
  JIM DIAMOND *POLYDOR (Univ): 843 847-2 (CD) -4 (MC)*
BOOTMEN (2001) Music score by CEZARY SKUBISZEWSKI
  -S/T- VAR.ARTISTS *BMG IMPORTS: 74321 78969-2 (CD)*
BOOTY CALL (1996) -S/T- with VARIOUS ARTISTS
  JIVE-ZOMBA (Pinn): CHIP 182 (CD) HIP 182 (2LP)
BORDER CAFE (BBC 09/06/2000) Music sco: COLIN WINSTON
  FLETCHER. title song by WILLY DOWLING.*SELECTION on*
  BBC WORLDWIDE (Pinn): WMSF 6025-2 (CD)
BORN FREE (1965) Music score: JOHN BARRY / title song
  (JB-Don Black) sung by MATT MONRO *new recording by*
  ROYAL SCOTTISH NATIONAL ORCH.*VARESE:VSD 6084 (CD)*
  see COLL.26,29,30,32,33,36,186,

BORN ROMANTIC (2001) Music score by SIMON BOSWELL
-S/T- VAR.ARTISTS *SONY TV (TEN): 501 824-2 (CD)*
BORN TO DANCE (1936) *feat* ELEANOR POWELL -S/T- selec.+
'GOING MY WAY' *GREAT MOVIE THEMES (BMG): CD 60031*
BORSALINO (1970) Music sco: CLAUDE BOLLING selection
AUVIDIS (Harmonia Mundi): K.1505 (CD)
BOSSA NOVA (2000) Music score by EUMIR DEODATO -S/T-
VERVE (UNIV): 543 714-2 (CD)
BOSTON KICKOUT (1996) Music score: DAVID ARNOLD -S/T-
SILVERTONE (Pinn): ORECD 543 (CD)
BOSS WOMEN (BBC1 17/07/2000) title music "Born On A
Sunday" by ART OF NOISE from 'The Seduction Of
Claude DEBUSSY' *ZTT (Pinn):ZTT 130(CD)(C) (CD/MC)*
BOUNCE (2000) Music score by MYCHAEL DANNA
-S/T- score *VARESE (Pinn): VSD 6194 (CD)*
-S/T- (songs and music from and inspired by)
EAST WEST (TEN): 8573 86881-2 (CD)
BOUNTY (Mutiny On The Bounty)(1984) Music by VANGELIS
theme *Coll* 'THEMES' *POLYDOR: 839518-2 (CD) -4 (MC)*
BOWFINGER (1999) Music score by DAVID NEWMAN -S/T-
VARESE (Pinn): VSD 6040 (CD)
BOY FROM MERCURY The (1997) Music: Various Arts -S/T-
OCEAN DEEP (Grapev/Polyg): OCD 004 (CD)
BOY WHO GREW TOO FAST (OPERA) Music & Libretto (Gian
Carlo Menotti) Royal Opera House Orch/Chor.(David
Syrus) - *TER (Koch): CDTER 1125 (CD)*
BOYFRIEND The - songs by Sandy Wilson
  1.30TH ANN.REVIV.LONDON CAST 1984 *feat* ROSEMARY ASHE
SIMON GREEN-JANE WELLMAN-ANNA QUAYLE-PETER BAYLISS
PADDIE O'NEIL-DEREK WARING and Company
<u>Highlights</u>: *SHOWTIME (MCI-THE): SHOW(CD)(MC) 027*
<u>Complete</u>: *TER (Koch): CDTER 1095 (CD)*
  2.ORIG BROADWAY CAST 1954 *feat:* JULIE ANDREWS & Comp
RCA (BMG): GDGK 60056 (CD)
  3.CLASSIC MUSICALS SERIES *feat:* JANE WELLMAN-SIMON
GREEN-ANNA QUAYLE-DEREK WARING-PETER BAYLIS *plus*
songs from 'ME AND MY GIRL' *KOCH INT: 34080-2 (CD)*
BOYS AND GIRLS (2000) Music score by STEWART COPELAND
-S/T- *POLYDOR (Univ): 810 058-2 (CD)*
BOYS DON'T CRY (1999) Music score: NATHAN LARSON -S/T-
KOCH INT (Koch): 38078-2 (CD) also KOCCD 8078 (CD)
BOYS FROM SYRACUSE songs Richard Rodgers-Lorenz Hart
OFF-BROADWAY REV.CAST 1963 *EMI: ZDM 764695-2 (CD)*
BOYZ UNLIMITED (C4 05/02/1999) Music by PHIL HARDING &
IAN CURNOW. theme "I Say A Little Prayer For You"
BRADY BUNCH The (USA TV) see *COLL.243,*
BRAINDEAD (1992) Music sco: PETER DASENT Var Artists:
-S/T- *NORMAL (Topic/Project/Dir): QDKCD 006 (CD)*
BRASSED OFF (1996) Music score TREVOR JONES *feat* The
GRIMETHORPE COLLIERY BAND -S/T- *RCA-CONIFER (BMG):*
09026 68757-2 (CD) & 75605 51368-2 (CD including
'CLASSIC BRASS' *album) see COLL.66,97,204,*
BRAVEHEART (1995) Music by JAMES HORNER -S/T- *LONDON*
UNIV: 448 295-2 (CD) see COLL.3,61,73,148,149,266,

BRAVO TWO ZERO (BBC1 03/1/1999) Music: DAVID FERGUSON
main theme on Coll 'The View From Now' on
CHANDOS: CHAN 9679 (CD) see COLL.104,
BREAD (UKGO 3/11/92 / BBC 1/5/86-91) Theme mus "Home"
DAVID MacKAY sung by The CAST *see COLL.3,20,42,*
BREAKFAST AT TIFFANY'S (1961) Music sco: HENRY MANCINI
song "Moon River" (Lyr: Johnny Mercer) -S/T- with
'ARABESQUE' *RCA CAMDEN (BMG): 74321 69878-2 (CD)*
-S/T- RCA:ND 89905 (CD) see COLL.61,73,170,
BREAKFAST CLUB (1985) Music score by KEITH FORSEY
-S/T- A.& M. (Univ): CDMID 179 (CD) AMC 5045 (MC)
BREAKING AWAY (1979) music by PATRICK WILLIAMS
NAXOS (Select): 8551155 (CD)
BREAKING GLASS (1980) mus.comp/perf by HAZEL O'CONNOR
-S/T- reis: SPECTRUM (Univ): 551 356-2 (CD)
BREAKING THE WAVES (1995) Music sco: JOACHIM HOLBEK
-S/T- Var.Art POLLYANNA (Pinn): POLLYPREM 001 (CD)
BRIDE OF CHUCKY (1997) Music score by GRAEME REVELL
-S/T- VAR.ARTISTS SPV (Koch): 0851858-2 (CD)
BRIDE OF FRANKENSTEIN The (1935) *see COLL.150,271,*
BRIDE OF THE RE-ANIMATOR (1990) Music sc: RICHARD BAND
+'RE-ANIMATOR' -S/T- *S.SCREEN Koch: FILMCD 082(CD)*
BRIDE OF THE WIND (2001) Music score: STEPHEN ENDELMAN
-S/T- DG (UNIV): 469 584-2 or 289 469 5842 (CD)
BRIDE WORE BLACK The - *see COLL.140,*
BRIDESHEAD REVISITED (C4 24/1/1998 orig 1981)
music score: GEOFFREY BURGON -S/T- *re-iss on MFP*
(EMI) CD(TC)MFP 6172 (CD/MC) see COLL.55,188,
BRIDGE ON THE RIVER KWAI (1957) Music: MALCOLM ARNOLD
LSO (R.Hickox) *CHANDOS: 9100 (CD)* "Colonel Bogey"
(Kenneth Alford) *see COLL.20,182,245,*
BRIDGE TOO FAR, A (1977) Music score by JOHN ADDISON
-S/T- reissue *RYKODISC (Vital): RCD 10746 (CD)*
BRIDGES OF MADISON COUNTY (1995) *see COLL.64,*
BRIDGET JONES DIARY (2001) VARIOUS ARTISTS SOUNDTRACK
VOLUME 1 *MERCURY (Univ): 548 796-2 (CD) -4 (MC)*
'BRIDGET JONES 2' songs 'inspired by' and others
VOLUME 2 *MERCURY (Univ): 586 598-2 (CD)*
BRIEF ENCOUNTER (1945) Mus: RACHMANINOV new collect:
'BRIEF ENCOUNTER: THE VERY BEST OF RACHMANINOV'
ERATO (TEN): 0630 18061-2 (CD) see COLL.73,269,
BRIGADOON - songs - Alan Jay Lerner & Frederick Loewe
1.ORIG 1954 FILM -S/T- w:GENE KELLY-CYD CHARISSE-VAN
JOHNSON / 23 tracks *EMI PREMIER: CDODEON 16 (CD)*
2.ORIG BROADWAY CAST 1947 w:DAVID BROOKS-MARION BELL
PAMELA BRITTON-LEE SULLIVAN *(BMG): GD(GK) 81001*
3.ORIG LONDON CAST 1988 *feat:*ROBERT MEADMORE-JACINTA
MULCAHY-MAURICE CLARK-LESLEY MACKIE-ROBIN NEDWELL-
IAN MACKENZIE STEWART *FIRST NIGHT (Pin) OCRCD 6022*
4.STUDIO RECORDING 1991 Ambrosian Chorus & London
Sinfonietta (John McGlynn) *EMI: CDC 754481-2 (CD)*
5.HIGHLIGHTS STUDIO RECORDING 1998) *feat* JANIS ELLIS
ETHAN FREEMAN-MAURICE CLARKE-MEG.KELLY & N.S.O.
(JOHN OWEN EDWARDS) *TER (Koch): CDTEH 6003 (CD)*

BRIGHT LEAF (1950) Music score by VICTOR YOUNG
  NEW RECORD.by MOSCOW SYMPHONY ORCH + 'UNINVITED'
  /'GREATEST SHOW ON EARTH'/'GULLIVER'S TRAVELS'
  MARCO POLO (Select): 8225063 (CD)
BRING IT ON (2000) Music score by CHRISTOPHE BECK
  -S/T- VARIOUS ARTISTS *EPIC (TEN): 500 989-2 (CD)*
BRING ON THE NIGHT (1986) Music by STING
  A.& M. (Univ): BRIND 1 (2CD) BRINC 1 (2MC)
BRINGING OUT THE DEAD (1999) Music sc: ELMER BERNSTEIN
  -S/T- *feat* THE CLASH/BRUCE SPRINGSTEEN/REM etc.on
  COLUMBIA (Ten): 496 457-2 (CD) -4 (MC)
BRITAIN AT WAR IN COLOUR (ITV 11/2000) Original music
  score by CHRIS ELLIOTT -S/T- *V.Artists:* VERA LYNN-
  HENRY HALL-FRANK SINATRA-HARRY JAMES-ANNE SHELTON-
  ANDREWS SISTERS-GRACIE FIELDS-GLENN MILLER etc.
  FIRST NIGHT (Pinn): REELCD 102 (CD)
BRITISH SONG CONTEST 2001 (BBC1 4/2001) *see page 352*
  (entry chosen for Eurovision Song Contest 2001)
  1st "No Dream Impossible" sung by Lindsay Dracass
  Universal: 15856-2 (CDs)
  2nd "Men" performed by Nanne *unavailable*
  3rd "That's My Love" by Tony Moore *unavailable*
  4th "Just Another Rainbow" Lucy Randell *unavailable*
BRITISH SONG CONTEST 2000 (BBC1 20/02/2000)
  (entry chosen for Eurovision Song Contest 2000)
  1st: "Don't Play That Song Again" (J.Springate-G.
  Shephard) Nicki French *RCA: 74321 76457-2 (Cds)*
  2nd: "Only The Women Know" (Kimberley Rew) sung by
  Six Chix *EMI: CDCHIX 001 (CDs) TCCHIX 001 (MC)*
  3rd: "Crazy" (C.Porter-T.Moore) sung by Catherine
  Porter *unavailable*
  4th: "I Won't Let You Do This To Me" (T.Bradley-P.
  Brown-M.Connaris) sung by Sexy Sadie *unavailable*
BRITS The (BRITANNIA MUSIC AWARDS) VARIOUS ARTISTS
  2001 SONY MUSIC: STVCD 105 (2CD)
  2000 SONY MUSIC: SONYTV 83CD (CD) SONYTV 83MC (MC)
BROADWAY MELODY OF 1936 (1935 MUSICAL) *feat* JACK BENNY
  ELEANOR POWELL-ROBERT TAYLOR+ 'BRO.MELODY OF 1940'
  GREAT MOVIE THEMES (TARGET-BMG): CD 60007 (CD)
BROADWAY MELODY OF 1938 (1937) -S/T- *f:* ELEANOR POWELL
  JUDY GARLAND *contains mus.from* 'Moon Over Miami'
  GREAT MOVIE THEMES (Target-BMG): CD 60030 (CD)
BROADWAY MELODY OF 1940 (40 MUSICAL) *feat* FRED ASTAIRE
  GEORGE MURPHY-ELEANOR POWELL +'BRO.MELODY OF 1936'
  GREAT MOVIE THEMES (TARGET-BMG): CD 60007 (CD)
BROKEDOWN PALACE (1999) Music score: DAVID NEWMAN
  -S/T- VAR.ARTISTS *MERCURY (Univ): 546 390-2 (CD)*
BROKEN ARROW (1996) Music score by HANS ZIMMER
  -S/T- reissue *MILAN (BMG): 74321 34865-2 (CD)*
BROKEN BLOSSOMS (1919) Contemporary score: CARL DAVIS
  see COLL.85,
BRONCO (USA tv 1950's/60's) *see COLL.245,*
BROOKSIDE (C4 2/11/82-2001) Theme music: DAVE ROYLANCE
  STEVE WRIGHT *deleted*

BROTHER (2000) Music score by JOE HISAISI -S/T- on
BMG IMPORTS: 74321 80263-2 (CD)
BROTHER FROM ANOTHER PLANET (1984) Music score: MASON
DARING -S/T- *Daring (Direct): DRCD 1007 (CD)*
BROTHER ON THE RUN (1974) Music: JOHNNY PATE-ADAM WADE
-S/T- *SANCTUARY Pinn:CMRCD 287 (CD) CMYLP 287 (LP)*
BROTHERS (2001) Music score by MELODEE SUTTON -S/T-
VARIOUS ARTISTS *WB (TEN): 9362 48058-2 (CD)*
BROTHERS (2000) Music score by JULIAN STEWART LINDSAY
-S/T- on *CONCORDE (AMD-Pinn): CONCD 2 (CD)*
BROTHERS The (BBC1 1971) Theme music DUDLEY SIMPSON
see COLL.42,
BRUISER (BBC2 28/02/2000) ser.music by NICK LOVE theme
"A Walk In The Black Forest" by HORST JANKOWSKI
BRUSH STROKES (BBC1 12/10/87) theme "Because Of You"
DEXYS MIDNIGHT RUNNERS on 'Very Best Of Dexys..'
MERCURY (Univ): 846 460-2 (CD) -4(MC) -1(LP)
BUBBLE BOY (2001) Music score by JOHN OTTMAN -S/T-
VARESE (Pinn): VSD 6283 (CD)
BUBBLING BROWN SUGAR (ORIG LONDON CAST 1977) VAR ARTS.
DRG (Pinn): CDSBL 13106 (CDx2)
BUCK ROGERS IN THE 25TH CENTURY (USA 1979 ITV) theme
music by STU PHILLIPS *see COLL.14,38,218,*
BUDDAH OF SUBURBIA The (BBC 3/11/93) title song & inc
idental music (David Bowie) sung by DAVID BOWIE &
ERDAL KIZILCAY feat LENNY KRAVITZ gtr -S/T- reiss
ARISTA (BMG): 74321 17004-2 (CD) -4 (MC)
BUDDY (1997) Music score: ELMER BERNSTEIN -S/T- on
VARESE (Pinn): VSD 5829 (CD) see COLL.40,
BUDDY (ORIG LONDON CAST 95 'LIVE' RECORDING) on
FIRST NIGHT (Pinn): CASTCD 55 (CD) CASTC 55 (MC)
BUDDY (O.LONDON CAST 89) PAUL HIPP-Gareth Marks-Enzo
Squillino *FIRST NIGHT (Pinn):QUEUECD 1 (CD)*
BUDDY - A LIFE IN MUSIC (SHOWS COLLECTION 1999) *with*
MIKE BERRY-JERRY ALLISON-SONNY CURTIS. 40TH YEAR
ANNIVERSARY TRIBUTE *CARLTON: 30362 00422 (CD)*
SHOWS COLLECTION (CHE): 3036 20042-2 (CD)
BUDDY'S SONG (90) *Feat:* Chesney Hawkes-Roger Daltrey
-S/T- *CHRYSALIS (EMI): CCD21 (CD) ZDD21 (MC)*
BUDGIE (LWT 9/4/71-72) theme "The Loner" NEIL HARRISON
see COLL.3,200,
BUDGIE THE LITTLE HELICOPTER (Sleepy Kid/HTV/ 4/1/94)
theme: PAUL K.JOYCE *MFP (EMI): TCMFP 6117 (MC)*
BUENA VISTA SOCIAL CLUB The (1999) Music by RY COODER
-S/T- *WORLD CIRCUIT USA (Pinn): WCD 050 (CD)*
BUFFY THE VAMPIRE SLAYER (TV USA 1996)(SKY1/BBC2 1999)
theme by NERF HERDER, score by WALTER MURPHY -S/T-
COLUMBIA (Ten): 496 633-2 (CD) -4 (MC)
BUGS BUNNY SHOW (Cart.USA) *see COLL.242,*

BUG'S LIFE, A (1998) Music & songs: RANDY NEWMAN "The
Time Of Your Life" performed by RANDY NEWMAN -S/T-
DISNEY-Edel (Vital): 010634-2DNY (CD) -4DNY (MC)

BUGSY MALONE (Show 1997) Music & songs: PAUL WILLIAMS
Or.London National Youth Theatre Cast *with* MICHAEL
STURGES-SHERIDAN SMITH-STUART PIPER-JANEE BENNETT-
ALEX LEA-PAUL LOWE-HANNAH SPEARITT-MALINDA PARRIS
TER (Koch): CDTER 1246
BUGSY MALONE (Film 1976) Music & songs: PAUL WILLIAMS
-S/T- *reissue RSO-POLYDOR (Univ): 831 540-2 (CD)*
BULLETS OVER BROADWAY (1994) dir: WOODY ALLEN / -S/T-
SONY CLASSICAL: SK 66822 (CD)
BULLITT (1968) Music sco: LALO SCHIFRIN -S/T- reissue
W.BROS (TEN): 9362 48085-2 (CD) also 45008-2(CD) +
ALEPH Koch:ALEPH 018 (CD) see COLL.95,142,250,
BULLY (2001) VARIOUS ARTISTS inc.EMINEM on
OCF ENTERTAINMENTS (Jetstar): OCF 0001 (CD)
BULWORTH (1998) Music score: ENNIO MORRICONE
-S/T- (songs) *INTERSCOPE (TEN): INTD 90160 (CD)*
-S/T- (score) *RCA VICTOR (BMG): 09026 63253-2 (CD)*
BURKE'S LAW (USA) *see COLL.84,245,*
BURN THE FLOOR (MUSIC INSPIRED BY THE STAGE SHOW)
MCA (Univ): MCD 60071 (CD)
BUSTER (1988) Music score: ANNE DUDLEY w. PHIL COLLINS
-S/T- *VIRGIN (EMI): CDV 2544 (CD) OVEDC 398 (MC)*
BUTCH CASSIDY AND THE SUNDANCE KID (1969) Music: BURT
BACHARACH "Raindrops Keep Falling On My Head" (B.
Bacharach-H.David) sung by B.J.THOMAS -S/T- *reiss:*
SPECTRUM (Univ): 551 433-2(CD)
BUTCHER BOY The (1998) Music score: ELLIOT GOLDENTHAL
EDEL-CINERAMA (Vital) 0022892CIN (CD)
BUTTERFLY BALL The (Film Musical 1974) Music sc: ROGER
GLOVER / Roger Glover & Friends -S/T- *CONNOISSEUR*
(Pinn): VSOPCD 139 (CD) VSOLP(MC) 139 (Dbl LP/MC)
BUTTERFLY KISS (BBC2 14/6/97) Music score: JOHN HARLE
see COLL.130,
BY JEEVES! (MUSICAL) Songs: ANDREW LLOYD WEBBER-ALAN
AYCKBOURN *feat:* STEVEN PACEY-MALCOLM SINCLAIR & Co
POLYDOR (Univ.): 533 187-2 (CD)
BYE BYE BIRDIE (MUSICAL 1960) ORIGINAL BROADWAY CAST
music: CHARLES STROUSE lyrics: LEE ADAMS *featuring*
CHITA RIVERA-DICK VAN DYKE-KAY MEDFORD-PAUL LYNDE
SONY CLASSICS (TEN): SMK 89254 (CD)
also remastered CAST Recording on
UNIVERSAL-IMS (UNIV): AA.3145 86432-2 (CD)

C ABARET - songs by John Kander and Fred Ebb
1.NEW BROADWAY CAST 1997 *w:* NATASHA RICHARDSON-
ALAN CUMMING-MARY LOUISE WILSON and Company
RCA VICTOR (BMG): 09026 63173-2 (CD)
2.NEW LONDON CAST 1986 *feat:* WAYNE SLEEP-VIVIENNE
MARTIN-CAROLINE CLARE-GRAZINA FRAME-KELLY HUNTER-
OSCAR QUITAK *FIRST NIGHT (Pinn): OCRCD 6010 (CD)*
3.STUDIO RECORDING *feat:* JONATHAN PRYCE-JUDI DENCH-
MARIA FRIEDMAN-GREGG EDELMAN-JOHN MARK AINSLEY
Complete: *TER (Koch): CDTER2 1210 (2CD)*
Highlights: *CURTAIN CALL-MCI (DISC): CURTCD 009 CD*

4.BROADWAY CAST 1966 *with* JILL HAWORTH-LOTTE LENYA-
   JACK GILDORD-JOEL GREY-BERT CONVY-PEG MURRAY-
   EDWARD WINTER *COLUMBIA (Ten): SMK 60533 (CD)*
5.ORIG LONDON CAST 1968 *feat* JUDI DENCH-LILA KEDROVA
   KEVIN COLSON-BARRY DENNEN *SONY: SMK 53494 (CD)*
6.FILM MUSICAL 1972 *featuring* LIZA MINNELLI -S/T-
   MCA (UNI): MCLD 19088 (CD)
7.SHOWS COLLECTION 1997 TOYAH WILLCOX-NIGEL PLANER
   & Comp.*CARLTON Shows: 3036 20039-2 (CD) -4(MC)*
8.(UNKNOWN SOURCE)
   VARESE (Pinn): VSD 5945 (CD)
CABIN IN THE SKY (1943) *f:* LOUIS ARMSTRONG-LENA HORNE
   ETHEL WATERS-EDDIE ANDERSON *re-mastered -S/T- on*
   EMI SOUNDTRACKS (EMI): CDODEON 31 (CD)
   Songs by VERNON DUKE and JOHN LaTOUCHE *selection*
   DEFINITIVE (Discovery): SFCD 33504 (CD)
CADFAEL (ITV 29/5/1994) music score by COLIN TOWNS
   -S/T- *SOUNDTRACKS EMI: 521 945-2 (CD) see COLL.42,*
CAESAR SMITH *see COLL.156,158,*
CAGNEY AND LACEY (USA81 BBC1 9/7/82) theme BILL CONTI
   see COLL.14,77,247,
CAINE MUTINY (1954) Music score: MAX STEINER
   see COLL.61,239,
CAL (1984) Music score: MARK KNOPFLER -S/T- *VERTIGO-*
   Univ: 822 769-2 (CD) / also on E.542 950-2 (CD)
   including 'PRINCESS BRIDE' and 'LOCAL HERO'
CALAMITY JANE - songs: Sammy Fain-Paul Francis Webster
   1.STUDIO RECORDING 1996 *featuring:* GEMMA CRAVEN
      CARLTON Shows Collect 30362 0030-2 (CD) -4 (MC)
   2.STUDIO R.1995 *w* DEBBIE SHAPIRO-TIM FLAVIN-SUSANNAH
      FELLOWS and Company
      Highlights: *CURTAIN CALL-MCI (DISC):CURTCD 007 CD*
      Complete: *TER (Koch): CDTER2 1215 (2CD)*
   3.FILM MUSICAL 1953 DORIS DAY -S/T- inc.'THE PAJAMA
      GAME' *COLUMBIA (TEN): 501 871-2 (CD)*
CALIFORNIA DREAMS (USA C4 25/4/93) Rock Drama TV Ser
   -S/T- *re-issue: GEFFEN MCA (UNI): GFLD 19301 (CD)*
CALL ME MADAM - songs by Irving Berlin
   1.ORIG LONDON CAST 1994 *feat* TYNE DALY-DAVID KERNAN
      JOHN BARROWMAN *DRG Pinn: DRGCD(DRGMC) 94761*
CALL MY BLUFF (revived BBC1 13/5/96-2001) theme music
   "Ciccolino" *unavailable*
CALLE 54 (2000) VAR.ARTISTS LATIN JAZZ CONCERT DOCUM.
   EMI SOUNDTRACKS: 532 000-2 (CD) 531 009-2 (2CDs)
CAMBERWICK GREEN (BBC1 1966) *see COLL.132,*
CAMELOT - songs by Alan Jay Lerner & Frederick Loewe
   1.FILM MUSICAL 1967 RICHARD HARRIS-VANESSA REDGRAVE
      -S/T- *W.Bros (TEN): 7599 27325-2 (CD)*
   2.REVIVAL LONDON CAST 1982 RICHARD HARRIS-FIONA FULL
      ERTON-ROBERT MEADMORE-ROBIN BAILEY-MICHAEL HOWE
      Complete: *TER (Koch): CDTER 1030 (CD)*
   3.ORIG LONDON CAST 1964 *w* LAURENCE HARVEY-ELIZABETH
      LARNER-NICKY HENSON-JOSEPHINE GORDON-KIT WILLIAMS
      BARRY KENT *FIRST NIGHT: OCRC 4 (MC) deleted*

4.ORIG BROADWAY CAST 1961 *feat* JULIE ANDREWS-RICHARD
  BURTON-ROBERT GOULET-R.McDOWELL *SONY: SK 60542 CD*
5.CLASSIC MUSICALS SERIES *featuring:* RICHARD HARRIS
  FIONA FULLERTON-ROBERT MEADMORE-MICHAEL HOWE etc.+
  songs from 'MY FAIR LADY' *Koch Int: 34079-2 (CD)*
CAMPION (BBC1 22/1/89) theme music by NIGEL HESS
  see COLL.5,137,
CAN-CAN (ORIG BROADWAY CAST 1953) Songs (Cole Porter)
  feat: GWEN VERDON-LILO-PETER COOKSON-HANS CONREID
  ERIK RHODES *ANGEL (EMI): ZDM 764664-2 (CD)*
CANDID CAMERA (1960's/70's) 'JONATHAN ROUTH'S CLASSIC
  CANDID CAMERA' *PULSE (BMG): PLS(CD)(MC) 272*
  see COLL.245,
CANDIDE -songs by Leonard Bernstein-Stephen Sondheim
             Richard Wilbur and John Latouche
1.1999 ROYAL NATIONAL THEATRE RECORDING
  FIRST NIGHT (Pinn): CASTCD 75 (CD) CASTMC 75 (MC)
2.1997 NEW BROADWAY CAST *RCA :0902 668835-2 (CD)*
3.1991 MUSICAL OPERA Studio Recording *w* JERRY HADLEY
  JUNE ANDERSON-CHRISTA LUDWIG-ADOLPH GREEN-NICOLAI
  GEDDA-DELLA JONES-KURT OLLMANN & L.S.O.(Bernstein)
  DG (Univ): 429734-2 (2CDs) -4 (2MC)
4.1988 MUSICAL OPERA Studio *feat* SCOTTISH OPERA CAST
  TER (Koch): CDTER 1156 Highlights: *CDTER 1006*
5.1956 ORIG BROADWAY CAST *w:* BARBARA COOK-MAX ADRIAN
  ROBERT ROUNSEVILLE-IRRA PETINA-WILLIAM OLVIS-LOUIS
  EDMONDS-C.BAIN *SONY Broadway: SK 48017 (CD)*
CANDYMAN 3:DAY OF THE DEAD (1999) Music: ADAM GORGONNI
  -S/T- IMPORT *BEYOND (USA): 578 218-2 (CD)*
CANNON (USA TV) *see COLL.124,246,*
CAPEMAN The (MUSICAL 1997/8) All songs by PAUL SIMON
  featuring RUBEN BLADES-MARC ANTHONY-EDNITA NAZARIO
  W.BROS (TEN): 9362 46814-2 (CD) -4 (MC)
CAPITAL CITY (Thames 26/9/89) theme music: COLIN TOWNS
  -S/T- *FIRST NIGHT (Pinn): SCENE(CD)(C) 18 (CD/MC)*
CAPRICORN ONE (1978) Music sco: JERRY GOLDSMITH -S/T-
  also containing music from 'OUTLAND') on *GNP USA*
  (ZYX): GNPD 8035 (CD) see COLL.114,115,232,
CAPTAIN BLOOD (1935) Music by ERICH WOLFGANG KORNGOLD
  IMPORT (DISCOV): TSU 0141 see COLL.160,240,
CAPTAIN BLOOD (1952) Mus.sco: VICTOR YOUNG new record:
  BRANDENBURG S.ORCH.(Kaufman) with other items on
  MARCO POLO (Select): 8.223607 (CD
CAPTAIN CORELLI'S MANDOLIN (2000) Music score: STEPHEN
  WARBECK / title song sung by RUSSELL WATSON -S/T-
  DECCA LONDON (Univ): 467 678-2 (CD) -4 (MC)
CAPTAIN FROM CASTILLE (1947) Music sco: ALFRED NEWMAN
  -S/T- including music from 'THE SNAKE PIT' (1947)
  TSUNAMI (Discov): TCI 0620/21 (2CD) see COLL.1,
CAPTAIN KANGAROO (USA) *see COLL.242,*

CAPTAIN SCARLET AND THE MYSTERONS (BBC2 1/10/93 orig
  ITV 29/9/67) music by BARRY GRAY *see COLL.2,24,38,*
  74,84,118,221,250,253,261,

CAPTIVE (1986) Music sco: MICHAEL BERKLEY-The EDGE
  -S/T- *VIRGIN (EMI): CDV 2401 (CD)*
CAR 54 WHERE ARE YOU (USA TV) *see COLL.243,*
CAR WASH (1976) T.theme: NORMAN WHITFIELD sung by ROSE
  ROYCE -S/T- reissue: *MCA (UNI): MCD 11502 (CD)*
CARAVAGGIO 1610 (1986) Music: SIMON FISHER TURNER
  -S/T- *reissued on DEMON (Pinn): DSCD 10 (CD)*
CARD The - songs by Tony Hatch and Jackie Trent
  ORIG LONDON CAST 1973 *w:* JIM DALE-MILLICENT MARTIN
  JOAN HICKSON-MARTI WEBB-ELEANOR BRON-ALAN NORBURN
  JOHN SAVIDENT *FIRST NIGHT (Pinn): OCRCD 6045 (CD)*
CARDINAL The (1963) Music score JEROME MOROSS / Coll.
  'Classic Film Music of JEROME MOROSS' with 'SEVEN
  WONDERS OF THE WORLD'/'PROUD REBEL'/'CLOSE UP'/'THE
  JAYHAWKERS'/'THE CAPTIVE CITY'
  SILVA CLASSICS (Koch): SILKD 6030 (2CD)
CAREER GIRLS (1998) featuring music by The CURE
  -S/T- *TWEED COUTURE (N.Note-Pinn): TWEEDCD 8 (CD)*
CAREFREE (1938) FILM MUSICAL *feat* FRED ASTAIRE-GINGER
  ROGERS -S/T- *selection on* 'Let's Swing and Dance'
  +songs fr.'FOLLOW THE FLEET'/'TOP HAT'/'SWINGTIME'
  GREAT MOVIE THEMES (Target-BMG): CD 60015 (CD)
  also available -S/T- + *songs from* 'SHALL WE DANCE'
  IRIS Mus-Chansons Cinema (Discov): CIN 007 (CD)
CARLA'S SONG (1996) Music score: GEORGE FENTON -S/T-
  DEBONAIR Records (Pinn): CDDEB 1005 (CD)
CARLITO'S WAY (1993) Mus sco: PATRICK DOYLE Songs V/A
  -S/T- (Songs) *EPIC (Ten): 474 994-2 (CD) deleted*
  -S/T- (Score) *VARESE (Pinn): VSD(VSC) 5463 CD/MC*
CARMEN - *mus:* Georges Bizet *libr:* H.Meilhac-L.Halevy
  1.FILM MUSICAL 1983 *w:* LAURA DEL SOL-PACO DE LUCIA
   ANTONIO GADES-CRISTINA HOYOS -S/T- *POLY (IMS):*
   E.817 247-2 (CD)
  2.FILM MUSICAL 1984 *w:* PLACIDO DOMINGO-JULIA MIGENES
   JOHNSON *ERATO: MCE 75113 (3MC) ECD 88037 (3CD)*
  3.STUDIO RECORDING *with* MARILYN HORNE as Carmen
   DG (Univ): 427 440-2 (3CD's)
CARMEN JONES songs by G.Bizet & Oscar Hammerstein II
  1.ORIG BROADWAY CAST 1943 *feat:* MURIEL SMITH-LUTHER
   SAXON-CARLOTTA FRANZELL-GLENN BRYANT-JUNE HAWKINS
   CD inc 'CARMEN FANTASY' performed by ISAAC STERN
   PEARL-PAVILION (Pinn): GEMMCD 0099 (CD)
  2.FILM MUSICAL 1954 *feat:* MARILYN HORNE-PEARL BAILEY
   LaVERN HUTCHINSON-MARVIN HAYES-OLGA JAMES-BERNICE
   PETERSON-BROCK PETERS -S/T- *(BMG): GD(GK) 81881*
  3.ORIG LONDON CAST 1991 *Direct:* SIMON CALLOW *with*
   WILHELMINA FERNANDEZ-SHARON BENSON-DAMON EVANS-
   MICHAEL AUSTIN-GREGG BAKER-KAREN PARKS-CLIVE ROWE
   DANNY JOHN JULES *EMI: CDJONES 1 (EL 754351-2)*
CARNIVAL OF SOULS (1998) *BIRDMAN (Cargo): BMR 012 (CD)*
CARO DIARIO - see under DEAR DIARY
CAROUSEL - songs: Richard Rodgers-Oscar Hammerstein II
  1.FILM MUSICAL 1956 *feat:* GORDON McRAE-SHIRLEY JONES
   -S/T- Remastered *EMI ANGEL: CDC 527 352-2 (CD)*

2.ORIG LONDON CAST 1993 JOANNA RIDING-KATRINA MURPHY
FIRST NIGHT (Pinn): OCRCD 6042 (CD) CASTC 40 (MC)
3.SHOWS COLLECTION 1993 *feat:* DAVE WILLETTS-CLAIRE
MOORE-SU POLLARD-IAN WALLACE-LINDA HIBBERD
CARLTON Shows: PWKS 4144 (CD) PWKMC 4144 (MC)

CARRIE (1976) Music score: PINO DONAGGIO -S/T- *reiss +
additional items RYKODISC (Vital): RCD 10701 (CD)*

CARRY ON... (UK COMEDY FILM SERIES FROM 1958-1991)
Music by ERIC ROGERS-BRUCE MONTGOMERY + Var.Arts
CITY OF PRAGUE PHILHARMONIC ORCH: Gavin Sutherland
WHITE LINE-ASV (Sel): WHL 2119 (CD) see COLL.59,

CASABLANCA (1943) Mus: MAX STEINER *vocal* DOOLEY WILSON
-S/T- + *dialogue EMI: 823 502-2 (CD)*
see COLL.73,105,239,

CASINO (1995) Songs by Various Artists
-S/T- (31 Tracks) on *MCA (UNI): MCAD 11389 (2CD)*

CASINO ROYALE (1967) Music score: BURT BACHARACH -S/T-
*VARESE (Pinn): VSD 5265 (CD) and CLASSIC (Vivante)
DAD 1033 (CD) see also COLL.193*

CASPER (1995) Music score by JAMES HORNER
-S/T- *MCA (UNI): MCD 11240 (CD)*

CASPER THE FRIENDLY GHOST (USA TV) *see COLL.149,242,*

CAST AWAY (2001) Music score by ALAN SILVESTRI -S/T-
VARESE (Pinn): VSD 6213 (CD)

CASTAWAY 2000 (BBC1 18/01/2000) series music by
SIMON MAY and SIMON LOCKYER *unavailable*

CASUALTY (BBC1 1986-2002) theme by KEN FREEMAN + song
"EVERLASTING LOVE" (Cason-Gayden) CASUALTY CAST
WARNER ESP (TEN): WESP 003CD (CDs) WESP 003C (MC)
also "STAY WITH ME BABY" sung by REBECCA WHEATLEY
BBC Worldwide (Pinn): WMSS 6022-2 (CDs) -4 (MC)
"Bound 4 Da Reload (Casualty)" by OXIDE & NEUTRANO
EAST WEST (TEN): OXIDE 01CD (CDs) inc.theme sample
for main 'CASUALTY' theme *see COLL.42,172,283,*

CAT O'NINE TAILS (1980) Music: ENNIO MORRICONE -S/T-
inc 'FOUR FLIES ON GREY VELVET'/'BIRD WITH THE
CRYSTAL PLUMAGE' on *DRG (Pinn): DRGCD 32911 (CD)*

CAT PEOPLE (1942) Music score: ROY WEBB *new rec.by the*
SLOVAK RADIO SYMPHONY ORCH (William T.Stromberg) +
suites 'SEVENTH VICTIM'(1943) 'BEDLAM'(1946) 'THE
BODY SNATCHER'(1945)'I WALKED WITH A ZOMBIE'(1943)
MARCO POLO (Select): 8.225125 (CD)   see COLL.275,

CATHEDRAL (BBC1 7/9/97) theme "Anna Of The Five Towns"
by NIGEL HESS *see COLL.137,*

CATLOW (1971) Music score: ROY BUDD -S/T- Collect also
feat 'SOLDIER BLUE' (1970) & 'ZEPPELIN' (1971) on
CINEPHILE (Pinn): CINCD 022 (CD)

CATS - songs by Andrew Lloyd Webber and Trevor Nunn
1.ORIG LONDON CAST 1981 *feat:* ELAINE PAIGE & Comp
POLYDOR: 817 810-2 (2CD) 817 810-4 (2MC)
'Highlights' 839415-2(CD) -1(LP) -4(MC) -5 (DCC)
2.CLASSIC MUSICALS SERIES *feat:* MARIA FRIEDMAN and
CLIVE CARTER w. MUNICH SYMPHONY ORCH (J.O.Edwards)
+*songs* 'PHANTOM OF THE OPERA' *KOCH Int: 34078-2CD*

CATS AND DOGS (2001) Music score by JOHN DEBNEY -S/T-
  VARESE (Pinn): VSD 6278 (CD)
CAT'S MEOW The (2001) Jazz standards peformed by IAN
  WHITCOMB -S/T- *BMG IMPORTS: 09026 63822-2 (CD)*
CATWEAZLE (LWT 1/3/70-71) theme TED DICKS *see COLL.2,*
CAUGHT UP (1998) *VIRGIN: CDVUS 139 (CD) VUSLP 109 (LP)*
CAVEMAN'S VALENTINE The (2001) Music score by TERENCE
  BLANCHARD -S/T- *DECCA USA IMP: 440 013 586-2M (CD)*
CD : UK (ITV 1998-2001) 40 track coll: 'CD UK YOU KNOW
  WHERE IT'S AT' *BMG UK: 74321 79285-2 (2CD) -4(2MC)*
  'MORE WICKED HITS' *UK: 74321 82369-2 (2CD) -4(2MC)*
CELEBRITY (1999) WOODY ALLEN'S SELECTION OF 30s & 40s
  songs -S/T- *MILAN (BMG): 74321 64071-2 (CD)*
CELL The (2000) Music score by HOWARD SHORE -S/T- feat
  LONDON PHILHARM.ORCH.& MASTER MUSICIANS OF JAJOUKA
  SILVA SCREEN (Koch): FILMCD 346 (CD)
CELL BLOCK 4 (1992) Music score (John Barnes) -S/T-
  MCA (UNI): MCD 10758 (CD)
CELTS The (C4 21/4/2000) Music score by KARL JENKINS
  -S/T- featuring ADIEMUS IV 'The Eternal Knot' on
  Virgin (EMI):CDVE 952 (CD) also see COLL 10,
CELTS The (BBC2 14/5/1987) Music score comp/perf by
  ENYA -S/T/- *WEA: 4509 91167-2 (CD) WX 498C (MC)*
CENTER STAGE (1999) Music score: GEORGE FENTON -S/T-
  VARIOUS ARTS on *EPIC (TEN): 498 227-2 (CD) -4 (MC)*
CENTRAL STATION (Central Do Brasil) (1998) Music score
  ANTONIO PINTO-JAQUES MORELEMBAUM -S/T- issued on
  BMG SOUNDTRACKS: 74321 63196-2 (CD)
CENTRE OF THE WORLD (2001) VARIOUS ARTISTS SOUNDTRACK
  SIX DEGREES KUDOS (Pinn): 6570 361041-2 (CD)
CENTURY (1993) Music score: MICHAEL GIBBS -S/T- *with*
  'CLOSE MY EYES' *IONIC-MUTE (Pinn): IONIC 10 (2CD)*
CHALLENGE The (1982) Music score: JERRY GOLDSMITH
  -S/T- *PROMETHEUS IMPORT: PCR 505 (CD)*
CHALLENGE The ORIG.LONDON CAST *TER: TERCD 1201 (2CD)*
CHAMPION THE WONDER HORSE (USA 56)(BBC1 7/11/92) theme
  song (Norman Luboff-Marilyn Keith) sung by FRANKIE
  LAINE *BEAR FAMILY (Rollecoaster): BCD 15632 (CDs)*
CHAMPIONS (1984) Music score: CARL DAVIS -S/T- *deleted*
  vers "Sometimes" Elaine PAIGE *(TEN): 2292 40511-2*
CHAMPIONS The (ITC 25/9/68 - 4/69) theme: EDWIN ASTLEY
  see COLL.2,24,74,131,250,
CHAMPIONS LEAGUE FOOTBALL *see* EUROPEAN CHAMP.LEAGUE
CHANGE OF HABIT *see* ELVIS PRESLEY INDEX p.348
CHANGING ROOMS (BBC2 4/9/96-2002) theme music by
  JIM PARKER *unavailable*
CHAPLIN (1992) Mus:JOHN BARRY *see COLL.26,30,32,66,69,*
CHARADE (1964) Music score: HENRY MANCINI *-S/T- with*
  'EXPERIMENT IN TERROR' *reissued on*
  RCA CAMDEN (BMG): 74321 72714-2 (CD) see COLL.170,
CHARGE OF THE LIGHT BRIGADE (1936) Music: MAX STEINER
  new rec SLOVAK STATE PHILHARMONIC *also with* 'THE
  TREASURE OF THE SIERRA MADRE'
  CENTAUR (Comp/Pinn): CRC 2367 (CD) see COLL.239,

CHARIOTS OF FIRE (1981) Music score: VANGELIS -S/T-
  POLYDOR (Univ): 490 737-2 / 549 095-2 (remastered)
  800 020-2 (CD)   see COLL.266,263,
CHARLIE BROWN (A BOY NAMED) (USA 80's/BBC1) Mus score
  composed and performed by The VINCE GUARALDI TRIO
  FANTASY (Complete): FCD 8430-2 (CD)
CHARLIE GIRL - songs by David Heneker and John Taylor
  1.NEW LONDON CAST 1986 *w:* PAUL NICHOLAS-CYD CHARISSE
  MARK WYNTER-DORA BRYAN-NICHOL.PARSONS-KAREN DAVIES
  LISA HULL *FIRST NIGHT (Pinn): OCRCD 6009(CD)*
CHARLIE'S ANGELS (FILM 2000) Music sc: EDWARD SHEARMUR
  -S/T- *COLUMBIA (TEN): 498 478-2 (CD) -4 (MC)*
CHARLIE'S ANGELS (TVUSA 1976) theme JACK ELLIOTT-ALLYN
  FERGUSON *see COLL.78,244,277*
CHARLY (1968) Music score by RAVI SHANKAR -S/T- on
  MOVING IMAGE (Cargo): MIE 007CD (CD) MIE 007 (LP)
CHARMED (USA1998/C5 01/04/2000) theme music "How Soon
  Is Now" (The SMITHS) by LOVE SPIT LOVE from the
  -S/T- of 'THE CRAFT' *COLUMBIA (TEN):484 152-2 (CD)*
  SMITHS on 'Singles' *WARNER (TEN): 4509 9909-2 (CD)*
CHARRO! *see* ELVIS PRESLEY INDEX p.348
CHASING THE DEER (1993) Music by JOHN WETTON -S/T- on
  BLUEPRINT (Pinn): BP 282CD BLUEPRINT (Sil.Sounds)
  6043 88124-2 (CD) CROMWELL (THE): CPCD 020 (CD)
CHE! (1969) Music score: LALO SCHIFRIN -S/T- *reissue*
  ALEPH (Koch): ALEP 006 (CD)
CHEERS (USA C4 6/1/84-93) theme "Where Everybody Knows
  Your Name" GARY PORTNOY *see COLL.14,244,*
CHELTENHAM FESTIVAL (BBC1 14/3/89-2000) theme music
  "Odissea" (Reverberi-Giordiano) RONDO VENEZIANO
  BMG (Discovery): 610.535 (CD)
CHERRY HARRY & RAQUEL (1969 RUSS MEYER) -S/T- inc:
  'MONDO TOPLESS' (66) 'GOOD MORNING & GOODBYE' (67)
  NORMAL/QDK (Dir/Greyhound/Pinn): QDK(CD)(LP) 014
CHESS - songs: Benny Andersson-Bjorn Ulvaeus-Tim Rice
  1.1986 Chess Pieces: The Best Of Chess *feat:* ELAINE
  PAIGE-BARBARA DICKSON-MURRAY HEAD-TOMMY KORBERG-
  DENIS QUILLEY-BJORN SKIFS-L.S.O.-AMBROSIAN SINGERS
  RCA (BMG): 74321 15120-2 (CD) -4 (MC)
  2.ORIG BROADWAY CAST: *POLYDOR (Univ): 847 445-2 (CD)*
CHEYENNE (USA TV 1958) *see COLL.245,*
CHEYENNE AUTUMN (1964) Music score by ALEX NORTH.
  SELECTION WITH 'CINERAMA SOUTH SEAS ADV. (1958) +
  'DRAGONSLAYER' (81) *LABEL X (Hot): ATMCD 2004 (CD)*
  also on LABEL X (Hot): LXCD 4 (CD)
CHICAGO - songs: John Kander and Fred Ebb
  1.ORIG LONDON CAST (1997) *feat:* UTE LEMPER-RUTHIE
  HENSHALL-HENRY GOODMAN-NIGEL PLANER-MEG JOHNSON
  RCA (BMG): 09026 63155-2 (CD) -4 (MC)
  2.ORIG BROADWAY CAST (1996) *featur:* ANN REINKING
  BEBE NUEWIRTH-JAMES NAUGHTON-JOEL GRAY and Comp
  RCA (BMG): 09026 68727-2 (CD) -4 (MC)
  3.ORIG NEW YORK CAST (1975, re-mastered 1998)
  RCA (BMG): 07822 18952-2 (CD)

CHICAGO BLUES (FILM) MUDDY WATERS-JB HUTTO-JUNIOR WELLS
JOE YOUNG-KOKO TAYLOR *CASTLE (Pinn): CLACD 425 (CD)*
CHICAGO HOPE (BBC1 1/4/1995) Mus: MARK ISHAM-JEFF RONA
-S/T- *SONIC (Grey-Cargo):SI 8702(CD) see COLL.172,*
CHICKEN RUN (2000,Nick Park) Music score: JOHN POWELL
and HARRY GREGSON WILLIAMS -S/T-
DREAMWORKS-BMG (BMG): 09026 63702-2
CHICO AND THE MAN (USA 74) theme song by JOSE FELICIANO
on 'My Name Is' *BMG IMPORTS: 74321 87206-2 (CD)*
CARLTON Ess.Gold (CHE): 30359 00232 (CD) -4(MC)
CHIGLEY (BBC1 1969) *see COLL.132,*
CHILDREN OF A LESSER GOD (1986) "Largo Ma Mon Tanto"
2nd m/m 'Concerto D.Min For Violins' (BACH) Music
music score by MICHAEL CONVERTINO -S/T- *GNP (ZYX)*
GNPD(GNP5)(GNPS)8007 (CD/MC/LP) also NAXOS 8551155
CHILDREN'S HOSPITAL (BBC1 19/10/93) mus DEBBIE WISEMAN
BMG (BMG): 74321 47589-4 (MC) see COLL.172,283,
CHIMERA (Anglia 7/9/91) theme music "Rosheen Du" by
NIGEL HESS sung by CHAMELEON *see COLLS 137,*
CHINATOWN (1974) Music score: JERRY GOLDSMITH -S/T-
VARESE (Pinn): VSD 5677 (CD)
CHIPS (USA TV 1980) theme: JOHN PARKER *see COLL.247,*
CHITTY CHITTY BANG BANG (2001) O.LONDON CAST MUSICAL
with MICHAEL BALL-EMMA WILLIAMS-ANTON RODGERS-BRIAN
BLESSED-NICHOLA McAULIFFE-RICHARD O'BRIEN & Company
recording to be confirmed
CHITTY CHITTY BANG BANG (1968) Music and songs by
RICHARD & ROBERT SHERMAN -S/T- *reissue + add.items*
DICK VAN DYKE-SALLY ANN HOWES-LIONEL JEFFRIES etc.
RYKODISC (Vital): RCD 10702 (CD) RAC 10702 (MC)
CHOCOLAT (2000) Music score by RACHEL PORTMAN -S/T-
SONY CLASSICS (TEN): SK 89472 (CD)
CHORUS LINE, A songs: Marvin Hamlisch-Edward Kleban
1.FILM SOUNDTRACK 1985 *feat:* MICHAEL DOUGLAS-TERENCE
MANN-ALYSON REED *reissue BGO (BMG): BGOCD 360 (CD)*
2.ORIGINAL BROADWAY CAST 1975 *w:* DONNA McKECHNIE-
PATRICIA GARLAND *COLUMBIA (Ten): SK 65282 (CD)*
CHRISTIE MALRY'S OWN DOUBLE ENTRY (2001) Music score by
LUKE HAINES -S/T- *HUT (EMI): CDHUT 65 (CD)*
CHRISTINE (1984) Music score: JOHN CARPENTER -S/T-
VARESE (Pinn): VSD 5240 (CD)
CHRISTIANE F.(1981) Music by DAVID BOWIE -S/T- *reissue*
EMI SOUNDTRACKS: 533 093-2 (CD)
CHRISTMAS CAROL: THE MOVIE (2001) Mus JULIAN NOTT -S/T-
EMI -S/T- 535 786-2 (enhanced CD) & 536 246-0 (CD)
CHRISTMAS CAROL, A (2000) Music score: STEPHEN WARBECK
-S/T- *VARESE (Pinn): VSD 6071 (CD)*
CHRISTOPHER COLUMBUS (1949) Music by Sir ARTHUR BLISS
new SLOVAK RADIO S.O.(Adriano) + 'Seven Waves Away'
(1956) *MARCO POLO (Select): 8.223315 (CD)*
CHRISTOPHER COLUMBUS: THE DISCOVERY (1992) Music score
CLIFF EIDELMAN -S/T- *VARESE (Pinn): VSD 5389 (CD)*
CHRONICLES OF NARNIA (BBC1 13/11/88) theme mus GEOFFREY
BURGON *see COLL.55, also BBC: ZBBC 1109/1110 (2MC)*

CIDER HOUSE RULES The (1999) Music sco: RACHEL PORTMAN
-S/T- *SONY CLASS (TEN): SK 89031 (CD) see COLL.202,*
CIDER WITH ROSIE (ITV 27/12/1998) Music sco: GEOFFREY
BURGON -ST- *SILVA SCREEN (Koch): FILMCD 306 (CD)*
CIMARRON STRIP (USA TV) *see COLL.246,*
CINDERELLA (DISNEY 1950) *see* WALT DISNEY INDEX p.341
CINDERELLA (MUSICAL SHOW 1957) with JULIE ANDREWS
Columbia IMPT.(Silva Screen): CK 02005 (CD)
CINDERELLA (SONGS FROM THE CLASSIC FAIRY TALE)
NEW RECORDINGS *VARESE (Pinn): VSD 5875 (CD)*
CINEMA PARADISO (1990) Music score ENNIO MORRICONE
DRG (Koch): DRGCD 99501 (CD)
see COLL.60,68,73,97,176,178,
CINERAMA SOUTH SEAS ADVENTURE (1958) Music score by
ALEX NORTH. *SELECTION* + 'CHEYENNE AUTUMN' (1964)
'DRAGONSLAYER' (81) *LABEL X (Hot): ATMCD 2004 (CD)*
CIRCUS The (1928) Mus sc: CHARLES CHAPLIN *see COLL.66,*
'FILM MUS.OF CHARLES CHAPLIN' *RCA: 09026 68271-2*
CIRQUE DU SOLEIL see 'ALEGRIA'/'QUIDAM'/'SALTIMBANCO'
CITIZEN KANE (1941) Music: BERNARD HERRMANN *(complete)*
AUSTRALIAN P.O.(TONY BREMNER) *feat* ROSAMUND ILLING
PREAMBLE-5th CONT (HOT-S.Screen): PRCD 1788 (CD)
also *SOUNDTRACK FACTORY (Discov): SFCD 33553 (CD)*
and *VARESE (Pinn): VSD 5806 (CD) see COLL.135,*
CITY CENTRAL (BBC1 04/04/1998-2000) Music theme and
incidental music by BARRY ADAMSON *unavailable*
CITY HALL (1995) Music score: JERRY GOLDSMITH -S/T- on
VARESE (Pinn): VSD 5699 (CD)
CITY LIGHTS (1931) Original Music composed by CHARLES
CHAPLIN. City Lights Orch conduct: CARL DAVIS
S.SCREEN (Koch): FILMXCD 326 / FILMCD 078 also on
SOUNDTRACK FACTORY (Discov): SFCD 33510 (CD) with
'MODERN TIMES' *see COLL.66,85,*
CITY OF ANGELS (O.LONDON CAST 1993) Songs (Cy Coleman-
L.Gelbart) MARTIN SMITH-ROGER ALLAM-HADYN GWYNNE-
HENRY GOODMAN-SUSANNAH FELLOWS-JOANNE FARREL
FIRST NIGHT (Pinn): OCRCD 6034 (CD)
CITY OF ANGELS (1998) Music score: GABRIEL YARED
-S/T- *WB (TEN): 9362 46867-2 (CD) -4 (MC)*
CITY OF INDUSTRY (1996) Music score: STEPHEN ENDELMAN
-S/T- *inc* MASSIVE ATTACK-BOMB THE BASS-LUSH-TRICKY
PHOTEX etc. *QUANGO-ISLAND (Univ): 524 308-2 (CD)*
CITY OF THE WALKING DEAD (1970) Music score: STELVIO
CIPRIANI -S/T- *LUCERTOLA (SRD): EFA 04362-2 (CD)*
CITY SLICKERS (1991) Music score: MARC SHAIMAN -S/T-
VARESE (Pinn): VSD 5321 (CD)
CIVIL ACTION, A (1998) Music score: DANNY ELMAN -S/T-
HOLLYWOOD-EDEL (Vit): 010087-2HWR (CD)
CIVIL WAR The (BBC2 30/3/91) theme "Ashokan Farewell"
by JAY UNGAR -S/T- incl: "Shenandoah"/"When Johnny
Comes Marching Home" & others - KEN BURNS -S/T- on
ELEKTRA-NONESUCH (TEN): 7559-79256-2(CD) -4(MC)
ALSO AVAIL: "The Civil War-It's Music & Sounds"
IMS-POLY E.432 591-2 (CD) also see COLL.108,

CLAIM The (2000) Music score by MICHAEL NYMAN on
  VENTURE-VIRGIN (EMI): CDVE   953 (CD)
CLAMBAKE *see* ELVIS PRESLEY INDEX p.348
CLANDESTINE MARRIAGE The (1999) Music score: STANISLAS
  SYREWICZ -S/T- *VENTURE-VIRGIN (EMI): CDVE 949 (CD)*
CLANGERS The (BBC1 1969) Music by VERNON ELLIOTT -S/T-
  TRUNK (SRD): SOUP 1CD (CD) SOUP 1LP (LP)
CLARISSA AND THE COUNTRYMAN (BBC2 20/10/2000) music by
  JANE ELLER *unavailable*
CLARISSA EXPLAINS IT ALL (USA TV) *see COLL.248,*
CLARKSON'S STAR CARS (BBC2 01/06/2000) title music by
  BEN SALISBURY *unavailable*
CLASH OF THE TITANS (1981) Music s: LAURENCE ROSENTHAL
  reissue with LONDON SYMPHONY ORCHEST (L.Rosenthal)
  FANTASY IMP (S.Screen): PNDL 14 & PEG A28693 (CD)
CLASS ACT, A (MUSICAL ABOUT MUSICALS) by EDWARD KLEBAN
  ORIG CAST RECORDING *BMG IMPORT: 09026 63757-2 (CD)*
CLEOPATRA (1963) Music score: ALEX NORTH *NEW RECORDING*
  VARESE (Pinn): VSD 26224-2 (2CD)
CLEOPATRA JONES (1973) Music score by J.J.JOHNSON and
  songs by JOE SIMON and MILLIE JACKSON -S/T- reiss
  WB (TEN): 9362 48090-2 (CD)
CLERKS (1994) Music score: SCOTT ANGLEY -S/T- V.Arts
  COLUMBIA (Ten): 477 802-2 (CD)
CLIVE ANDERSON ALL TALK (BBC1 6/10/96) title mus "All
  Talk" by ELVIS COSTELLO & ATTRACTIONS *unavailable*
CLIVE BARKER'S A-Z OF HORROR (BBC2 4/10/97) series
  title music by TOT TAYLOR on 'WATERLAND' album
  TWEED COUTURE (Pinn/Vital): TWEEDCD 001 (CD)
CLOCKERS (1995) Music score by STANLEY CLARKE-TERENCE
  BLANCHARD -S/T- *MCA (UNI): MCD 11304 (CD)*
CLOCKING OFF (BBC1 23/01/2000) Music score composed &
  conducted by MURRAY GOLD *unavailable*
CLOCKWORK ORANGE, A (1971) Electronic music by WALTER
  'WENDY' CARLOS -S/T- *WARNER Ten: 7599 27256-2 (CD)*
  see COLL.84,88,97,219,
CLOSE ENCOUNTERS OF THE THIRD KIND (1977) music by
  JOHN WILLIAMS -S/T- *COLLECTOR SPECIAL EDITION*
  ARISTA (BMG): 07822 19004-2
  JOHN WILLIAMS Nat.Phil.Orch *RCA: RCD 13650 (CD)*
  see COLL.121,220,232,237,280,
CLOSE MY EYES (1991) Music sco: MICHAEL GIBBS -S/T- +
  'CENTURY' on *IONIC-MUTE (Pinn): IONIC 10 (2CD)*
CLOSE SHAVE, A (Wallace & Gromit) (1995) Mus by JULIAN
  NOTT *Video: BBC (Pinn): BBCV 5766 (VHS) see also*
  'GRAND DAY OUT'/'WRONG TROUSERS'
CLOSER TO HEAVEN (SHOW 2001) Songs by NEIL TENNANT and
  CHRIS LOWE featuring PAUL KEATING and others
  EPIC (TEN): 504 516-2 (CD)
CLOSER YOU GET The (2000) Music score: RACHEL PORTMAN
  -S/T- (VARIOUS) *RCA VICT (BMG): 09026 63601-2 (CD)*
CLOSET (2000) Music score by VLADIMIR COSMA on Coll
  with 'JAGUAR'(1996) and 'THE DINNER GAME' (1998)
  DRG USA (Pinn): DRGCD 9522 (CD)

CLOTHES SHOW The (BBC1 1987-1997) theme "In The Night" by PET SHOP BOYS (re-mix version *unavailable*) orig 'Disco' *EMI: CDP 746 450-2 (CD) TC-PRG 1001 (MC)*

CLUELESS (1995) Music sco: DAVID KITAY -S/T- V.Arts *CAPITOL (EMI): CDEST 2267 (CD)*

COAL MINER'S DAUGHTER (1980) biopic of LORETTA LYNN -S/T- *MCA (IMS-UNIVERSAL): AA88 170 122-2 (CD)*

COASTAL COMMAND (1942) Music score: VAUGHAN WILLIAMS on 'Film Music' RTE CONCERT ORCH (Andrew Penny) on *MARCO POLO (Sel):8.223665 (CD) see COLL.49,120,*

COCKTAIL (1988) Music score: J.PETER ROBINSON -S/T- on *ELEKTRA (TEN): 960806-2 (CD)*

COCOON (1985) Music: JAMES HORNER inc Michael Sembello *IMP (S.Screen): PNDL 13 (CD) see COLL.148,232,*

COCOON 2 'The Return' (1989) Music score: JAMES HORNER -S/T- *VARESE Pinn: VSD 5211 (CD) see COLL.149,*

COLBY'S The (USA TV) *see COLL.247,*

COLD FEET (ITV 15/11/1998) music score by MARK RUSSELL theme "Female Of The Species" re-mix: SPACE -S/T- *GLOBAL TV (BMG): 74321 72607-2 (2CDs) -4(2MC)* 'MORE COLD FEET' (VARIOUS ARTISTS) available on *GLOBAL TV (BMG): 74321 78961-2 (CD) -4 (MC)* *orig* SPACE track from 'SPIDERS' *GUT (BMG): GUTCD 1* 'COLD FEET' theme by MARK RUSSELL & 'Female.'theme on *COLL.260,* 'TV 2000' *SONY: SONYTV82CD (CD)* 'COLD FEET' (V.Arts comp) *UNIV MUS: 585 913-2 (2CD)*

COLD HEAVEN (1992) Music score: STANLEY MYERS Suite on *INTRADA (S.Screen): MAF 7048D (CD) also includes* Suite from film 'TRUSTING BEATRICE' (S.MYERS)

COLD LAZARUS (BBC1 5/96) Music sc: CHRISTOPHER GUNNING -S/T- includes music from 'KARAOKE' feat tracks by BING CROSBY-HANK WILLIAMS-CRAIG DOUGLAS etc. *SILVA SCREEN (Koch): FILM(CD)(C) 181 (CD/MC)*

COLD ROOM The (1994) Music score: MICHAEL NYMAN -S/T- *SILVA SCREEN (Koch): FILMCD 157 (CD)*

COLDITZ (BBC1 19/10/72) "Colditz March" ROBERT FARNON *see COLL.123,200,*

COLOR OF MONEY The (1986) Mus: ROBBIE ROBERTSON +songs -S/T- *MCA USA: MCAD 6189 (CD)*

COLOR PURPLE The (1986) Music sco: QUINCY JONES +Songs Tata Vega -S/T- *QWEST Imp (S.Scr): 925389-2 (2CDs)*

COLT 45 (USA TV) *see COLL.245,*

COLUMBO (USA) - *see COLL.124,*

COMA (1978) Music score by JERRY GOLDSMITH -S/T- inc: music from 'LOGAN'S RUN' on *CHAPTER III (USA IMPT): CHA 0136 (CD)*

COMANCHEROS The (1961) Music score by ELMER BERNSTEIN *FSM CLASSICS (USA Ltd Ed.): FSMCD Vol 2.No.6 (CD)* *see COLL.40,*

COMEBACK (1982) Music by ERIC BURDON & His BAND -S/T- *BURNING AIRLINES (UNIV): PILOT 081 (2CD)*

COMEDY PLAYHOUSE (BBC1 1960s) theme "Happy Joe" by RON GRAINER *see COLL.6,24,253,*

COMMITMENTS The (1991) -S/T- (Various Atists covers)
  MCAD 10286 (CD) MCAC 10286 (MC)
  COMMITMENTS 2   *MCA (UNI): MCLD 19312 (CD)*
COMMITTED (1999)
  -S/T- *GOLD CIRCLE (Prop): GC 0200 (CD)*
COMPANY - songs: Stephen Sondheim
  1.ORIG LONDON CAST 1995/6   ADRIAN LESTER-SHEILA GISH
    SOPHIE THOMPSON-CLIVE ROWE-PAUL BENTLEY and Comp.
    FIRST NIGHT (Pinn): CASTCD 57 (CD) CASTC 57 (MC)
  2.ORIG BROADWAY CAST 1995
    EMI PREM.West End (EMI): PRMFCD 2 (CD) DELETED
  3.ORIG LONDON CAST 1972 *w* ELAINE STRICH-BETH HOWLAND
    GEORGE COE-SUSAN BROWNING-LARRY KERT and Company
    Sony Broadway: SMK 53496 (CD)
  4.ORIGINAL BROADWAY CAST 1970 *with* ELAINE STRITCH-
    DEAN JONES-BARBARA BARRIE-DONNA McKECHNIE & Comp.
  5.COMPANY IN JAZZ by The TROTTER TRIO
    VARESE (Pinn): VSD 5673 (CD)
COMPANY OF WOLVES The (1984) Music by GEORGE FENTON
  -S/T- reissue *JAY-TER (SSD): CDJAY 1338 (CD)*
CON AIR (1997) Music sco: MARK MANCINA & TREVOR RABIN
  -S/T- (import only) *POLY: E.162 099-2 (CD)*
CONAN THE ADVENTURER (TV) music score: CHARLES FOX
  -S/T- *SONIC IMAGE (Cargo): 78282 78801-2 (CD)*
CONAN THE BARBARIAN (1981) Music sco: BASIL POLEDOURIS
  -S/T- *MILAN (BMG): 111 262 (CD)*
  see *COLL.62,217,266,*
CONAN THE DESTROYER (1983) Music sco: BASIL POLEDOURIS
  VARESE (S.Screen): VSD 5392 (CD) see *COLL.217,*
CONFIDENTIALLY YOURS (1983 'Vivement Dimanche') Music
  GEORGES DELERUE on *Coll* 'TRUFFAUT & DELERUE ON
  THE SCREEN' *DRG (Pinn): 32902 (CD)*
CONFORMIST The (1970) Music sco: GEORGES DELERUE -S/T-
  + -S/T- score from 'TRAGEDY OF A RIDICULOUS MAN'
  DRG (Pinn): DRGCD 32910 (CD)
CONNECTION The (1961) Mus: FREDDIE REDD-JACKIE McLEAN
  -S/T- re-iss *BOPLICITY (Complete): CDBOP 019 (CD)*
CONRACK (1974) Music sco: JOHN WILLIAMS main theme on
  Collection 'POSEIDON ADVENTURE' *(limited edit.)* on
  RETROGRADE (S.Screen/MFTM): FSMCD Vol.1 No.2 (CD)
CONSPIRACY THEORY The (1997) Music sco: CARTER BURWELL
  -S/T- (score) - *SNAPPER (Pinn): SMMCD 612 (CD)*
  -S/T- (songs, V.Art) *TVT (Pinn): TVT 81302 (CD)*
CONTACT (USA MUSICAL 1999) ORIGINAL CAST RECORDING on
  BMG IMPORTS: 09026 63764-2 (CD)
CONTACT (1997) Music score: ALAN SILVESTRI -S/T- V.Art
  WB (TEN): 9362 46811-2 (CD) -4 *(MC)*
CONTAMINATION (1981) Music score by GOBLIN -S/T- *Imp*
  CINEVOX (Prime): CDMDF 340CD (CD)
CONTENDER The (2000) Music score by LARRY GROUPE -S/T-
  including music from 'DETERRENCE' (Larry Groupe) on
  CITADEL USA IMP: STC 77132 (CD)
CONTRACT ON CHERRY STREET (1977 TVM) Music score by
  JERRY GOLDSMITH -S/T- *PROMETHEUS Imp: PCR 503 (CD)*

COOK THE THIEF HIS WIFE AND HER LOVER The (1989) Music
MICHAEL NYMAN -S/T- *VIRGIN (EMI): (CD)(TC)VE 53*

COOKIE'S FORTUNE (1998) Music score: DAVE STEWART
"Cookie's Blues" by DAVE STEWART with CANDY DULFER
-S/T- *ARISTA (BMG): 74321 66110-2 (CD)*

COOL HAND LUKE (1967) Music score: LALO SCHIFRIN -S/T-
ALEPH (Koch): ALEP 022 (CD)

COOL RUNNINGS (1993) Music score: HANS ZIMMER songs by:
WAILING SOULS-JIMMY CLIFF-DIANA KING-TIGER etc.
-S/T- reissue: *COLUMBIA (Ten): 474 840-2 (CD)*

COOL WORLD (1992) Music score: MARK ISHAM -S/T- score
VARESE (Pinn): VSD 5382 (CD)

COOLEY HIGH (1975) Music sc: FREDDIE PERREN -S/T- *feat*
SMOKEY ROBINSON & MIRACLES-TEMPTATIONS-MARY WELLS-
SUPREMES etc. *SPECTRUM (Univ): 551 547-2 (CD)* also
IMS-UNIV: AA.12157676-2 (CD)

COP LAND (1997) Music score: HOWARD SHORE -S/T-
RCA-MILAN (BMG): 74321 53128-2 (CD)

COPACABANA (O.LONDON CAST 1994) Songs: BARRY MANILOW
f: GARY WILMOT *FIRST NIGHT (Pinn): OCRCD 6047(CD)*

COPYCAT (1996) Music score: CHRISTOPHER YOUNG -S/T-
MILAN (BMG): 74321 33742-2 (CD)

CORN IS GREEN The (1978) Music score by JOHN BARRY
NEW VERSION inc 'THEY MIGHT BE GIANTS'/'WALKABOUT'
and others *SILVA SCREEN (Koch): FILMCD 339 (CD)*

CORNBREAD EARL AND ME -S/T- *feat:* The BLACKBYRDS on
BGP/ACE (Pinn): CDBGPM 094 (CD) BGPD 1094 (LP)

CORONATION STREET (Granada 09/12/1960-2002) original
theme music by ERIC SPEAR / 40TH ANNIVERSARY ALBUM
orig theme + 41 NO.1's from the last 4 decades
BMG TV: 74321 81197-2 (2CD) -4 (2MC) see COLL.253,

CORRUPTOR The (1998) Music score by CARTER BURWELL
-S/T- score *VARESE (Pinn): VSD 6014 (CD)*
-S/T- songs *JIVE (Pinn): 052 311-2 (CD)*

COSBY SHOW The (USA C4 20/1/85) series theme mus by:
STU GARDNER-BILL COSBY *see COLL.14,248,*

COTTON CLUB The (1985) Music score: JOHN BARRY -S/T-
reissue: *GEFFEN-MCA (UNI): GED 24062 (CD)*
see COLL.26,32,61,

COTTON MARY (1999) Music score by RICHARD ROBBINS
-S/T- *RCA (BMG): 74321 71345-2 (CD)*

COUNT DRACULA (1970) Music sco: BRUNO NICOLAI -S/T-
PAN Imprt (Silva Screen): PAN 2502 (CD)

COUNT OF LUXEMBOURG The (OPERETTA) Music: FRANZ LEHAR
English lyr:ERIC MASCHWITZ *New Sadlers Wells Cast*
English Highlights *TER (Koch): CDTER 1050 (CD)*

COUNTDOWN (C4 from 2/11/1982-2001) theme & incidental
music by ALAN HAWSHAW *unavailable*

COUNTESS MARITZA (OPERETTA) Mus: EMERICH KALLMANN Engl
ish lyr: NIGEL DOUGLAS *New Sadlers Wells Cast*
English Highlights *TER (Koch): CDTER 1051 (CD)*

COUNTRY HOUSE (BBC2 04/08/2000) theme music by HOWARD
GOODALL *unavailable*

COUNTRY PRACTICE (Australian TV) *see COLL.172,*

COUNTRYMAN (1982) Reggae music -S/T- *feat:* BOB MARLEY & WAILERS-ASWAD-TOOTS & MAYTALS-LEE SCRATCH PERRY -S/T- *Reggae Refresh-ISLAND (UNIV): RRCD 60 (CD)*

COUPLING (BBC2 12/05/2000) theme song "Perhaps Perhaps Perhaps" sung by MARI WILSON *unavailable.* VERSION by DORIS DAY on *SONYTV 67CD* and *494 464-2 (CD)*

COURIER The (88) Music score: DECLAN McMANUS (ELVIS COSTELLO) -S/T- *VIRGIN (EMI):CDV 2517 (CD)*

COURT JESTER The (1955) Songs (Sylvia Fine-Sammy Cahn) with DANNY KAYE -S/T- also incl.songs from 'HANS CHRISTIAN ANDERSEN' *VARESE (Pinn): VSD 5498 (CD)*

COUSIN BETTE (1998) Music score: SIMON BOSWELL -S/T- *RCA VICTOR (BMG): 09026 63168-2 CD)*

COVER GIRL (1944) Songs: JEROME KERN-IRA GERSHWIN -S/T- selection with 'GOOD NEWS' on *GREAT MOVIE THEMES (BMG): CD 60035 (CD)*

COWBOYS The (1971) Music score: JOHN WILLIAMS -S/T- *VARESE (Pinn): VSD 5540 (CD)*

COX AND BOX (OPERETTA by GILBERT and SULLIVAN) LEON BERGER (bar) IAN KENNEDY (ten) DONALD FRANCKE (bass) KENNETH BARCLAY (piano) *COMPLETE OPERETTA DIVINE ART (Celtic Music): 2.4104 (CD, 1998)*

COYOTE UGLY (2000) -S/T- LEANN RIMES-DON HENLY-INXS-EMF SNAP-CHARLIE DANIELS BAND-RARE BLEND-TAMARA WALKER -S/T- *CURB LONDON (TEN): 8573 85254-2 (CD)*

CRACKER: To Be A Somebody (ITV 10/10/1994) score music by DAVID FERGUSON *see COLL.104,*

CRADLE WILL ROCK The (0.1985 USA CAST) Music by DAVID ROBBINS-MARK BLITZSTEIN *feat* JOHN HOUSEMAN & PATTI LuPONE *JAY-TER (SSD): CDJAY2 1300 (2CD)* -S/T- (1999) *RCA (BMG) 09026 63577-2 (CD)*

CRAFT The (1995) Music sc: GRAEME REVELL 2 soundtracks music score -S/T- *VARESE (Pinn): VSD 5732 (CD)* songs V.Art -S/T- *SONY: 484 152-2 (CD) -4 (MC)*

CRAZY FOR YOU - songs by George and Ira Gershwin
   1.ORIG LONDON CAST 1993 *w* RUTHIE HENSHALL-KIRBY WARD *FIRST NIGHT (Pinn): OCRCD 6055 (CD)*
   2.ORIG BROADWAY CAST 1992 *EMI: CDC 754618-2 (CD)*

CRAZY IN ALABAMA (1999) Music score by MARK SNOW -S/T- *SILVA SCREEN (Koch): FILMCD 322 (CD)*

CRAZY BEAUTIFUL (2001) Music score by PAUL HASLINGER -S/T- (V.ARTS) *HOLLYWOOD (Vital) 013 096-2HWR (CD)*

CREATURE (Peter Benchley's) (1997) Music score by JOHN VAN TONGEREN -S/T- *INTRADA (USA): MAF 7081 (CD)*

CREATURE FROM THE BLACK LAGOON (54) Mus: Hans J.Salter +mus.from 'HITLER' (61) 'BLACK SHIELD OF FALWORTH' (54) 'INCREDIBLE SHRINKING MAN'(57)(Hans J.Salter) *INTRADA (Koch): MAF 7054CD (CD) see COLL.220,249,*

CREATURES THE WORLD FORGOT - *see COLL.249,*

CREW The (2000) Music score by STEVE BARTEK -S/T- with VARIOUS ARTISTS on *MILAN USA (BMG) (- CD)*

CRICKET (1) TEST CRICKET (C4 22/07/1999) "Mambo No.5" (P.Prado) LOU BEGA *RCA: 74321 69672-2 (CDs) -4 (MC)* 'A LITTLE BIT OF MAMBO' *RCA: 74321 68861-2 (CD)*

CRICKET (2) *(see also* **WORLD CUP)** BBC theme music
'SOUL LIMBO' by BOOKER T.& MGs *see COLL.3,101,122,*
CRIME AND PUNISHMENT IN SUBURBIA (2000) Music score by
MICHAEL BROOK -S/T- *BMG IMP: 74321 78827-2 (CD)*
CRIME STORY (USA 1989) Theme "Runaway" (Del Shannon-
Max Crook) 'DEL SHANNON-COMPLETE CAREER ANTHOLOGY
1961-1990 *RAVEN (Australian Imp): RVCD 51 (2CD)*
CRIMES OF PASSION (1984) Music score by RICK WAKEMAN
-S/T- *PRESIDENT (BMG): RWCD 3 (CD)*
CRIMETIME (1996) Music: DAVID A.STEWART -S/T- inc V/A
POLLYANNA Prod (Pinn): POLLYPREM 002 (CD)
CRIMEWATCH UK (BBC1 7/6/1984-2001) theme mus "Rescue
Helicopter" (Emergency) JOHN CAMERON *see COLL.5,*
CRIMSON PIRATE (1952) *see COLL.120,240,*
CROCODILE DUNDEE (1986) Music score: PETER BEST -S/T-
SILVA SCREEN (Koch): FILMCD 009 (CD)
CROCODILE DUNDEE IN L.A. (2001) Music: BASIL POLEDOURIS
-S/T- *SILVA SCREEN (Koch): FILMCD 350 (CD)*
CROCODILE SHOES (BBC1 10/11/94) music: TONY McANANEY
"Crocodile Shoes" sung by JIMMY NAIL -S/T- on
EAST WEST (TEN): 4509 98556-2 (CD) -4 (MC) title
CROCODILE SHOES 2 (BBC1 14/11/96) *featur* JIMMY NAIL
-S/T- *EAST WEST (TEN): 0630 16935-2 (CD) -4 (MC)*
CROSSING DELANCEY (1988) Music sc: PAUL CHIHARA -S/T-
VARESE (Pinn) VSD 5201 (CD)
CROSSROADS (ITV revived 05/03/2001) theme TONY HATCH
unavailable TV version arrangement
CROSSROADS (Central 2/11/64 - 4/4/88 | 4510 episodes)
Orig theme 'Crossroads' TONY HATCH 1964-1987 *also*
PAUL McCARTNEY & WINGS on 'VENUS and MARS'*(EMI)*
see COLL.2,24,74,131,200,253,
CROUCHING TIGER HIDDEN DRAGON (2000) Music by YO-YO MA
and TAN DUN -S/T- *SONY CLASSICS: SK 89347 (CD)*
CROW The (1993) Music score: GRAEME REVELL + Var.Arts
-S/T- (score) *VARESE (Pinn): VSD 5499 (CD)*
-S/T- (songs) *WB (TEN): 7567 82519-2(CD) 4(MC)*
CROW The (2): CITY OF ANGELS (1996) Music sco: GRAEME
REVELL -S/T- *HOLLYWOOD-POLY (Univ): 533 147-2 (CD)*
CROW The (3): SALVATION (2000) Music score by MARCO
BELTRAMI -S/T- *KOCH INT: 33370-2 (CD)*
CROWD The (1928 silent) Contemporary score by CARL
DAVIS *see COLL.85,* 'The SILENTS'
CROWN COURT (Granada 1972) closing theme mus "Distant
Hills" SIMON PARK ORCHESTRA *see COLL.250,*
CROWN GREEN BOWLS *see COLL.122,*
CRUEL INTENTIONS (1998) Music score: EDWARD SHEARMUR
-S/T- score *VARESE (Pinn): VSD 6200 (CD)*
-S/T- songs (V.Arts) *VIRGIN (EMI): CDVUS 158 (CD)*
CRUEL SEA The (1953) *see COLL.161,208,*
CRUISE The (BBC1 12/1/98) title mus: JOHN HARLE sung
by BBC CONCERT ORCHESTRA & BBC SINGERS.JOHN HARLE
album 'SILENCIUM' *ARGO (Univ): 458 356-3 (CD)*
JANE McDONALD album "Jane McDonald" on *FOCUS-GUT*
(Vital) FMCD 001 (CD) FMMC 001 (MC)

CRUMB (BBC2 26/12/96) Music: DAVID BOEDDINGHAUS-CRAIG
  VENTRESCO -S/T- *RYKODISC (Vital): RCD 10322 (CD)*
CRUSADE (USA 1998) Music score by EVAN CHEN -S/T- on
  SONIC IMAGES (Greyhound): 7828 278910-2 (CD)
CRY FREEDOM (1987) Music: GEORGE FENTON-JONAS GWANGWA
  -S/T- *MCA (USA Import): MCAD 6224 (CD)*
CRY THE BELOVED COUNTRY (1995) JOHN BARRY *see COLL.26,*
CRYING GAME The (1992) Music score: ANNE DUDLEY -S/T-
  feat Var.Arts *reissue: POLYDOR: 517024-2 (CD)*
CURSE OF THE CAT PEOPLE (1944) Music score: ROY WEBB
  CLOUD NINE IMPORT: CNS 5008 (CD) see COLL.84,
CURSE OF THE MUMMY'S TOMB (1964) Music: CARLO MARTELLI
  -S/T- *GDI (ABM/UNIVERSAL): GDI 016 (CD)*
CUTTHROAT ISLAND (1995) Mus sco: JOHN DEBNEY with LSO
  SILVA SCR (Koch): FILMCD 178 (CD) see COLL.240,
CYRANO DE BERGERAC (1950) Music score: DIMITRI TIOMKIN
  on Coll 'HIGH NOON' *RCA (BMG): 09026 62658-2 (CD)*
CYRANO DE BERGERAC (1990) Music sco: JEAN-CLAUDE PETIT
  -S/T- *COLOSSEUM (Pinn): CST 348046 (CD)*
  see also 'JEAN DE FLORETTE' and see COLL 60,
D AD (BBC1 25/9/97) theme "Tijuana Taxi" HERB ALPERT &
  HIS TIJUANA BRASS 'The Very Best Of HERB ALPERT'
  A.& M.(Univ): CDMID 170 (CD) CMID 170 (MC)
  theme2 "Go Daddy Go" arr.by JULIAN STEWART LINDSAY
DAD'S ARMY (BBC1 31/07/1968-1977) series theme song
  "Who Do Think You Are Kidding Mr.Hitler"
  (Jimmy Perry-Derek Taverner) sung by BUD FLANAGAN
  see COLL.2,24,74,
DADDY LONG LEGS *see COLL.1,*
DAKTARI (USA TV) *see COLL.243,*
DALES DIARY The (YTV only) theme music "Overture" from
  'The Wasps' (VAUGHAN WILLIAMS) complete version on
  EMI CLASSICS: CDM 565 130-2 (CD)
DALLAS (USA 1980/BBC1 1978-6/10/1991) theme music:
  JERROLD IMMEL *see COLL.42,117,244,*
DALZIEL AND PASCOE (BBC1 16/3/96-2001) orig music by
  BARRINGTON PHELOUNG *unavailable*
DAMAGE (1993) Music score: ZBIGNIEW PREISNER -S/T-
  VARESE (Pinn): VSD 5406 (CD)
DAMES (1934) *SOUNDTRACK FACTORY (Discov): SFCD 33517*
  (CD) / COLLECTION with 'SAN FRANCISCO'/'SUZY' on
  GREAT MOVIE THEMES (Targ-BMG): CD 60022 (CD)
DAMES AT SEA - songs by Jim Wise with George Haimsohn
  and Robin Miller. ORIG UK TOURING CAST 1989 *with*
  BRIAN CANT-SANDRA DICKINSON-JOSEPHINE BLAKE etc.
  TER (Koch): CDTER 1169 (CD)
DAMBUSTERS The (1955) Music: ERIC COATES *see COLL.120,*
DANCE A LITTLE CLOSER (Musical) Music: CHARLES STROUSE
  Lyrics: ALAN JAY LERNER *Original Broadway Cast* on
  TER (Koch): CDTER 1174 (CD)
DANCE WITH ME (1998) Music score: MICHAEL CONVERTINO
  V.ARTS -S/T- *EPIC (Ten): 491 125-2 (CD) -4 (MC)*
DANCER IN THE DARK (2000) Music: BJORK 'SELMER SONGS'
  ONE LITTLE INDIAN Pinn: TPLP 151CD (CD) 151LP (LP)

DANCES WITH WOLVES (1990) Music sco: JOHN BARRY -S/T-
  EPIC (TEN): 467 591-2(CD) -4(MC) ZK 66817 (CDspec)
  see COLL.26,30,32,36,37,73,146,182,204,277,279,
DANCING AT LUGHNASA (1998) Music score: BILL WHELAN
  -S/T- *SONY CLASSICS: SK 60585 (CD)*
DANGER MAN (ITV 11/9/1960-68) Theme mus "High Wire" by
  EDWIN ASTLEY -S/T-*RAZOR & TIE (Koch): RE 21512(CD)*
  see COLL.2,5,24,74,250,251,
DANGERFIELD (2) BBC1 1998/1999 ser) theme & incidental
  music by RAY RUSSELL *unavailable*
DANGERFIELD (1) (BBC1 1995-1998 ser)theme & incidental
  music by NIGEL HESS *see COLL.4,137,172,*
DANGEROUS GROUND (1997) Music sc: STANLEY CLARKE -S/T-
  CHIPS-ZOMBA (Pinn): CHIP 181 (CD) HIP 181 (2LP)
DANGEROUS LIAISONS (1988) Music Score: GEORGE FENTON
  -S/T- *VIRGIN EMI:CDV 2583 (CD) see COLL.64,97,197,*
DANGEROUS MOONLIGHT (1941) Theme 'Warsaw Concerto' by
  RICHARD ADDINSELL *see COLL.9,49,235,267,269,*
DANIEL BOONE (USA) *see COLL.242,*
DANTE'S PEAK (1997) Music score: JOHN FRIZZELL with
  main theme composed by JAMES NEWTON HOWARD -S/T-
  VARESE (Pinn): VSD 5793 (CD)
DANZON (1992) Music sco: DANZONERA DIMAS-FELIPE PEREZ
  -S/T- *DRG (Pinn): CDSBL 12605 (CD)*
DARK ADAPTED EYE, A (BBC1 02/01/1994) Music score by
  DAVID FERGUSON *see COLL.104,*
DARK AT THE TOP OF THE STAIRS (1960) *see COLL.239,*
DARK CITY (1997) Music score: TREVOR JONES -S/T- on
  SNAPPER (Pinn): SMMCD 615 (CD)
DARK CITY (1950) *see COLL.219,273,*
DARK EYES (1987) Music score: FRANCIS LAI -S/T- on
  DRG (Pinn): CDSBL 12592 (CD)
DARK HALF The (1992) Music sc: CHRISTOPHER YOUNG -S/T-
  VARESE (Pinn): VSD 5340 (CD)
DARK OF THE SUN (1967) Music score by JACQUES LOUSSIER
  -S/T- inc 'GUNS FOR SAN SEBASTIAN' (E.MORRICONE)
  CHAPTER III (USA): CHA 0134 (CD)
DARK SHADOWS (USA Soap 1966-70) "Quentin's Theme" by
  Charles Randolph Green / ROBERT COBERT ORCHESTRA
  -S/T-*VARESE: VSD 5702 (CD) see COLL.219,243,*
DARK STAR (1974) Music score: JOHN CARPENTER -S/T-
  VARESE (Pinn): VSD 5327 (CD) see COLL.57,
DARLING BUDS OF MAY The (YTV 07/04/1991) theme music
  PIP BURLEY sco: BARRIE GUARD + ENGLISH LIGHT ORCH
  -S/T- *SOUNDTRACKS EMI: 520 685-2 (CD) see COLL.42,*
DARLING LILI (1970) Music score by HENRY MANCINI
  -S/T- *RCA EUROPE (Discovery): 74321 66500-2 (CD)*
DARTS (BBC1/2 All Competitions) Theme mus "Cranes" by
  by DOUGLAS WOOD GROUP *see COLL.122,*
DAS BOOT (W.Germany) *see* 'BOAT The' *see COLL.265,*
DASTARDLY AND MUTTLEY *see COLL.244,259,*
DATELINE LONDON theme "Cutty Sark" *see COLL.27,29,*
DAVE ALLEN (Carlton/Noel Gay 7/1/93) theme "Blarney's
  Stoned" ALAN HAWKSHAW *see COLL.231,*

DAVID COPPERFIELD (1970) Music score by MALCOLM ARNOLD
   new score recording by MOSCOW SYMPHONY ORCHESTRA
   (W.Stromberg, cond) *inc* 'ROOTS OF HEAVEN' score on
   MARCO POLO (Select): 8225167 (CD)
DAVY CROCKETT (1955) Theme s "Ballad Of Davy Crockett"
   FESS PARKER on 'Americana' *BEAR FAMILY: BCD 15625*
DAWN OF THE DEAD (Film) - *see under* ZOMBIES

DAWSON'S CREEK (USA) (C4 2/5/1998) theme mus "I Don't
   Want To Wait" composed & performed by Paula Cole.
   'Songs from Dawson's Creek' *feat* PAULA COLE-CURTIS
   STEIGERS-SEAN MULLINS-SIXPENCE NONE THE RICHER etc
   COLUMBIA (Ten): 494 369-2 (CD) -4 (MC)
   'Dawsons Creek 2' *SONY (TEN):500 924-2 (CD) -4(MC)*
   "Kiss Me" SIXPENCE..+theme on 'TV 2000' *SONYTV82CD*
DAY AT THE RACES, A (1937) feat The MARX BROTHERS
   DEFINITIVE (Discovery): SFCD 33503 (CD)
DAY THE EARTH STOOD STILL The (1951) Music sc: BERNARD
   HERRMANN *DECCA (Univ): 443 899-2 (CD) also incl*
   JOURNEY TO THE CENTRE OF THE EARTH-SEVENTH VOYAGE
   OF SINBAD-FAHRENHEIT 451-THREE WORLDS OF GULLIVER
   also avail: Symphonic Suite (Nat.PO-Fred Steiner)
   with 'The Kentuckian' *PREAMBLE (USA Imp) PRCD 1777*
DAY THE FISH CAME OUT (1967) Music: MIKIS THEODORAKIS
   -S/T- *SAKKARIS (Pinn): SR 50088 (CD)*
DAYS OF HOPE (Musical 91) Songs: HOWARD GOODALL Orig.
   London Cast *TER (Koch): CDTER 1183 (CD)*
DAYS OF WINE AND ROSES The (1962) *see COLL.170,*
DAZED AND CONFUSED (1994) ALICE COOPER-DEEP PURPLE-
   KISS-ZZ TOP -S/T- *GIANT (BMG): 74321 16675-2 (CD)*
DEAD MAN (1995) Music score: NEIL YOUNG
   -S/T- *WB (TEN): 9362 46171-2 (CD)*
DEAD MAN ON CAMPUS (1998) Music sco: MARK MOTHERSBAUGH
   -S/T- *DREAMWORKS: DRMD 5003-2 (CD)*
DEAD MAN WALKING (1995) Music score by DAVID ROBBINS
   -S/T- (songs) *COLUMBIA (Ten): 483 534-2(CD) -4(MC)*
DEAD POETS SOCIETY (1989) Music score: MAURICE JARRE
   -S/T- *MILAN (BMG): CDCH 558 (CD)* inc:'THE YEAR OF
   LIVING DANGEROUSLY' (M.Jarre)
DEAD PRESIDENTS (1995) Music score by DANNY ELFMAN
   -S/T- (score) *CAPITOL (EMI): 7248 35818-2 (CD)*
   -S/T- (songs 1) *EMI PREM: PRDCD 4 (CD)*
   -S/T- (songs 2) *EMI PREM: PRMDCD 5 (CD)* *DELETED*
DEADFALL (1968) Music sco: JOHN BARRY / song "My Love
   Has Two Faces" (John Barry-Jack Lawrence) sung by
   SHIRLEY BASSEY. solo guitar: RENATA TARRAGO -S/T-
   RETROGRADE IMPORT: FSM 80124-2 (CD) *see COLL.26,*
DEATH AND THE MAIDEN (1994) Music sco: WOJCIECH KILAR
   -S/T- on *ERATO (BMG): 4509 99727-2 (CD)*
DEATH IN VENICE (1971) Music: GUSTAV MAHLER (Symphony
   numbers 3 & 5) -S/T- *SONY Fra (Discov): SK 70097
   (CD) ST 70097 (MC) NAXOS: 8551151 (CD)*
DEATH LINE (1972) Music: WIL MALONE-JEREMY ROSE -S/T-
   SPINNEY (SRD): SPINNEY 002CD (CD) SPINNEY 002 (LP)

DEATH OF A SCOUNDREL (1956) *see under* 'KING KONG' 1933
DEATH WISH (1974) Music score: HERBIE HANCOCK
  -S/T- *reissue SONY JAZZ: 491 981-2 (CD)*
DEEP BLUE SEA (1999) Music score by TREVOR RABIN
  Songs: *WARNER (TEN): 9362 47485-2 (CD) -4 (MC)*
  Score: *VARESE (Pinn): VSD 6063 (CD)*
DEEP END OF THE OCEAN (1999) Music sc: ELMER BERNSTEIN
  -S/T- *RCA BMG SOUNDTRACKS: 74321 66520-2 (CD)*
DEEP IMPACT (1997) Music score: JAMES HORNER -S/T- on
  SONY Classics: SK 60690 (CD) ST 60690 (MC)
DEEP RED (Profondo Rosso) *DRGCD (Pinn): 32903 (CD)*
DEEP RISING (1998) Music score: JERRY GOLDSMITH -S/T-
  EDEL-HOLLYWOOD (Vital) 012120-2HWR
DEEP The (1977) Music by JOHN BARRY *see COLL.26,*
DEEP THROAT (1973) Music by JULIUS WECHTER'S MARIMBA
  BAND -S/T- IMP *BONK (SRD): XXX1CD (CD) XXX1LP (LP)*
DEERHUNTER The (1978) Music sco: STANLEY MYERS -S/T-
  CAPITOL (S.Screen) 92058-2(CD) -4(MC) 'Cavatina'
  perf.by John WILLIAMS *see COLL.61,123,188,204,*
DEFENCE OF THE REALM (BBC1 8/8/96) theme m. "School Of
  Mysteries" JOHN HARLE on 'SILENCIUM' *see COLL.130,*
DEKALOG (Ten Commandments)(1988) Mus:ZBIGNIEW PREISNER
  -S/T- with KATOWICE SYMPH.ORCH.*SILVA SCREEN (Koch)*
  SILKD 6029 (CD) & AMPLITUDE (Discov): AMP 709 (CD)
DELIA'S HOW TO COOK (BBC2 13/10/1998) music: GUY DAGUL
  original theme by FATHER JAMES WALSH *unavailable*
DELIVERANCE (1972) M: ERIC WEISSBERG "Duelling Banjos"
  feat STEVE MANDELL -S/T-*WB (TEN):9362 48088-2 (CD)*
DELUSION (1991) Music sco: BARRY ADAMSON *MUTE:*
  IONIC 4 (LP) IONIC 4C (MC) IONIC 4CD (CD)
DEMOLITION MAN (1993) Music s: ELLIOT GOLDENTHAL
  -S/T- *VARESE (Pinn): VSD 5447 (CD)*
DEMPSEY & MAKEPEACE (LWT 11/1/85) ser.theme music by
  ALAN PARKER *see COLL.4,250,*
DENNIS THE MENACE (USA TV) *see COLL.242,*
DEPARTMENT S (ITC 9/3/1969) theme music: EDWIN ASTLEY
  see COLL.2,24,74,250,
DEPUTY The - *see COLL.24,157,*
DERSU UZALA (1975) Music score by ISAAC SCHWARTZ
  KBS S.O.(Jordania) *KOCH CLASSICS: 37273-2 (CD)*
DESERT ISLAND DISCS (BBC) theme "By The Sleepy Lagoon"
  by ERIC COATES. compilation "CASTAWAY'S CHOICE' on
  BBC AUDIO INT. (Pinn): WMEF 00267 (2CDs)
DESERT SONG - songs by Sigmund Romberg - Oscar Hammer
  stein II and Otto Harbach
  1. ORIG LONDON CAST 1927 *w* EDITH DAY-PHEBE BRUNE-GENE
    GERRARD-CLARICE HARDWICKE-DENNIS HOEY-BARRY MACKAY
    plus music from 'NEW MOON (1929) 'BLUE TRAIN' (27)
    PEARL (Pavilion): GEMMCD 9100(CD)
  2. STUDIO RECORDING *w:* GORDON MacRAE-DOROTHY KIRSTEN
    + music from 'New Moon' and 'The Student Prince'
    HMV (EMI): CDM 769 052-2 (CD)
  3. STUDIO RECORDING *with:* MARIO LANZA *also music from*
    The STUDENT PRINCE RCA (BMG) GD(GK)60048 (CD/MC)

DESPERATELY SEEKING SUSAN (1985) Score: THOMAS NEWMAN
+'Making Mr.Right' *VARESE (Pinn): VCD 47291 (CD)*
DESTRY RIDES AGAIN (O.LONDON CAST 1979) Songs: HAROLD
ROME *featuring* JILL GASCOINE and Co. / Recording
TER (Koch): CDTER 1034
DETECTIVE The (BBC 1968) Mus: RON GRAINER *see COLL.6,*
DETROIT ROCK CITY (1999) Music score by
VAR.ARTISTS -S/T- *MERCURY (Univ): 546 389-2 (CD)*
DEUCE BIGALOW MALE GIGOLO (2000) Music score by TEDDY
CASTELUCCI -S/T- incl: BLONDIE-ERIC BURDON-MARVIN
GAYE-HOT CHOCOLATE-KC & SUNSHINE BAND-1OCC etc.
EDEL-HOLLYWOOD (Vital) 012 252-2HWR (CD)
DEVIL AND DANIEL WEBSTER The (aka 'All That Money Can
Buy) (1941) music score: BERNARD HERRMANN / Suite
UNICORN KANCHANA (Harmonia Mundi): UKCD 2065 (CD)
also on 'CONCERTO MACABRE' *KOCH INT: 37609-2 (CD)*
DEVIL IN MISS JONES The (1972) SOUNDTRACK on
OGLIO (Direct): OGL 81597-2 (CD)
DEVIL RIDES OUT The (1968) Music score: JAMES BERNARD
-S/T- *GDI (RMG-Univ): GDICD 013 (CD)*
see COLL.130,138,150,151,
DEVIL'S ADVOCATE (1997) Music sco: JAMES NEWTON HOWARD
-S/T- *MADFISH-SNAPPER (Pinn): SMMCD 611 (CD)*
DEVIL'S TOOTHPICK The (1992) Doc.Brazilian/USA music:
GILBERTO GIL-BILLY COBHAM-KENIA-LARRY CORYELL etc.
CTI-KUDU (New Note-Pinn): CTI 10122 (CD)
DEVOTION (1943) Music score by ERICH WOLFGANG KORNGOLD
New R: MOSCOW SYMPHONY ORCH (William T.Stromberg)
MARCO POLO (Select): 8.225038 (CD)
DIAL M.FOR MURDER (1954) Music by DIMITRI TIOMKIN
see COLL.141,144,
DIAMONDS (1999) Music score by JOEL GOLDSMITH
-S/T- *VARESE (Pinn): VSD 6107 (CD)*
DIAMONDS (1975) Music score by ROY BUDD -S/T- *reissue*
CASTLE (Pinn): CINCD(LP) 003 (CD/LP) see COLL.54,
DIAMONDS ARE FOREVER (1971) Music score: JOHN BARRY
-S/T- *EMI: CZ 554 see COLL.26,28,29,36,45,46,47,*
222, see also JAMES BOND FILM INDEX p.346
DICK (1999) Music score by JOHN DEBNEY -S/T- on
VIRGIN (EMI): CDVUS 164 (CD)
DICK BARTON (ITV 1978) theme music "Devil's Galop" by
CHARLES WILLIAMS *see COLL.50.100,119,*
DICK POWELL THEATRE (USATV 1961) *see COLL.131,182,253,*
DICK VAN DYKE SHOW (USATV 1962) *see COLL.75,242,,*
DIDIER (1997) Music score: PHILIPPE CHANY
XIII BIZ (Discovery): LBS 1097010-2 (CD)
DIE HARD (1988) Music score by MICHAEL KAMEN -S/T-
VARESE (Pinn): VSD 5208
DIE HARD 2: DIE HARDER (1989) Mus: MICHAEL KAMEN -S/T-
VARESE (Pinn): VSD 5273
DIE HARD 3: WITH A VENGEANCE (1995) Music sco: MICHAEL
KAMEN *w:* V/A -S/T- *RCA (BMG): 09026 68306-2 (CD)*
DIE HALBSTARKEN (WOLFPACK 1956) Music: MARTIN BOTTCHER
-S/T- *BEAR FAMILY (Rollecoaster): BCD 16403 (CD)*

DIFFERENT FOR GIRLS (1998) Music sco: STEPHEN WARBECK
VARIOUS ARTISTS -S/T- *OCEAN DEEP: OCD 010 (CD)*
DIFFERENT STROKES (USA TV) *see COLL.247,*
DIFFERENT WORLD, A (USA series C4 from 22/9/88) theme
music (Stu Gardner-Bill Cosby-Dawnn Lewis) sung by
ARETHA FRANKLIN (USA TV) *see COLL.248,*
DINNER GAME (LE DINER DES CONS 1998) Music score by
VLADIMIR COSMA on Coll with 'CLOSET'(2000) and
'LE JAGUAR' (1996) *DRG USA (Pinn): DRGCD 9522 (CD)*
DINOSAUR (2000) Music score by JAMES NEWTON HOWARD
-S/T- *HOLLYWOOD-DISNEY (Vital): 011 261-2DNY (CD)*
DINOSAURS The (USA TV Ser 93) music by PETER MELNICK
TV -S/T- *NARADA Cinema (Pinn): ND 66004 (CD)*
DIRTY DANCING (1987) Music score: JOHN MORRIS + V.Arts
'MORE DIRTY DANCING' *74321 36915-2 (CD) -4 (MC)*
'LIVE' music *RCA (BMG): PK 90336 (MC)*
'COLLECTORS EDIT' *RCA (BMG): 0786 367786-2 (2CDs)*
DIRTY DINGUS MAGEE (1970) Music score by JEFF ALEXANDER
-S/T- with 'DIRTY DOZEN' (Frank De VOL) on
CHAPTER III (USA): CHA 0132 (CD)
DIRTY DOZEN The (1967) Music score by FRANK DE VOL
-S/T- with 'DIRTY DINGUS MAGEE'(Jeff ALEXANDER) on
CHAPTER III (USA): CHA 0132 (CD)
DIRTY HARRY (ANTHOLOGY) Music scores by LALO SCHIFRIN
*ALEPH (Koch): ALEP 003 (CD) also available on
SIMPLY VINYL (Telstar): SVLP 82 (LP) also WB (TEN)
8573 87357-2 (CD)* + 'SUDDEN IMPACT'/'MAGNUM FORCE'
DISAPPEARANCE OF FINBAR The (1995) Music score by DAVY
SPILLANE -S/T- V.Arts *SNAPPER (Pinn): SMACD 504*
DISCWORLD (TERRY PRATCHETT'S) (C4) 'SOUL MUSIC' album
PLUTO (Direct): TH 030746 (CD)
DISH The (2000) Music score by EDMUND CHOI -S/T- on
VARESE (Pinn): VSD 6226 (CD)
DISORDERLIES (1987) Music: RAY PARKER JNR & others
-S/T- *re-issued on SPECTRUM (Univ): 551 137-2 (CD)*
DISTANT DRUMS (1951) Music score by MAX STEINER plus
-S/T- scores (Steiner) from 'MY GIRL TISA' (1948)
'SOUTH OF ST.LOUIS' (1948) 'CLOAK & DAGGER' (1946)
SCREEN ARCHIVES ENT (USA IMPT.): SAECSR 0001 (2CD)
DIVA (1982) Music score VLADIMIR COSMA / 'La Wally' by
WILHELMENA FERNANDEZ -S/T- *DRG (Pinn): DRGCD 9523*
see COLL.60,122,197,
DIVORCE ME DARLING (1997 LONDON REVIVAL) Songs: SANDY
WILSON) *feat:* RUTHIE HENSHALL-KEVIN COLSON-MARTI
WEBB-TIM FLAVIN-JOAN SAVAGE-LINZI HATELY & Comp.
JAY-TER (SSD): CDJAY 1273 (CD)
DIXON OF DOCK GREEN (BBC1 50s-70s) theme "An Ordinary
Copper" (Jeff Darnell) *deleted*
DO THE RIGHT THING (1989) Music by BILL LEE featuring
WYNTON MARSALIS and others -S/T- *import reissue
UNIVERSAL MUSIC: AA.40014618-2 (CD)*
DOBERMANN (1997) Music: SCHYZOMANIAC; FRANCOIS ROY-
JEAN JACQUES HERTZ-PHILLIPE MALLIER feat BRUNE
-S/T- *ISLAND France: (Discovery): 524 412-2 (CD)*

DOBIE GILLIS (USA TV) *see COLL.242,*
DOC HOLLYWOOD (1991) Music score: CARTER BURWELL -S/T-
  VARESE (Pinn): VSD 5332 (CD)
DOCTOR AT LARGE (ITV 1971) theme "Bond Street Parade"
  by ALAN TEW *see COLL.231,*
DOCTOR AT THE TOP (BBC1 21/2/1991)
  see also 'DOCTOR IN THE HOUSE' *see COLL.2,*
DOCTOR DOLITTLE (FILM 1998) VARIOUS ARTISTS -S/T- on
  ATLANTIC (TEN): 7567 83113-2 (CD) -4(MC) -1(LP)
DOCTOR DOLITTLE 2 (2001) Music score: DAVID NEWMAN
  -S/T- VARIOUS ARTISTS *RCA (BMG): 8081 32005-2 (CD)*
DOCTOR DOLITTLE (O.LONDON CAST 1998) PHILLIP SCHOFIELD
  & Comp. *FIRST NIGHT (Pinn):CAST(C)(CD) 68 (MC/CD)*
DOCTOR DOLITTLE (1967) songs by LESLIE BRICUSSE -S/T-
  feat: REX HARRISON-SAMANTHA EGGAR-ANTHONY NEWLEY
  reissued -S/T- SPECTRUM (Univ): 554 527-2 (CD)
DOCTOR FAUSTUS (1967) Music sc: MARIO NASCIMBENE -S/T-
  + 'FRANCIS OF ASSISI' *DRG (Pinn) DRGCD 32965 (CD)*
DOCTOR FINLAY'S CASEBOOK (BBC1 1962-71) theme music
  "March from 'A Little Suite' No 2 (TREVOR DUNCAN)
  see COLL.4,24,45,74,119,172,
DOCTOR IN THE HOUSE (LWT 70) *see COLL 4,*
DOCTOR JEKYLL AND MS.HYDE (1994) Music: MARK McKENZIE
  -S/T- *INTRADA (Silva Screen Imp): MAF 7063D (CD)*
DOCTOR KILDARE (USA 61) Theme music: JERRY GOLDSMITH
  see COLL.172,245,
DOCTOR NO (1962) Music score: MONTY NORMAN-JOHN BARRY
  -S/T- reiss *EMI PREM (EMI):CZ 558 (CD)*
  see COLL.45,47,61,also JAMES BOND FILM INDEX p.346
DOCTOR QUINN: MEDICINE WOMAN (USA/ITV 28/5/93) orig
  music by WILLIAM OLVIS -S/T- with Various Artists
  SONIC IMAGE (Cargo-Greyhound): SI 8804 (CD)
DOCTOR STRANGELOVE (1963) Music: LAURIE JOHNSON
  see COLL.61,88,156,157,
DOCTOR WHO (BBC1 23/11/63-93) orig theme RON GRAINER
  'DOCTOR WHO Volume 1: The Early Years (1963-1969)
  BBC Radiophonic Workshop
  BBC WORLDWIDE (Pinn): WMSF 6023-2 (CD)
  'DOCTOR WHO Volume 2: New Beginnings (1970-   )
  BBC Radiophonic Workshop
  BBC WORLDWIDE (Pinn): WMSF 6024-2 (CD)
  -
  'MUSIC FROM THE TENTH PLANET'
  OCHRE (Cargo/SRD): OCH 060 (MCD)
  'TERROR OF THE ZYGONS'/'THE SEEDS OF DOOM' Music
  by GEOFFREY BURGON BBC (Pinn): WMSF 6020-2 (CD)
  'THIRTY YEARS AT THE RADIOPHONIC WORKSHOP' (BBC)
  Music Var.Arts *BBC (Pinn) BBCCD 871 (CD) see also*
  (1) 'DR.WHO - VARIATIONS ON A THEME' various comp.
  SILVA SCREEN (Koch): FILMCD 706 (CD)
  'DOWNTIME' (Doctor Who Video) music: IAN LEVENE
  SILVA SCREEN (Koch): FILMCD 717 (CD)
  'SHAKEDOWN' Music MARK AYRES
  SILVA SCREEN (Koch): FILMCD 718 (CD)

DOCTOR WHO: EVOLUTION 'MUSIC FROM DOCTOR WHO' feat
music of RON GRAINER-KEFF McCULLOCH & DOMINIC GREEN
PRESTIGE-NOVA (Pinn): CDSGP 0320 (CD)
DOCTOR WHO: VENGEANCE ON VAROS *BBC: ZBBC 1932 2MC*
DOCTOR WHO: MUSIC FROM THE TENTH PLANET
OCHRE (Cargo/SRD): OCH 050 (CD)

'WHO IS DOCTOR WHO' Various Artists and Orchestras
BBC RADIOPHONIC WORKSHOP-FRAZER HINES-JON PERTWEE
JACK DORSEY ORCH-ERIC WINSTONE ORCH-ROBERT TOVEY-
EARTHLINGS-MALCOLM LOCKYER ORCHESTRA-GO GO'S etc.
RPM (Pinn): RPM 200 (CD)

the theme music of DOCTOR WHO :
see COLL.2,5,8,38,42,74,83,218,237,247,283,

DOCTOR WILLOUGHBY (ITV 14/11/1999) theme music by
    DAVE MACKAY on 'AS SEEN ON TV' *see COLL.20,*
DOCTOR ZHIVAGO (1965) Music score: MAURICE JARRE
    -S/T- *reissue: EMI Premier (EMI): CDODEON 1 (CD)*
    see COLL.73,153,161,
DOCTORS The (2000 BBC1 26/03/2000) series title music:
    by MIKE BADGER-PAUL HEMMINGS *unavailable*
DOCTORS The (1969 BBC1) m: TONY HATCH *see COLL.24,131,*
DOGMA (1999) Music score by HOWARD SHORE -S/T- *IMPORT*
    MAVERICK-WARNER (TEN): 9362 47597-2 (CD)
DOLLARS - see 'HEIST'
DOLLY SISTERS The (1945) BETTY GRABLE-JUNE HAVER inc.
    songs from 'ROSE OF WASHINGTON SQUARE' and
    'GOLD DIGGERS OF 1933' *TARGET (BMG) CD 60009 (CD)*
DOLORES CLAIBORNE (1995) Music score: DANNY ELFMAN
    -S/T- *VARESE (Pinn): VSD 5602 (CD)*
DOLPHINS (2000) Music by STING and STEVE WOOD -S/T-
    ARK 21 (Univ): 810 057-2 (CD) also
    POLYDOR (Univ): 159 145-2 (CD)
DON QUIXOTE (2000) Music score: RICHARD HARTLEY -S/T-
    VARESE (Pinn): VSD 6142 (CD) also
DON QUIXOTE (Spanish TV mini-ser) music score: LALO
    SCHIFRIN -S/T- *PROMETHEUS (S.Scr): PCD 132 (CD)*
DONNIE BRASCO (1997) Music score: PATRICK DOYLE
    -S/T- (songs) *HOLLYWOOD (Univ.): 162 102-2 (CD)*
    -S/T- (score) *VARESE (Pinnacle): VSD 5834 (CD)*
DON'T GO BREAKING MY HEART (1998) Music sc: ROLFE KENT
    -S/T- *SOUNDTRACK (Pinn): STRACK 101 (CD)*
DON'T LOOK NOW (1973) Music sco: PINO DONAGGIO -S/T-
    TER (Koch): CDTER 1007
DON'T SAY A WORD (2001) Music score by MARK ISHAM
    -S/T- *VARESE (Pinn): VSD 6291 (CD)*
DOOGIE HOWSER MD (USA) *see COLL.14,203,248,*
DOORS The (1991) Music sco: BUDD CARR Orig songs by
    JIM MORRISON & DOORS -S/T- *ELEKTRA (TEN): 7599
    61047-2 (CD) EKT 85C (MC) EKT 85 (LP)*
DOUBLE IMPACT (1991) Music score: ARTHUR KEMPEL -S/T-
    S.SCREEN (Koch): FILMCD 110 (CD)

DOUBLE INDEMNITY (1944) Music sco: MIKLOS ROZSA Suite
   on Coll *'FILM NOIR CLASSICS'* with 'THE KILLERS' +
   'THE LOST WEEKEND' *feat* NEW ZEALAND S.O.cond.by
   JAMES SEDARES on *KOCH INT (Koch): 37375-2 (CD)*
DOUBLE LIFE OF VERONIQUE (1991) Music sco: ZBIGNIEW
   PREISNER Choral music by VAN DEN BUDENMAYER -S/T-
   VIRGIN (EMI): CDVE 939 (CD)
DOUBLE TROUBLE see ELVIS PRESLEY INDEX p.348
DOWN BY LAW (1987) Music sco: JOHN LURIE & TOM WAITS
   also includes 'VARIETY' -S/T- music: JOHN LURIE
   MADE TO MEASURE (New Note-Pinn): MTM 14 (CD)
DOWN FROM THE MOUNTAIN (2001) VAR.ARTS (OH BROTHER
   WHERE ART THOU) S/T *MERCURY (UNIV): 170 221-2 (CD)*
DOWN IN THE DELTA (1998) Music score: STANLEY CLARKE
   -S/T- STEVIE WONDER-LUTHER VANDROSS-THE LEVERTS-
   VIRGIN (EMI): CDVUS 153 (CD) VUSMC 153 (MC)
DOWN TO EARTH (BBC1 28/08/2000) music score: SHERIDAN
   TONGUE / song "After All This Time" performed by
   TONY HADLEY -S/T- *DECCA (UNIV): 470 173-2 (CD)*
DOWN TO EARTH (2001) Music score by JAMSHIED SHARIFI
   EPIC (TEN): 502 008-2 (CD)
DOWN TO YOU (1999) VARIOUS ARTISTS SOUNDTRACK
   EPIC (TEN): 497 613-2 (CD)
DOWNHILL CITY (2000) -S/T- with VARIOUS ARTISTS
   CLEAR SPOT (Cargo/Koch/Pinn): EFACD 05418-2 (CD)
DR. *see under* DOCTOR
DRACULA AD 1972 (1972) Music score by MIKE VICKERS
   -S/T- *GDI (UNIV): 516 425-2 (CD)*
DRACULA 2000 VARIOUS ARTISTS Soundtrack on
   -S/T- *COLUMBIA (TEN): 501 545-2 (CD)*
DRACULA - see COLL.82,90,126,127,138,150,219,249,
DRACULA (1931) CONTEMPORARY SCORE (1999) composed by
   Philip Glass *and featuring the* Kronos Quartet
   NONESUCH-WARNER (Ten): 7559 79542-2 (CD)
DRACULA (1992) Music score by WOJCIECH KILAR -S/T-
   COLUMBIA (Ten): 472 746-2 (CD)
DRACULA (HAMMER STORY featuring CHRISTOPHER LEE & The
   HAMMER CITY ORCHESTRA) *BGO (Pinn): BGOCD 240 (CD)*
DRAGNET (USA TV 1950s) theme: WALTER SCHUMANN
   see COLL.75,77,242,
DRAGON: THE BRUCE LEE STORY (1993) Mus: RANDY EDELMAN
   -S/T- *MCA (UNI): MCAD 10827 (CD)*
DRAGONHEART (1996) Music score: RANDY EDELMAN -S/T-
   MCA (UNI): MCAD 11449 (CD)
DRAGONHEART 2: A NEW BEGINNING (2000) Music score by
   MARK McKENZIE -S/T- *VARESE 9Pinn): VSD 6170 (CD)*
DRAGONSLAYER (1981) Music score: ALEX NORTH. *SELECTION
   WITH* 'CHEYENNE AUTUMN' (1964) 'CINERAMA SOUTH SEAS
   ADVENTURE' (1958) *LABEL X (Hot): ATMCD 2004 (CD)*
DRAT THE CAT! (MUSICAL) sgs: MILTON SCHAFER-IRA LEVIN
   1997 USA STUDIO *w:* SUSAN EGAN-JASON GRAAE-JONATHAN
   FREEMAN-JUDY KAYE on *VARESE (Pinn): VSD 5721 (CD)*
DRAUGHTSMAN'S CONTRACT The (1983) Mus: MICHAEL NYMAN
   -S/T- *CHARISMA (Virgin-EMI): CASCD 1158 (CD)*

DREAM LOVER (1994) Music sco: CHRISTOPHER YOUNG -S/T-
  KOCH Screen Rec (Koch): 387002 (CD)
DREAM OF OLWEN The *see* 'WHILE I LIVE' +
  see COLL.235,267,268,
DREAM WITH THE FISHES (1998) VARIOUS ARTISTS -S/T- on
  SNAPPER (Pinn): SNACD 811 (CD)
DRIFTWOOD (1996) Music score: CARL DAVIS -S/T- on
  OCEAN DEEP (Grapev/Polyg): OCD 003 (CD)
DRIVE ME CRAZY (2000) VARIOUS ARTISTS -S/T- on
  JIVE (Pinn): 922 036-2 (CD)
DRIVEN (2001) Music score by BT (BRIAN TRANSEAU) -S/T-
  CURB-LONDON (TEN): 0927 41012-2 (CD)
DRIVING MISS DAISY (1989) Music sco HANS ZIMMER songs
  Eartha Kitt-Louis Armstrong -S/T- *VARESE (Pinn):*
  VSD 5246 (CD) VSC 5246 (MC) see COLL.122,197,
DROP DEAD GORGEOUS (1999) Music sc: MARK MOTHERSBAUGH
  -S/T- (VARIOUS ARTS) *SIRE (TEN): 4344 3106-2 (CD)*
DROP ZONE (1994) Music score HANS ZIMMER -S/T- on
  VARESE (Pinn): VSD 5581 (CD)
DROWNING BY NUMBERS (1988) Music score: MICHAEL NYMAN
  -S/T- *VENTURE (Virg-EMI): CDVE 23 (CD)*
DUBARRY WAS A LADY (1943) *feat:*LUCILLE BALL-GENE KELLY
  RED SKELTON-TOMMY DORSEY ORCH + *songs from* 'SKY'S
  THE LIMIT'/'42ND STR.' *TARGET (BMG):CD 60010 (CD)*
DUCHESS OF DUKE STREET The (UKGo 2/11/92 orig BBC 76)
  theme music: ALEXANDER FARIS *see COLL.42,200,*
DUCK SOUP (1933) Songs by BERT KALMAR and HARRY RUBY
  selection DEFINITIVE (Discovery): SFCD 33501 (CD)
DUCKMAN (USA TV) *see COLL.248,*
DUDE WHERE'S MY CAR (2000) VAR.ARTISTS SOUNDTRACK inc:
  GRAND THEFT AUDIO-TREBLE CHARGER-SUPERDRAG-WEEN
  -S/T- *LONDON (Univ): 4344 31156-2 (CD)*
DUE SOUTH (BBC1 9/5/95) mus: (Jack Lenz-John McCarthy-
  Jay Semko) theme by JAY SEMKO & CRASH TEST DUMMIES
  + NORTHERN PIKES-SARAH MacLACHLAN-KLAATU-GUESS WHO
  FIGGY DUFF-BLUE RODEO-LOREENA McKENNITT-PAUL GROSS
  -S/T- VOLUME 1: (VARIOUS ARTISTS)
  NETTWERK (Pinn): 62428 40004-2 (CD) -4 (MC)
  -S/T- VOLUME 2: (VARIOUS ARTISTS)
  NETTWERK (Pinn): 62428 40007-2 (CD) -4 (MC)
DUEL AT DIABLO (1966) Music score: NEAL HEFTI / with
  'HORSE SOLDIERS' (1959 DAVID BUTTOLPH score)
  TARAN (Silver Sounds): W 9105 (CD)
DUEL IN THE SUN (1946) m:DIMITRI TIOMKIN *see COLL.255,*

DUEL OF HEARTS, A (1990) Music score: LAURIE JOHNSON
  see COLL.156,158,
DUELLISTS The (1977) *see COLL.120,240,*
DUETS (2000) Music score by DAVID NEWMAN -S/T- inc V/A
  -S/T- *HOLLYWOOD-EDEL (Vital): 012 241-2HWR (CD)*
DUKES OF HAZZARD (USA 79) Theme 'Good Ol'Boys' (WAYLON
  JENNINGS) *see COLL.247,*
DULCIMA (Film 1971) Music score: JOHNNY DOUGLAS Theme
  DULCIMA (THE-DISC): DLCD 110 (CD) DLCT 110 (MC)

DUMB AND DUMBER (1994) Music sc: TODD RUNGREN -S/T-
  Revis.Re-iss RCA (BMG): 74321 48059-2 (CD) -4(MC)
DUMBO (1941) -S/T- *DISNEY-EDEL (Vital) - (CD)*
  - *see* WALT DISNEY INDEX p.341
DUNE (USA TV mini series 2000) music by GRAEME REVELL
  -S/T- *GNP USA (ZYX): GNPD 8071 (CD)*
DUNE (1984) Music score: BRIAN ENO and TOTO. Complete
  Score with 30m of previously unreleased music on
  USA IMP: PNDL 15 (CD) / POLY-IMS: E.823 770-2 (CD)
DURANGO (1999) Music score by MARK McKENZIE -S/T-
  INTRADA Import (Silva Screen): MAF 7087 (CD)
DUSTY SPRINGFIELD STORY The (ORIG CAST RECORDING)
  OCEAN DEEP (Univ): OCD 015 (CD)
DYING YOUNG (91) Music sco: JAMES NEWTON HOWARD theme:
  KENNY G.-S/T- *ARISTA (BMG): 261952 (CD) 411952(MC)*
DYNAMITE BROTHERS The (1973) Music by CHARLES EARLAND
  -S/T- *BEAT GOES PUBLIC (Pinn): CDBGPM 120 (CD)*
DYNASTY (UKGO 8/3/93 orig BBC1 82 (USA 80) theme music
  BILL CONTI *see COLL.42,117,244,*
E.R. (USA/C4 1/2/95) theme music: JAMES NEWTON HOWARD
  -S/T- *WEA (TEN): 7567 82942-2 (CD) -4 (MC)*
  see COLL.139,172, and 'HIT TV'
E.T. (The Extra Terrestrial) (1982) Music comp & cond
  JOHN WILLIAMS -S/T- *MCA (UNI): MCLD 19021 (CD)*
  see COLL.121,220,281,
EAGLE HAS LANDED The (1976) Music sco: LALO SCHIFRIN
  -S/T- *ALEPH (Koch): ALEP 009 (CD) also on*
  WB (TEN): 8573 84366-2 (CD)
EARLY TRAVELLERS IN NORTH AMERICA (BBC2 23/07/1992)
  Music score by TOT TAYLOR -S/T- on
  TWEED COUTURE (Pinn): TWEEDCD 12 (CD)
EARTH: FINAL CONFLICT (USA/SKY1 1/1998) theme & incid.
  music score by MICKY ERBE and MARIBETH SOLOMON
  SONIC IMAGES (Cargo): SID 8920 (8282 78920-2) (CD)
EARTH STORY (BBC2 1/11/1998) music composed,conducted
  and produced by DEBORAH MOLLISON (piano, synths)
  -S/T- BBC PRODUCTION *CHANDOS/BBC: CHAN 9688 (CD)*
EARTHQUAKE (1974) Music score by JOHN WILLIAMS -S/T-
  VARESE (Pinn): VSD 5262 (CD) see COLL.257,
EAST IS EAST (1998) Music score by DEBORAH MOLLISON
  -S/T- *feat* BLUE MINK/JIMMY CLIFF/DEEP PURPLE/DAVE
  & ANSELL COLLINS/GEORGIE FAME/HOLLIES/McGUINNESS
  FLINT/SUPERGRASS *EMI RECORDS: 523 361-2 (CD)*
EAST OF EDEN (1954) Music score: LEONARD ROSENMAN *new
  Recording with* LONDON SINFONIETTA (J.ADAMS) incl:
  'REBEL WITHOUT A CAUSE' (1955 Leonard Rosenman)
  NONESUCH (TEN): 7559 79402-2 (CD) also: LEONARD
  ROSENMAN complete score + 'GIANT'/'REBEL WITHOUT A
  A CAUSE' *CINERAMA (S.Scr): CIN 2206-2(2CD) -4(2MC)*
EAST WEST (2000) Music score by PATRICK DOYLE perf.by
  BULGARIAN SYMPHONY ORCHESTRA and CHOIR -S/T- on
  SONY CLASSICS: SK 64429 (CD)
EASTENDERS (BBC1 19/2/1985-2002) theme by SIMON MAY &
  LESLIE OSBORNE *see COLL.42,283,*

EASTER PARADE (FILM MUSICAL (1948) Songs by IRVING
   BERLIN *featuring* FRED ASTAIRE-JUDY GARLAND -S/T-
   SOUNDTRACK FACTORY (Discov): SFCD 33523 (CD) also
   EMI PREMIER: CDODEON 4 (CD) see COLL.196,
EASY COME EASY GO see ELVIS PRESLEY INDEX p.348
EASY RIDER (1969) Music: STEPPENWOLF-ELECTRIC PRUNES-
   JIMI HENDRIX EXPERIENCE-BYRDS-ROGER McGUINN..-S/T-
   MCA (UNI): MCLD 19153 (CD) MCLC 19153 (MC)
   SIMPLY VINYL (Telstar): SVLP 26 (LP)
EAT DRINK MAN WOMAN (1993) Music score: MADER -S/T-
   VARESE (Pinn): VSD 5528 (CD)
ECHO FOUR-TWO (A.Rediff.24/8/1961) theme music by
   LAURIE JOHNSON see COLL.24,157,
ED TV (1998) Music score by RANDY EDELMAN -S/T- V.ART:
   REPRISE (TEN): 93624 7310-2 (CD) -4 (MC)
ED WOOD (1994) Music score: HOWARD SHORE -S/T- reissue
   EDEL-HOLLYWOOD (Vital) 012 002-2HWR (CD)
EDGE The (1997) Music score: JERRY GOLDSMITH -S/T- on
   RCA (BMG): 09026 68950-2 (CD)
EDGE OF DARKNESS (BBC2 10/5/92 orig 4/11/85) Theme mus
   ERIC CLAPTON-MICHAEL KAMEN see COLL.159,
EDGE OF SEVENTEEN *RAZOR & TIE (Koch): RE 82847-2 (CD)*
EDUCATING RITA (1983) Music score by DAVID HENTSCHEL
   -S/T- reissue *C5 (Pinn): C5CD 587 (CD)*
EDWARD II (1991) Music score: SIMON FISHER TURNER
   -S/T- *MUTE (Pinn): IONIC 8CD (CD) IONIC 8LP (LP)*
EDWARD AND MRS.SIMPSON (ITV 8/11/78) Mus: RON GRAINER
   see COLL.6,
EDWARD SCISSORHANDS (1990) Music by DANNY ELFMAN -S/T-
   MCA (UNI): MCLD 19303 (CD) see COLL.63,82,219,
EDWIN DROOD (MUSICAL 1986) see Mystery Of Edwin Drood
EERIE INDIANA (USA) see COLL.14,
EGYPTIAN The (1954) Music score by ALFRED NEWMAN and
   BERNARD HERRMANN *new rec:* MOSCOW SYMPHONY ORCH (W.
   Stromberg) *MARCO POLO (Select): 8225078 (CD)*
EIGER SANC TION The (1975) Music score: JOHN WILLIAMS
   -S/T- reissue *VARESE (Pinn): VSD 5277 (CD)*
EIGHT HEADS IN A DUFFELBAG (1997) Mus sc: ANDREW GROSS
   -S/T- *VARESE (Pinn): VSD 5835 (CD)*
EL CID (1961) Music score: MIKLOS ROZSA *New Recording*
   COMPLETE SCORE New Zealand Symphony Orchestra on
   KOCH INTernat.Class (Koch): 37340-2 (CD) -4(MC)
   see COLL.61,146,213,266,
ELECTION (1999) VARIOUS ARTISTS -S/T- on
   SIRE (Ten): 4344 31057-2 (CD)
ELECTRA (1975) Music score: MIKIS THEODORAKIS -S/T-
   SAKARIS (Pinn): SR 50090 (CD)
ELECTRIC DREAMS (1984) m: GIORGIO MORODER-PHILIP OAKEY
   -S/T- *VIRGIN (EMI): CDVIP 127 (CD) TCVIP 127 (MC)*
ELEGIES For Angels Punks & Raging Queens (ORIG LONDON
   CAST 1993) *First Night (Pinn): OCRCD 6035 (CD)*
ELEPHANT MAN The (1980) Music score: JOHN MORRIS plus
   'Adagio' (Samuel BARBER) sco *MILAN (BMG): 199 862
   (CD)* see COLL.105,

ELIZABETH (C4 2000) Music score by ANDY PRICE with the
  CITY OF PRAGUE PHILHARM. & CLIFTON CATHEDRAL CHOIR
  CHANNEL FOUR MUSIC (Univ): C4M 0002-2 (CD)
ELIZABETH (1998) Music score: DAVID HIRSCHFLEDER -S/T-
  DECCA (Univ): 460 796-2 (CD)
ELMER GANTRY (1960) Music score: ANDRE PREVIN -S/T- on
  RYKODISC (Vital): RCD 10732 (CD)
ELMO IN GROUCHLAND (2000) VARIOUS ARTISTS -S/T- on
  SONY WONDER (TEN): 498 056-2 (CD)
ELVIRA MADIGAN (1987) 'Piano Con.No.21'K.467' (MOZART)
  NAXOS (Select): 8551153 (CD)
EMERGENCY WARD 10 (ATV 1957-1967) closing theme music
  "Silks and Satins" PETER YORKE *see COLL.5,119,*
EMMA (1995) Music score by RACHEL PORTMAN -S/T- on
  EDEL-HOLLYW (Vit): 012 069-2HWR (CD) see COLL.202,
EMMERDALE (FARM) (Yorkshire 16/10/72-2001) theme mus
  by TONY HATCH *see COLL.2,200,*
EMPEROR'S NEW GROOVE(2000) Music score by JOHN DEBNEY
  -S/T- feat TOM JONES-STING-EARTHA KITT-STING etc.
  DISNEY-EDEL (Vital): 012 278-2DNY (CD)
EMPIRE STRIKES BACK The (Star Wars 2) Music score by
  JOHN WILLIAMS / Special-Edition SOUNDTRACK (1997)
  RCA (BMG): 09026 68747-2 (Deluxe 2CD)
  RCA (BMG): 09026 68773-2 (Slimline 2CD) -4 (2MC)
  see COLL.218,232,238,280,281,
ENCHANTED APRIL (BBC2 05/04/1992) Music score by
  RICHARD RODNEY BENNETT rec.by BBC PHILHARMONIC
  ORCHESTRA on *CHANDOS: CHAN 9867 (CD)*
END OF DAYS (1999) Music score by JOHN DEBNEY
  -S/T- (score) *VARESE (Pinn): VSD 6099 (CD)*
  -S/T- (songs) *GEFFEN (Univ): 490 508-2 (CD)*
END OF THE AFFAIR (1999) Music score by MICHAEL NYMAN
  -S/T- *SONY (TEN): SK 51354 (CD)*
END OF THE VIOLENCE (1997) Music score: RY COODER
  -S/T- (score) *OUTPOST (BMG): OPD 30007 (CD)*
  -S/T- (songs) *OUTPOST (BMG): OPD 30008 (CD)*
ENEMY AT THE GATES (2000) Music score by JAMES HORNER
  -S/T- *SONY CLASSICS (TEN): SK 89522 (CD)*
ENEMY OF THE STATE (1997) Music sco: TREVOR RABIN and
  HARRY GREGSON WILLIAMS -S/T- issued on
  HOLLYWOOD-EDEL (Vital) 010200-2HWR (CD)
ENGLAND OF ELIZABETH The (1956 travel short) Music by
  VAUGHAN WILLIAMS *MARCO POLO (Select) 8.223665(CD)*
ENGLISH PATIENT The (1996) Music sco: GABRIEL YARED
  -S/T- *FANTASY (Pinn): FCD 16001 (CD)* also on Coll
  'SHINE'/'THE PIANO' *VARESE (Pinn): VSD 25982 (2CD)*
  see COLL.64,67,97,204,
ENIGMA (2001) Music score: JOHN BARRY -S/T- V.ARTISTS
  UNIVERSAL MUSIC: 467 864-2 (CD)
ENTER THE DRAGON (1973) Music sco: LALO SCHIFRIN -S/T-
  WEA (TEN): 7599 26380-2 (CD) and 9362 48074-2 (CD)
ENTERPRISE Star Trek spin-off (USATV 2001) theme music
  "Faith In My Heart" sung by RUSSELL WATSON from
  album 'Encore' *UNIVERSAL: 470 300-2 (CD) -4 (MC)*

ENTRAPMENT (1999) Music score: CHRISTOPHER YOUNG -S/T-
RESTLESS USA (BMG): 74321 73518-2 (CD)
EQUALIZER The (USA 29/10/86) theme by STEWART COPELAND
-TV S/T- *IRS: DMIRF 1029 (CD) see COLL.14,248,*
EQUINOXE (1992) Music by Various Artists -S/T-
VARESE (Pinn): VSD 5424 (CD)
EQUUS (1977) Music score: RICHARD RODNEY BENNETT -S/T-
RYKODISC (Vital): RCD 10726 (CD)
ERIN BROCKOVICH (2000) Music sco: THOMAS NEWMAN -S/T-
SONY CLASSICAL (TEN): SK 89239 (CD)
ESCAPE FROM L.A. (1996) Music sco: SHIRLEY WALKER-J.C.
score -S/T- *MILAN (BMG): 74321 40951-2 (CD)*
songs -S/T- *WEA: 7567 92714-2 (CD) -4 (MC)*
ESCAPE FROM NEW YORK (1981) Music sco: JOHN CARPENTER-
ALAN HOWARTH -S/T- *SILVA SCREEN (Koch): FILMCD 327
(CD) + DAGORED (Koch): RED 124 (LP) also on
VARESE (Pinn): VCD 47224 (CD)*
ESCAPE ME NEVER (1947) Mus sc: ERICH WOLFGANG KORNGOLD
"Ballet Fantasy" MOSCOW SYMPH.ORCH (Stromberg) and
'ANOTHER DAWN' *MARCO POLO (Select): 8.223871 (CD)*
suite also on *CHANDOS:CHAN 8870 (CD) see COLL.160,*
ESCORT The - see 'LA SCORTA'
ETERNITY AND A DAY (1998) Music sco: ELENI KARAINDROU
-S/T- *ECM Import: 465 125-2 (CD)*
EUREKA STREET (BBC1 13/09/1999) Mus.sco: MARTIN PHIPPS
BBC WORLDWIDE (Pinn): WMSF 6016-2 (CD)
EURO 2000 European Football Champ. (09Jun-02July 2000)
BBC *theme* "Canto Della Terra" sung ANDREA BOCELLI
from 'SOGNO' *POLYDOR (Univ): 547 221-2 (CD) -4(MC)*
ITV *theme* "Theme from Young Person's Guide To The
Orch." (BENJAMIN BRITTEN) *EMI: CDM 567 451-2 (CD)*
England *song* "Jerusalem" by FAT LES *EMI: CDR 6540*
Europe *theme* "Campione 2000" by E.TYPE *(Polydor)*
Alb 'England Anthems Album' *UNIV: 467 133-2 (CD)*
EUROPA EUROPA (1991) Music score: ZBIGNIEW PREISNER
-S/T- also inc.mus. 'OLIVIER OLIVIER' (Preisner)
DRG (Pinn): DRGCD 12606 (CD) DRGMC 12606 (MC)
EUROPEAN CHAMPIONS LEAGUE Football (ITV 1992-2002)
"Champion League Anthem" TONY BRITTEN *unavailable*
EUROPEAN FIGURE SKATING CHAMPIONSHIPS (BBC 1/2) theme
"Mornings At Seven" JAMES LAST ORC on 'By Request'
POLY (Univ): 831 786-2 (CD) see also 'ICE SKATING'
EUROTRASH (C4 from 1993) theme mus "St.Tropez" (F.Lai)
BRIGITTE BARDOT on 'A SONG FOR EURTRASH'
EMI UK: 495 062-2 (CD)
EUROVISION SONG CONTEST 'COPENHAGEN 2001' (complete)
ALL 23 ENTRIES FROM THE 2001 SONG CONTEST
BMG EURO IMPORT: 74321 84292-2 (CD)
EUROVISION SONG CONTEST (2001) (Denmark BBC1 12/5/2001)
2001 winning song: "Everybody" sung by TANEL PADAR-
DAVE BENTON (2XL) - Estonia (198 pts.)
2000 UK entry: "No Dream Impossible" by LINDSAY
DRACASS (placed 15th and scored 28 points)
UNIVERSAL: 158 56-2 (CDs)

EUROVISION SONG CONTEST (2001) - *see also page 352*

EUROVISION SONG CONTEST 'STOCKHOLM 2000' (complete)
ALL 24 ENTRIES FROM THE 2001 SONG CONTEST
BMG EURO IMPORT: 74321 76587-2 (2CD)
EUROVISION SONG CONTEST (2000) (Sweden BBC1 13/5/2000)
2000 winning song: "Fly On The Wings Of Love" sung
by OLSEN BROTHERS Denmark (195 pts.)(24 countries)
LIBERTY (EMI): 888 804-2 (CDs) WITHDRAWN BY EMI
2000 UK entry: "Don't Play That Song Again" by
NICKI FRENCH (placed 16th and scored 28pts.)
RCA (BMG): 74321 76457-2CDs)
2000 Russia "Solo" by ALSOU & BRAINSTORM (2nd)
UNIVERSAL (Univ): cat.number unconfirmed
2000 Estonia entry "Once In a Lifetime" by INES
EDEL (Vital) cat.number unconfirmed

EUROVISION SONG CONTEST *1956-1999* - Various Artists
UNIVERSAL IMPT: 541 347-2 (2CD) - see COLLECTIONS

EUROVISION SONG CONTEST 1999 'ISRAEL 1999' complete
HMV IMPORT: IMP 2062 (2CD)

EUROVISION SONG CONTEST (1999) (UK) BBC1 29/5/1999)
99 winning song: "Take Me To Your Heaven" sung by
CHARLOTTE NILSSON Sweden (163pts) (23 countries)
ARISTA (BMG): 74321 68695-2 (CDs)
99 UK entry: "Say It Again" performed by PRECIOUS
placed joint 12th with 38pts. *EMI: CDEM 544 (CDs)*
EUROVISION SONG CONTEST (1998) (UK) BBC1 9/5/1998)
98 winning song: "Diva" perf.by DANA INTERNATIONAL
Israel scored 174pts (25 countries) recorded on
DANCEPOOL (Ten): DANA 1CD (CDs)
98 UK entry: "Where Are You" performed by IMAANI
placed 2nd with 167pts. *EMI: CDEM 510 (CDs)*
Other songs unreleased in the UK
EUROVISION SONG CONTEST (1997)(Ireland) BBC1 3/5/1997)
97 winning song: "Love Shine A Light" performed by
KATRINA & THE WAVES UK score 227pts (25 countries)
on *ETERNAL (TEN): WEA 106(CD)(C)(T) (CDs/MC/12"s)*
97 runner up: "Mysterious Woman" performed by MARC
ROBERTS Ireland scored 157pts. recorded on *RITZ
(Pinn): RITZCD 305 (CDs) RITZC 305 (MC)*
Interval Music: composed by RONAN KEATING perf.by
by BOYZONE *Other songs unreleased in the UK*
EUROVISION SONG CONTEST (1996) (Norway) BBC1 18/5/96)
96 winning song: "The Voice" perform: EIMEAR QUINN
for IRELAND scored 162 pts (23 Countries) recorded
POLYDOR (Univ): 576 884-2 (CD) 576 884-4 (MC)
96 UK entry: "Ooh Aah Just A Little Bit" by GINA G.
(77pts - 7th) *ETERNAL (TEN): WEA 041(CD)(C)(T)*
Interval Music: composed by EGIL MONN-IVERSEN perf:
NORWEGIAN RADIO ORCH cond: FRODE THINGNAES. song by
MORTEN HARKET 'Heaven's Not For Saints Let It Go'

EUROVISION SONG CONTEST (1995) (Ireland) BBC1 13/5/95)
95 winning song: "Nocturne" perform: SECRET GARDEN
for NORWAY scored 148 pts (25 Countries) recorded
POLYDOR: 856 978-2 (CD) 856 978-4 (MC)
95 UK entry: "Love City Groove" by LOVE CITY GROOVE
(76pts - 10th) *PLANET 3: GXY 2003CD (CDs)*
Interval Music: "Lumen" by MICHEAL O'SUILLEABHAIN
VENTURE VIRGIN (EMI): VENDX 5 (CDs) VENCX 5 (MC)

EUROVISION SONG CONTEST (1994) (Ireland) (BBC1 30/4/94)
94 winning song: "Rock'n'Roll Kids"(Brendan Graham)
by PAUL HARRINGTON & CHARLIE McGETTIGAN for IRELAND
scored 226pts (25 Countries) *Roc Kids M (Grapevine
/Poly): RNRK(CD)(MC)(SP) 1 (CDs/MC/7"s) deleted*
94 UK entry: "Lonely Symphony" (De Angelis-Dean) by
FRANCES RUFFELLE (63pts-10th) *VIRGIN: VSCCD(VSC)
(VS) 1499 (CDs/MC/7"s)* / Interval Music (1994)
"RIVERDANCE" by BILL WHELAN *see also* 'RIVERDANCE'

EUROVISION SONG CONTEST (1993) (Ireland) (BBC1 15/5/93)
93 winning song: "In Your Eyes" (Jimmy Walsh) sung
by NIAMH KAVANAGH for IRELAND scored 187 pts (25 Co
untries) *ARISTA: 74321 15415-2(CDs) -4(MC) -7(7")*
93 UK entry:"Better The Devil" (Dean Collinson-Red)
SONIA (164 pts-2nd) *ARISTA (BMG): 74321 14687-2CDs*

EUROVISION SONG CONTEST (1992) (Sweden) (BBC1 9/5/92)
92 winning song: "Why Me"(Johnny Logan)LINDA MARTIN
scored 155 points (23 Countries) *Columbia deleted*
92 UK entry: "One Step Out Of Time" (Tony Ryan-Paul
Davies-Victor Stratton) MICHAEL BALL (139 pts- 2nd)
Poly: PZCD 206 (CDs) PO 206 (7") POCS 206 deleted

EUROVISION SONG CONTEST (1991) (Rome) (BBC1-4/5/91)
91 winning song: "Fangad Av En Stormvind' (Captured
By A Love Storm) CAROLA (Sweden) scored 146 points
(22 Countries) *RCA: PB 44649(7") PD 44650(CDs)
also* "Le Dernier Qui A Parle" (Last One Who Speaks)
AMINA (France) 146 Pts *Philips: PH 45 (7") PHMC 45*
91 UK entry "A Message To Your Heart" (Paul Curtis)
SAMANTHA JANUS (47pts-11th) *Hollywood HWD(T)(CD)104*

EUROVISION SONG CONTEST (1990) (Yugoslav)(BBC1 5/5/90)
90 winning song "Insieme 1992" (All Together Now)by
TOTO COTUGNO (Italy) scored 149 pts (22 countries)
on *Odeon (EMI): (12)ODO 113 (12"s/7"s) deleted*
90 UK entry "Give A Little Love Back To The World"
(Paul Curtis) sung by EMMA (87 points placed 6th)
recorded on *Big Wave (BMG): BWR 33 (7"s) deleted*

EUROVISION SONG CONTEST 1956-1999 - VARIOUS ARTISTS
UNIVERSAL SWE (Silver Sounds): 541 347-2 (2CD)

EUROVISION THEME MUSIC "Te Deum In D.Major" (Marc-Antoi
ne Charpentier) Academy Of St.Martin-In-The Fields
(Neville Marriner) *EMI: CDC 754 284-2 (CD)* also
English Chamber Orch *EMI: CZS 767 425-2 (2CD)*

EVE'S BAYOU (1997) Music sco: TERENCE BLANCHARD -S/T-
SONIC IMAGES (Cargo-Greyhound): SI 8707 (CD)

EVEN COWGIRLS GET THE BLUES (1993) Music & songs (k.d.
   lang) -S/T- *Sire-WB (TEN)*: 9362 45433-2(CD)
EVENING SHADE (USA) *see COLL.14,248,*
EVENT HORIZON (1997) Music sc: MICHAEL KAMEN + V.Arts.
   -S/T- *INTERNAL (Univ)*: 828 939-2 (CD)
EVER AFTER (1998) Music score: GEORGE FENTON -S/T- on
   DECCA (Univ): 460 581-2 (CD)
EVER DECREASING CIRCLES (BBC1 29/1/84 & 03/2000) theme
   "Prelude No.15 Op.34 Allegretto" (D.SHOSTAKOVICH)
   vers.by TATYANA NIKOLAIVA *HYPERION: CDA 66620 (CD)*
EVERLASTING PIECE - see 'AN EVERLASTING PIECE'
EVERY SUNDAY (1936) DEANNA DURBIN-JUDY GARLAND -S/T-
   selection with 'ZIEGFELD GIRL' on
   GREAT MOVIE THEMES (BMG): CD 60026 (CD)
EVERY WOMAN KNOWS A SECRET (ITV 18/03/1999) Music by
   NIGEL HESS *CHANDOS: CHAN 9750 (CD)*
EVERYBODY'S FINE (1990,It) Music score: ENNIO MORRICONE
   -S/T- *CAM ORIG SOUNDTRACKS (HOT):p 493 189-2 (CD)*
EVERYONE SAYS I LOVE YOU (1996) Mus: DICK HYMAN / Songs
   on *RCA Victor (BMG)*: 09026 68756-2 (CD)
EVIL OF FRANKENSTEIN *see COLL.127,,*
EVIL UNDER THE SUN (1982) Music of COLE PORTER arranged
   and conducted by JOHN LANCHBERRY *reissue* -S/T- on
   DRG USA (Pinn): DRGCD 12615 (CD)
EVITA - songs by Tim Rice and Andrew LLoyd Webber
   1.FILM 1996 *feat* MADONNA-JONATHAN PRYCE-ANTONIO BANDE
     RAS-JIMMY NAIL etc.-S/T- *SIRE (TEN)*: 9362 463462-2
     (CD) -4 *(MC)* / "Don't Cry For Me Argentina" MADONNA
     WEA: W.0384CD (CDs) W.0384C (MCs)
   2.STUDIO RECORDING 1976 *with* JULIE COVINGTON and Comp
     MCA (UNI): DMCXC 503 (CD)
   3.ORIG BROADWAY CAST 1979 *feat:* PATTI LuPONE-MANDY
     PATINKIN-BOB GUNTON-MARK SYERS-JANE OHRINGER & Comp
     MCA (UNI): MCDW 453 (2LP)
   4.**ORIG LONDON CAST 1978** *w:* ELAINE PAIGE-DAVID ESSEX
     MCA (UNI): DMCG 3527 (CD) MCGC 3527 (MC)
     see COLL.88,199,
   5.EVITA (4CD SET) *UNIVERSAL-IMS:AAM CAD 211008 (4CD)*
EVOLUTION (2001) Music score by JOHYN POWELL -S/T- on
   VARESE (Pinn): VSD 6256 (CD)
EXCALIBUR (1981) Music score incl.unused music cues
   TREVOR JONES *OLD WORLD MUSIC (Imp)*: OWM 9402 (CD)
   see COLL.61,62,83,
EXISTENZ (1999) Music score by HOWARD SHORE -S/T- on
   RCA VICTOR (BMG): 09026 63478-2 (CD)
EXIT (Film) Music score: TANGERINE DREAM -S/T-
   VIRGIN (EMI): CDV 2212 (CD) OVEDC 166 (MC)
EXIT TO EDEN (1994) Music score: PATRICK DOYLE -S/T-
   VARESE (Pinn): VSD 5553 (CD)
EXIT WOUNDS (2001) Music sco: JEFF RONA-DAMON BLACKMAN
   -S/T- Various Artists *VIRGIN (EMI)*: CDVUS 194 (CD)
EXODUS (1960) Music score by ERNEST GOLD -S/T- *reissue*
   IMPORT: 7446 599833-2 (CD) also on *TELARC (BMG)*:
   CD 80168 (CD) - *see COLL.112,*

EXORCIST The (1973) Music sco: JACK NITZSCHE -S/T-
V.composers MIKE OLDFIELD-KRYSZTOF PENDERECKI-HANS
WERNER HENZE-GEORGE CRUM-ANTON WEBERN-DAVID BORDEN
WEA FRA (Discov): 9362 46294-2 (CD)
EXORCIST II: The Heretic (1977) Music ENNIO MORRICONE
-S/T- *reissue WB (TEN): 9362 46992-2 (CD)*
EXPERIENCE (Rock 1968) JIMI HENDRIX EXPERIENCE feat:
Jimi HENDRIX-Noel REDDING-Mitch MITCHELL *reissue*
-S/T- BRILLIANT (Target-BMG): BT 33045 (CD) also
CHARLY (Koch/Pinn): CDGR 246 (CD) / SNAP 004 (CD)
NECTAR (Pinn): NTRCD 036 (CD) NTRC 036 (MC)
EXPERIMENT IN TERROR (1962) Music by HENRY MANCINI
-S/T- reissue with 'CHARADE' on
RCA CAMDEN (BMG): 74321 72714-2 (CD)
EXPOSED (1983) *see COLL.87,*

EYES WIDE SHUT (1999) Music score: JOCELYN POOK -S/T-
REPRISE (TEN): 9362 47450-2 (CD) -4 (MC)
see COLL.97,
F 1 **(Formula 1 Grand Prix)**(ITV 7/3/97-2001) theme mus
by JAMIROQUAI *unavailable*
F.B.I.(USA TV) *see COLL.175,239,242,*
F.B.I.STORY (1959) Music by MAX STEINER *see COLL.239,*
FABULOUS BAKER BOYS (1989) Music score: DAVE GRUSIN
reissue -S/T- GRP USA (BMG): GRP 2002-2 (CD)
FACE (1997) Music sco: ANDY ROBERTS-PAUL CONROY-ADRIAN
CORKER -S/T- *feat V/A ISLAND (Univ): CID 8061 (CD)*
FACE / OFF (1997) Music score: JOHN POWELL -S/T-
EDEL-HOLLYWOOD (Vital) 012125-2HWR (CD)
FACE TO FACE (BBC2 18/9/95) theme mus "Overture to Les
Francs Juges" Op.3 (BERLIOZ) *vers* Chicago S.Orch
(Solti) *DECCA (Univers.): 417 705-2 (CD)*
FACE TO FACE (1967) Music score ENNIO MORRICONE *Import*
with 'BIG GUNDOWN' *MASK (S.Screen): MK 701 (CD)*
FACULTY The (1998) Music score: MARCO BELTRAMI -S/T-
COLUMBIA (Ten): 493 038-2 (CD) -4 (MC)
FAHRENHEIT 451 (1966) Music score by BERNARD HERRMANN
SEATTLE SO *VARESE: VSD 5551 (CD) see COLL.140,*
ORIG -S/T- *TSUNAMI (Sil.Screen): TSU 0136 (CD)*
FALCON CREST / THE FALL GUY (USA TV) *see COLL.14,247,*
FALL OF THE ROMAN EMPIRE - *see COLL.254,*

FALLEN IDOL (1948) Music score: WILLIAM ALWYN *suite by*
London S.O.*Richard Hickox CHANDOS: CHAN 9243 (CD)*
FAME (USA/BBC1 82-12/2/85) *reissue of* KIDS FROM FAME
RCA: (BMG): ND 90427 (CD) theme by ERICA GIMPEL
RCA: (BMG): PK 89257 (MC)
FAME (FILM MUSICAL 80) M: MICHAEL GORE-DEAN PITCHFORD
IRENE CARA *see COLL.2,*
FAME (THE MUSICAL)(ORIG LONDON CAST 95) *feat:* LORRAINE
VELEZ-RICHARD DEMPSEY-SONIA SWABY and Company on
POLYDOR-RUG (Univ): 529 109-2 (CD) -4 (MC)
FAME THE MUSICAL (Various) 1999 ORIG USA RECORDING
DRG USA (Pinn): DRGCD 19010 (CD)

FAMILY AFFAIRS (C5 30/3/1997-2001) series theme music
    by RICK TURK *unavailable* / song "Family Affair"
    (S.Stewart) ROLAND GIFT *UNIVERSAL-ISLAND*
FAMILY AT WAR, A (ITV 12/5/70) Theme: Ist mm Symphony
    No.6 in E.Minor (VAUGHAN WILLIAMS) *var.recordings*
FAMILY MAN The (2000) Music score by DANNY ELFMAN
    -S/T- with VAR.ARTS.*LONDON (TEN): 431 151-2 (CD)*
FAMILY OF MY OWN, A (BBC1 05/01/2000) theme music by
    LEVEL 42 "Something About You" on 'Very Best'
    POLYDOR (Univ): 559 373-2 (CD) -4 (MC)
FAMILY WAY The (1966) Music score: PAUL McCARTNEY
    (arr/prod:George Martin) Suite on 'The Family Way'
    PHILIPS (Univ): 454 230-2 (CD)
FAN The (1996) Mus.sc: HANS ZIMMER *feat* MASSIVE ATTACK
    -S/T- *SNAPPER (Pinn): SMMCD 613 (CD)*
FANTASIA (1941) New Rec.of complete class.film music
    NAXOS (Select): 8551166 (CD) see COLL.64,195,
FANTASIA 2000 (1999) Mus: SORCERER'S APPRENTICE *DUKAS*
    PINES OF ROME *RESPIGHI*; 5TH SYMPH.*BEETHOVEN*; PIANO
    CONC.NO.2 *SHOSTAKOVICH*; RHAPSODY IN BLUE *GERSHWIN*
    CARNIVAL OF THE ANIMALS *SAINT-SAENS*; POMP AND CIRC
    UMSTANCE MARCH *ELGAR*; FIREBIRD SUITE *STRAVINSKY*
    Chicago S.O.(James Levine) -S/T- *DISNEY-EDEL (Vit)*
    010 558-2DNY (CD) see also DISNEY INDEX p.341
FANTASTIC PLANET (LA PLANETE SAVAGE) (1973) Music
    score composed and performed by ALAIN GORAGUER
    -S/T- *DC RECORDINGS (Vital): DC 33(CD)(LP)*
FANTASTIC VOYAGE (1966) Music sco: LEONARD ROSENMAN
    complete score *Ltd Ed.Imp Coll* 'POSEIDON ADV.'
    RETROGRADE (S.Screen/MFTM): FSMCD Vol.1 No.3 (CD)
FANTASTICKS The - songs by Harvey Schmidt & Tom Jones
    1.ORIG BROADWAY CAST 1960 *with:* JERRY ORBACH-RITA
    GARDNER-KENNETH NELSON *TER (Koch): CDTER 1099*
    2.JAPAN TOUR CAST REC. *DRG (Pinn) DRGCD 19005 (CD)*
FANTASY ISLAND (USA TV) *see COLL.247,*

FAR FROM HOME: ADVENTURES OF YELLOW DOG (1996) Music:
    JOHN SCOTT -S/T- *JOHN SCOTT (S.Scr): JSCD 118(CD)*
FAR FROM THE MADDING CROWD (1967) Mus: RICHARD RODNEY
    BENNETT -S/T- *CHAPTER III (S.Sounds) CHPT 1005-2CD
    new recording by* BBC PHILHARMONIC ORCHESTRA on
    CHANDOS: CHAN 9867 (CD)
FARANDOLE (1944) *see* 'HUNCHBACK OF NOTRE DAME' (1956)

FAREWELL TO ARMS, A (1957) Mus: MARIO NASCIMBENE -S/T-
    +'SONS AND LOVERS' *DRG (Pinn): DRGCSD 32962 (CD)*
    also avail: inc.mus. from 'The Barefoot Contessa'
    on *LEGEND Import (Silva Screen): LEGENDCD 11 (CD)*
FAREWELL TO MY CONCUBINE (1993) Music sco: ZHAO JIPING
    -S/T- *VARESE (Pinn): VSD 5454 (CD)*
FARGO (1996) Mus.sco: CARTER BURWELL + 'BARTON FINK'
    -S/T- *SNAPPER (Pinn): SMMCD 614 (CD)*
FARINELLI: IL CASTRATO (1995) Classical music -S/T-
    AUVIDIS Travelling (Harmonia Mundi): K.1005 CD)

FARMING (BBC 1950's) theme music "A Quiet Stroll"
CHARLES WILLIAMS *see COLL.119,*
FARSCAPE (USA) (BBC2 29/11/1999) Music by SUBVISION
and GUY CROSS -S/T- *GNP CRESCENDO (USA) (- CD)*
FAST AND THE FURIOUS (2001) Music score by BRIAN TYLER
-S/T- VARIOUS ARTS *DEF JAM (UNIV): 548 832-2 (CD)*
FASTER PUSSYCAT (1968) V/A with 'LORNA'/'VIXEN' -S/T-
NORMAL-QDK MEDIA (Pinn/Greyh/Dir) QDKCD 008 (CD)
FATAL ATTRACTION (1987) Music sco: MAURICE JARRE -S/T-
GNP USA (ZYX) GNPD 8011 (CD) opera m: "Un Bel Di"
(Madam Butterfly) (PUCCINI) *see COLL.153,154,197,*
FATHER CHRISTMAS (C4-25/12/91) music: MIKE HEWER perf:
Phoenix Chamber Orch (Julian Bigg) narrated by Mel
Smith -S/T- *COLUMBIA (TEN): 469 475-2 (CD) -4 (MC)*
FATHER OF THE BRIDE (1991) Music score: ALAN SILVESTRI
-S/T- *VARESE (Pinn): VSD 5348 (CD)*
FAWLTY TOWERS (BBC2 1975/79) theme by DENNIS WILSON
see COLL.283,
FEAR AND LOATHING IN LAS VEGAS (1998) VARIOUS ARTISTS
-S/T- *GEFFEN (BMG): GED 25218 (CD)*
FEAR IS THE KEY (1972) Music score by ROY BUDD -S/T on
CINEPHILE Pinn: CINCD(LP) 002 (CD/LP) see COLL.48.
FEARLESS VAMPIRE KILLERS (67) M: KRZYSTOF KOMEDA -S/T-
+'ROSEMARY'S BABY' *POLONIA (S.Scr): POLONIA CD 160*
FEDS (1988) Music score and songs: RANDY EDELMAN -S/T-
GNP (Greyhound/ZYX) GNPD 8014 (CD)
FETCH THE VET (CITV 18/09/2000) t.music by PHIL BUSH
see COLL.285,
FELICIA'S JOURNEY (1999) Music score by MYCHAEL DANNA
-S/T- *MILAN (BMG): 74321 71772-2 (CD)*
FENN STREET GANG The (LWT 24/9/71) theme "The Dandy"
DENIS KING *see COLL.3,*
FEVER (2000) Music score by JOE DELIA -S/T- (USA) on
PACIFIC TIME ENTERTAINMENT (USA): (- CD)
FEVER PITCH (1996) Music: NEIL MacCOLL & BOB HEWERDINE
-S/T- *BLANCO Y NEGRO (TEN): 0630 18453-2 (CD)*
FIDDLER ON THE ROOF - songs Jerry Bock-Sheldon Harnick
  1. FILM MUSICAL 1971 *feat* TOPOL -S/T- *30th anniversary
     edit.+ prev.unreleased tracks EMI: 535 266-2 (CD)
     UNITED ARTISTS (EMI): CDP 746091-2 (CD)*
  2. CARLTON SHOWS COLLECTION 1995 *feat:* ANTHONY NEWLEY
     TRACEY MILLER-MARION DAVIES-LINDA HIBBERT-NICK
     CURTIS-DAVID HITCHEN *CARLTON: 30362 0014-2(CD)*
  3. STUDIO RECORDING 1968 *featuring:*
     ROBERT MERRILL-MOLLY PICON-ROBERT BOWMAN-ANDY COLE
     LONDON FESTIVAL ORCHESTRA (Stanley Black) *reissue:
     DECCA (Univ): 448 949-2 (CD)*
  4. ORIG LONDON CAST 1967 *inc:* TOPOL-MIRIAM KARLIN-
     SANDOR ELES-HEATHER CLIFTON-LINDA GARDNER-
     *SONY West End (TEN): SMK(SMT) 53499 (CD/MC)
     SONY CLASSICAL (TEN): SMK 89546 (CD)*
FIELDS OF AMBROSIA sgs: MARTIN SILVESTRI-JOEL HIGGINS
ORIG LONDON CAST *feat:* CHRISTINE ANDREAS & Comp.
FIRST NIGHT (Pinn): CASTCD 58 (CD)

FIERCE CREATURES-DON'T PET THEM (1996) Music score:
JERRY GOLDSMITH -S/T- *VARESE (Pinn): VSD 5792 (CD)*
FIFTEEN MINUTES (2000) Music score: ANTHONY MARINELLI-
J.PETER ROBINSON -S/T- VARIOUS ARTISTS
MILAN-BMG IMPORTS: 74321 84668-2 (CD)
FIFTEEN-TO-ONE (C4 11/1/1988-2002) mus.by PAUL McGUIRE
FIFTH ELEMENT The (1997) Music sco: ERIC SERRA -S/T-
VIRGIN (EMI): CDVIRX 63 (CD) MCVIRX 63 (MC)
FIFTY-FIVE DAYS AT PEKING (1961) Mus: DIMITRI TIOMKIN
on 'HIGH NOON' *RCA (BMG): 09026 62658-2 (CD)*
FIGHT CLUB (1999) Music by the DUST BROTHERS -S/T- on
RESTLESS-RCA (BMG): 74321 71643-2 (CD)
SIMPLY VINYL (Vital): SVLP 161 (LP)
FILM 2001 WITH JONATHAN ROSS (BBC1 1972-2001) *theme:*
"I Wish I Knew How It Would Feel To Be Free" by
BILLY TAYLOR TRIO on 'FILM 2000 WITH JONATHAN ROSS'
VIRGIN: VTDCD(MC) 328 (2CD/MC) see COLL.104,200,283,
FILTH AND THE FURY The (2000) Music: The SEX PISTOLS
-S/T- *VIRGIN (EMI): CDVD 2908 (CD)*
FINAL FANTASY: THE SPIRITS WITHIN (2001) Music: ELLIOT
GOLDENTHAL -S/T- *SONY CLASSICS: SK 89697 (CD)*
FINDERS KEEPERS - *see under* 'MUDHONEY'
FINDING FORRESTER (2001) VAR.JAZZ ARTISTS SOUNDTRACK on
SONY JAZZ (TEN): 501 765-2 (CD)
FINIAN'S RAINBOW - songs by Burton Lane & E.Y.Harburg
1.ORIGINAL BROADWAY CAST 1947 *inc:* ELLA LOGAN-ALBERT
SHARPE-DONALD RICHARDS-DAVID WAYNE-ANITA ALVAREZ
SONY CLASSICS (TEN): SMK 89208 (CD)
2.REVIVAL BROADWAY CAST 1960 *with:* JEANNE CARSON
RCA (Silva Screen): 1057-2 (CD) 1057-4 (MC)
3.REPRISE MUSICAL REPERTORY COMPANY *including* 'KISS
ME KATE'/'SOUTH PACIFIC'/'GUYS & DOLLS'
REPRISE (TEN): 9362 47775-2 (4CD set)
FIORELLO (O.BROADWAY C.1959) Songs (Jerry Bock-Sheldon
Harnick) TOM BOSLEY-PATRICIA WILSON-ELLEN HANLEY
EMI ANGEL: ZDM 565 023-2 (CD)
FIRE OVER ENGLAND (1937) see *COLL.7,8,*
FIREBALL XL5 (ATV/ITV 25/3/63) theme song: BARRY GRAY
by DON SPENCER see *COLL.2,24,38,74,84,218,242,250,*
FIREMAN SAM (BBC/SC4-88) theme music: Ben HENEGHAN and
IAN LAWSON *sung by* MALDWYN POPE see *COLL.132,285,*
FIRST BLOOD (82) Music: JERRY GOLDSMITH voc: DAN HILL
-S/T- *INTRADA (S.Scr): FMT 8001D (CD) see* 'RAMBO'
also on VARESE (Pinn): VSD 6155 (CD)
FIRST GREAT TRAIN ROBBERY (1978) see 'WILD ROVERS'
FIRST MEN IN THE MOON The (1964) Music score: LAURIE
JOHNSON *CLOUD NINE:ACN 7015 (CD) see COLL.156,158,*
FIRST OF THE FEW (1942) Music incl: "Spitfire Prelude
and Fugue" (WILLIAM WALTON) L.P.Orch (Sir A.Boult)
HMV: ED 2911129-4 (MC) with 'Things To Come'
FIRST SNOW OF WINTER (BBC1 1998) see *COLL.20,*
FISHER KING The (1991) Music sco: GEORGE FENTON -S/T-
arts include Harry Nilsson-Brenda Lee-Chill Rob.G
MCA (UNI): MCAD 10249 (CD) MCAC 10249 (MC)

FIST OF FURY (1972) Music score by JOSEPH KOO -S/T-
  YX (CARGO): YX 7001 (LP)
FISTFUL OF DOLLARS, A (1964) Music sc: ENNIO MORRICONE
  -S/T- complete *inc* 'FOR A FEW DOLLARS MORE' (1965)
  /'ONCE UPON A TIME IN THE WEST' (1968)
  RCA (BMG): 74321 66040-2 (CD) also 'A FISTFUL OF
  SOUNDS' *SIMPLY VINYL (Telstar): SVLP 83 (LP)*
  see COLL.175,178,204,277,279,
FISTFUL OF DYNAMITE, A (Duck You Sucker!) (1971) Music
  ENNIO MORRICONE *DRG USA (Pinn) DRGCD 32907 (CD)*
  see COLL.177,
FITZ The (BBC2 04/08/2000) theme music: SHARON SHANNON
  incidental music by PHIL POPE *unavailable*
FIVE DAYS AND FIVE NIGHTS (FILM) Music: D.SHOSTAKOVICH
  mus.score inc.music from 'THE GADFLY' (1955)
  NAXOS (Select): 8.553299 (CD)
FIVE EASY PIECES (1970) *Coll NAXOS (Sel): 8551156 (CD)*
FIVE FINGERS (1952) Music score by BERNARD HERRMANN
  new score recording MOSCOW SYMPHONY ORCH conduct.by
  WILLIAM STROMBERG inc: 'SNOWS OF KILIMANJARO' score
  MARCO POLO (Select): 8.225168 (CD)
FIVE GUYS NAMED MOE (O.LONDON CAST 1991) Song & Dance
  Review w.music by LOUIS JORDAN *feat:* CLARKE PETERS
  FIRST NIGHT (Pinn): CAST(C)(CD) 23 DELETED 1998
  'Five Guys Named Moe'(L.JORDAN) *MCA:MCLD 19048 CD*
  L.JORDAN & TYMPANY 5 *BANDSTAND (H.Mund):BDCD 1531*
FIVE HEARTBEATS The (1991) Various Arts -S/T- *VIRGIN
  Movie Music (EMI): CDVMM 4 (CD) TCVMM 4 (MC)*
FIX The (1997 LONDON CAST) JOHN BARROWMAN-PHILIP QUAST
  FIRST NIGHT (Pinn): CASTCD 62 (CD) CASTC 62 (MC)
FLAME AND THE ARROW (1950) MAX STEINER *see COLL.239,*
FLAMING STAR *see* ELVIS PRESLEY INDEX p.348
FLAMINGO KID The (1984) Music sco: CURT SOBELL + V/A
  -S/T- *re-issue SPECTRUM (Univ): 551 539-2 (CD)*
FLASH GORDON (1980) Music & Songs: QUEEN -S/T- reiss:
  EMI: CDP 789 499-2 (CD) TCPCSD 137 (MC)
FLASHDANCE (1983) Mus: GIORGIO MORODER t.song IRENE
  CARA -S/T- *CASABLANCA: 811 492-2(CD) PRIMC 111(MC)*
FLASHPOINT (1985) Music score: TANGERINE DREAM -S/T-
  ONE WAY (Greyhound): 18507 (CD)
FLEET'S IN (1942) DOROTHY LAMOUR-BETTY HUTTON -S/T-
  selections with 'YOLANDA AND THE THIEF' on
  GREAT MOVIE THEMES (BMG): CD 60033 (CD)
FLEMISH FARM The (1943) Music score: VAUGHAN WILLIAMS
  MARCO POLO (Select): 8.223665 (CD)
FLESH AND THE DEVIL (1926) Contemporary score by CARL
  DAVIS *see COLL.85,215,*
FLETCH (1985) Music: HAROLD FALTERMEYER + STEPHANIE
  MILLS-KIM WILDE-DAN HARTMAN *MCA: DMCF 3284(CD)*
FLIGHT OF THE DOVES (1971) Music score by ROY BUDD
  song DANA -S/T- *CINEPHILE (Pinn): CINCD 010 (CD)*
FLIGHT OF THE PHOENIX (1970) Music: JERRY GOLDSMITH
  with 'PATTON' (GOLDSMITH, 1970) on
  RETROGRADE (S.Screen/MFTM): FSMCD Vol.2 No.2 (CD)

FLIM FLAM MAN The (1967) Music score: JERRY GOLDSMITH
  -S/T- *including score from* 'A GIRL NAMED SOONER'
  RETROGRADE (FSM): FSMCD VOL.2 NO.9 (CD)
FLINTSTONES The (USA 61/85) "Meet The Flinstones" (H.
  Curtin) TV-S/T- reiss: *MCI (MCI-THE): MCCD(MCTC)
  181 (CD/MC) see COLL.259,*
FLINTSTONES The (FILM 1993) Music: HOYT CURTIN & oth)
  MCA (UNI): MCD 11045 (CD) and MCA 11100 (CD)
FLIPPER (USA 1964) *see COLL.242,*
FLORA THE RED MENACE - songs: John Kander & Fred Ebb
  OFF BROADWAY CAST 1987 *TER (Koch): CDTER 1159 (CD)*
FLORADORA (ORIG LONDON CAST 1899) Mus (Leslie Stuart)
  Lyrics (Ernest Boyd-Jones and Paul Rubens)
  PEARL (Harmonia Mundi): OPALCD 9835 (CD)
FLOYD COLLINS (Musical 1996 USA) Songs: ADAM GUETELL
  w: CHRISTOPHER INNVAR-JESSE LENAT-THERESA McCARTHY
  NONESUCH (TEN): 7559 79434-2 (CD)
FLUBBER (1997) Music score by DANNY ELFMAN -S/T- *reiss
  EDEL-DISNEY (Vital) 017 566-2DNY (CD)*
FLUCHTWEG ST.PAULI (1971) Music: PETER SCHIRMANN -S/T-
  CRIPPLED DICK-HOT WAX (Greyh-SRD):EFA 27611-2 (CD)
FLY The (1986) Music score: HOWARD SHORE -S/T- on
  VARESE (Pinn): VCD 47272 (CD)
FLYING DOWN TO RIO (1933 MUSICAL) FRED ASTAIRE-GINGER
  ROGERS-DOLORES DE RIO *incl.songs from* 'HOLLYWOOD
  HOTEL' *TARGET (BMG): CD 60008 (CD)*
FOG The (1979) Music score by JOHN CARPENTER
  *SILVA SCREEN (Koch): FILMCD 342 (CD) / also on
  VARESE (Pinn): VCD 47267 (CD) also see COLL.57,*
FOLLIES - songs by Stephen Sondheim
  1.ORIG LONDON CAST 1987 *feat:* JULIA McKENZIE-DIANA
  RIGG-DANIEL MASSEY-DAVIE HEALEY-DOLORES GRAY & Co
  FIRST NIGHT (Pinn): OCRCD 6019 (CD)
FOLLOW THAT DREAM *see* ELVIS PRESLEY INDEX p.348
FOLLOW THE BOYS (1944) VARIOUS -S/T- SELECTIONS on
  GREAT MOVIE THEMES: (Targ-BMG): CD 60032 (CD)
FOLLOW THE FLEET (1936) FILM MUSICAL *feat* FRED ASTAIRE
  GINGER ROGERS -S/T- *sel.on* 'Let's Swing and Dance'
  +songs from 'SWING TIME'/'TOP HAT'/'CAREFREE'
  GREAT MOVIE THEMES (Target-BMG): CD 60015 (CD)
  -S/T- + songs from 'SWING TIME' *IRIS Mus-Chansons
  Cinema (Discovery): CIN 006 (CD) also see COLL.21,*
FOLLYFOOT (ITV 1971) theme "Lightning Tree" (Steve
  Fracis) sung by The SETTLERS *see COLL.5,*
  and "Meadow Mist" *MARCO POLO: 8223517 (CD)*
FOOD & DRINK (BBC2 26/10/1999) 99/2000 ser.theme music
  by STEVE BROWN *unavailable* / 1993-98 theme: SIMON
  MAY *COLL* 'NEW VINTAGE' *ARC Total: CDART102 DELETED*
FOOTBALL *see* EUROPEAN CHAMPIONS LEAGUE/MATCH OF T.DAY
FOOTLIGHT PARADE (1933 MUSICAL) *inc:* JAMES CAGNEY-JOAN
  BLONDELL-RUBY KELLER DICK POWELL *incl.songs from*
  'STAR SPANGLED RHYTHM' *TARGET (BMG): CD 60013 (CD)*
FOOTLOOSE (Rock Film 1984) Music by KENNY LOGGINS
  -S/T- *reissue COLUMBIA: CBS 493 007-2 (CD)*

FOOTLOOSE (ORIGINAL BROADWAY CAST RECORDING)
   FIRST NIGHT (Pinn): CASTCD 74 (CD)
FOR A FEW DOLLARS MORE (1965) Music: ENNIO MORRICONE
   -S/T- complete with 'A FISTFUL OF DOLLARS' (1964)
   'ONCE UPON A TIME IN THE WEST' (1968)
   RCA (BMG): 74321 66040-2 (CD)   see *COLL.175,178,*
FOR ME AND MY GAL (1942) *feat:* JUDY GARLAND-GENE KELLY
   reissued -S/T- *EMI ODEON: CDODEON 12 (CD)*
FOR RICHER OR POORER (1997) Music score: RANDY EDELMAN
   -S/T- *VARESE (Pinn): VSD 5891 (CD)*
FOR ROSEANNA - see 'ROSEANNA'S GRAVE'
FOR THE BOYS (1991) Music sco: DAVE GRUSIN with BETTE
   MIDLER -S/T- *ATLANTIC TEN: 7567 82329-2(CD) -4(MC)*
FOR THE LOVE OF THE GAME (1998) Music score by BASIL
   POLEDOURIS -S/T- *VARESE (Pinn): VSD 6092 (CD)*
FOR WHOM THE BELL TOLLS (1943) see *COLL.284,*
FOR YOUR EYES ONLY - *see* JAMES BOND FILM INDEX p.346
   see *COLL.46,47,*
FORBIDDEN GAMES (1952) *COLL: NAXOS: 8551171 (CD)*
FORBIDDEN PLANET (1954) Music sco: LOUIS & BEBE BARRON
   -S/T- *GNP USA (Greyhound):PRD 001 (CD) PR 001 (LP)*
   also SILVA SCREEN: FILMXCD 190 (2CD) see COLL.233,
FORCES OF NATURE (1998) Music score: JOHN POWELL -S/T-
   DREAMWORKS-POLY: DRD 50111 or 450 111-2 (CD)
FOREVER AMBER (1947) Music score: DAVID RAKSIN. *NEW*
   COMPLETE RECORDING on VARESE (Pinn): VSD 5857 (CD)
FOREVER KNIGHT (USA TV series) music sco: FRED MOLLIN
   -S/T- *GNP (ZYX): GNPD 8043 (CD)*
FOREVER PLAID (O.LONDON CAST 1993) American 50s/60s
   Hit Musical *FIRST NIGHT (Pinn):CASTCD 33 (CD)*
FORMULA ONE GRAND PRIX (ITV 7/3/97-2001) theme music
   by JAMIROQUAI *special arrangement / unavailable*
FORREST GUMP (1993) Music sco: ALAN SILVESTRI + V.Arts
   -S/T- songs *EPIC TEN:504 494-2 (2CD) see COLL.182,*
FORSYTE SAGA The (BBC1 1967) Theme "Elizabeth Tudor"
   Three Elizabeths ERIC COATES see *COLL.2,24,74,*
FORTY-SECOND STREET - *see under* 42ND STREET
FOSSE THE MUSICAL (1999)
   (O.BROADWAY CAST) *RCA (BMG): 09026 63379-2 (CD)*
   (O.LONDON CAST 99) *RCA (BMG): 74321 72157-2 (CD)*
FOUR FEATHER FALLS (ITV 25/02/1960) t.song: BARRY GRAY
   MICHAEL HOLLIDAY 'EP Collect' *SEE FOR MILES (Pinn)*
   SEECD 311 (CD) see COLL.3,15,
FOUR FLIES ON GREY VELVET (1971) Mus: ENNIO MORRICONE
   -S/T- inc 'BIRD WITH THE CRYSTAL PLUMAGE' +
   'CAT O'NINE TAILS' *DRG (Pinn): DRGCD 32911 (CD)*
FOUR HORSEMEN OF THE APOCALYPSE (1921) Contemporary
   score by CARL DAVIS *see Collections* 'The SILENTS'
FOUR IN THE MORNING (1965) Music sco: JOHN BARRY -S/T-
   reiss.with 'ZULU' -S/T- *RPM (Pinn): RPM 195 (CD)*
   also on PLAY IT AGAIN (Koch): PLAY 002 (CD)
FOUR JILLS IN A JEEP (1944) DICK HAYMES-BETTY GRABLE
   CARMEN MIRANDA-JIMMY DORSEY + mus. 'Lady Be Good'
   GREAT MOVIE THEMES (Target-BMG): CD 60029 (CD)

FOUR WEDDINGS AND A FUNERAL (1993) Music sco: RICHARD
RODNEY BENNETT -S/T- *VERTIGO (Univ):516 751-2 (CD)*
new recording by BBC PHILHARMONIC ORCHESTRA on
CHANDOS: CHAN 9867 (CD) also see COLL.64,95,

FOURTH KING The Music score by ENNIO MORRICONE -S/T-
DRG (Pinn): DRGCD 12622 (CD)

FOX The (1967) Music score by LALO SCHIFRIN
-S/T- *WB (TEN) 9362 47880-2 and 8573 87364-2 (CDs)*
ALEPH (Koch): ALEP 017 (CD)

FOX AND THE HOUND The - *see* WALT DISNEY INDEX p.341

FOXBAT (1977) Music score by ROY BUDD *reissued -S/T-*
inc 'INTERNECINE PROJECT' and 'SOMETHING TO HIDE'
CINEPHILE CINCD 019 (CD)

FRANCES (1982) Music sco JOHN BARRY *see COLL.26,32,37,*

FRANCIS OF ASSISI (1961) Music: MARIO NASCIMBENE -S/T-
with 'DOCTOR FAUSTUS' *DRG (Pinn): DRGCD 32965 (CD)*

FRANKENSTEIN (1931) Music score by DAVID BROEKMAN on
SOUNDTRACK FACTORY (Discov): SFCD 33554 (CD)

FRANKENSTEIN (1973) Music score by JAMES BERNARD -S/T-
GDI (Apex/Univ): GDICD 011 (CD)
see COLL.273, see also 'MARY SHELLEY'S..'

FRANKENSTEIN AND THE MONSTER FROM HELL - *see COLL.127,*

FRANKENSTEIN CREATED WOMAN (1966) *see COLL.127,*

FRANKENSTEIN MUST BE DESTROYED *see COLL.126,*

FRANKIE AND JOHNNY *see* ELVIS PRESLEY FILM INDEX p.348

FRANKIE STARLIGHT (1995) Music score: ELMER BERNSTEIN
-S/T- *VARESE (Pinn): VSD 5679 (CD) see COLL.40,*

FRASIER (USA 93/C4 20/4/94) title mus by BRUCE MILLER
DARRYL PHINNESSEE song "Tossed Salads and Scrambled
Eggs" performed by KELSEY GRAMMER on COLL 'FRASIER'
BMG IMPORTS: 74321 82419-2 (CD) / *theme vers.also*
available on 'HIT TV' *VARESE (Pinn): VSD 5957 (CD)*

FRED (BBC2 1/10/84) + **FRED DIBNAH STORY** (BBC2 28/8/96)
LIFE WITH FRED (BBC2 10/3/94) series theme music
"Carnival Of Venice" Op.77 (BRICCIALDI) version by
JAMES GALWAY flute *RCA (BMG): 09026 68882-2 (CD)*

FRED DIBNAH'S MAGNIFICENT MONUMENTS (BBC2 17/02/2000)
original music by ELIZABETH PARKER *unavailable*

FREDDIE AS F.R.O.7 1992 M: DAVID DUNDAS-RICK WENTWORTH
-S/T- *MCI (THE-DISC): FRO7 CD1(CD) FRO7 MC1(MC)*

FREDDY GOT FINGERED (2001) Music score by MIKE SIMPSON
-S/T- *RESTLESS (VITAL): PIASREST 002CD (CD)*

FREDDY'S DEAD: THE FINAL NIGHTMARE (A NIGHTMARE ON ELM
STREET 6)(1991) Mus: BRIAN MAY -S/T- *METAL BLADE*
(Pinn): CDZZORRO 33 (CD) ZORRO 33 (LP)

FREE ENTERPRISE (2000) Music score by SCOTT SPOCK -S/T-
VARIOUS ARISTS on *UNFORSCENE (Pinn): 40009-2 (CD)*

FREE WILLY (1993) Mus: BASIL POLEDOURIS *see COLL.182,*

FREE WILLY 2: The Adventure Home (1995) Music: BASIL
POLEDOURIS -S/T- *SM: 480 739-2 / -4 deleted*

FREE WILLY 3: The Rescue (1997) Music: CLIFF EIDELMAN
-S/T- *VARESE (Pinn): VSD 5830 (CD)*

FREEJACK (1991) Music score: TREVOR JONES -S/T- *reiss*
MORGAN CREEK (Univ): 002247-2 (CD)

FREEWHEELERS The (ITV 70's) theme music "Private Eye"
LAURIE JOHNSON *see COLL.3,156,*
FRENCH KISS (1995) Music score: JAMES NEWTON HOWARD
-S/T- *MERCURY (Univ): 528 321-2 (CD) -4 (MC)*
FRENCH LIEUTENANT'S WOMAN The (1981) Music: CARL DAVIS
'Adagio' Sonata in D.K576 (MOZART) John Lill (pno)
-S/T- *DRG (Pinn): DRGCD 6106 (CD)*
FRENCH TWIST - *see* 'GAZON MAUDIT'
FRENZY (1972) Music score by RON GOODWIN *see CLL.141,*
FRESH PRINCE OF BEL-AIRE (USA 1990/BBC2 14/1/91)
music by WILL SMITH *see COLL.248,*
FRIDAY (1994) Music sco: HIDDEN FACES -S/T- *PRIORITY
VIRGIN (EMI): CDPTY 117 (CD) PTYMC 117 (MC)*
FRIDAY NIGHT'S ALL WRIGHT (ITV 13/11/1998) theme music
"Shaft" by ISAAC HAYES *VIRGIN (EMI): VTCD 59 (CD)*
FRIDAY THE 13TH (TV Series) (USA 89)(ITV-13/7/90) mus
score by FRED MOLLIN -S/T- on *GNP Crescendo USA
(Greyhound): GNPD 8018 (CD) GNPS(5) 8018 (LP/MC)*
FRIED GREEN TOMATOES (1992) Music score: THOMAS NEWMAN
-S/T- *MCA: MCAD 10461 (CD)*
FRIENDLY PERSUASION (1956) Music sco: DIMITRI TIOMKIN
t.song (D.Tiomkin-P.F.Webster) sung by PAT BOONE
-S/T- *VARESE (Pinn): VSD 5828 (CD)*
FRIENDS (NZ/C4 28/4/95) theme mus "I'll Be There For
You" (Michael Skloff-Allee Willis) by REMBRANDTS
-S/T- *(TEN): 9362 46008-2 (CD) 9362 46008-4 (MC)*
'FRIENDS AGAIN' *REPRISE: 9362 47100-2 (CD) -4(MC)*
see COLL.139,260,- 'TV 2000' *SONYTV82CD*
FRITZ THE CAT (1971) Music sco: ED BOGAS-RAY SHANKLIN
CHARLES EARLAND -S/T- inc 'Heavy Traffic' score
*FANTASY (Pinn): FCD 24745 (CD) also available on
MOVING IMAGE (Cargo/Silver Sounds): MIE 003 (LP)*
FROG DREAMING Music score by BRIAN MAY -S/T- also inc:
'THE WILD DUCK' (music by SIMON WALKER)
SOUTHERN CROSS (HOT): SCCD 1019 (CD)
FROG PRINCE The (1984) Music score: ENYA -S/T- *re-iss
SPECTRUM (Univ): 551 099-2 (CD)*
FROM DAWN TIL DUSK (1995) Music score: GRAEME REVELL
-S/T- *EPIC Soundtrax (Ten): 483 617-2 (CD)*
FROM HELL (2001) Music score by TREVOR JONES -S/T- on
VARESE (Pinn): VSD 6296 (CD)
FROM RUSSIA WITH LOVE (1963) Music: JOHN BARRY title
song (L.Bart) MATT MONRO -S/T- *EMI: CZ 550 (CD)*
see COLL.26,31,34,35,36,45,46,75,171,186,222,
see also JAMES BOND FILM INDEX p.346
FROST - *see under* 'TOUCH OF FROST'
FUGITIVE The (USA ABC/QM 1963-66) theme by PETE RUGOLO
LONDON STUDIO SYMPHONY ORCH (Harry Rabinowitz) on
SILVA SCREEN (Koch): FILMCD 326 (CD)
see COLL.24,75,84,245,261,
FUGITIVE The (1993) Music: JAMES NEWTON HOWARD -S/T-
ELEKTRA (TEN): 7599 61592-2 (CD) see COLL.252,
FULL CIRCLE (The Haunting Of Julia) (1976) Music score
COLIN TOWNS -S/T- *KOCH Screen (Koch): 38703-2(CD)*

FULL METAL JACKET (1987) Songs by various artists
  -S/T- *W.BROS (TEN): 925 613-2 (CD) -4 (MC)*
  also with 'CLOCKWORK ORANGE' and 'BARRY LYNDON'
  WARNER ESP: 9362 47517-2 (3CD set)
FULL MONTY The (FILM 1996) Music: ANNE DUDLEY -S/T-
  HOT CHOCOLATE-TOM JONES-M.PEOPLE-SERGE GAINSBOURG-
  STEVE HARLEY & COCKNEY REBEL-GARY GLITTER-WILSON
  PICKETT-IRENE CARA-DONNA SUMMER-SISTER SLEDGE etc
  Volume 1 *RCA (BMG): 09026 68904-2 (CD) -4 (MC)*
  Volume 2 *RCA (BMG): 74321 60448-2 (CD) -4 (MC)*
  see COLL.95,
FULL MONTY The (SHOW ORIG BROADWAY CAST) songs: DAVID
  YAZBECK *BMG IMPORTS: 09026 63739-2 (CD)*
FUN IN ACAPULCO *see* ELVIS PRESLEY INDEX p.348
FUNNY BONES (1995) Music score: JOHN ALTMAN -S/T- on
  EDEL UK (Vital): 002930-2EDL (CD)
FUNNY FACE (1957) Songs: GEORGE & IRA GERSHWIN *with:*
  AUDREY HEPBURN-FRED ASTAIRE-KAY THOMPSON-MICHEL
  AUCLAIR *VERVE (Univ): 531 231-2 (CD)*
FUNNY GIRL - songs by Jule Styne and Bob Merrill
  FILM SOUNDTRACK 1968 *feat:* BARBRA STREISAND -S/T-
  COLUMBIA (Ten): 462 545-2 (CD) -4 (MC)
FUNNY THING HAPPENED ON THE WAY TO THE FORUM, A
  songs by Stephen Sondheim
  1.FILM 1966 -S/T- *RYKODISC (Vital): RCD 10727 (CD)*
  2.JAZZ VER: TROTTER TRIO *VARESE (Pinn):VSD 5707 (CD)*
FUNNY WOMEN (BBC2 4/10/97) theme "Funny Face" (G.& I.
  I.Gershwin) by FRED ASTAIRE 'FUNNY FACE' -S/-T
  VERVE (Univ): 531 231-2 (CD)
FURIA (1999) Music score by BRIAN MAY -S/T-
  EMI PARLOPHONE: 528 585-2 (CD)
FURY The (1978) Music sc: JOHN WILLIAMS / LONDON S.O.
  -S/T- import *VARESE (Pinn): VSD 5264 (CD)*
G.B.H. (C4 6/6/91) mus: RICHARD HARVEY-ELVIS COSTELLO
  -S/T- music by ELVIS COSTELLO & RICHARD HARVEY
  DEMON (Pinn): DSCD 4(CD) DSCASS 4(MC) DSLP4 (LP)
G.I.BLUES (1960) feat ELVIS PRESLEY remastered -S/T-
  RCA (BMG): 07863 67460-2 / 07863 66960-2 (CD) -4
  also on CASTLE MUSIC (Pinn): ELVIS 106 (LP)
  see also ELVIS PRESLEY INDEX p.348
G.I.JANE (1997) Music score: TREVOR JONES -S/T- on
  POLYDOR: 162 109-2 (CD)
GADFLY The (1955) Music Suite Op.97A (D.SHOSTAKOVICH)
  score incl.music from 'FIVE DAYS AND FIVE NIGHTS'
  NAXOS (Select): 8.553299 (CD) recording also on
  CFP (EMI) CDCFP 4463 (CD) -4 (MC)
GALAPAGOS IN 3D (2001) Music score by MARK ISHAM -S/T-
  MILAN (BMG IMPORTS): 74321 81968-2 (CD)
GALLIPOLI (1981) *see COLL.197,*
GAMBLER The (1997) Mus: TCHAIKOVSKY adapt: BRIAN LOCK
  -S/T- *VIRGIN CLASSICS (EMI): VC 545 312-2 (CD)*
GAME OF DEATH (1979) Music score: JOHN BARRY c/w NIGHT
  GAMES (Barry) *SILVA SCREEN (Koch):FILMCD 123 (CD)*
  GAME OF DEATH also on *DAGORED (Koch): RED 121 (LP)*

GAME ON (Hat-Trick for BBC2 27/2/95) theme music "When I Find My Heaven" by The GIGOLO AUNTS on 'Flippin' Out' *FIRE Records (Pinn): FIRECD 35 (CD)*

GAMEKEEPER The (BBC1 28/7/95) Music by The IRON HORSE -S/T- 'Voice Of The Land'-THE IRON HORSE on *KLUB (Gord.Duncan/Ross/Topic): CD(ZC)LDL 1232 (CD/MC)*

GANG RELATED (1998) -S/T- featuring VARIOUS ARTISTS *DEATH ROW (RMG/UNIVERSAL MUSIC): DROW 104 (2CD) PRIORITY-VIRGIN (EMI): CDPTY(PTYMC) 149 (CD/MC)*

GANGSTER NO.1 (C4 2000) Music by JOHNNY DANKWORTH-NEIL HANNON and Various Artists -S/T- on *CHANNEL 4 MUSIC-UNIVERSAL (Univ): C4M 0003-2 (CD)*

GANGWAY (1937) md: Louis Levy / 4 songs on 'LOUIS LEVY MUSIC FROM T.MOVIES' *EMPRESS KOCH: RAJCD 884 (CD)*

GARDEN The (1990) Music sc: SIMON FISHER TURNER -S/T- *IONIC (Pinn): IONIC 5C (MC) IONIC 5CD (CD)*

GARDEN OF DELIGHT (I GUARDIANI DEL CIELO) (2000 Italy) Music sco: ENNIO MORRICONE voc:ANTONELLA RUGGIERO -S/T- *RCA IMPORT (BMG IMP): 74321 72050-2 (CD)*

GARDEN OF EVIL (1954) Music score: BERNARD HERRMANN *new record:* MOSCOW SYMPHONY ORCH. (W.Stromberg) *also feat suite from* 'PRINCE OF PLAYERS' (1955) *MARCO POLO (Select): 8.223841 (CD) see COLL.1,*

GARDENER'S WORLD (BBC2/Catalyst) theme music 1993-98 series by NICK WEBB & GREG CARMICHAEL (ACCOUSTIC ALCHEMY) title track from "NATURAL ELEMENTS" on *GRP (New Note-BMG): GRP 01412 (CD)*

GARY RHODES NEW BRITISH CLASSICS "Pulsewidth" by The APHEX TWIN from 'Selected Ambient Works Vol.1" *APOLLO (3MV/Pinn): AMB 3922CD (CD) AMB 3922 (2LP)*

GAS FOOD AND LODGING (1992) Music sc: BARRY ADAMSON & V.Arts) *IONIC (RTM/Pinn): IONIC 9(C)(CD) (MC/CD)*

GASLIGHT *see COLL.8,*

GATTACA (1997) Music score: MICHAEL NYMAN -S/T- *VIRGIN VENTURE (EMI): CDVE 936 (CD) TCVE 936 (MC)*

GAUNTLET The (1977) Music score by JERRY FIELDING -S/T- on *WARNER (TEN): 9362 47882-2 (CD)*

GAZON MAUDIT (FRENCH TWIST) (1995) Music: MANUEL MALOU -S/T- *VIRGIN (EMI): CDVIR 49 (CD)*

GENDERQUAKE (C4 9/7/96) op.theme music "Ebben Ne Andro Lontano" from 'La Wally' (Catalini) sung by LESLEY GARRETT 'DIVA' *S.Screen (Koch): SONGCD 903 (CD)*

GENERAL The (1997) Music sco: RICHIE BUCKLEY songs by Var.Artists including VAN MORRISON-BRENDAN GLEESON -S/T- *HUMMINGBIRD (Dir/ADA/Pinn): HBCD 0018 (CD)*

GENERAL HOSPITAL (ITV 70's series) *theme (1)* "Girl In The White Coat" DEREK SCOTT *theme (2)* "Red Alert" *see COLL.172,200,*

GENERAL HOSPITAL (USA TV) *see COLL.246,*

GENERAL'S DAUGHTER The (1999) Music by CARTER BURWELL -S/T- *MILAN (BMG): 74321 69474-2 (CD)*

GENERATION GAME *see* JIM DAVIDSON'S GENERATION GAME

GENESIS (1986) Music composed/performed by RAVI SHANKAR -S/T- *MILAN (BMG IMPORTS): 74321 77741-2 (CD)*

GENEVIEVE (1953) Music score composed & performed by
  LARRY ADLER "Genevieve Waltz"/"Love Theme"/"Blues"
  'Best Of Larry Adler' *EMI GOLD: CD(TC)MFP 6259*
  "Genevieve Waltz" on *EMI: CD(TC)EMS 1543 (CD/MC)*
GENTLE BEN (USA TV) *see COLL.246,*
GENTLEMEN PREFER BLONDES - songs: Jule Styne-Leo Robin
  1.REVIVAL BROADWAY RECORDING 1995 *with:* K.T.SULLIVAN
  DRG (Pinn): DRGCD (DRGMC) 94762 (CD/MC)
GEORGE OF THE JUNGLE (1997) Music score: MARC SHAIMAN
  -S/T- *DISNEY (Vit) 010 444-2DNY (CD) see COLL.243,*
GERMINAL (1993) Music: JEAN LOUIS ROCQUES with ORCHES
  TRE NAT.DE LILLE -S/T- *VIRGIN (EMI) CDVIR 28 (CD)*
GET CARTER (2000) Music by TYLER BATES, theme ROY BUDD
  -S/T- score *SILVA SCREEN (Koch): FILMCD 348 (CD)*
  -S/T- songs *SILVA SCREEN (Koch): FILMCD 347 (CD)*
GET CARTER (1971) Music score by ROY BUDD -S/T- on
  CINEPHILE-CASTLE (Pinn):CMEDD 017 (2CD) +CINCD 001
  + *ESSPR 656 (CDs) ESSLP 656 (LP) see COLL.54,250,*
GET REAL (1997) Music score by JOHN LUNN -S/T- V.Arts.
  ARISTA (BMG): 74321 66590-2 (CD)
GET SHORTY (1996) Music score: JOHN LURIE -S/T- V.Arts
  US3-BOOKER T.& MG's-MORPHINE-GREYBOY etc.
  ANTILLES-ISLAND (Univ): 529 310-2 (CD) -4 (MC)
GET SMART (USA TV 60s) *see COLL.175,242,*
GET WELL SOON (BBC1 2/11/97) title theme song "In Over
  My Head" by CHRISTIE HENNESSEY sung by ALED JONES
  COALITION (TEN): COLA 032CD (CDs) COLA 032C (MC)
GHOST (1990) Music sco: MAURICE JARRE feat "Unchained
  Melody" (Alex North-Hy Zaret) - RIGHTEOUS BROTHERS
  -S/T- re-issue *MILAN (BMG): 4321 34278-2 (CD)*
  see COLL.61,73,153,154,191,
GHOST AND MRS.MUIR (1947) Music sco: BERNARD HERRMANN
  1-*DEFINITIVE (Discovery): SFCD 33508 (CD)*
  2-*VARESE (Pinn): VSD 5850 (CD)*
  3-*SILVA SCREEN (Koch) FILMCD 162(CD)*
  4-*SILVA SCREEN (Koch) FILMXCD 308 (2CD)*
  5-*VARESE (Pinn): VSD 5937 (CD) COLL.1,135,142*
GHOST AND MRS.MUIR (USA TV) *see COLL.246,*
GHOST AND THE DARKNESS (1997) Music s: JERRY GOLDSMITH
  -S/T- *EDEL-HOLLY (Vital) 012 089-2HWR (CD) COLL.3,*
GHOSTDOG: THE WAY OF THE SAMURAI (2000) Music by RZA
  -S/T- *EPIC (TEN): 496 146-2 (CD)*
GHOST HUNTER (BBC1 04/01/2000) music: DAVID CHILTON
GHOST IN MONTE CARLO, A (1990) music: LAURIE JOHNSON
  see COLL.156,158,
GHOST OF FRANKENSTEIN The (1942) music: CHARLES PREVIN
  new rec: SLOVAK RADIO SYMPHONY ORCH (William
  Stromberg,cond) *MARCO POLO (Select): 8.225124 (CD)*
GHOST SHIP The - *CNS 5008 (CD)*
GHOST SQUAD *see COLL.24,251,*
GHOST WORLD (2001) Music score by DAVID KITAY -S/T- on
  SHANACHIE (Proper): SHANCD 6056 (CD)
GHOSTBUSTERS (1984) Music sco: ELMER BERNSTEIN Title
  song: RAY PARKER JR -S/T- *ARISTA (BMG) 258720 (CD)*

GHOSTS OF MARS (2001) Music sco: JOHN CARPENTER -S/T-
VARESE (PINN): VSD 6286 (CD)
GI BLUES (1960) ELVIS PRESLEY -S/T- remastered *RCA BMG
07863 66960-2 (CD)* / *CASTLE (Pinn): ELVIS 106 (LP)*
see ELVIS PRESLEY INDEX p.348
GIANT (1956) Music: DIMITRI TIOMKIN suite on 'Western
Film World Of D.Tiomkin' LONDON STUDIO S.ORCH.
(L.Johnson) *U.KANCHANA (H.Mundi) UKCD 2011 (CD)*
also avail: complete score + 'EAST OF EDEN'/'REBEL
WITHOUT A CAUSE' *TSUNAMI (S.Screen):TSU 0201 (CD)*
GIDGET (USA TV) *see COLL.253*
GIGI - songs by Alan Jay Lerner and Frederick Loewe
  1.FILM MUSICAL 1958 LESLIE CARON-MAURICE CHEVALIER
  -S/T- *42 trks MGM (EMI Premier): CDODEON 10 (CD)*
  2.ORIG LONDON CAST 1985 *w:* SIAN PHILLIPS-BERYL REID-
  AMANDA WARING-JEAN PIERRE AUMONT-GEOFFREY BURRIDGE
  JOHN AARON *FIRST NIGHT (Pinn): OCRCD 6007 (CD)*
GILBERT & SULLIVAN OVERTURES LIGHT OPERA PRO-ARTE ORCH
(Sir M.Sargent) *CFP (EMI): CD(TC)CFP 4529 (CD/MC)*
GILDA (1946) Music score by HUGO FRIEDHOFER plus songs
SOUND TRACK FACTORY (Discovery): SFCD 33536 (CD)
GILLIGAN'S ISLAND (USA) *see COLL.242,*
GIMME GIMME GIMME (BBC2 08/01/1999) music: PHILIP POPE
arrang.of "Gimme Gimme Gimme" (Andersson-Ulvaeus)
TV version unavailable. ABBA version on *POLYDOR*
GIRL 6 (96)   PRINCE -S/T- *WEA:9362 46239-2(CD) -4(MC)*
GIRL CRAZY (1943) Songs by GEORGE & IRA GERSHWIN *feat:*
JUDY GARLAND-MICKEY ROONEY-TOMMY DORSEY ORCHESTRA
*SOUNDTRACK FACTORY (Discov): SFCD 33530 (CD) also
EMI SOUNDTRACKS: CDODEON 30 (CD)* new recording on
VIRGIN (EMI): VM 561247-2 (CD)
GIRL FIGHT (2000) Music score: TEDDY SHAPIRO -S/T-
VARIOUS ARTS *EMI IMPORT SOUNDTRACK: 529 194-2 (CD)*
GIRL FROM U.N.C.L.E. (USA TV) *see COLL.246,*
GIRL HAPPY *see* ELVIS PRESLEY INDEX p.348
GIRL INTERRUPTED (1999) Music score by MYCHAEL DANNA
-S/T- (V/A) *MILAN-RCA (BMGF): 74321 75484-2 (CD)*
IMP USA (Greyhound/Cargo): TVT 01658 16500-2 (CD)
GIRL NAMED SOONER, A (1975) Music sco: JERRY GOLDSMITH
-S/T- *including score from 'FLIM-FLAM MAN'* on
RETROGRADE (FSM): FSMCD VOL.2 NO.9 (CD)
GIRL ON A MOTORCYCLE (1968) Music by LES REED -S/T-
*RPM (Pinn): RPM 171 (CD) also available on
DAGORED (Cargo/APex/Silver Sounds): RED 1081 (LP)*
GIRL WHO CAME TO SUPPER The - songs by Noel Coward
  1.NOEL COWARD SINGS HIS SCORE (1963)
  DRG (Pinn): DRGCD 5178 (CD)
GIRL WITH BRAINS IN HER FEET The (1998) Music score by
ROB LANE -S/T- with VARIOUS ARTISTS inc: TOM JONES
SYMPOSIUM-SLADE-SWEET-STEREOPHONICS and others
V2 (Pinn): VVR 100265-2 (CD)
GIRLS GIRLS GIRLS *see* ELVIS PRESLEY INDEX p.348
GIVE MY REGARDS TO BROAD STREET (1984) PAUL McCARTNEY
J.LENNON -S/T- *EMI:CDP 789 268-2 (CD)*

GLADIATOR (2000) Music by HANS ZIMMER and LISA GERRARD
  feat METROPOLITAN ORCH & ENGLISH CHAMBER CHOIR
  -S/T- VOLUME 1 *DECCA-UNIVERSAL MUS: 467 094-2 (CD)*
  -S/T- VOLUME 2 *DECCA-UNIVERSAL MUS: 013 192-2 (CD)*
GLADIATORS (ITV 9/96) theme "Boys Are Back In Town"
  (P.Lynnot) GLADIATORS *RCA (BMG):74321 41699-2 CDs*
GLASS The (ITV 27/5/2001) Music by RICHARD G.MITCHELL
  -S/T- *ARISTA (BMG): 74321 87355-2 (CD)*
GLASS HOUSE (2001) Music score by CHRISTOPHER YOUNG
  -S/T- *VARESE (Pinn): VSD 6282 (CD)*
GLASS MOUNTAIN The (1949) Music score by NINO ROTA
  MANTOVANI ORC *HORATIO NELSON (THE): CDSIV 6128(CD)*
  see COLL.211,235,268,
GLENN MILLER STORY The (1954) Universal Studio Orch
  -S/T- *MCA (UNI): MCLD 19025 (CD)*
GLOBAL SUNRISE (BBC 1/1/97) Music score: BRIAN BENNETT
  -S/T- *OCEAN DEEP (Grapev/Poly): OCD 002 (CD)*
GLOBE TREKKER (Sat.C1/2002) Var.Instrumental mus -S/T-
  BMG: Vol.1: 74321 87177-2 (CD) Vol.2: 87178-2 (CD)
GLORY (1989) Music score: JAMES HORNER w. Boys Choir
  Of Harlem -S/T- *VIRGIN: CDV(TCV)V 2614 (CD/MC)*
GO! (1998) VARIOUS ARTS -S/T- *feat* NO DOUBT-LEFTFIELD-
  NATALIE IMBRUGLIA-FATBOY SLIM-AIR and others
  HIGHER GROUND SONY: HIGH 8CD (CD) HIGH 8MC (MC)
GO INTO YOUR DANCE (1935) DUBIN-WARREN songs with AL
  JOLSON-RUBY KEELER -S/T- + songs from 'MELODY FOR
  TWO'/'YOU CAN'T HAVE EVERYTHING'/'YOU'LL NEVER GET
  RICH' *GREAT MOVIE THEMES (BMG): CD 60014 (CD)*
GOBLIN MARKET (O.OFF BROADWAY CAST 1987) Songs: POLLY
  PENN-PEGGY HARMON from Christina Rossetti story
  feat TERRY KLAUSNER-ANN MORRISON and Company
  JAY-TER (SSD: CDJAY 1237 (CD)
GODFATHER The (1972) Mus sc: NINO ROTA -S/T- *MCA (UNI)*
  MCLD 19022 (CD) SUITE: *S.Screen (Koch): FILMCD 077*
  see COLL.61,175,211,
GODFATHER II (1974) Music sco: NINO ROTA -S/T- *reiss*
  MCA (UNI): MCAD 10232 (CD)
GODFATHER III (1991) M: CARMINE COPPOLA. Theme: NINO
  ROTA. voc, HARRY CONNICK JR -S/T- *SONY: 467 813-2*
  see COLL.73,204,
GODFATHER TRILOGY - The Milan Philharmonic Orchestra
  CARMINE COPPOLA cond.Milan Philh.Orch music from 3
  GODFATHER Films (Music: NINI ROTA-CARMINE COPPOLA)
  SILVA SCREEN (Koch): FILMCD 344 (CD)
GODMONEY (1997) -S/T- *V2 (34MV-Pinn):VVR 100060-2 (CD)*
GODS AND MONSTERS (1999) Music score: CARTER BURWELL
  -S/T- *RCA (BMG): 09026 63356-2 (CD)*
GODSPELL - songs by Stephen Schwartz
  1.FILM -S/T- 1973 *feat:* VICTOR GARBER-DAVID HASKELL-
  JERRY STOKA-LYNNE THIGPEN-ROBIN LAMONT -*S/T*-
  ARIOLA (S.Screen): ARCD 8337 (CD) ACB6 8337 (MC)
  2.O.BROADWAY CAST 71 *feat* DAVID HASKELL-LAMAR ALFORD
  JOHANNE JONAS-ROBIN LAMONT-SONIA MANZANO-STEPHEN
  NATHAN-JEFFREY MYLETT *ARIOLA IMP: ARCD 8304 (CD)*

3.STUDIO RECORDING 1993 JOHN BARROWMAN-CLAIRE BURT
JACQUELINE DANKWORTH-RUTHIE HENSHALL-GLYN KERSLAKE
PAUL MANUEL-CLIVE ROWE-SAMANTHA SHAW-DARREN DAY
Highlights: *CURTAIN CALL-MCI (Disc): CURTCD 006 CD*
Complete: *TER (Koch): CDTER 1204 (CD)*
GODZILLA (Film Ser.) - *see COLL.82,138,174,*
GODZILLA 2000 (aka GODZILLA MILLENNIUM) (2000)
    Music score by TAKAYUKI HATTORI -S/T- on
    GNP CRESCENDO (Import): GNPD 8065 (CD)
GODZILLA (1954-1984) Var.music scores from Japanese
    monster series NEW SYMPHONIC DIGITAL RECORDINGS
    VARESE (Pinn): VSD 5920 (CD) see also COLLECTIONS
    'MONSTER MANIA' (compil.) *VARESE: VSD 5969 (CD)*
GODZILLA (1954-1984) Var.music from the TOHO FILMS
    Music by AKIRA IFUKUBE & others
    BEST OF GODZILLA 1 *SILVA SCREEN (Koch): FILMCD 201*
    BEST OF GODZILLA 2 *SILVA SCREEN (Koch): FILMCD 177,*
GODZILLA (1998) Music score: DAVID ARNOLD / Var.Arts
    COLUMBIA-SONY (Ten): 489 610-2 (CD) -4 (MC) -8 (MD)
GODZILLA Vs MEGAGUIRUS (2000) Music by MICHURU OSHIMA
    -S/T- *IMPORT GNP USA: GNPD 8072-2 (CD)*
GOHATTO (1999) Music score by RYUICHI SAKAMOTO -S/T-
    BMG IMPORTS: 74321 76688-2 (CD)
GOING FOR A SONG (BBC1 1971-2000) theme mus "Prelude"
    from 'The Birds' (RESPIGHI) *various recordings*
GOING MY WAY (1944) *feat* BING CROSBY -S/T- select +
    'BORN TO DANCE' *GREAT MOVIE THEMES (BMG): CD 60031*
GOING STRAIGHT (BBC1 24/2/1978) - *see COLL.283,*

GOLD DIGGERS (1995) Music score: JOEL McNEELY -S/T-
    VARESE (Pinn): VSD 5633 (CD)
GOLD DIGGERS OF 1933 (MUSICAL) DICK POWELL-RUBY KEELER
    ER-JOAN BLONDELL-GINGER ROGERS *includes songs from*
    'ROSE OF WASHINGTON SQUARE' & 'THE DOLLY SISTERS'
    TARGET (BMG): CD 60009 (CD)
GOLD RUSH The (1925) Music: CHARLES CHAPLIN *see*
    'FILM MUS.OF CHARLES CHAPLIN' *RCA: 09026 68271-2*
    MAX TAK ORCH *BASTER (Direct): BASTER 309050 (CD)*
GOLDEN APPLE The (MUSICAL 1954) Songs: JEROME MOROSS-
    JOHN LATOUCHE *featur:* PRISCILLA GILLETTE-STEPHEN
    DOUGLASS-KAYE BALLARD-JONATHAN LUCAS-JACK WHITING
    Broadway Cast Rec. *RCA (BMG): 09026 68934-2 (CD)*
GOLDEN BOWL The (1999) Music score by RICHARD ROBBINS
    -S/T- (score) *MILAN (BMG): 74321 78472-2 (CD)*
GOLDEN BOY (SHOW 1964) Songs CHARLES STROUSE-LEE ADAMS
    O.BROADWAY C.feat: SAMMY DAVIS JNR-BILLY DANIELS-
    PAULA WAYNE-LOUIS GOSSETT-LOLA FALANA-KEN.TOBEY
    RAZOR & TIE (Koch): RE 82177-2 (CD)
GOLDEN EARRINGS (1947) Music score: VICTOR YOUNG *feat*
    MURVYN VYE with MARLENE DIETRICH-RAY MILLAND -S/T-
    extracts including music from 'GONE WITH THE WIND'
    GREAT MOVIE THEMES (Delta-BMG): CD 60050 (CD)
GOLDEN GIRLS The (USA)(C4 1/8/86) Theme "Thank You For
    Being a Friend" (Andrew GOLD) *see COLL.247,*

GOLDEN VOYAGE OF SINBAD (1973) Music sco: MIKLOS ROSZA
Complete score: *PROMETHEUS (S.Scr): PCD 148 (CD)*
see *COLL.213,214,240,*
GOLDENEYE - see JAMES BOND FILM INDEX p.346
see *COLL.46,47,*
GOLDFINGER (1964) Mus: JOHN BARRY title song (J.Barry
L.Bricusse-A.Newley) sung by SHIRLEY BASSEY -S/T-
-S/T- *reissue EMI PREMIER (EMI): CZ 557 (CD)*
see *COLL.26,28,29,36,46,47,171,175,*
see also JAMES BOND FILM INDEX p.346
GOLF (BBC1/2 1970s-2002) theme music "Chase Side Shoot
Out" (Brian Bennett) by BRIAN BENNETT *deleted*
GOMER PYLE (USA TV) see *COLL.243,*
GONDOLIERS The - songs by Gilbert and Sullivan
  1.D'OYLY CARTE OPERA COMPANY - New Symph Orchestra
   (Isadore Godfrey) *LONDON (Univ): 425 177-2 (CDx2)*
  2.NEW SADLERS WELLS OPERA STUDIO RECORDING
   TER: CDTER2 1187 (2CD)
  3.PRO-ARTE ORCHESTRA (Sargent) GLYNDEBOURNE FESTIVAL
   CHOIR Soloists:Geraint Evans-Alexander Young-Owen
   Brannigan-R.Lewis *EMI: CMS 764 394-2 (2CDs)*
  4.DOYLY CARTE OPERA ORCH & CHORUS *with* 'RUDDIGORE'
   PEARL (Harmonia Mundi): GEMS 0135 (3CDs)
GONE IN 60 SECONDS (2000) Music score by TREVOR RABIN
-S/T- (songs) V/A *MERCURY (Univ): 542 793-2 (CD)*
-S/T- (score)   *VARESE (Pinn): VSD 6182 (CD)*
GONE TO TEXAS Music score: DENNIS McCARTHY -S/T- *IMPT.
IMPRT (Silva Screen): PCD 142 (CD)*
GONE WITH THE WIND (1939) Music sco: MAX STEINER -S/T-
with addition.unissued items *digitally re-mastered
EMI ODEON (EMI): CDODEON 27 (2CD)* also available:
National Philharmonic Orchestra (Charles Gerhardt)
*RCA RED SEAL (BMG): GD 80452 (CD) GK 80452 (MC)
DEFINITIVE (Discovery): SFCD 33532 (CD)*
GONE WITH THE WIND Music score by MAX STEINER
-S/T- extracts including music & songs from movie
'GOLDEN EARRINGS' (1947) music by VICTOR YOUNG on
GREAT MOVIE THEMES (Delta-BMG): CD 60050 (CD)
see *COLL.69,239,*
GOOD MORNING VIETNAM (1988) Music score: ALAN MASON +
Var.Arts -S/T- *A.& M: CDMID 163 (CD) CMID 163 (MC)*
GOOD NEWS (1947) *feat* JUNE ALLYSON -S/T- selections +
'COVER GIRL' *GREAT MOVIE THEMES (BMG): CD 60033*
GOOD NEWS! MUSIC THEATRE OF WICHITA Songs B.G.DeSylva
Lew Brown-Ray Henderson *inc* KIM HUBER-ANN MORRISON
LINDA MICHELE-MICHAEL GRUBER *TER (Koch):CDTER 1230*
GOOD ROCKIN'TONITE (ORIG.LONDON CAST 1992) *JACK GOOD'S*
nostalgic look back at the 50's *with* PHILIP BIRD-
TIM WHITNALL-GAVIN STANLEY-JOE BROWN and Company
FIRST NIGHT (Pinn): OCRCD 6026 (MC/CD)
GOOD THE BAD & THE UGLY (1966) Music: Ennio Morricone
-S/T- *LIBERTY (EMI): CDP 748 408-2 (CD) also on
DAGORED (Koch): RED 1301 (2LPs)*
see *COLL.75,171,175,176,177,178,*

GOOD WILL HUNTING (1997) Music sco: DANNY ELFMAN -S/T-
EMI PREMIER SOUNDTRACKS (EMI): 823 338-2 (CD)
GOODBYE AGAIN (1961) Music score: GEORGES AURIC
see *COLL.190*,
GOODBYE CHARLIE BRIGHT (2000) Music score: IVOR GUEST
-S/T- VARIOUS ARTISTS *TELSTAR (BMG): TCD 3187 (CD)*
GOODBYE GIRL O.LONDON CAST 1996 (Marvin HAMLISCH-Don
BLACK) *featur* GARY WILMOT-ANN CRUMB and Company
FIRST NIGHT (Pinn): CASTCD 63 (CD) CASTC 63 (MC)
FIRST NIGHT (Pinn): SCORECD 44 (CDsingle)
GOOBYE MR.CHIPS (O.CHICHESTER CAST 1979) *w:* JOHN MILLS
TER (Koch): CDTER 1025 see *COLL.7*,
GOODFELLAS The (1990) Music score: CHRISTOPHER BROOKS
-S/T- *ATLANTIC (TEN): 7567 82152-2 (CD)*
GOODIES The (BBC1 1970-1980) Music: BILL ODDIE-MICHAEL
GIBBS 'Best Of' feat BILL ODDIE-GRAEME GARDEN-TIM
BROOKE TAYLOR on *CASTLE PIE (Pinn): PIESD 243 (CD)*
GOODNIGHT SWEETHEART (BBC1 18/11/93-1999) title song
(RAY NOBLE) TV version by NICK CURTIS *unavailable
original by* AL BOWLLY with RAY NOBLE ORCHESTRA on
EMI: CDP 794 341-2 (CD) / incidental music by
Anthony & Gaynor SADLER *unavailable* 'GOODNIGHT
SWEETHEART' & others sung by ELIZABETH CARLING
(Phoebe) on *UNIVERSAL: 547 548-2 (CD) -4 (MC)*
GOODTIME CHARLEY (MUSICAL) Songs: LARRY GROSSMAN & HAL
HACKADY Broadway Cast *RCA (BMG): 09026 68935-2 CD*
GORKY PARK (1983) Music sco: JAMES HORNER -S/T- reiss:
VARESE (Pinn): VCD 47260 (CD)
GORMENGHAST (BBC2 17/01/2000) Music by RICHARD RODNEY
BENNETT with Choral music by JOHN TAVENER. played
by BBC PHILHARMONIC, The ACADEMY OF ANCIENT MUSIC
with The TEMPLE CHURCH CHOIR and JAKE ARDITTI
SONY CLASSICAL (TEN): SK 89135 (CD)
also available: IRMIN SCHMIDT: GORMENGHAST on
SPOON-MUTE (Vital): SPOONCD 44 (CD)
GOTHIC (1987) Music: THOMAS DOLBY feat Screaming Lord
Byron (Tim Spall) -S/T- *VIRGIN (EMI): CDV 2417*
GOVERNESS The (1997) Music sco: EDWARD SHEARMUR -S/T-
SONY CLASSICS: SK 60685 (CD)
GRADUATE The (1967) Songs: PAUL SIMON & ART GARFUNKEL
-S/T- *COLUMBIA (Ten): 40-32359 (MC) CD 32359 (CD)*
also on *SIMPLY VINYL (Telstar): SVLP 39 (LP)*
GRAFFITI BRIDGE (1990) Mus: PRINCE -S/T- *Paisley Park
WB (TEN): 759927493-2 (CD) WX(C) 361 (LP/MC)*
GRAND CANYON (1992) Music score: JAMES NEWTON HOWARD
-S/T- *MILAN (BMG): 262493 (CD) 412493 (MC)*
GRAND DAY OUT,A (Wallace & Gromit) music: JULIAN NOTT
v/o PETER SALLIS -S/T- with 'The Wrong Trousers'
BBC: ZBBC 1947 (MC) BBC Video: BBCV 5155
(Grand Day Out) *BBCV 5155* (Wrong Trousers) *(VHS)*
GRAND NATIONAL (BBC Grandstand) opening music theme
from film "Champions" 1983 (CARL DAVIS) *DELETED*
GRAND PRIX (BBC 1978-1996) theme "The Chain" orig by
FLEETWOOD MAC from 'Rumours' *WEA: K2 56344 (CD)*

GRAND PRIX (ITV from 1997)
  see under F1 (FORMULA 1) *also see COLL.101,*
GRANDSTAND (BBC1 began 8/10/1958-2002) *THEME MUSIC*
  76-2002 KEITH MANSFIELD *see COLL.3,101,122,*
  1958 "News Scoop" LEN STEVENS *see COLL.5,122,*
GRANGE HILL (BBC1 1978-96) *theme mus (1978-1989)*
  "Chicken Man" (ALAN HAWKSHAW) *deleted*
  1990-2001 theme PETER MOSS *unavailable*
GRASS HARP The (USA BROADWAY MUSICAL PLAY)
  ORIG BROADWAY CAST *VARESE (Pinn): VSD 6010 (CD)*
GRATEFUL DAWG (2000) GRATEFUL DEAD FILM DOCUMENTARY
  -S/T- ACCOUSTIC DISC (Koch): ACD 46 (CD)
GREASE - songs by Jim Jacobs-Warren Casey-Gibb Bros
  John Farrar-Louis St.Louis-S.Simon and others
  1. FILM MUS.1978 JOHN TRAVOLTA-OLIVIA NEWTON JOHN
     FRANKIE VALLI-STOCKARD CHANNING-FRANKIE AVALON
     POLYDOR (Univ): 044041-2 (CD) 044041-4 (MC) and
  2. O.LONDON CAST 1993 CRAIG McLACHLAN-DEBBIE GIBSON
     VOYD EVANS & Co *Epic (SM): 474 632-2 (CD) -4 (MC)*
  3. STUDIO RECORD 1994 JOHN BARROWMAN-SHONA LINDSAY
     ETHAN FREEMAN-MARK WYNTER-SALL ANN TRIPLETT & Comp
     Highlights: *CURTAIN CALL-MCI (DISC): CURTCD 004 CD*
     Complete: *TER (Koch): CDTER 1220 (CD)*
  4. CARLTON SHOWS COLL (Studio 93) CARL WAYNE-MICHAELA
     STRACHAN *CARLTON: PWKS(PWKMC) 4176 (CD/MC)*
  5. NEW BROADWAY CAST 1994 *RCA (BMG): 09026 62703-2 CD*
  6. STUDIO RECORDING VARIOUS ARTISTS *HALLMARK (ABM):*
     30395-2 (CD) -4 (MC)
  7. ALL THE HIT SONGS VARIOUS ARTISTS
     CASTLE PIE (Pinn): PIESD 078 (CD)
GREAT BALLS OF FIRE ORIG.LONDON CAST HIGHLIGHTS 1999
  FIRST NIGHT (Pinn): SCORECD 47 (CD)
GREAT CARUSO The (1950) feat the voice of MARIO LANZA
  RCA GOLD (BMG): GD(GK) 60049 (CD/MC)
GREAT COMPOSERS The (BBC2 7/12/1998) CLASSICAL MUSIC
  SELECTION *TELDEC/BBC/WARNER: 3984 21856-2 (2CD)*
GREAT DAY IN HARLEM, A (1995) Var.Arts CD *(not -S/T-)*
  ART BLAKEY-GENE KRUPA-DUKE ELLINGTON-DIZZY
  GILLESPIE-COUNT BASIE *SONY JAZZ (SM):460500-2 (CD)*
GREAT ESCAPE The (1962) Mus sco: ELMER BERNSTEIN -S/T-
  reiss *RYKODISC (Vital): RCD 10711 (CD, 09.1998)*
  also on *INTRADA USA (Koch Int): MAFCD 7025 (CD)*
  see COLL.40,123,146,
GREAT EXPECTATIONS (BBC1 12/04/1999) Mus: PETER SALEM
  BBC WORLDWIDE (Pinn): WMSF 6012-2 (CD)
GREAT EXPECTATIONS (1997) Music score: PATRICK DOYLE
  ATLANTIC (TEN): 7567 83058-2 (CD) -4 (MC)
GREAT EXPECTATIONS (ORIG CAST THEATR CLWYD, MOLD 1993)
  Songs: MIKE READ *featur* DARREN DAY-CHRIS CORCORAN-
  ELIZABETH RENEHAN-TAMARA USTINOV and Company
  TER (Koch): CDTEP 500 (CD) and CDTER 1209 (CD)
GREAT RACE The (1965) Music score: HENRY MANCINI -S/T-
  reissue with score from 'THE PARTY' (1968) on
  RCA CAMDEN (BMG): 74321 82238-2 (CD)

GREAT ROCK AND ROLL SWINDLE (1980) Music: SEX PISTOLS -S/T- *full VIRGIN (EMI): TCVD 2510(2MC) CDVD 2510 (2CDs) highlights: OVED 234 (LP) OVEDC 234 (MC)*

GREAT TRAIN ROBBERY (FIRST) - see *COLL.115,*

GREAT UNDERTAKINGS (C4 03/02/2000) theme "Come On Up To The House" by TOM WAITS from 'Mule Variations' *EPITAPH USA (Pinn): 65472 (CD) 65474 (MC)*

GREAT ZIEGFELD The (1936) ARTHUR LANGE (music dir) extracts on *DEFINITIVE (Discov): SFCD 33534 (CD)*

GREATEST AMERICAN HERO (USA TV) see *COLL.244,*

GREATEST SHOW ON EARTH The (1952) Music score: VICTOR YOUNG *NEW RECORDING by* MOSCOW SYMPHONY ORCHESTRA + *suites from* 'THE UNINVITED'/'GULLIVER'S TRAVELS' *MARCO POLO (Select): 8225063 (CD)*

GREATEST STORY EVER TOLD (1960) Music s: ALFRED NEWMAN -S/T- *RYKODISC (Vital): RCD 10734 (CD)*

GREED (1924 silent) Contemporary score by CARL DAVIS see *COLL.85,* 'The SILENTS'

GREEN ACRES (USA TV) see *COLL.242,*

GREEN BIRD (MUSICAL) ORIGINAL USA CAST RECORDING on *DRG USA (New Note-Pinn): DRGCD 12989 (CD)*

GREEN CARD (1991) Music score HANS ZIMMER -S/T- *VARESE (Pinn): VSD 5309 (CD) VSC 5309 (MC)*

GREEN HORNET The (USA TV) see *COLL.221,243,*

GREEN MILE The (1999) Music score by THOMAS NEWMAN -S/T- *WB (TEN): 9362 47584-2 (CD)*

GREENWICH MEAN TIME (1998) Music score: GUY SIGSWORTH -S/T- (VAR.ARTISTS) *ISLAND (Univ): CID 8092 (CD)*

GREENWILLOW (ORIG N.Y.CAST 1960) Songs: FRANK LOESSER *feat:* ANTHONY PERKINS-CECIL KELLAWAY-PERT KELTON *DRG USA (Pinn): DRGCD 19006 (CD)*

GREY FOX The (1982) Music score: MICHAEL CONWAY -S/T- *DRG (Pinn): CDSL 9515 (CD) + NAXOS: 8551172 (CD)*

GREY OWL (2000) Music score by GEORGE FENTON -S/T- *IMPORT (Discovery): LXE 710 (CD)*

GREYSTOKE: THE LEGEND OF TARZAN LORD OF THE APES (1984) *Coll: NAXOS (Sel): 8551160 (CD)*

GRIDLOCK'D (1997) Mus score: STEWART COPELAND V.ARTS -S/T- *DEATH ROW (RMG/UNIV): DROW 105 (CD)* also *MERCURY (Univ): 534 684-2 (CD) -4 (MC)*

GRIFTERS The (1990) ELMER BERNSTEIN see *COLL.40,*

GRIMLEYS The (ITV 08/03/1999) VAR.ARTISTS COMPILATIONS 'GRIMLEYS'VOL.1' *GLOBAL TV (BMG): RADCD 157 (CD)* 'GRIMLEYS VOL.2' *BMG TV: 74321 84268-2 (2CD)* theme "Bye Bye Baby" BAY CITY ROLLERS *ARISTA (BMG) 74321 26575-2 (CD)* closing theme "Mama Weer All Crazee Now" by SLADE *POLYDOR: 537 105-2 (CD)*

GRINCH The (2000) (HOW THE GRINCH STOLE CHRISTMAS) Music score by JAMES HORNER -S/T- score/soundtrack *INTERSCOPE UNIV: 490 765-2 (CD)*

GRINCH The (1965) Music score by ALBERT HAGUE -S/T- on *MERCURY (UNIV): 528 438-2 (CD)*

GRIND (O.BROADWAY CAST 1985) Songs (LARRY GROSSMAN and
  ELLEN FITZHUGH) *with* Ben Vereen-Leilani Jones & Co
  TER (Koch): CDTER 1103 (CD)
GRIZZLY ADAMS - *see* 'LIFE AND TIMES OF GRIZZLY ADAMS'
GROUND FORCE (BBC2 1997-2001) theme music by JIM PARKER
  performed by The BLACK DYKE MILLS BAND
  -S/T- *BBC MUSIC (Pinn): WMSF 6015-2 (CD) -4 (MC)*
  also avail: 'ALAN TITCHMARSH IN A COUNTRY GARDEN'
  (Classics Selection) *SONY CLASS: SONTV 85CD (CD)*
GROUNDHOG DAY (1092) Music score: GEORGE FENTON -S/T-
  Imp: CB 53760 (CD) deleted / see COLL.195,269,
GROUPIE GIRL (1970) Various Artists -S/T- *reissue with*
  'BEYOND THE VALLEY OF THE DOLLS' (1970) V.Artists
  SCREEN GOLD (Greyhound): SGLDCD 0010 (CD)
GROWING PAINS (BBC1 16/5/92) theme music: NIGEL HESS
  see COLL.137,247,
GUIDE FOR THE MARRIED MAN (1967) Music score by JOHNNY
  WILLIAMS -S/T- *FSM (USA): FSM VOL.3 NO.5 (CD)*
GULLIVER'S TRAVELS (1939) Music score by VICTOR YOUNG
  NEW RECORDING by MOSCOW SYMPHONY ORCHEST.+ *suites
  from* 'THE UNINVITED'/'THE GREATEST SHOW ON EARTH'
  MARCO POLO (Select): 8225063 (CD)
GULLIVERS TRAVELS (C4 7/4/96) mus score: TREVOR JONES
  -S/T- *RCA IMPT (Silva Screen): RCA 68475-2 (CD)*
GUMMO (1998) V.ARTS -S/T- *DOMINO (Vit): WIGCD 052 (CD)*
GUN LAW (also known as GUN SMOKE)(USA 55-75)
  theme music (Koury-Spencer) *see* **GUNSMOKE**
GUN SHY (2000) Music score by ROLFE KENT -S/T- on
  HOLLYWOOD-EDEL (Vital): 011 708-2HWR (CD)
GUNS FOR SAN SEBASTIAN (1968) Music score by ENNIO
  MORRICONE -S/T- inc: 'DARK OF THE SUN' (JACQUES
  LOUSSIER) on *CHAPTER III (USA): CHA 0134 (CD)*
GUNS OF NAVARONE The (1961) Music sco: DIMITRI TIOMKIN
  -S/T- suite *U.KANCHANA: DKPCD 9047 (CD) DELETED*
  see COLL.61,123,254,265,
GUNSMOKE *see COLL.245,*
GUYS AND DOLLS - songs by Frank Loesser
  1.50th Anniversary edition VARIOUS ARTISTS
    DRG USA (Koch): DRGCD 19017 (CD)
  2.REV.LONDON N.THEATRE CAST 1982 IAN CHARLESON-JULIE
    COVINGTON-DAVID HEALY-BOB HOSKINS-JULIA McKENZIE
    reiss MFP (EMI): CD(TC)MFP 5978 (CD/MC)
  3.ORIG BROADWAY CAST 1950 ROBERT ALDA-VIVIENE BLAINE
    STUBBY KAYE *MCA: MCLD 19155 / MCAD(MCAC) 10301*
  4.NEW BROADWAY CAST 1991 Walt Bobbie-John Carpenter-
    Steve Ryan-Ernie Sabella-Herschel Sparber
    RCA (BMG): 09026 61317-2(CD) -4(MC) -5(DCC)
  5.CARLTON SHOWS COLLECT.1995 DENNIS LOTIS-BARBARA
    WINDSOR-KEITH MICHELL-BERNARD CRIBBINS and Company
    CARLTON SHOWS Collect: 30362 0013-2 (CD) -4 (MC)
  6.STUDIO RECORDING 1995 EMILY LOESSER-GREGG EDELMAN
    TIM FLAVIN-DAVID GREEN-KIM CRISWELL-DON STEPHENSON
    <u>Complete:</u> *TER (Koch): CDTER 1228 (CD)*
    <u>Highlights:</u> *TER (Koch): CDTEH 6007 (CD)*

7.Songs by FRANK LOESSER / 'The Best Of'
   VARIOUS ARTISTS *EMPORIO (Disc): EMPRCD 802 (CD)*
8.REPRISE MUSICAL REPERTORY COMPANY *including* 'KISS
   ME KATE'/'SOUTH PACIFIC'/'FINIAN'S RAINBOW'
   REPRISE (TEN): 9362 47775-2 (4CD set)
   also as a single CD on 9362 45014-2 (CD)
GYPSY - songs by Jules Styne and Stephen Sondheim
   1.ORIG BROADWAY CAST 1959 *w.*ETHEL MERMAN and Company
     COLUMBIA USA IMPORT: CK 32607 (CD) JST 32607 (MC)
   2.ORIG LONDON CAST 1973 ANGELA LANSBURY-DEBBIE BOWEN
     JUDY CANNON-ZAN CHARISSE-BARRIE INGHAM and Company
     RCA IMPORT: 60571-2 (CD) 60571-4 (MC)
H ACKERS (1996) Music score: SIMON BOSWELL -S/T- *feat:*
   STEREO MCs-ORBITAL-LEFTFIELD-UNDERWORLD-PRODIGY...
   EDEL-CINERAMA (Vital) 002256-2 CIN (CD)
HADDON HALL (MUSICAL) Songs by Sir ARTHUR SULLIVAN and
   SYDNEY GRUNDY. EDINBURGH PRINCE CONSORT CHORUS &
   ORCH (David Lyall) *DIVINE ART (D1 Mus) 21201 (2CD)*
HADLEIGH (Yorkshire 29/10/69-76) theme mus: TONY HATCH
   see COLL.2,131,200,
HAIR - songs by Galt McDermott-Jerome Ragni-James Rado

   1.1979 Film Cast, Re-mastered 20th anniv.edition)
     RCA (BMG): 07863 67812-2 (CD)
   2.ORIG BROADWAY CAST 1968 STEVE CURRY-RONALD DYSON
     MELBA MOORE *RCA Victor (BMG): BD 89667 (CD)*
   3.ORIG LONDON CAST 1968 PAUL NICHOLAS-VINCE EDWARDS
     OLIVER TOBIAS *POLYDOR (Univ): 519 973-2 (CD)*
   4.CARLTON SHOWS COLLECTION 1995 CARL WAYNE-NICOLA
     DAWN-BOBBY CRUSH-JOHN HOWARD *prod:* Gordon Lorenz
     CARLTON Shows Collect: 30362 0015-2 (CD) -4 (MC)
   5.STUDIO RECORDING - SHOWS COLLECTION
     SHOWTIME (Disc): SHOWCD 055 (CD)
HAIR BEAR BUNCH (USA 1971) "Help It's The Hair Bear
   Bunch'(H.Curtain-Roland-Williams) *see COLL.259,*
HAIRDRESSER'S HUSBAND (1990) Music score: MICHAEL NYMAN
   M.NYMAN BAND *SILVA SCREEN (Koch): DM 2490-2 (CD)*
HALF COCKED (1995) *feat* VARIOUS ARTISTS -S/T- *MATADOR*
   (Vital): OLE 152-2 (CD) -1 (LP)
HALLOWEEN (THE BEST OF HALLOWEEN 1-6) S/track Master
   VARESE (Pinn): VSD 5773 (CD)
   see COLL.57,83,138,150,219,
HALLOWEEN 1 (1978) Music sc: JOHN CARPENTER -S/T- Imp
   VARESE USA (Pinn): VSD 5970 (CD) & VCD 47230 (CD)
HALLOWEEN 2 (1981) Music sco: JOHN CARPENTER -S/T- Imp
   VARESE USA (Pinn): VCD 47152 (CD)
HALLOWEEN 3 (1983) Mus: ALAN HOWARTH-J.CARPENTER -S/T-
   VARESE (Pinn): VSD 5243 (CD)
HALLOWEEN 4 (1988) Music sco: ALAN HOWARTH -S/T- Impt
   VARESE (Pinn: VSD 5205 (CD) see COLL.58,
HALLOWEEN 5 (1989) Music sco: ALAN HOWARTH -S/T- Impt
   VARESE (Pinn): VSD 5239 (CD) see COLL.58,
HALLOWEEN 6 (1995) Music score: ALAN HOWARTH -S/T-
   VARESE (Pinn): VSD 5678 (CD)

HAMISH MACBETH (BBC1 Scot 26/3/95) series music by
   JOHN LUNN *deleted*
HAMLET (2000) Music score by CARTER BURWELL
   -S/T- score: *VARESE (Pinn): VSD 6125 (CD)*
   -S/T- songs: *RYKODISK: RCD 10495*
HAMLET (1990) Music score ENNIO MORRICONE -S/T-
   VIRGIN (EMI): CDVMM 3 (CD)
HAMLET (1964 USSR) Music: SHOSTAKOVICH score performed
   by BELGIAN RADIO SYMPHONY ORCHESTRA (Shostakovich)
   RCA Navigator Classics (BMG): 74321 24212-2 (CD)
HAMLET (1948) Music score: WILLIAM WALTON inc.mus.from
   'As You Like It' *CHANDOS (Chandos): CHAN 8842 (CD)*
HAMMETT (1982) Music score by JOHN BARRY -S/T-
   PROMETHEUS IMPORT: PCR 506 (CD)
HANCOCK (BBC 60s) m: DEREK SCOTT *see COLL.2,24,74,253,*
HAND THAT ROCKS THE CRADLE (1991) Music: GRAEME REVELL
   -S/T- *reiss EDEL-HOLLYWOOD (Vital) 013 304HWR (CD)*
HANDFUL OF DUST, A (1988) Music by GEORGE FENTON -S/T-
   OCEAN DISQUE (Pinn) CDLTD 071 + ***DRG:DRGCD 6110 (CD)***
HANDMAID'S TALE The (1990) Music sco: RYUICHI SAKAMOTO
   -S/T- *GNP (ZYX): GNPD 8020 (CD)*
HANGED MAN The (ITV 1975) Music score: ALAN TEW feat:
   BULLET -S/T- *DC Records (Vital): DC 015(CD)(LP)*
HANGING GARDEN The (1998) Music score: JOHN ROBY -S/T-
   VIRGIN (EMI): CDVIR 72 (CD)
HANGING TREE (1959) Music by MAX STEINER *see COLL.239,*
HANGING UP (2000) Music score by DAVID HIRSCHFELDER
   -S/T- (score) *VARESE (Pinn): VSD 6120 (CD)*
HANGOVER SQUARE (1945) Music score: BERNARD HERRMANN
   Suite on 'CONCERTO MACABRE' *KOCH INT: 37609-2 (CD)*
   -S/T- with 'HATFUL OF RAIN'/'ON DANGEROUS GROUND'
   TSUNAMI (S.Screen): TCI 0610 (CD) see COLL.268,
HANNAH 1939 (ORIG USA CAST) Songs: BOB MERRILL
   TER (Koch): CDTER 1192 (CD)
HANNAH AND HER SISTERS (1986) Music: COUNT BASIE Orch
   + HARRY JAMES ORCH -S/T- *MCA (UNI): IMCAC 6190(MC)*
   see COLL.64,
HANNAY (ITV 06/01/1988) music: DENIS KING *see COLL.20,*
HANNIBAL (2000) Music score by HANS ZIMMER -S/T- on
   LONDON (UNIV): 467 696-2 (CD) note "VIDE COR MEUM"
   from 'LA VITA NUOVA'(Dante Poem Setting with music
   by PATRICK CASSIDY) *unavailable*
HANOVER STREET (1979) Music: JOHN BARRY *see COLL.26,*
HANS ANDERSEN - songs by Frank Loesser
   1.FILM MUSICAL 1952 *feat:* DANNY KAYE 'Very Best Of
   MCA (UNI): MCLD 19049 (CD) MCLC 19049(MC) also on
   VARESE (Pin): VSD 5498 (CD) inc 'THE COURT JESTER'
   2.ORIG LONDON CAST 1974/77 TOMMY STEELE-SALLY ANN
   HOWES-ANTHONY VALENTINE-SIMON ANDREWS-LILA KAYE-
   MILO O'SHEA-COLETTE GLEASON-BOB TODD *reiss on 1CD*
   DRG-New Note (Pinn): DRGCD 13116 (CD)
HAPPY BIRTHDAY SHAKESPEARE (BBC 23/04/2000) end song
   "You Get What You Give" by The NEW RADICALS on
   MCA (Univ): MCSTD 48111 (CDs)

HAPPY DAYS (USA 74) *orig theme* "Rock Around The Clock"
(J.De Knight-M.Freedman) BILL HALEY & THE COMETS
MCA Rec (BMG) Title theme "Happy Days" (N.Gimbel-
Chas Fox) PRATT & McLAIN *see COLL.244,*

HAPPY TEXAS (1999) Music score by PETER HARRIS with a
V.ARTISTS -S/T- *BMG IMP (BMG): 077822 18898-2 (CD)*

HAPPY TRAILS (USA TV) *see COLL.242,*

HARBOUR LIGHTS (BBC1 18/02/1999) theme and score by
JOE CAMPBELL and PAUL HART *unavailable*

HARD BOILED (1993) music score: MICHAEL GIBBS -S/T-
IONIC-MUTE (RTM-Pinn): IONIC 11CD (CD)

HARD DAY'S NIGHT (1964) *Sgs* JOHN LENNON-PAUL McCARTNEY
BEATLES & GEORGE MARTIN -S/T- *PARLOPHONE EMI:*
CDP 746 437-2 (CD) PCS 3058 (LP) TCPCS 3058 (MC)

HARD RAIN (1998) Music by CHRISTOPHER YOUNG.conductor:
PETE ANTHONY -S/T- *MILAN (BMG): 74321 56425-2 (CD)*

HARD TARGET (1993) Music score: GRAEME REVELL -S/T- on
VARESE (Pinn): VSD 5445 (CD)

HARD TIMES: THE MUSICAL (2000) (Songs by CHRISTOPHER
TOOKEY) ORIG LONDON CAST (Highlights) on
FIRST NIGHT (Pinn): SCORECD 48 (CDs)

HARDBALL (2001) Music score by MARK ISHAM -S/T- on
COLUMBIA (TEN): 504 876-2 (CD)

HARDCASTLE AND McCORMICK (USA TV) *see COLL.14,203,247,*

HARDER THEY COME The (1971) Music & songs: JIMMY CLIFF
-S/T- *MANGO ISLAND: RRCD 61 (CD) RRCT 61 (MC)*

HARMAGEDDON (1982) Music score by KEITH EMERSON -S/T-
VOLCANO (Cargo): CPC 83003 (CD)

HARPIST The (1997) Music score: BRIAN BENNETT -S/T-
OCEAN DEEP (Grapevine/Polyg): OCD 011 (CD)

HARRY AND THE HENDERSONS (USA 90 BBC1 27/9/91) theme
"Your Feet's Too Big" (Ada Benson-F.Fisher & Ink
Spots) TV vers.sung by LEON REDBONE *unavailable*
INK SPOTS on *FLAPPER (Pinn): PASTCD 9757 (CD)*

HARRY POTTER AND THE PHILOSOPHER'S STONE (2001)
Music score by JOHN WILLIAMS -S/T-
ATLANTIC/EAST WEST (TEN): 07567 930865 (2CD/CDrom)
ATLANTIC/EAST WEST (TEN): 07567 834914 (MC)

HARRY HE'S HERE TO HELP (2000) Music by DAVID SINCLAIR
WHITAKER / also "Piano Sonata No.5" KV283 (Mozart)
-S/T- *VIRGIN (EMI): CDVIR 129 (CD)*

HARRY'S GAME (Yorkshire 25/10/82) music: PAUL BRENNAN
CLANNAD 'Ultimate Coll.'*(BMG) 74321 48674-2 (CD)*
see COLL.108,188,

HART TO HART (USA TV) *see COLL.244,*

HARUM SCARUM - see ELVIS PRESLEY FILM INDEX p.348

HARVEST (Regain) (1937) Music: ARTHUR HONEGGER suite
on *MARCO POLO (Select): 8.223467 (CD)*

HARVEY GIRLS The (1946) Songs: HARRY WARREN-JOHNNY
MERCER *feat:* JUDY GARLAND-RAY BOLGER-JOHN HODIAK
-S/T- *reiss: SOUNDTRACK FACTORY (Dir): SFCD 33527*

HATARI! (1962) Music: HENRY MANCINI -S/T- reiss.with
'HIGH TIME' *RCA CAMDEN (BMG): 74321 82239-2 (CD)*
also see COLL.61,170,258,

HAUNTED (1995) Music score: DEBBIE WISEMAN -S/T-
  SILVA SCREEN (Koch): TRXCD 2002 (CD)
HAUNTING The (1999) Music score: JERRY GOLDSMITH
  VARESE (Pinn): VSD 6054 (CD)
HAVE GUN-WILL TRAVEL (USA 57) "The Ballad Of Paladin"
  (Richard Boone-J.Western-S.Rolfe) JOHNNY WESTERN
  'Americana' *COLUMB: 468 121-2 (CD) see COLL.243,*
HAVE I GOT NEWS FOR YOU (BBC2 28/9/90-2002 theme tune
  performed by BIG GEORGE *see COLL.283,*
HAWAII 5-0 (USA 1968-80) theme music: MORTON STEVENS
  see COLL.77,83,124,200,242,243,
HAWAIIAN EYE (USA TV) *see COLL.243,*
HAZARD OF HEARTS, A (1987) Music by LAURIE JOHNSON
  see COLL.156,158,
HE GOT GAME (1998) Music score: AARON COPLAND
  -S/T- score: *SONY CLASSICS: SK 60593 (CD)*
  -S/T- songs: *MERCURY (Univ): 558 130-2 (CD)*
HE'S GOT THE GAME (1998) Mus: AARON COPLAND songs by
  PUBLIC ENEMY -S/T- *MERCURY: 558 130-2 (CD) -4(MC)*
HEAD (1968) Music performed by The MONKEES featuring:
  MICKEY DOLENZ-DAVY JONES-MIKE NESMITH-PETER TORK
  -S/T- *RHINO/ATLANTIC (TEN): 4509 97659-2 (CD)*
HEADS AND TAILS (BBC TV) *see COLL.132,*
HEAR MY SONG (1991) Music: JOHN ALTMAN Josef Locke's
  v/o VERNON MIDGLEY -S/T- *WEA: 7599 24456-2 (CD)*
  JOSEF LOCKE on 'Hear My Song' EMI: CDGO 2034 (CD)
HEART IN WINTER, A (Un Coeur En Hiver) (1991) Music sc
  (Philippe Sarde)'Sonata for Piano,Violin & Cello'
  (RAVEL) Complete mus *ERATO (TEN): 4509 92408-2(CD)*
  also on NAXOS 8551159 (CD)
HEART OF MIDNIGHT (1988) Music score: YANNI -S/T-
  SILVA SCREEN (Koch): FILMCD 119 (CD) see COLL.45,
HEARTBEAT (YTV 10/4/1992-2001) theme "Heartbeat"
  (N.Petty-Bob Montgomery) TV ver.sung by NICK BERRY
  'MOMENTS' *UNIVERSAL MUSIC: 584 093-2 (2CD)*
  'HEARTBEAT THE 10TH ANIVERSARY' Various Arts COLL
  GLOBAL TV (BMG): 74321 78963-2 (2CD) -4 (2MC) and
  'HEARTBEAT THE GOLD COLLECTION' (Various Artists)
  GLOBAL: RAD(CD)(MC) 90 (2CD/MC) also see COLL.77,
HEARTBREAK HIGH (Aust.94/BBC2 27/9/94) Various Music
  -S/T- *WEA (TEN): 4509 99938-2 (CD)*
HEARTBREAKERS (2001) Music score JOHN DEBNEY and theme
  by DANNY ELFMAN -S/T- (Various Artists) on
  RCA VICTOR BMG IMPORTS: 09026 63770-2 (CD)
HEARTBREAKERS (1984) Music sco: TANGERINE DREAM -S/T-
  SILVA SCREEN (Koch): FILMCD 163 (CD)
HEARTS AND BONES (BBC1 30/04/2000) music MARTIN PHIPPS
HEARTS IN ATLANTIS (2001) Music score by MYCHAEL DANNA
  -S/T- *IMPORT DECCA LONDON USA: 016 035-23 (CD)*
HEAT AND DUST (1982) *NAXOS (Select): 8551151 (CD)*
HEATHCLIFF - songs by John Farrar and Tim Rice
  1.LIVE 1996 RECORDING *feat* CLIFF RICHARD *with* HELEN
    HOBSON-SARA HAGGERTY and GORDON GILTRAP *(guitar)*
    EMI UK: CD(TC)EMD 1099 (2CD/MC)

2.STUDIO ALBUM 1995 *featuring* CLIFF RICHARD *with*
OLIVIA NEWTON JOHN-KRISTINA NICHOLS and others
EMI: CD(TC)EMD 1091 (CD/MC) *DELETED*.

HEAVEN'S GATE (1980) Music score by DAVID MANSFIELD
-S/T- reissue *RYKODISC (Vital): RCD 10749 (CD)*
see *COLL.83,279,*

HEAVEN'S PRISONERS (1995) Music score: GEORGE FENTON
-S/T- (songs) *CODE BLUE-WEA: 7567 82848-2 / -4*
-S/T- (score) *DEBONAIR (Pinn): CDDEB 1004 (CD)*

HEAVY (1994) Music score: THURSTON MOORE -S/T- on
CINERAMA-EDEL (Vital) 0022642CIN (CD)

HEAVY METAL (1981) Music score: ELMER BERNSTEIN + V/A:
-S/T- reiss.*COLUMBIA (Ten): 486 749-2 (CD)*

HEAVY METAL 2: F.A.K.K.2 ANIMATED ROCK FEATURE SEQUEL
VARIOUS ARTISTS *BMG IMPORTS: 74321 73234-2 (CD)*

HEAVY TRAFFIC (1973) Music sco: ED BOGAS-RAY SHANKLIN-
CHARLES EARLAND -S/T- inc 'Fritz The Cat' score on
FANTASY (Pinn): FCD 24745 (CD) also on
AKARMA (Greyhound/Silver Sounds): MIE 004 (LP)

HEDWIG AND THE ANGRY INCH (SHOW 2000) Music and songs
by STEPHEN TRASK. *ORIGINAL LONDON CAST (PLAYHOUSE)*
feat MICHAEL CERVERIS-ELIZABETH MARSH-NOAH TAYLOR
ATLANTIC-EAST WEST (TEN): 7567 83160-2 (CD) -4(MC)

HEIST (aka DOLLARS) (1971) Music score by QUINCY JONES
WB (TEN): 9362 47879-2 (CD)

HELL UP IN HARLEM (1973) includes music by EDWIN STARR
-S/T- *MOTOWN (UNIV): 013 739-2 (CD)*

HELLO AGAIN (1987) Music sco: WILLIAM GOLDSTEIN -S/T-
MULTIMEDIA IMP (Silver Sounds): 7956 76005-2 (CD)

HELLO DOLLY - songs by Jerry Herman /
1.FILM MUSICAL 1969 -S/T- *featur* BARBRA STREISAND
CASABLANCA (S.Screen): 810368-2 (CD) -4 (MC)
2.SHOWS COLLECT. *CARLTON: 30362 0025-2 (CD) -4 (MC)*

HELLRAISER (1987) Music score: CHRISTOPHER YOUNG -S/T-
S.SCREEN (Koch): FILMCD 021(CD) see *COLL 138,219,*

HELLRAISER 2 'Hellbound' (1988) Mus: CHRISTOPHER YOUNG
-S/T- *GNP (Greyh/ZYX): GNP(C)(D) 8015 (LP/MC/CD)*

HELLRAISER III 'Hell On Earth'(92) Music: RANDY MILLER
-S/T- (SCORE) *GNP (ZYX): GNPD 8233 (CD) GNP5*
8233 (MC) (SONGS) *S.Screen: 480007-2(CD) -4(MC)*

HELLRAISER IV: BLOODLINE (95) Music sco: DANIEL LICHT
feat Northwest Sinfonia and Chorus (Pete Anthony)
-S/T- *SILVA SCREEN (Koch): FILMCD 179 (CD)*

HELL'S BELLES (1969) Music score by LES BAXTER -S/T-
SIDEWALK (Greyhound): 5919 (LP)

HELP (1965) Songs: JOHN LENNON-PAUL McCARTNEY -S/T-
EMI: CDP 746 439-2 (CD) TC-PCS 3071 (MC) PCS (LP)

HELP I'M A FISH (2001) Music score by SOREN HYLDGAARD
-S/T- *RCA (BMG): 74321 87464-2 -4 (MC)*

HENRY FOOL (1998) Music score: HAL HARTLEY -S/T- on
ECHO STATIC (Cargo-Greyhound): ECHO 105 (CD)

HENRY V (1944) Music: WILLIAM WALTON / *NEW REC:* RTE
ORCH (Andrew Penny) *NAXOS (Select): 8553343 (CD)*
see *COLL.69,120,235,*

HENRY V (1944) Music sco: WILLIAM WALTON *sel:* 'WALTON
FILM MUSIC' LONDON PHILHARM.ORCH cond: CARL DAVIS
EMI:CDM 565585-2 (CD) also BOURNEMOUTH SYMPH.ORCH.
(Litton) *LONDON DECCA (Univ): 448 134-2(CD)*

HENRY V (1989) Music score by PATRICK DOYLE with the
CBSO (Simon Rattle) -S/T- *EMI: CDC 749919-2 (CD)*
see *COLL.64,266,*

HENRY VIII (C4 15/3/98) m: ADRIAN THOMAS see *COLL.20,*

HENRY'S CAT (BBC 1984) see *COLL.132,*

HERCULES (1997, WALT DISNEY) Music: ALAN MENKEN -S/T-
DISNEY-EDEL (Vital) WD 60864-2 (CD)
see *also* WALT DISNEY FILM INDEX p.341

HERCULES The Legendary Journeys (TV Series 1995) music
score and incidental music by JOSEPH LoDUCA
-S/T-   VOLUME 1   *VARESE (Pinn): VSD 5660 (CD)*
-S/T-   VOLUME 2   *VARESE (Pinn): VSD 5884 (CD)*
-S/T-   VOLUME 3   *VARESE (Pinn): VSD 6032 (CD)*
-S/T-   VOLUME 4   *VARESE (Pinn): VSD 6183 (CD)*
'YOUNG HERCULES' *VARESE (Pinn): VSD 5983 (CD)*
see *COLL.38,84,*

HERE COME THE WAVES (1945 MUSICAL) *feat* BING CROSBY +
BETTY HUTTON *incl.songs from* 'BATHING BEAUTY' and
'THIS GUN FOR HIRE' *TARGET (BMG): CD 60001 (CD)*

HERE ON EARTH (2000) Music score by ANDREA MORRICONE
-S/T- *COLUMBIA (TEN): 497 860-2 (CD)*

HERE WE GO ROUND THE MULBERRY BUSH (1967) Mus: STEVIE
WINWOOD and The SPENCER DAVIS GROUP -S/T- re-iss:
RYKODISC (Vital): RCD 10717 (CD)

HERE'S HARRY (BBC1 1960s) theme music "Comedy Hour"
by IVOR SLANEY see *COLL.3,*

HETTY WAINTHROP INVESTIGATES (BBC1 3/1/96) ser.theme
music by NIGEL HESS *on* 'A-Z OF BRITISH TV THEMES
VOL.3' *PLAY IT AGAIN (Koch): PLAY 010 (CD) and*
'WORLD OF SOUND' *BBC Worldw (Koch): 33635-2 (CD)*
see *COLL.4,137,283,*

HEY LOVE ORIG USA CAST on *VARESE (Pinn): VSD 5772 (CD)*

HEY MR.PRODUCER! (C4 00/12/1998) CAMERON MACKINTOSH
TRIBUTE CONCERT SUMMER 1998 with VARIOUS ARTISTS
FIRST NIGHT (Pinn): ENCORE CD 9 (2CD)

HI-LO COUNTRY The (1997) Music score: CARTER BURWELL
-S/T- *TVT (USA IMPORT) TVT 8290 (CD)*

HIDEAWAY (1994) Music score: TREVOR JONES -S/T- on
INOIC-MUTE/RTM (Disc): IONIC 12CD (CD)

HIDEOUS KINKY (1998) Music score: JOHN KEANE -S/T-
SILVA SCREEN (Koch): FILMCD 311 (CD)

HIGH AND THE MIGHTY The Music score: DIMITRI TIOMKIN
RCA (BMG): 09026 62658-2 (CD) see *COLL.258,*

HIGH ART (1997) Music by SHUDDER TO THINK -S/T- on
REEL SOUNDS (Pinn): 63467 79735-2 (CD)

HIGH CHAPARRAL The (USA BBC1 67) music: DAVID ROSE
see *COLL.246,*

HIGH FIDELITY (2000) Music score by HOWARD SHORE -S/T-
HOLLYWOOD-EDEL (Vital) 010 918-2HWR (CD) also on
HOLLYWOOD-EDEL (Vital) 011 218-2HWR (CD) -1 (2LP)

HIGH NOON (1952) Music score: DIMITRI TIOMKIN suite on
'Western Film World Of D.Tiomkin' LONDON STUDIO SO
(L.Johnson) *UN.KANCHANA (H.Mundi) UKCD 2011 (CD)*
Song "Do Not Forsake Me" sung by TEX RITTER
BEAR FAMILY: BCD 15625 (CD) see COLL.255,
HIGH ROAD TO CHINA (1984) Music sco: JOHN BARRY -S/T-
SOUTHERN CROSS (Hot): SCCD 1030 (CD) see COLL.26,
HIGH SOCIETY - songs by Cole Porter
  1.FILM MUSICAL 1956 SOUNDTRACK *inc* BING CROSBY-GRACE
  KELLY-FRANK SINATRA-CELESTE HOLM and Company -S/T-
  CAPITOL EMI: CDP 793787-2 (CD)
  2.ORIGINAL BROADWAY REVIVAL CAST 1998
  DRG (Pinn): DRGCD 19011 (CD)
HIGH SPIRITS (1988) Music score: GEORGE FENTON -S/T-
  GNP (ZYX/Greyhound) GNPD 8016 (CD) GNP5 8016 (MC)
HIGH TIME (1960) Music: HENRY MANCINI -S/T- reiss.with
  'HATARI' *RCA CAMDEN (BMG): 74321 82239-2 (CD)*
  also RCA IMPORT: 74321 62998-2 (CD score only)
HIGHER AND HIGHER (1943 MUSICAL) *inc* FRANK SINATRA-MEL
  TORME-VICTOR BORGE *includ.songs from* 'STEP LIVELY'
  TARGET (BMG): CD 60004 (CD)
HIGHLANDER (1986) Music score: MICHAEL KAMEN Songs by
  Queen (6='A Kind Of Magic') *EMI: CDP 746267-2 (CD)*
HIGHLANDER: End Game (2000) Music by STEPHEN GRAZIANO
  and NICK GLENNIE SMITH -S/T- on *GNP CRESCENDO USA
  (ZYX):GNPD 8067-2 (CD)*
HIGHLANDER: Final Dimension (1994) Mus: PETER ROBINSON
  -S/T- *EDEL (Vital) EDL 28892 (CD)*
HIGHLANDER (TV s.1992) theme "Princes Of The Universe"
  QUEEN ('A Kind Of Magic') *EMI: CDP 746 267-2 (CD)*
HIGHWAY PATROL (USA TV 1950's) *see COLL.245,*
HIGHWAY TO HEAVEN (USA)(ITV 7/6/87) theme: DAVID ROSE
  see COLL.14,247,
HILARY AND JACKIE (1998) Music sc: BARRINGTON PHELOUNG
  -S/T- *SONY CLASSICS: SK 60394 (CD)*
HILL STREET BLUES (USA TV 1980) Music by MIKE POST
  O.TV -S/T- *SILVA SCREEN (Koch): SILVAD 3510 (CD)*
  see COLL.14,77,117,203,244,250,
HIMALAYA (1999) Music score by BRUNO COULAIS -S/T- on
  VIRGIN 9EMI): CDVIR 120 (CD)
HINDLE WAKES (1927 silent) Contemporary music score by
  IN THE NURSERY -S/T- *ITN CORPORAT. CORP 023 (2CD)*
HIP-HOP YEARS The (C4 23/09/1999) 'The Hip Hop Years
  -Music from the Channel 4 Series' (VARIOUS ARTS)
  VIRGIN-COLUMBIA/C4 (Ten): MOOD(CD)(C)66 (2CD/2MC)
HISTORY OF BRITAIN (BBC2 30/09/2000 by SIMON SCHAMA)
  Music: JOHN HARLE solo voice of EMMA KIRKBY with
  BBC SINGERS and BBC CONCERT ORCHESTRA -S/T- on
  BBC WORLDWIDE (Pinn): WMSF 6040-2 CD
HISTORY OF MR.POLLY (1949) Music score: WILLIAM ALWYN
  Suite from film played by London Symphony Orch
  (Richard Hickox) on *CHANDOS: CHAN 9243 (CD)*
HIT THE DECK (1955) feat DEBBIE REYNOLDS-TONY MARTIN-
  ANN MILLER-JANE POWELL -S/T- *RHINO to be confirmed*

HITCHHIKERS GUIDE TO THE GALAXY (BBC2 1981) *theme*: TIM
SOUSTER *other mus*: PADDY KINGSLAND *BBC:ZBBC 1035
(MC set) BBCCD 6001(CD set)*
HITLER (1961) *see* 'BLACK SHIELD OF FALWORTH' (54)
HMS BRILLIANT (BBC1 26/7/95) music: JOHN HARLE. title
theme "Light" sung by SARAH LEONARD *see COLL.130*,
HMS PINAFORE - (operetta) songs by Gilbert & Sullivan
  1.D'OYLY CARTE OPERA (STUDIO 1999)
    TER (Koch): CDTER2 1259 (2CD)
  2.New Sadlers Wells 87 NIKOLAS GRACE-LINDA ORMISTON
    Complete: *TER (Koch): CDTER 1150 (2CD)*
  3.D'OYLY CARTE OPERA COMPANY - New Symphony Orchest
    (I.Godfrey) *LONDON (Univ): 414 283-2 (CDx2)*
  4.PRO-ARTE ORCH Malcolm Sargent GLYNDEBOURNE FESTIV.
    CHOIR +'TRIAL BY JURY' *EMI: CMS 764397-2 (2CD)*
  5.D'OYLY CARTE OPERA COMPANY CAST (1949)
    PEARL-PAVILION (Harmonia Mundi): GEMMCD 0096 (CD)
HOBSON'S CHOICE (1953) Music sco: MALCOLM ARNOLD suite
+other MALCOLM ARNOLD works *KOCH Int: 37266-2 (CD)*
'Film Music' *CHANDOS: CHAN 9100 (CD) see COLL.20*,
HOGAN'S HEROES (USA TV) *see COLL.243*,
HOLBY CITY (BBC1 12/01/1999-2002) theme music composed
and performed by KEN FREEMAN *unavailable*
HOLE The (2001) Music score by CLINT MANSELL -S/T- V/A
UNIVERSAL MUSIC: 556 474-2 (CD)
HOLIDAY (BBC1 1999-2001) theme STEVE BROWN *unavailable*
(BBC1 series 1992-1999) theme by PAUL HARDCASTLE
on 'FIRST LIGHT' *CONNOISSEUR COLL: NSPCD 516 (CD)*
HOLIDAY HOTEL (ITV 18/07/2000) title music composed by
PAUL BOROSS-HENRY MARSH *unavailable*
HOLIDAY IN MEXICO (1946) *feat* JANE POWELL-XAVIER CUGAT
plus 'WEEKEND IN HAVANA' selections on
GREAT MOVIE THEMES (BMG): CD 60036 (CD)
HOLIDAY INN (1942) *feat* BING CROSBY & FRED ASTAIRE
SOUNDTRACK FACTORY (Discovery): SFCD 33551 (CD)
ALSO with 'TWO FOR TONIGHT' & 'ROAD TO MOROCCO' on
GREAT MOVIE THEMES (Target-BMG): CD 60027 (CD)
HOLIDAY SWAPS (BBC1 12/04/1999) title theme music
"Marvellous" LIGHTNING SEEDS from 'Jollification'
COLUMBIA Sony: 477 237-2 (CD) -4 (NC)
HOLLOW MAN (2000) Music score by JERRY GOLDSMITH -S/T-
VARESE (Pinn): VSD 6171 (CD)
HOLLYOAKS (Mersey Prod C4 23/10/95) theme music by
STEVE WRIGHT & GORDON HIGGINS -S/T- 'MUSIC FOR A
HOLLYOAKS GENERATION' *UNIVERSAL M: 585 314-2 (2CD)*
HOLLYWOOD CANTEEN (1944) VARIOUS -S/T- SELECTION on
GREAT MOVIE THEMES (Targ-BMG): CD 60024 (CD)
HOLLYWOOD HOTEL (1937 MUSICAL) *w*: DICK POWELL-ROSEMARY
& LOLA LANE *includ.songs from* 'FLYING DOWN TO RIO'
TARGET (BMG): CD 60008 (CD)
HOLY SMOKE (1999) Music score by ANGELO BADALAMENTI
"Holy Holy" NEIL DIAMOND; "Primitive" ANNIE LENNOX
-S/T- *MILAN (BMG): 74321 71528-2 (CD)*
HOME ALONE (1990) Music: JOHN WILLIAMS *see COLL.281*,

HOME ALONE 2 (1992) -S/T- Music sore by JOHN WILLIAMS
    ARISTA (BMG): 07822 11000-2(CD) -4
HOME ALONE 3 (1999) Music score: NICK GLENNIE SMITH
    -S/T- *EDEL-HOLLYWOOD (Vital) 012138-2HWR (CD)*
HOME AND AWAY (Australia)(ITV 13/2/1989-2000) -S/T-
    theme by MIKE PERJANIK sung by KAREN BODDINGTON
    & MARK WILLIAMS *MUSHROOM (Pinn.Imps): D.93463 (CD)*
    MUSIC FROM THE TV SER.*S.T.W.(Pinn): STW 19CD (CD)*
HOME FRONT (BBC2 12/04/1994-2001) theme music by
    TONY & GAYNOR SADLER (LOGORHYTHM) *unavailable*
HOMEBOY (1988) Music score: ERIC CLAPTON-MICHAEL KAMEN
    -S/T- *VIRGIN (EMI): CDV 2574 (CD)*
HOMEGROWN (1996) Music score by TREVOR RABIN -S/T-
    WILL IMPORT (Silver Sounds): 7801 63365-2 (CD)
HONEST (2000) Music sco: DAVID A.STEWART w. ALL SAINTS
    ISLAND (UNIV): CID 8097 (CD)
HONEYMOONERS The (USA TV) *see COLL.243,*
HONG KONG PHOOEY (USA TV) *see COLL.246,259,*
HOOK (1991) *see COLL.121,240,280,281,*
HOPALONG CASSIDY (USA TV) *see COLL.245,*
HOPE AND GLORY (BBC1 22/06/1999) CLASSICAL MUSIC -S/T-
    -S/T- *BBC MUSIC (Pinn): WMSF 6014-2 (CD)*
HOPE FLOATS (1998) Music score: DAVE GRUSIN
    -S/T- score: *RCA VICTOR (BMG): 09026 63255-2 (CD)*
    -S/T- songs: *EMI PREM: 493 402-2 (CD) -4 (MC)*
HORIZON (BBC2) title music: WILFRED JOSEPHS other mus
    ELIZABETH PARKER (BBC Radio.Workshop) *unavailable*
HORRORS OF THE BLACK MUSEUM *see COLL.138,150,151,*
HORSE OF THE YEAR SHOW (BBC1) theme: "A Musical Joke"
    in F (K.522) 'Musikalischer Spass' 4th mm (MOZART)
    see COLL.101,
HORSE SOLDIERS (1959) Music: DAVID BUTTOLPH / score
    with 'DUAL AT DIABLO' (1966 NEAL HEFTI score)
    TARAN (Silver Sounds): W 9105 (CD)
HORSE WHISPERER The (1998) Music score: THOMAS NEWMAN
    -S/T- score *EDEL-HOLLYWOOD (Vital) 012137-2 (CD)*
    -S/T- songs *UNIVERSAL (BMG): UMD 80503 (CD)*
HORSEMAN ON THE ROOF The (1995) Music sco: JEAN CLAUDE
    PETIT -S/T-*AUVIDIS-TRAVELLING (H.Mundi): 1139-2 CD*
HOT MIKADO (ORIG LONDON CAST 1995) *feat:* SHARON BENSON
    FIRST NIGHT (Pinn): OCRCD 6048 (CD)
HOT MILLIONS (1968) Music score: LAURIE JOHNSON
    see COLL.156,158,
HOT SHOE SHUFFLE (ORIG AUSTRALIAN CAST 1993) *inc* DAVID
    ATKINS-RHONDA BURCHMORE-JACK WEBSTER-TAP BROTHERS
    FIRST NIGHT (Pinn): OCRCD 6046 (CD)
HOT SHOTS (1991) Music score: SYLVESTER LEVAY -S/T-
    VARESE (Pinn): VSD 5338 (CD)
HOTEL DU NORD (1938) Music score by MAURICE JAUBERT
    selection on *AUVIDIS (Harmonia Mundi): K.1502 (CD)*
HOUNDS OF ZAROFF (1932 aka THE MOST DANGEROUS GAME)
    Music: MAX STEINER *new recording by* MOSCOW S.O.
    cond: WILLIAM T.STROMBERG also incl.score to 'SON
    OF KONG' (1933) *MARCO POLO (Select): 8225166 (CD)*

HOUSE OF FRANKENSTEIN (1944) Music sco: HANS SALTER &
PAUL DESAU *new rec:* MOSCOW SYMPH.ORCH.(Stromberg)
MARCO POLO (Select): 8.223748 (CD) see COLL.249,

HOUSE ON HAUNTED HILL (1999) Music score by DON DAVIS
-S/T- *VARESE (Pinn):* VSD 6088 (CD)

HOUSE PARTY (1990) VARIOUS.ARTISTS -S/T- *import reiss*
UNIVERSAL MUSIC: AA 40014593-2 (CD)

HOW NOW DOW JONES (USA MUSICAL 1998) ORIGINAL BROADWAY
CAST REC.on *RCA VICTOR (BMG):* 09026 63581-2 (CD)

HOW STELLA GOT HER GROOVE BACK (1998) VAR.ARTS -S/T-
MCA (UNI): MCD 11806 (CD)

HOW THE EMPEROR GOT HIS GROOVE BACK - *see under*
EMPEROR'S NEW GROOVE

HOW THE GRINCH STOLE CHRISTMAS - SEE 'GRINCH'

HOW THE WEST WAS WON (1962) Music score: ALFRED NEWMAN
-S/T- *deleted / see COLL.63,258,277,279,*

HOW TO MARRY A MILLIONAIRE (1953) Mus: CYRIL MOCKRIDGE
-S/T- *FSM GOLDEN CLASSICS USA: VOL4. NO.2 (CD)*

HOW TO SUCCEED IN BUSINESS WITHOUT REALLY TRYING 1967
Music: NELSON RIDDLE with songs by FRANK LOESSER
RYKODISC (Vital): RCD 10728 (CD)

HOW TO BE A PLAYER (DEF JAM'S) (1997) VARIOUS ARTISTS
DEF JAM (Univ): 537 973-2 (CD) -1 (2LP)

HOWARD GOODALL'S BIG BANGS (C4 12/03/2000) Music from
TV series with HOWARD GOODALL / Various Artists
-S/T- *METRONOME (CRC-Pinn):* (METCD 1043 (CD)

HOWARD GOODALL'S CHOIR WORKS (C4 8/3/1998)
HOWARD GOODALL with Various Choirs and soloists
ASV (Select): CDCCA 1028 (CD)

HOWARD THE DUCK (aka HOWARD A NEW BREED OF HERO)(1986)
Music score by JOHN BARRY / *this recording also
includes* 'THE BLACK HOLE' (JOHN BARRY, 1979)
MASK (USA Import): MK 703 (CD)

HOWARDS END (1992) Music score: RICHARD ROBBINS -S/T-
NIMBUS (Nimbus): NI 5339 (CD) NC 5339 (MC)

HOWARDS' WAY (BBC1 1/9/85-1990) theme music: SIMON MAY
LESLIE OSBORNE / SIMON MAY ORCH "Barracuda" theme
"Always There" sung by MARTI WEBB *see COLL.283,*

HU-DU-MEN (1996) Music score by YOSHIHIDE OTOMO -S/T-
SOUND FACTORY (Impetus): STK 005CD (CD)

HUCKLEBERRY HOUND (USA TV) *see COLL.243,259,*

HUDSON HAWK (1991) Music: MICHAEL KAMEN-ROBERT KRAFT
-S/T- *VARESE (Pinn):* VSD 5323 (CD)

HUDSUCKER PROXY The (1994) Music score: CARTER BURWELL
-S/T- *VARESE (USA):* VSD 5477 (CD)

HUMAN JUNGLE The (ITC 63/C4 87) theme: BERNARD EBBING
HOUSE by JOHN BARRY ORCH *see COLL.3,27,29,*

HUMAN TRAFFIC (1999) CLUB MUSIC -S/T- by PETE TONG +
PRIMAL SCREAM-ORBITAL-PUBLIC ENEMY-PETE HELLER-
UNDERWORLD-C.J.BOLLAND *FFRR (Uni):* 556 109-2 (CD)

HUMORESQUE (1946) Mus.score: FRANZ WAXMAN.*new record*
LONDON SYMPHONY ORCHESTRA conduct: ANDREW LITTON
feat: NADJA SALERNO-SONNENBERG (violin)
NONESUCH-WB (TEN): 7559 79464-2 (CD)

HUNCHBACK OF NOTRE DAME The (1939) Mus: ALFRED NEWMAN
Suite by MOSCOW SYMPHONY ORCH.& CHORUS (William T.
Stroberg) 'BEAU GESTE' (1939) 'ALL ABOUT EVE' (39)
MARCO POLO (Select): 8.223750 (CD)
HUNCHBACK OF NOTRE DAME (1956) Music sco: GEORGES AURIC
new rec (Suite) MOSCOW SYMPHONY ORCH (Adriano) and
suites 'FARANDOLE' (1944) 'LOLA MONTEZ' (1955)
MARCO POLO (Select): 8.225070 (CD)
HUNCHBACK OF NOTRE DAME (1996 Disney) Mus ALAN MENKEN
Lyr STEPHEN SCHWARTZ *song* "Someday" by ETERNAL
EMI FIRST AVENUE: CDEMS 439 (CDs) TCEM 439 (MC)
-S/T- W.DISNEY: WD 77190-2 (CD) see DISNEY p.341
HUNDRED ACRES, A (Antelope West/C4 23/2/90) theme by
NIGEL HESS *see COLL.137,*
HUNGER The (1982) Music: MICHAEL RUBINI-DENNY JAEGER+
music "Lakme" (DELIBES) "Solo Cello Suites" (BACH)
VARESE (Pinn): VSD 47261(CD) -S/T- also available
MILAN (BMG): CDCH 004 (CD) inc.'THE YEAR OF LIVING
DANGEROUSLY' *see COLL.154,*
HUNLEY The (1999) Music score by RANDY EDELMAN -S/T-
MILAN (BMG): 73138 35878-2 (CD)
HUNT FOR RED OCTOBER (1989) Music: BASIL POLEDOURIS
-S/T- *MCA (UNI): MCLD 19306 (CD)*
HUNTER (USA77)(ITV 5/85)   *see COLL.14,203,247,*
HUNTERS: THE WORLD OF PREDATORS AND PREY (1995)
Mus: The RESIDENTS -S/T- *MILAN (BMG): 31169-2 (CD)*
HUNTING OF THE SNARK (MUSICAL) MIKE BATT / ORIG 1988
CONCEPT ALBUM *FIRST NIGHT (Pinn): CASTCD 24 (CD)*
HUNTING VENUS (ITV 31/03/1999) starring MARTIN CLUNES
TV -S/T- *COLUMBIA (Ten): 494 300-2 (CD) -4 (MC)*
HURLYBURLY (1998) Music score: DAVID BAERWALD -S/T-
USA INPORT: WILL 33658 (CD)
HURRICANE The (1998) Music score by CHRISTOPHER YOUNG
-S/T- *UNIVERSAL MUSIC: 170 116-2 (CD)*
HURRICANE STREETS (1998) Music score: THEODORE SHAPIRO
-S/T- (VAR.ARTISTS) *POLYDOR (Univ): 557 067-2 (CD)*
I AIM AT THE STARS (1960) Music score: LAURIE JOHNSON
see COLL.156,158,
I AND ALBERT (O.LONDON CAST 1972) Songs: **Charles Strou
se-Lee Adams** *feat:* POLLY JAMES-SVEN B.TAUBE-LEWIS
FIANDER-RAEWYN BLADE *JAY-TER (SSD):CDJAY 1353 (CD)*
I BURY THE LIVING (1957) *see under* 'RETURN OF DRACULA'
I DREAM OF JEANNIE (USA 60s) *see COLL.242,*
I DREAMED OF AFRICA (2000) Music score: MAURICE JARRE
VARESE (Pinn): VSD 6143 (CD)
I LOVE LUCY (USA 1950s) *see COLL.242,*
I LOVE MY WIFE (O.BROADWAY CAST) Songs by CY COLEMAN-
MICHAEL STEWART *DRG (Pinn): CDRG 6109 (CD)*
I LOVE THE 90's (BBC2 18/08/2001) COLLECTION OF 1990s
V.ARTISTS CHART HITS *VIRGIN (EMI): VTDCD 410 (2CD)*
I LOVE YOU PERFECT (TVM 1989) Music score: YANNI -S/T-
SILVA SCREEN (Koch): FILMCD 122 (CD)
I LOVE YOU YOU'RE PERFECT NOW CHANGE (USA REVUE 1996)
O.CAST RECORDING *VARESE (Pinn): VSD 5771 (CD)*

I REMEMBER MAMA (MUSICAL 1985) Songs: Richard Rodgers
Martin Charnin *World premiere record* Sally Anne
HOWES-George HEARN-Ann MORRISON-Sian PHILLIPS-Gay
SOPER-Patricia ROUTLEDGE *TER (Koch): CDTER 1102*
I SPY (USA TV) *see COLL.124,*
I WALK THE LINE (1970) Music by JOHNNY CASH and CARL
PERKINS *with* 'LITTLE FAUSS AND BIG HALSY' (1970)
BEAR FAMILY (Rollercoaster): BCD 16130 (2CD)
I WALKED WITH A ZOMBIE (1943) *see COLL.275,*
I WANT TO LIVE (1958) Music score: JOHN MANDEL -S/T-
feat SHELLEY MANNE-GERRY MULLIGAN-RED MITCHELL etc
RYKODISC (Vital): RCD 10743 (CD)
I WENT DOWN (1997) Music score: DARIO MARIANELLI -S/T-
OCEAN DEEP (Grapevine-Polyg): OCD 008 (CD)
IBIZA UNCOVERED (SKY1 6/7/97) theme mus "Magic Carpet
Ride" by The MIGHTY DUB KATZ on *LONDON-FRR (Univ):*
FCD 306(CDs) FX 306(12"s) / 'IBIZA UNCOVERED' with
V/A (Vol.1) *VIRGIN: VTDCD 168 (2CD) VTDMC 168 (MC)*
V/A (Vol.2) *VIRGIN: VTDCD 177 (2CD) VTDMC 177 (MC)*
IBIZA UNCOVERED: THE RETURN *VTDCD(MC) 255 (2CD/MC)*
ICE HOUSE The (BBC1 05/04/1997) Music score by
DAVID FERGUSON *see COLL.104,*
ICE PALACE (1960) Music by MAX STEINER *see COLL.239,*
ICE SKATING (BBC 1978-1998) theme "Mornings At Seven"
JAMES LAST ORCH 'By Request' *POLY: 831 786-2 (CD)*
ICE STORM The (1996) Music: MYCHAEL DANNA -S/T- V.ARTS
VELVET (Pinn): VEL 79713-2 (CD)
ICEMAN (1984) Music score by BRUCE SMEATON -S/T- on
SOUTHERN CROSS (Hot): SCCD 1006 (CD)
IDLE HANDS (1998) VARIOUS ARTISTS -S/T-
TIMEBOMB (Cargo): 43526 (CD)
IF (1968) Music sco: MARC WILKINSON *score unavailable*
also used "African Sanctus" from 'MISSA LUBA'
(Congolese African Mass) available version on
PHILIPS (Univ): 426 836-2 (CD) -4 (MC)
IGNATIO (Film) Music VANGELIS -S/T- *813 042-2 (CD)*
IL BAGNO TURCO (TURKISH BATH) (1997) TRANSCENDENTAL
MUSIC (Var) *TSUMAMI IMP (Discov): TOS 0305 (CD)*
IL POSTINO - *see* 'POSTMAN The'
I'LL DO ANYTHING (1993) Music score HANS ZIMMER -S/T-
VARESE (Pinn): VSD 5474 (CD)
I'LL FLY AWAY (USA TV) *see COLL.248,*
ILLUSTRATED MAN The (1969) Music sco: JERRY GOLDSMITH
TARAN (Silver Sounds): W.9102 (CD)
I'M GETTING MY ACT TOGETHER AND TAKING IT ON THE ROAD
Songs: Nancy Ford-Gretchen Cryer O.LOND.CAST 1981
DIANE LANGTON-BEN CROSS *TER (Koch): CDTER 1006*
I'M NO ANGEL (1933) *JASMINE: JASCD 102 (CD)*
IMAGINE - THE MOVIE (1988) Mus: JOHN LENNON -S/T- *EMI*
CDP 790 803-2 (CD) TCPCSP 722 (MC) PCSP 722 (LP)
IMMORTAL BELOVED (1994) Mus.extr.(BEETHOVEN-ROSSINI)
-S/T- *Sony: SK 66301 (CD) SM 66301 (MD)*
IMPOSTERS The (1998) Music score: GARY DE MICHELE
-S/T- V.ARTISTS *RCQ (BMG): 09026 63172-2 (CD)*

IN A LAND OF PLENTY (BBC2 10/01/2001) theme "Saffron"
(J.Pook-H.Brough) sung by JOCELYN POOK from album
'Untold Things' *REAL WORLD-ISL (EMI):CDRW 93 (CD)*
IN AN OUT (1997) Music score: MARC SHAIMAN -S/T- V/A
MOTOWN (Univ): 530 841-2 (CD)
IN DREAMS (1998) Music score: ELLIOT GOLDENTHAL -S/T-
VARESE (Pinn): VSD 6001 (CD)
IN LIKE FLINT (1967) Music score: JERRY GOLDSMITH also
inc 'OUR MAN FLINT' *VARESE (Pinn): VSD 5935 (CD)*
IN THE ARMY NOW (1993) Music score: ROBERT FOLK -S/T-
INTRADA (Silva Screen): MAF 7058CD (CD)
IN THE BLOOD (BBC2 13/5/96) t.mus: GILES SWAYNE -S/T-
RYKODISC (Vital): RCD 20172(CD) RACS 20174(MC)
IN THE HEAT OF THE NIGHT (1967) Music sc: QUINCY JONES
title sung by RAY CHARLES -S/T- inc.mus.from 'THEY
CALL ME MR.TIBBS' *RYKODISC (Vital): RCD 10712 (CD)*
and TARAN *(Silv.Sounds): W.9106 (CD)* see *COLL.248,*
IN THE MOOD FOR LOVE (2000) Music by MICHAEL GASLASSO
-S/T- *VIRGIN (EMI): CDVIR 125 (CD)*
IN TOO DEEP (1998) Music score: CHRISTOPHER YOUNG
-S/T- (songs) *COLUMBIA (Ten): 495 295-2 (CD)*
-S/T- (score) *VARESE (Pinn): VSD 6072 (CD)*
IN TOWN TONIGHT (BBC 1950s) see *COLL.45,46,100,119,*

INCREDIBLE HULK The (USA 1978) theme mus: JOE HARNELL
see *COLL.14,200,221,247,*
INCREDIBLE SHRINKING MAN The (1957) mus: FRED CARLING
& ED LAWRENCE + 'CREATURE FROM THE BLACK LAGOON
(54) 'HITLER'(61) 'BLACK SHIELD OF FALWORTH' (54)
INTRADA (Koch): MAF 7054CD (CD) see *COLL.219,249,*
INDECENT PROPOSAL (1993) Music: JOHN BARRY see *COLL.26,*

INDEPENDENCE DAY (1996) Music sco: DAVID ARNOLD -S/T-
RCA-20th Cent.Fox (BMG): 09026 68564-2 (CD)
see *COLL.61,220,257,*
INDIAN SUMMER (2000) Music score by MICK RONSON -S/T-
BURNING AIRLINES (Universal): PILOT 057 (CD)
INDIANA JONES & THE LAST CRUSADE (1989) Mus.score:JOHN
WILLIAMS -S/T- *WB: K925883-2 (CD)* see *COLL.121,*
INDIANA JONES & THE TEMPLE OF DOOM (1984) Music: JOHN
WILLIAMS see *COLL.121,*
INFERNO (1980) Music score: KEITH EMERSON *-S/T- reiss*
CINEVOX (Koch/Silva Screen): CDMF 3060 (CD)
INHERIT THE WIND - see *COLL.112,*

INN OF THE SIXTH HAPPINESS The (1958) Mus sco: MALCOLM
ARNOLD Suite on 'Film Music' London Symphony Orch
(R.Hicox) *CHANDOS: CHAN 9100 (CD)*
INNOCENT SLEEP The (1995) Music sco: MARK AYRES cond.
by Nic Raine / vocalist LESLEY GARRETT -S/T-
SILVA SCREEN (Koch): FILMCD 167 (CD)
INSIDER The (2000) Music by LISA GERRARD-PIETER BOURKE
-S/T- *COLUMBIA (TEN): 496 458-2 (CD) -4 (MC)*
INSPECTOR GADGET (USA TV) see *COLL.244,*

INSPECTOR MORSE (ITV 1987-2000) theme and original
music by BARRINGTON PHELOUNG *NEW COLLECT (2000):*
'THE MAGIC OF INSPECTOR MORSE' on *VIRGIN (EMI):*
VTDCD 353 (2CDs) VTDMC 353 (2MC) / also available:
Coll: 'INSPECTOR MORSE III' theme & incidental
classical *VIRGIN: CDVIP 178 (CD) TCVIP 178 (MC)*
'ESSENTIAL INSPECTOR MORSE COLL' *VIRGIN (EMI):*
VTCD 62 (CD) VTMC 62 (MC) see COLL.77,188,
INSTINCT (1999) Music score by DANNY ELFMAN -S/T- on
VARESE (Pinn): VSD 6041 (CD)
INTERNECINE PROJECT The (1974) Music score by ROY BUDD
-S/T- + music from 'SOMETHING TO HIDE' (1971) on
CINEPHILE (Pinn): CINCD 019 (CD) see COLL.54,
INTO THE ARMS OF STRANGERS (2000) Music LEE HOLDRIDGE
-S/T- *CHAPTER III (Silver Sounds) CHPT 1006-2 (CD)*
-S/T- *GOLD CIRCLE (Proper) GCE 1006-2 (CD)*
INTO THE WOODS (MUSICAL) Songs by STEPHEN SONDHEIM
Orig.London Cast 1990 *feat:* IMELDA STAUNTON-JULIA
McKENZIE-JACQUELINE DANKWORTH-ANN HOWARD-RICHARD
DEMPSEY-NICHOLAS PARSONS-CLIVE CARTER and Company
RCA VICTOR (BMG): RD 60752 (CD)
INVADERS The (USA 66) theme music: DOMINIC FRONTIERE
(USA TV) *see COLL.220,246,*
INVASION OF THE SAUCER MEN (1957) Music by RONALD STEIN
-S/T- with 'IT CONQUERED THE WORLD' (1956 R.Stein)
PERCEPTO USA Import: PERCEPTO 005 (CD)
INVINCIBLE (2001) Music score by HANS ZIMMER -S/T- on
BMG IMPORTS: 74321 89821-2 (CD)
INVISIBLE MAN RETURNS (1940) Music score: HANS SALTER-
FRANK SKINNER *new record* MOSCOW SYMPHONY ORCHESTRA
(Stromberg) on *MARCO POLO (Select): 8.223748 (CD)*
also includes THE WOLF MAN and SON OF FRANKENSTEIN
IOLANTHE (operetta) songs by Gilbert and Sullivan
1.D'OYLY CARTE OPERA COMPANY New S.Orch Of London
(I.Godrey) *LONDON (Univ): 414 145-2 (2CD) -4 (MC)*
2.PRO-ARTE ORCHEST (Malcolm Sargent) & GLYNDEBOURNE
FESTIVAL CHOIR Soloists: George Baker-Ian Wallace-
Alex.Young-Owen Brannigan *EMI: CMS 764400-2 (2CDs)*
3.D'OYLE CARTE OPERA (JOHN PRYCE JONES, musical dir)
feat: JILL PERT-RICHARD STUART-ELIZABETH WOOLLETT-
PHILIP BLAKE-JONES *TER (Koch): CDTER2 1188 (2CD)*
IPCRESS FILE (1965) Music: JOHN BARRY see *COLL.26,*
IPI TOMBI (MUSICAL 1975) Music by BERTHA EGNOS / ORIG
S.AFRICAN CAST *NOVA-PRESTIGE (Pinn): CDGSP 0577 CD*
IRISH AND HOW THEY GOT AWAY WITH IT, The (1997 USA)
based on FRANK McCOURT'S biogr. 'Angela's Ashes'
O.CAST RECORDING *VARESE (Pinn):VSD 5916 (CD)*
IRMA LA DOUCE (1963) Mus: MARGUERITE MONNOT, md: ANDRE
PREVIN -S/T- *RYKODISC (Vital): RCD 10729 (CD)*
IRON AND SILK (1991) Music score: MICHAEL GIBBS -S/T-
IONIC (RTM/Pinn): IONIC 7CD (CD)
IRON GIANT The (1999) Music score: MICHAEL KAMEN
-S/T- (score): *VARESE (Pinn): VSD 6062 (CD)*
-S/T- (songs): *WARNER (Ten): 8122 75943-2 (CD)*

IRON MASK (1929) Contemporary score by CARL DAVIS
  see *COLL.85*, 'The SILENTS'
IRON WILL (1993) -S/T- Music score: JOEL McNEELY -S/T-
  VARESE (Pinn): VSD 5467 (CD)
IRONSIDE see *COLL.83,124,200,242,261,*
ISN'T SHE GREAT (2000) Music sco: BURT BACHARACH -S/T-
  DECCA (UNIV): 466 981-2 (CD)
IT CONQUERED THE WORLD (1956) Music by RONALD STEIN
  -S/T-+ 'INVASION OF THE SAUCER MEN' (1957 R.Stein)
  PERCEPTO USA Import: PERCEPTO 005 (CD)
IT HAPPENED AT THE WORLD'S FAIR see ELVIS INDEX p.348
IT HAPPENED IN BROOKLYN (1946) FRANK SINATRA -S/T-
  SELECTIONS with 'VARIETY GIRL' -S/T- selection on
  GREAT MOVIE THEMES (BMG): CD 60034 (CD)
IT TAKES A THIEF (USA TV) see *COLL.124,246,*
IT'S A KNOCKOUT! (revival) (C5 03/09/1999) theme music
  "Bean Bag" HERB ALPERT & TIJUANA BRASS *A.& M.delet*
IT'S A MAD MAD MAD MAD WORLD (1963) Music: ERNEST GOLD
  -S/T- *reiss + addit.RYKODISC (Vit): RCD 10704 (CD)*
  see *COLL.112,*
IT'S A WONDERFUL LIFE (1946, Frank Capra) music score:
  DIMITRI TIOMKIN / Coll of songs inspired by movie
  DEBUTANTE (Univ): 555 346-2 (CD) -4 (MC)
IT'S GARRY SHANDLING SHOW (USA TV) see *COLL.248,*
IT'S MY PARTY (1995) Music sco: BASIL POLEDOURIS -S/T-
  VARESE (Pinn): VSD 5701 (CD)
ITALIAN JOB The (1960) Music score by QUINCY JONES inc
  "Self Preservation Society" by PETER KING and
  "On Days Like These" sung by MATT MONRO
  -S/T- *MCA (Univ):MCD 60074-2 (CD) MCA 60074-1 (LP)*
ITN NEWS (Orig 60s-70s theme) 'Non Stop' JOHN MALCOLM
  see *COLL.119,* see also NEWS AT TEN
IVAN THE TERRIBLE (1943) Music by PROKOFIEV *new vers:*
  FRANKFURT RADIO SYMPHONY ORCH (Dmitri Kitoenko)
  RCA VICTOR Red Seal (BMG): 09026 61954-2 (CD)
  other recordings: PHILHARMONIA ORCH (Neeme Jarvi)
  Linda Finnie (mez-sop) Nikita Storojev (bass-bar)
  CHANDOS (Chandos): CHAN 8977 (CD)
  PHILHARMONIC ORCH (Riccardo Muti) Ambrosian Chorus
  (J.McCarthy) *EMI CDM 769584-2 (CD) EG 769584-4(MC)*
  TCHAIKOVSKY SYMPHONY ORCHEST (Vladimir Fedoseyev)
  NIMBUS (Nimbus): NI 5662/3 (2CD)
IVANHOE (1951) Music sco: MIKLOS ROZSA *new digital rec*
  featur: Sinfonia of London (Bruce Broughton)
  INTRADA (Silva Screen): MAF 7055CD (CD)
  -S/T- + MADAME BOVARY/QUO VADIS/PLYMOUTH ADVENTURE
  TICKERTAPE USA Impt.(S.Screen): TT 3001 (CD)
IVOR THE ENGINE (BBC1 26/1/1976) music: VERNON ELLIOTT
  UNIVERSAL VIDEO: 078 144-3 (VHS complete col.epis)
JACK (1996) Music: MICHAEL KAMEN song "Star" sung by
  BRYAN ADAMS -S/T- *EDEL-HOLLY.(Vital) 012063-2 (CD)*
JACK DEE'S HAPPY HOUR (BBC1 10/04/2000) t.music arr.by
  GLEN TILBROOK *unavailable. Orig by* TED HAWKINS on
  'HAPPY HOUR' *ROUNDER (ADA/Direct): ROUCD 2033 (CD)*

JACK FROST (1998) Music score: TREVOR RABIN -S/T- on
  MERCURY (UNIV): 538 598-2 (CD)
JACK OF HEARTS (BBC1 04/08/1999) Music by: MARK THOMAS
  title theme sung by BONNIE TYLER *unavailable*
JACKIE BROWN (1998) Various Artists -S/T-
  W.BROS (TEN/Greyhound): 9362 46841-2 (CD) -4 (MC)
JACOB'S LADDER (1990) Music sco: MAURICE JARRE -S/T-
  VARESE (Pinn): VSD 5291 (CD)
JACQUES BREL IS ALIVE AND WELL AND LIVING IN PARIS
  ORIGINAL LONDON CAST with VARIOUS ARTISTS
  TER (Koch): CDTEM2 1231 (2CD)
JAGUAR Le (1996) Music score by VLADIMIR COSMA on Coll
  with 'CLOSET'(2000) and 'THE DINNER GAME' (1998)
  DRG USA (Pinn): DRGCD 9522 (CD)
JAILBAIT (2000) VARIOUS ARTISTS SOUNDTRACK on
  MCA-UNIVERSAL-IMS: AA 314541395-2 (CD)
JAILHOUSE ROCK (1957) ELVIS PRESLEY remastered -S/T-
  *RCA (BMG) :07863 67453-2 (CD) / SANCTUARY (Pinn):
  ELVIS 111 (LP)* see also ELVIS PRESLEY INDEX p.348
JAKE'S PROGRESS (C4 12/10/95) music by RICHARD HARVEY
  & ELVIS COSTELLO -S/T- *DEMON (Pinn): DSCD 14 (CD)*
JAMAICA INN (ITV 9/5/83) Mus: FRANCIS SHAW *see COLL.5,*
JAMES BOND (theme) (MONTY NORMAN)
  see COLL.27,29,36,45,46,94,171,175,222,250,
  see also JAMES BOND FILM INDEX p.346
JANE EYRE (1995) Music score ALLESIO VLAD & CLAUDIO
  CAPONI -S/T- *DRG (N.Note-Pinn): DRGCD 12619 (CD)*
JANE EYRE (1971) Music score by JOHN WILLIAMS
  SILVA SCREEN (Koch): FILMCD 204 (CD)
JANE EYRE (1943) Music score: BERNARD HERRMANN new
  1994 recording by SLOVAK RADIO SYMPHONY ORCHESTRA
  *MARCO POLO (Select): 8.223535 (CD) also available
  SOUNDTRACK FACTORY (Discov): SFCD 33519 (CD) and
  Fox-Arista (BMG):07822 11006-2 +'LAURA'* (D.RAKSIN)
JASON AND THE ARGONAUTS (1963) Music: BERNARD HERRMANN
  New Studio Rec BRUCE BROUGHTON conduct.the LONDON
  SINFONIA *INTRADA-BALTIC (S.Screen): MAP 7083 (CD)*
  see COLL.135,266,
JASON KING (ITC 15/7/1971-1972) theme LAURIE JOHNSON
  see COLL.83,156,158,250,
JAWBREAKER (1999) Music score: STEPHEN ENDELMAN -S/T-
  VARESE (Pinn): VSD 6013 (CD)
JAWS (1975) Music score: JOHN WILLIAMS
  COLLECTORS EDITION on *DECCA (Univ): 467 045-2 (CD)*
  *-S/T- re-iss: MCA MASTERS (BMG): MCLD 19281 (CD)
  NEW RECORDING by* ROYAL SCOTTISH NATIONAL ORCHESTRA
  cond.by JOEL McNEELY *VARESE (Pinn): VSD 6078 (CD)*
  see COLL.121,220,280,281,
JAWS 2 (1978) Music score: JOHN WILLIAMS -S/T-
  VARESE (Pinn): VSD 5328 (CD)
JAY AND SILENT BOB STRIKE BACK (2001) m:JAMES L.VENABLE
  -S/T- score *VARESE (Pinn): VSD 6277 (CD)*
  -S/T- songs *ISLAND (UNIV): 14713-2 (CD)*
JAYHAWKERS The (1959) Mus JEROME MOROSS *see* 'CARDINAL'

JAZZ ON A SUMMER'S DAY (1959) NEWPORT JAZZ FESTIVAL
 CHARLY RECORDS: SDVD 001 (CD/DVD) / also available
 SOUND TRACK FACTORY (Discov): SFCD 33539 (CD) +
 sel. GREAT MOVIE THEMES (BMG): CD 60039 (CD)
JAZZ SINGER The (1980) NEIL DIAMOND -S/T- *reiss:*
 COLUMBIA (Ten): 483 927-2 (CD) -4 (MC)
JEAN DE FLORETTE (1987) Music score: JEAN-CLAUDE PETIT
 main theme ad.from "La Forza Del Destino" (Verdi)
 Orchestra De Paris with Toots Thieleman *(harmonica)*
 SILVA SCREEN Koch:FILMCD 328 (CD)see COLL.60,61,64,
JEEVES AND WOOSTER (Granada 22/4/90) mus: ANNE DUDLEY
 vers.by GRAHAM DALBY & THE GRAHAMOPHONES on Coll
 'Transatlantique' *PRESIDENT: PCOM 1128 (CD)*
 see also BY JEEVES (Musical)
JEFFERSONS The (USA TV) *see COLL.244,*
JEFFREY (1995) Music score: STEPHEN ENDELMAN -S/T-
 VARESE (Pinn): VSD 5649 (CD)
JEKYLL AND HYDE (ORIGINAL BROADWAY CAST RECORDING)
 Music by FRANK WILDHORN, lyr.by LESLEY BRICUSSE
 FIRST NIGHT (Pinn): CASTCD 71 (CD)
JELLIKINS (ITV/GMTV 1999) Music & songs by DAVID LOWE
 featuring voice of RIK MAYALL.14 song soundtrack
 JELLISTAR (Univ): 153 709-2 (CD) see COLL.285,
JELLO IS ALWAYS RED The (Songs: CLARK GESTNER)
 ORIGINAL CAST with The Original Cabaret Songs of
 CLARK GESTNER *HARBINGER (Pinn): HCD 1502 (CD)*
JEOPARDY (USA TV) *see COLL.243,*
JERRY MAGUIRE (1996) Music score: DANNY BRAMSON
 -S/T- reissue *EPIC (Ten): 486 981-2 (CD) -8 (md)*
JERRY'S GIRLS (O.BROADWAY C.1984) Songs: **Jerry Herman**
 CAROL CHANNING-LESLIE UGGAMS *TER: CDTER2 1093 2CD*
JESUS (SKY 21/04/2000) Music: PATRICK WILLIAMS -S/T-
 (mus.from & inspired by)*CAPITOL-EMI:851 730-2 (CD)*
JESUS CHRIST SUPERSTAR - songs by Tim Rice and Andrew
 LLoyd Webber
  1.ORIG LONDON CAST 1996 *feat:* STEVE BALSALMO-ZUBIN
  VARTA-JOANNA AMPILL and Company
  REALLY USEFUL-Polydor: 533 735-2 (CD) -4 (MC)
  Highlights *REALLY USEFUL: 537 686-2 (CD) -4 (MC)*
  2.FILM MUSICAL 1973 *w:* YVONNE ELLIMAN-TED NEELY-CARL
  ANDERSON-BARRY DENNEN *MCA deleted*
  3.ORIG LONDON CAST 1972 PAUL NICHOLAS-DANA GILLESPIE
  IE-PAUL JABARA & Comp *MCA (UNI): MCFC 2503 (MC)*
  4.STUDIO RECORD 1972 MURRAY HEAD-IAN GILLAN-YVONNE
  ELLIMAN *MCA (UNI): DMCX 501 (CD)*
  5.HIGHLIGHTS FROM 20TH ANNIVERSARY (1992)
  with: PAUL NICHOLAS-CLAIRE MOORE-KEITH BURNS & Co
  FIRST NIGHT (Pinn): OCRCD 6031 (CD)
  6.STUDIO RECORD 1995 DAVE WILLETTS-CLIVE ROWE-ISSY
  VAN RANDWYCK-BILLY HARTMAN-ETHAN FREEMAN
  CURTAIN CALL-MCI (DISC-THE): CURTCD 012 (CD)
  7.CLASSIC MUSICALS SERIES *feat:* DAVE WILLETS-CLIVE
  ROWE-ISSY VAN RANDWYCK-CHRISTOPER BIGGINS and Co.
  + *songs* 'ASPECTS OF LOVE' *KOCH Int: 34083-2 (CD)*

8.ORIG MASTERWORKS EDIT. DAVE WILLETTS-CLIVE ROWE
    ISSY VAN RANDWYCK-ETHAN FREEMAN-CHRIS.BIGGINS
    TER (Koch): CDTER 9026 (2CD)
9.JESUS CHRIST SUPERSTAR (4CD set) *UNIVERAL (IMS)*
    AAM CAD 211757 (4CD)
JESUS OF NAZARETH(1977) Music score by MAURICE JARRE
    -S/T- *CASTLE MUSIC (Pinn): CMRCD 278 (CD)*
JESUS' SON (2000) Music score: JOE HENRY -S/T- with
    V.ARTS on *MAMMOTH-EDEL (Vital) 011 327-2MAM (CD)*
JETSONS The (USA TV 62) - *see COLL.242,259,*
JEWEL IN THE CROWN (ITV/Granada 9/1/1984)
    music score by GEORGE FENTON *deleted*
JFK - *see COLL.3,64,280,281,*
JIM DAVIDSON'S GENERATION GAME (BBC1 1998-2001 series)
    title music by EMERSON LAKE & PALMER *unavailable*
JIM'LL FIX IT (BBC1 1975) - *see COLL.132,*
JO WHILEY (C4 05/05/1999) title music by DAMIAN HARRIS
    V.ARTIST COLL 'The Incredible Sound Of Jo Whiley'
    INCREDIBLE (Ten): INC7CD (2CD) INC7MC (2MC)
JOAN AND LESLIE (BBC 1950s) theme "Miss Melanie"
    RONALD BINGE *MARCO POLO 9Sel): 8223515 (CD)*
JOAN OF ARC: The MESSENGER (1999) Music by ERIC SERRA
    -S/T- *COLUMBIA-SONY CLASSICS (Ten): SK 66537 (CD)*
JOE 90 (ATV/ITC 29/9/68-69) theme music BARRY GRAY
    see COLL.24,38,74,84,118,250,253,
JOHN PEEL'S SOUNDS OF THE SUBURBS (C4 27/02/1999)
    Collect.from TV ser.on influential British music
    SHIFTY (Pinn-Disc): SHIFTY 9901 (2CD)
JOHNNY BELINDA (1948) Music: MAX STEINER *see COLL.239,*
JOHNNY COOL (1963) Music score: BILLY MAY -S/T- *reiss*
    RYKODISC (Vital): RCD 10744 (CD)
JOHNNY STACCATO (USA 1959) theme mus: ELMER BERNSTEIN
    see COLL.124,
JOHNS (1996) music score by CHARLES BROWN -S/T- on
    VARESE (Pinn): VSD 5778
JOLSON STORY The (1946) V.ORIG -S/T- Film songs on
    GREAT MOVIE THEMES: (Targ-BMG): CD 60021 (CD)
JOLSON: THE MUSICAL (1995) Victoria Palace London
    BRIAN CONLEY and Company - ORIG CAST RECORDING on
    FIRST NIGHT (Pinn): CASTCD 56 (CD) CASTC 56 (MC)
JONATHAN CREEK (BBC1 10/5/97) theme music "Variations
    On A Theme" 'Danse Macabre' (Saint-Saens) arrang:
    JULIAN STEWART LINDSAY *unavailable*
JONATHAN LIVINGSTON SEAGULL (1973) Music: NEIL DIAMOND
    -S/T- *re-iss SONY: 467607-2 (CD)* with 'BEAUTIFUL
    NOISE'/'JAZZ SINGER' *SONY (Ten): 488676-2 (3CD)*
JONNY QUEST (USA TV) *see COLL.243,*
JOSEPH and THE AMAZING TECHNICOLOR DREAMCOAT - songs
    by Tim Rice and Andrew Lloyd Webber
    1.ORIG LONDON REVIVAL CAST 1991 *with:* JASON DONOVAN
    POLYDOR-REALLY USEFUL (Univ):511 130-2(CD) -4(MC)
    (Jason Donovan & Comp) *also* "Any Dream Will Do"
    "Close Every Door To Me"/"Pharaoh's Story"
    Phillip Schofield *POLY: RUR(CD)(CS)11(7"/CDs/MC)*

2. ORIG LONDON CAST 1973 GARY BOND-PAUL BROOKE-IAN
   CHARLESON-JOAN HEAL-JEREMY JAMES TAYLOR-GAVIN REED
   MCA (UNI): MCLD 19023 (CD)
3. STUDIO RECORD. PAUL JONES-TIM RICE-GORDON WALLER
   MIKE SAMMES SINGERS and GEOFF LOVE & HIS ORCHESTRA
   CFP (EMI): CC 242 (CD) HR 8200 (MC)
4. STUDIO RECORD. DONNY OSMOND-MARIA FRIEDMAN-RICHARD
   ATTENBOROUGH-JOAN COLLINS-CHRISTOPHER BIGGINS & Co
   REALLY USEFUL: CDRUG 1000 (CD) MCRUG 1000 (MC)

JOSEPH MERRICK ELEPHANT MAN (OPERA 2001) composed by
   LAURENT PETITGIRARD. *feat:* NATHALIE STUTZMANN and
   NICHOLAS RIVENCQ-ROBERT BREAULT-MARIE DEVELLEREAU
   SOPHIE KOCH-CELENA NELSON & MONTE CARLO PHILH.ORCH
   LE CHANT DU MONDE (H.Mundi): LDC 2781139/40 (2CD)

JOSHUA JONES (BBC TV) see *COLL.132,*

JOSIE AND THE PUSSYCATS (TV) *see COLL.244,259,*
JOSIE AND THE PUSSYCATS (FILM 2001) -S/T- VAR.ARTISTS
   EPIC (TEN): 503 179-2 (CD)
JOUR DE FETE (Jacques Tati 1948) Music sc: JEAN YATOVE
   -S/T- selection on 'Orig Music From His Films' on
   POLY (Discov): 836 983-2 (CD) see also MON ONCLE
JOURNEY TO THE CENTRE OF THE EARTH (1959) Music score:
   BERNARD HERRMANN + 4 songs sung by PAT BOONE
   VARESE (Pinn): VSD 5849 (CD) see COLL.1,
JOURNEY TO THE CENTRE OF THE EARTH (1999) Music score:
   BRUCE ROWLAND *VARESE Pinn): VSD 6069 (CD)*
JOURNEYS TO THE BOTTOM OF THE SEA (BBC2 13/03/2000)
   series music by JAI YEN *unavailable*
JOY LUCK CLUB The - *see COLL.202,*
JOY RIDE (2001) Music score by MARCO BELTRAMI -S/T-
   VARESE (Pinn): VSD 6290 (CD)
JUAREZ (1939) Music score by ERICH WOLFGANG KORNGOLD
   + *mus.from* 'PRIVATE LIVES OF ELIZABETH AND ESSEX'/
   'THE SEA WOLF' new record.by NEW ZEALAND SYMPHONY
   ORCHESTRA (cond: James Sedares) *KOCH: 37302-2 (CD)*
JUBILEE (1978) *V.A.* BRIAN ENO-ADAM & ANTS-WAYNE COUNTY
   & THE ELECTRIC CHAIRS-CHELSEA-SUZI PINNS-MANEATERS
   AMILCAR -S/T- *reissued EG-POLYG: EGCD 34 (CD)*
   also CAROLINE (Vital/Cargo/Greyhound): 1112 (CD)
JUDGEMENT AT NUREMBERG (1961) Music score: ERNEST GOLD
   -S/T- *RYKODISK (Vit): RCD 10723 (CD) see COLL.112,*
JUICE (1992) Music sco HANK SHOCKLEE & The Bomb Squad
   -S/T- Naughty By Nature-Erik B.& Rakim-Big Daddy
   Kane-Salt'n'Pepa *reis: MCA (UNI): MCLD 19308 (CD)*
JUKE BOX JURY 1959 (BBC1) theme "Hit and Miss" JOHN
   BARRY 7 + 4 *see COLL.3,27,29,283,*
JULES ET JIM (1961) Music score: GEORGES DELERUE
   -S/T- *PROMETHEUS IMPORT: PCD 103 (CD) also on*
   NONESUCH (TEN): 7559 79404-2 (CD)
JULIE AND THE CADILLACS (FILM MUSICAL 1999) -S/T-
   RED BALL (Recognition/Universal): BALLCD 114 (CD)
JULIET BRAVO (UKGo 5/11/92 orig 30/8/80) theme: DEREK
   GOOM arr.of BACH melody *see COLL.42,77,*

JUMANJI (1995) Music score: JAMES HORNER -S/T-
   SONY 481 561-2(CD)
JUMPIN'JACK FLASH (1986) Music score: THOMAS NEWMAN
   -S/T- *reissued on SPECTRUM (Univ): 551 138-2 (CD)*
JUNGLE BOOK The (1940) Music score: MIKLOS ROZSA
   -S/T- with 'THIEF OF BAGHDAD' *COLOSSEUM (Pinn):*
   CST 348044 (CD) also -S/T- mus from 'SPELLBOUND'
   (Miklos Rozsa) *FLAPPER (Pinn): PASTCD 7093 (CD)*
JUNGLE BOOK (1967) *Songs by* RICHARD & ROBERT SHERMAN
   -S/T- *W.DISNEY: WD 70400-2 (CD) -4 (MC)*
   see also WALT DISNEY INDEX p.341
JUNGLE BOOK (1994) Music sco: BASIL POLEDOURIS -S/T-
   MILAN (BMG): 74321 24861-2 (CD)
JURASSIC PARK (1993) Music score: JOHN WILLIAMS -S/T-
   MCA: MCD 10859(CD) see COLL.66,82,121,220,281,
JURASSIC PARK III (2001) Music score by DON DAVIS and
   JOHN WILLIAMS -S/T- *DECCA (UNIV): 014 325-2 (CD)*
JUST CAUSE (1994) Music sc: JAMES NEWTON HOWARD -S/T-
   VARESE (Pinn): VSD 5596 (CD)
JUST GOOD FRIENDS (BBC1 22/9/83) theme (John Sullivan)
   PAUL NICHOLAS *FIRST NIGHT (Pinn): CAST(C)(CD) 43*
JUST VISITING (2001) -S/T- *VARESE (Pinn) VSD 6239 (CD)*
JUST WILLIAM (Talisman/BBC1 13/11/94 music composed &
   directed by NIGEL HESS *see COLL.4,137,*
JUSTINE (1969) Music score: JERRY GOLDSMITH -S/T- *Imp*
   TSUNAMI (Silva Screen): TSU 0119 (CD)
K2 (1991) Music score: HANS ZIMMER -S/T-
   VARESE (Pinn): VSD 5354 (CD)
K-PAX (2001) Music score by EDWARD SHEARMUR -S/T- on
   DECCA-LONDON (Univ): 016 19-2 (CD)
KAMA SUTRA (1997) Mus sco: MYCHAEL DANNA / the Sarangi
   played by ARUNA NARYAN KALLE -S/T- issued on
   COLOSSEUM (Pinn): CST 348063 (CD)
KANSAS CITY (1997) VAR.JAZZ ARTS Collection (inspired
   by the film) *GIANTS OF JAZZ/DELTA (BMG): CD 53300*
KARAOKE (BBC1 28/4/96) Music sco: CHRISTOPHER GUNNING
   -S/T- includes music from 'COLD LAZARUS' + tracks
   by BING CROSBY-HANK WILLIAMS-CRAIG DOUGLAS etc.
   SILVA SCREEN (Koch): FILM(CD)(C) 181 (CD/MC)
KAT AND THE KINGS (MUSICAL) Songs: DAVID KRAMER
   O.CAST (STUDIO) *FIRST NIGHT (Pinn): CASTCD 64 (CD)*
   O.CAST LIVE REC *FIRST NIGHT (Pinn): CASTCD 67 (CD)*
KAVANAGH QC (ITV 3/1/95) music by ANNE DUDLEY and JOHN
   KEANE -S/T- *VIRGIN (EMI): VTCD(VTMC) 134 (CD/MC)*
KEEP THE ASIPIDISTRA FLYING (1997) Music by MIKE BATT
   EMI CLASSICS: CCD 556 613-2 (CD)
KEEPING THE FAITH (2000) Music score: ELMER BERNSTEIN
   -S/T- songs *EDEL-HOLLYW (Vital): 012 275-2HWR (CD)*
KERN GOES TO HOLLYWOOD (ORIG LONDON CAST 85) Songs by
   Jerome Kern-Dorothy Fields etc. *feat* ELAINE DELMAR
   DAVID KERNAN-ELISABETH WELCH-LIZ ROBERTSON & Comp.
   FIRST NIGHT (Pinn): OCRCD 6014 (CD)
KEVIN AND PERRY GO LARGE (BBC 2000) -S/T- VARIOUS ARTS
   -S/T- *VIRGIN (EMI): VTDCDX 298 (CD) VTDMC 298 (MC)*

KEY TO REBECCA The (USATV mini-ser 85) mus sco: J.A.C.
REDFORD -S/T- *PROMETHEUS (Silva S): PCD 123 (CD)*
KHARTOUM (1966) Music score: FRANK CORDELL -S/T- inc
'RING OF BRIGHT WATER' *ARTEMIS (Hot) ARTF 003 (CD)*
KID GALAHAD see ELVIS PRESLEY INDEX p.348
KIDNAPPED (1971) Music score by ROY BUDD -S/T- on
CINEPHILE (Pinn): CINCD 015 (CD) also available
with 'WHERE'S JACK' (ROY BUDD,1969) on
TICKERTAPE USA IMPORT: TT 3008 (CD)
KIDS ARE ALRIGHT The (1979) Music by PETE TOWNSHEND
-S/T- featuring THE WHO (Remastered -S/T-)
POLYDOR (UNIV): 543 694-2 (CD)
KIDS FROM FAME - *see under 'FAME'*
KIDS IN THE HALL BRAIN CANDY (1996) Mus: CRAIG NORTHEY
DOUG ELLIOTT-PAT STEWARD -S/T- *MATADOR (Vital):*
OLE 1832(CD) OLE 1831(LP) see COLL.248,
KIKA (1993) music of various artists -S/T- *Import* on
IMPORT MUSIC SERVICES (IMS): E.517 572-2 (CD)
KIKUJIRO SOMMER (2000) Music score: JOE HISAISHI
-S/T- *ALHAMBRA (USA) IMPORT: A.8954 (CD)*
KILLER TONGUE The (1996) Music and songs by FANGORIA
-S/T- on *EDEL-CINERAMA (Vital) 002269-2CIN (CD)*
KILLERS The (1946) Music sco: MIKLOS ROZSA selection
'LUST FOR LIFE' *VARESE (Pinn): VSD 5405 (CD)* also
on 'FILM NOIR CLASSICS' *see* 'DOUBLE INDEMNITY'
KILLING FIELDS The (1984) Music sco: MICHAEL OLDFIELD
-S/T- *VIRGIN (EMI): CDV 2328 (CD) MIKECD 12 (CD)*
see *COLL.64,*
KILROY (BBC1 12/10/87-2002) theme music composed and
arranged by ROBERT HOWES *unavailable*
KIMBERLY (1999) Music score by BASIL POLEDOURIS and
ERIC COLVIN -S/T- *VARESE (Pinn): VSD 6080 (CD)*
KIND HEARTS AND CORONETS (1949) *see COLL.161,*

KINDERGARTEN COP (1990) Music sc: RANDY EDELMAN -S/T-
VARESE (Pinn): VSD(VSC) 5305 (CD/MC)
KING AND I The (1999 Animated Musical) -S/T- on
SONY CLASSICS: SK 63386 (CD) ST 63386 (MC)
KING AND I The - songs by R.Rodgers & O.Hammerstein II
1.ORIGINAL LONDON CAST 2000 ELAINE PAIGE-JASON SCOTT
LEE-AURA DEVA-SEAN GHAZI and Company
WEA (TEN): 8573 84389-2 (CD) -4 (MC)
2.FILM MUSICAL 1956 YUL BRYNNER-DEBORAH KERR *(sung
by* MARNI NIXON) RITA MORENO-TERRY SAUNDERS -S/T-
remastered *EMI: CDC 527 351-2 (CD)*
3.ORIGINAL BROADWAY CAST 1996
TER (Koch): CDTER2 1214 (2CD)
4.ORIG BROADWAY CAST 1951 YUL BRYNNER-GERTRUDE
LAWRENCE-DORETTA MORROW-LARRY DOUGLAS & Company
MCA (UNI): MCLD 19156 (CD)
5.STUDIO RECORDING 1992 JULIE ANDREWS-BEN KINGSLEY-
LEA SALONGA-PEABO BRYSON-MARILYN HORNE-ROGER MOORE
MARTIN SHEEN-HOLLYWOOD BOWL SO.cond: JOHN MAUCERI
PHILIPS: 438 007-2 (CD) -4(MC) -5 (DCC) -1 (LP)

6.STUDIO RECORD.1994 VALERIE MASTERSON-CHRISTOPHER
LEE-JASON HOWARD-HARRY WILLIAMS-TINUKE OLAFIMIHAN
SALLY BURGESS-BEA JULAKASIUN and Company
TER (Koch): CDTEH 6006 (CD) / SHOWTIME: SHOWCD 024
7.CLASSIC MUSICALS SERIES *feat:* VALERIE MASTERSON
THOMAS ALLEN-MURIEL DICKINSON & MUNICH SYMPH.ORCH.
+ *songs from* 'OKLAHOMA!' *KOCH Int: 34077-2 (CD)*
KING CREOLE (1958) ELVIS PRESLEY remastered -S/T-
*RCA (BMG): 07863 67454-2 (CD) -4 (MC) / SANCTUARY
(Pinn):ELVIS 112 (LP) see* PRESLEY FILM INDEX p.348
KING KONG (1933) Music score by MAX STEINER
(1) *RESTORED MAX STEINER SCORE BY JOHN MORGAN*
MOSCOW SYMPHONY ORCHESTRA (WILLIAM J.STROMBERG)
MARCO POLO (Select): 8.223763 (CD)
(2) NATIONAL PHILHARM ORCH (FRED STEINER) *New Rec.*
SOUTHERN CROSS (Hot): SCCD 901 (CD) also on
LEGEND-5TH CONTINENT (Silva Screen): LXCD 10
(3) *COLLECTION* 'THIS IS CINERAMA' (1955) 'DEATH OF
A SCOUNDREL' (1956) *LABEL X (Hot): ATMCD 2005 (CD)*
see *COLL.61,174,239,*
KING KONG (1976) Music score: JOHN BARRY -S/T- *IMPORT*
MASK (S.Screen): MK 702 (CD) see *COLL.26,37,174,*
KING OF KINGS (1961) M: MIKLOS ROZSA see *COLL.213,215,*
KING OF THE HILL (USA/C4 01/08/1997) theme music by
The REFRESHMENTS / VARIOUS ARTISTS -S/T- on
ELEKTRA (TEN): 7559 62441-2 (CD)
KING RAT (1965) Music score by JOHN BARRY -S/T- reiss
COLUMBIA LEGACY (TEN): 502 389-2 (CD)
KING'S THIEF (1955) Music sc: MIKLOS ROZSA new record:
BRANDENBURG S.O. *MARCO POLO (Sel): 8.223607 (CD)*
KING'S THIEF (1955) Music sco MIKLOS ROZSA *(complete)*
TICKERTAPE USA Impt.(S.Screen): TT 3012 (CD)
KINSEY (BBC1 2/4/91) mus: DAVE GREENSLADE see *COLL.5,*
KIPPER (CITV 05/09/1997) mus: BOB HEATLIE see *COLL.285*
KISMET - songs by Robert Wright and George Forrest
adapted from the music of Alexander Borodin
1.ORIG -S/T- 1955 *reissue EMI ODEON: CDODEON 23 (CD)*
2.STUDIO 1964 *reissue LONDON (Univ): 452 488-2 (CD)* ·
3.ORIG BROADWAY CAST 1953 *with:* ALFRED DRAKE & Comp
SONY CLASSICS (TEN): SMK 89252 (CD)
4.STUDIO REC.1990 VALERIE MASTERSON-DONALD MAXWELL
DAVID RENDALL-ROSEMARY ASHE-BONAVENTURA BOTTONE-
RICHARD VAN ALLAN Philharmonia Orch:John O.Edwards
Highlights: *SHOWTIME (MCI-THE): SHOW(CD)(MC) 014*
Complete: *TER: CDTER2-1170 (2CD)*
5.STUDIO REC.1992 *with:* SAMUEL RAMEY-JULIA MIGENES-
JERRY HADLEY-MANDY PATINKIN-DOM DE LUISE-RUTH ANN
SWENSON *SONY BROADWAY: SK 46438 (CD)*
KISS ME KATE - songs by Cole Porter
1.ORIG FILM -S/T- 1953 KATHRYN GRAYSON-HOWARD KEEL
ANN MILER etc. *EMI ODEON (EMI): CDODEON 25 (CD)*
2.ORIG BROADWAY CAST 1948 *with:* LISA KIRK-PATRICIA
MORISON-ALFRED DRAKE-HARRY CLARK-HAROLD LANG & Com
COLUMB (Ten): SK 60536(CD) / EMI: ZDM 764760-2(CD)

3.ORIG BROADWAY CAST 1999 recording conducted by PAUL
GEMIGNANI *DRG USA (Koch-BMG): DRGCD 12988 (CD)*
4.ORIG LONDON CAST 1987 *w:* FIONA HENDLEY-PAUL JONES-
EARLENE BENTLEY-JOHN BARDEN-TIM FLAVIN and Company
reissued on FIRST NIGHT (Pinn): OCRCD 6020 (CD)
5.STUDIO RECORD.1991 *with:* JOSEPHINE BARSTOW-THOMAS
HAMPSON-KIM CRISWELL-GEORGE DVORSKY & Company.
EMI: CDS 754 033-2 (2CDs) EX 754 033-4 (2 MC)
6.STUDIO RECORD.1995 THOMAS ALLEN-DIANA MONTAGUE
Complete: *TER (Koch): CDTER2 1212 (2CD)*
7.STUDIO RECORDING 1996 *with* EDMUND HOCKRIDGE
JANINE ROEBUCK-JACKIE JEFFERSON *pr: GORDON LORENZ*
CARLTON SHOWS Coll (CHE): 30362 00332 (CD) -4(MC)
8.REPRISE MUSICAL REPERTORY COMPANY *includ* 'FINIAN'S
RAINBOW'/'SOUTH PACIFIC'/'GUYS & DOLLS'
REPRISE (TEN): 9362 47775-2 (4CD set)
KISS OF THE DRAGON (2001) Music score: CRAIG ARMSTRONG
-S/T- *VIRGIN (EMI): CDVUS 210 (CD)*
KISS OF THE SPIDER WOMAN (ORIG LONDON CAST 1992) *feat:*
CHITA RIVERA-BRENT CARVER-ANTHONY CRIVELLO & Comp:
reissued on FIRST NIGHT (Pinn): OCRCD 6030 (CD)
KISS OF THE VAMPIRE 1964 m:JAMES BERNARD *see COLL.126,*
KISSIN' COUSINS *see* ELVIS PRESLEY INDEX p.348
KISSING A FOOL (1997) Music score: JOSEPH VITARELLI
"At Last" sung by ETTA JAMES others songs by the
MIGHTY BLUES KINGS -S/T- *VARESE (Pinn): VSD 5922*
KNACK The (65) Music score: JOHN BARRY -S/T- *reissue*
RYKODISC (Vital): RCD 10718 (CD) / KEN MACKINTOSH
ORCH 'Mac's Back' *Presid: PLCD 532 / see COLL.26,*
KNIFE IN THE WATER (1962) Mus sc: KRZYSZTOF KOMEDA +
'CRAZY GIRL' *POWER BROS (Har.Mundi): PB 00145 (CD)*
KNIGHT RIDER (USA 1982 ITV 1983/C5 1997) theme (Glen
Larson-S.Phillips) *see COLL.14,38,221,247,*
KNIGHT'S TALE, A (2001) Music score by CARTER BURWELL
-S/T- *COLUMBIA (TEN): 503 096-2 (CD)*
KNOTS LANDING (USA BBC1 79) theme mus: JERROLD IMMEL
see COLL.244,
KOJAK (USA 73) theme music: BILLY GOLDENBERG
see COLL.77,83,84,117,124,200,
KOLCHAK THE NIGHT STALKER (USA TV) *see COLL.219,246,*
KOLYA (1997) Music score: ODREJ SOUKUP inc.Classical
-S/T- *PHILIPS (Univ): 456 432-2 (CD)*
KONGA - *see COLL.151,*
KOYAANISQATSI (1982) Music score: PHILIP GLASS -S/T-
NONESUCH (TEN): 7559 795192-9 (2CD)
KPAX - *see* K-PAX
KRAMER V KRAMER (1979) Music by VIVALDI and PURCELL
-S/T- *SONY FR.(Discov): SK 73945(CD) ST 73945 (MC)*
KREMMEN THE MOVIE featuring KENNY EVERETT *reissued on*
EMI GOLD-LFP (EMI): LFPS 1554 (MC)
KULL THE CONQUEROR (1997) Music score: JOEL GOLDSMITH
-S/T- *VARESE (Pinn): VSD 5862 (CD)*
KUNDUN (1997) Music score: PHILIP GLASS -S/T- on
Nonesuch (TEN): 7559 79460-2 (CD) -4 (MC)

L'AMANT see 'LOVER The'

L.A.CONFIDENTIAL (1997) Music score: JERRY GOLDSMITH
-S/T- score *VARESE (Pinn): VSD 5885 (CD)*
-S/T- songs *RESTLESS (BMG):74321 52596-2 (CD)*
L.A.LAW (USA)(ITV 7/9/88) theme music: MIKE POST
see *COLL.14,203,254*
LA BAMBA (1987) Music: MILES GOODMAN-CARLOS SANTANA
featuring Los Lobos -S/T- reissue:
SLASH-LONDON (Ten): 3984 28226-2 (CD)
Orig Ritchie Valens songs on ACE: CDCHD 953 (CD)
LA CAGE AUX FOLLES (MUSICAL 1983) Songs: Jerry Herman
Orig Broadway Cast feat: GEORGE HEARN-GENE BARRY-
JAY GARNER-JOHN WEINER-ELIZABETH PARRISH & Company
RCA VICTOR (BMG): BD 84824 (CD)
LA CAVA (MUSICAL 2000) Songs: LAURENCE O'KEEFE-STEPHEN
KEELING-JOHN CLAFLIN-SHAUN McKENNA.
O.LONDON CAST RECORDING from *DRESS CIRCLE RECORDS*
LA DERNIER METRO see LAST METRO The
LA DOLCE VITA (1960) Music score b NINO ROTA -S/T- on
CAM IMPT.(HOT): 493 095-2 (CD) see COLL.212,
LA DONNA INVISIBLE (-) Music by ENNIO MORRICONE -S/T-
DAGORED (Cargo-S.Sounds-BMG): RED 109-2(CD) -1(LP)
LA FEMME NIKITA (USA/C5 12/9/1997) theme m: MARK SNOW
-S/T- inc.songs *TVT (Cargo-S.Scr): TVT 8170-2 (CD)*
see *COLL.229,*
LA FETE SAUVAGE TV Soundtrack Music by VANGELIS -S/T-
Polydor Impt (Discovery): 841 198-2 (CD)
LA FLEUR DE MON SECRET - see FLOWER OF MY SECRET
LA FOLIE, A (1994) Music: MICHAEL NYMAN feat MICHAEL
NYMAN BAND -S/T- Impt *(DISCOVERY): 839 949-2 (CD)*
LA GLOIRE DE MON PERE - see 'GLORY OF MY FATHER'
LA GRANDE ILLUSION (1937) Music by JOSEPH KOSMA -S/T-
SOUND TRACK FACTORY (Discov): 33545 (CD)
LA PASSIONE (1996) Music by CHRIS REA -S/T- on
EAST WEST (TEN): 0630 16695-2 (CD) -4 (MC)
LA PLANETE SAVAGE (Fantastic Planet) (1973) Music
score composed and performed by ALAIN GORAGUER
-S/T- *DC RECORDINGS (Vital): DC 33(CD)(LP)*
LA REINE MARGOT - see QUEEN MARGOT
LA REVOLUTION FRANCAISE 1789-1794 (SHOW 1990) Songs:
Alain Boublil and Claude Michel Schonberg / Orig
PARIS Cast on *FIRST NIGHT (Pinn): OCRCD 6006 (CD)*
also on *WAGRAM (Discovery/Cargo): 306241-2 (CD)*
LABYRINTH (1986) Music score: TREVOR JONES-DAVID BOWIE
-S/T- re-issue FAME-MFP *(EMI): CDFA 3322 (CD)*
LADIES MAN The (2000) Music score: MARCUS MILLER -S/T-
V.ARTISTS *UNIVERSAL MUSIC (IMS):AA 4450 276-2 (CD)*
LADY AND THE HIGHWAYMAN (1988) Music by LAURIE JOHNSON
see *COLL.156,158,*
LADY AND THE TRAMP The (1956) Songs: PEGGY LEE-J.BURKE
Music: OLIVER WALLACE sung by **Peggy Lee** -S/T-
WALT DISNEY: WD 6021328 (CD) DISNEY INDEX p.341

LADY BE GOOD (1941) -S/T- ELEANOR POWELL-ANN MILLER-
JIMMY DORSEY ORCH + *m.from* 'Four Jills In A Jeep'
GREAT MOVIE THEMES (Target-BMG): CD 60029 (CD)
LADY BE GOOD (ORIG BROADWAY CAST) Songs (George & Ira
Gershwin) *ELEKTRA NONESUCH (TEN):7559 79308-2 (CD)*
LADY CAROLINE LAMB (1972) Music score: RICHARD RODNEY
BENNETT / 'Molto Vivo' new recording by BBC
PHILHARMONIC ORCHESTRA on *CHANDOS: CHAN 9867 (CD)*
LADY IN THE DARK (SHOW) Songs: KURT WEILL-IRA GERSHWIN
1997 STUDIO RECORDING *with* MARIA FRIEDMAN-ADRIAN
DUNBAR-STEVEN E.MOOORE *TER (Koch): CDTER 1244 (CD)*
LADY SINGS THE BLUES The (1972) Music: MICHEL LEGRAND
Songs of Billie Holiday sung by DIANA ROSS -S/T-
re-issued MOTOWN-POLYDOR (Univ): 530 135-2 (2CD)
LADYHAWKE (1985) Mus sc: ANDREW POWELL -S/T-
GNP (ZYX): GNPD 8042 (CD)
LADYKILLERS The (1955) Music: TRISTRAM CARY other mus
'Minuet No.5 In E.Op.11'(BOCCHERINI) *see COLL.161,*
LAKE PLACID (1999) Music score by JOHN OTTMAN -S/T-
VARESE (Pinn): VSD 6055 (CD)
LAMMBOCK (2001) -S/T- *ZYX : ZYX 55240-2 (CD)*
LAMPIES The (BBC1 12/10/2001) mus.by MCASSO "Light Up
The World" + theme "La La La It's The Lampies"
PLEASE MUSIC (Blue Crest-Pinn): LAMPCD 001 (CDs)
LAND AND FREEDOM (1994) Music score: GEORGE FENTON
-S/T- *DEBONAIR (Pinn): CDDEB 1001 (CD)*
LAND GIRLS The (1998) Music score: BRIAN LOCK -S/T-
SILVA SCREEN (Koch): FILMCD 300 (CD) see COLL.3,
LAND OF SMILES (*Operetta* by FRANZ LEHAR-LUDWIG HERZER
FRITZ LOHNER) feat: RICHARD TAUBER-MARGIT SUCHY-
*KOCH: 31373-2 (CD) French Highlights + MERRY WIDOW
etc. EMI BELLE EPOQUE: CZS 767 872-2 (2CD)*
LAND OF THE GIANTS (USA 68 / C4 10/1/93) theme music:
JOHN WILLIAMS *see COLL.38,84,218,246,*
LAND OF THE TIGER (BBC2 17/11/1997) orig music by
NICHOLAS HOOPER *BBC WORLDW (Pinn):WMSF 6005-2 (CD)*
LAND WITHOUT MUSIC (FILM OPERETTA 1936) RICHARD TAUBER
-S/T- excerpts *PEARL (H.Mundi): GEMM 263 (LP)*
LARKRISE TO CANDLEFORD (NAT.THEATRE STAGE PROD.1978)
Mus: ALBION BAND *CHARISMA/VIRGIN: CDSCD 4020 (CD)*
LASSIE (USA TV) *see COLL.245,*
LAST CASTLE The (2001) Music score by JERRY GOLDSMITH
-S/T- *DECCA LONDON (Univ): 016 193-2 (CD)*
LAST COMMAND The (1955) Music sco: MAX STEINER / song
"Jim Bowie" (Steiner-Clare) sung by GORDON MacRAE
TARAN (Silver Sounds): W 9109 (CD)
LAST DAYS OF CHEZ NOUS (1992) Music sc: PAUL GRABOWSKY
-S/T- *DRG USA (Pinn): DRGCD 12607 (CD)*
LAST DAYS OF DISCO The (1998) Music score: MARK SUOZZO
-S/T- *WORK-COLUMBIA Sony: 49213-2 (CD) -4 (MC)*
LAST DRAGON (1985) V/A -S/T- MISHA SEGAL-WILLIE HUTCH-
NORMAN WHITFIELD etc.*MOTOWN (UNIV): 530 386-2 (CD)*
LAST EMPEROR (1988) Mus: DAVID BYRNE-RYUICHI SAKAMOTO
CONG SU -S/T- *VIRGIN: CDV 2485 (CD) OVEDC 366*

LAST EXIT TO BROOKLYN (1989) Music sco: MARK KNOPFLER
  -S/T- *VERTIGO (Univ): 838 725-2 (CD)*
LAST MAN STANDING (1996) Music score/songs: RY COODER
  -S/T- *VERVE-POLYDOR (Univ): 533 415-2 (CD)*
LAST METRO The (1980) + 'THE WOMAN NEXT DOOR' (1981)
  music by GEORGES DELERUE *DRG (Pinn): 32902 (CD)*
LAST NIGHT (1998) Music score -S/T- on
  SONY CLASSICS: SK 60830 (CD)
LAST NIGHT OF THE PROMS (BBC1)
  'THE BEST PROMS ALBUM IN THE WORLD EVER' (Various)
  VIRGIN (EMI): VTDCD 323 (CD)
LAST OF ENGLAND The (1987) Music: SIMON FISHER TURNER
  -S/T- *MUTE: IONIC 1 (LP) CDIONIC 1 (CD)*
LAST OF THE MEDICINE MEN The (BBC2 28/09/2000)
  Music: MICHAEL ORMISTON and KEITH WAITHE -S/T- on
  BBC WORLDWIDE (Pinn): WMSF 6031-2 (CD)
LAST OF THE MOHICANS (1992) Music: TREVOR JONES-RANDY
  EDELMAN -S/T- *MORGAN CREEK (Vit): 002241-2MCM (CD)*
  new recording on VARESE (Pinn): VSD 6161 (CD)
  see COLL.3,61,97,279,
LAST OF THE SUMMER WINE The (BBC1 12/11/1973-2000)
  theme music by RONNIE HAZLEHURST *deleted*
LAST RUN The (1971) Music score by JERRY GOLDSMITH
  -S/T- inc 'WILD ROVERS' (1971 Jerry Goldsmith) on
  CHAPTER III (USA IMPORT): CHA 0135 (CD)
LAST SEPTEMBER (1999) Music score by ZBIGNIEW PREISNER
  SILVA SCREEN (Koch): SILKD 6027 (CD)
LAST STAND AT SABRE RIVER (1998) Music: DAVID SHIRE
  -S/T- *INTRADA (Koch/S.Screen): MAF 7078CD (CD)*
LAST STARFIGHTER The (1984) Music s: CRAIG SAFAN -S/T-
  reissue *INTRADA (Koch/S.Screen): MAF 7066CD (CD)*
LAST SUNSET - *see COLL.112,*
LAST TANGO IN PARIS (1972) Music score: GATO BARBIERI
  -S/T- *RYKODISC (Vital): RCD 10724 (CD)*
LAST TEMPTATION OF CHRIST (1988) Music: PETER GABRIEL
  -S/T-'Passion' *R.WORLD-VIRG: RW(CD)(MC)(LP)(MD) 1*
LAST TIME I COMMITTED SUICIDE The (1997) Jazz -S/T-
  BLUE NOTE (EMI): CDP 836 736-2 (CD)
LAST VALLEY The (1970) Music score by JOHN BARRY
  New Record CITY OF PRAGUE PHILH.ORCH conducted by
  NIC RAINE *SILVA SCREEN (Koch): FILMXCD 355 (CD)*
  and *-S/T- TICKERTAPE USA:TT 3003 (CD) see COLL.26,*
LATER (WITH JOOLS HOLLAND) (BBC2) Compilation featur
  BLUE/OASIS/PAUL WELLER/SUPERGRASS/ELASTICA etc.
  ISLAND (Univ): CID 8053 (CD)
LAURA (1944) Music score: DAVID RAKSIN -S/T- on
  *SOUNDTRACK FACTORY (Discov): SFCD 33518 (CD) also
  with 'JANE EYRE' (1943) FOX-ARISTA (BMG): 07822
  11006-2(CD) see COLL.61,69,*
LAUREL & HARDY 'Legends Of The 20th Century' (Coll)
  EMI: 522 816-2 (CD) - see COLL.165,245,
LAUTREC (2000) (MUSICAL) - *see page 345*
LAUTREC (1998) -S/T- *XIIIBIS (Discov) LBSA 98009-2 CD*
LAVERNE AND SHIRLEY (USA TV) *see COLL.244,*

LAW AND ORDER (USA TV) *see COLL.203,248,*
LAWMAN (USA TV) *see COLL.245,*
LAWNMOWER MAN 2: BEYOND CYBERSPACE (95) Music score:
   ROBERT FOLK *-S/T- VARESE (Pinn): VSD 5698 (CD)*
LAWRENCE OF ARABIA (1962) Music score: MAURICE JARRE
   -S/T- LONDON PHILHARMONIC ORCH conduct by MAURICE
   JARRE *CINEPHILE-CASTLE (Pinn): CINCD 008 (CD)* also
   The PHILHARMONIA ORCHESTRA (cond: TONY BREMNER) on
   SILVA SCREEN (Koch): FILMCD 719 (CD reissue 2000)
   others: VARESE (Pinn): VSD 5263 (CD) VSC 5263 (MC)
   see COLL.123,153,154,
LE BOSSU (1998) Music score: PHILIPPE SARDE *-S/T-* on
   VIRGIN (EMI): 845 348-2 (CD)
LE COLONEL CHABERT (1994) *SELECTION OF CLASSICAL MUSIC*
   AUVIDIS (Harmonia Mundi): K.1003 (CD)
LE GOUT DES AUTRES (2000) JEAN CHARLES JARRELL arranger
   UNIVERSAL FRANCE (Discov) 464 658-2 (CD)
LE JOUR ET LA NUIT (1997) Music score: MAURICE JARRE
   -S/T- imp WEA FRANCE (Discovery): 0630 18006-2 (CD)
LE PROF (1999) Music score by JEAN CLAUDE PETIT
   -S/T- SONY CLASSICS (TEN): SK 89247 (CD)
LEAVE HER TO HEAVEN (1945) Music score: ALFRED NEWMAN
   -S/T- with 'ALL ABOUT EVE' (A.Newman, 1945)
   FSM CLASSICS: FSMCD Vol 2.No.8 (CD) / see COLL.1,
LEAVE IT TO BEAVER (1997) Music s: RANDY EDELMAN *-S/T-*
   VARESE (Pinn): VSD 5838 (CD) see COLL.242,
LEAVING HOME (C4 29/9/96) 20th Century Orchestral mus
   CITY OF BIRMINGHAM SYMPH.ORCH cond: SIMON RATTLE
   -S/T- EMI CDM 566 136-2 (2CDs) CDM 566 137-2 (2CD)
LEAVING LAS VEGAS (1994) Music sc: MIKE FIGGIS + V/A
   -S/T- IRS-A.& M.(Univ): 540 476-2 (CD)
LEGALLY BLONDE (2001) Music score by ROLFE KENT *-S/T-*
   POLYDOR (UNIV): 493 078-2 (CD)
LEGEND (1986) *note: this film has two -S/T-*
   Music *(1)* JERRY GOLDSMITH Lyrics (John Bettis)
   VARESE (Pinn): VSD 6203 (CD) and Music *(2)*
   TANGERINE DREAM *and also feat* "Is Your Love Strong
   Enough" by BRYAN FERRY / "Loved By The Sun" by JON
   ANDERSON *-S/T- reiss: VARESE (Pinn): VSD 5645 (CD)*
LEGEND OF 1900 (1999) Music score by ENNIO MORRICONE +
   Roger Waters *-S/T- SONY CLASS (Ten): SK 66767 (CD)*
LEGEND OF BAGGER VANCE (2000) Mus score RACHEL PORTMAN
   -S/T- CHAPTER III (Silver Sounds) CHPT 1009-2 (CD)
   also on GOLD CIRCLE (Proper): GCE 1009-2 (CD)
LEGEND OF THE GLASS MOUNTAIN *see* GLASS MOUNTAIN
LEGENDS OF THE FALL (1994) Music s: JAMES HORNER *-S/T-*
   EPIC (Ten): 478 511-2 (CD)
LENNY'S BIG ATLANTIC ADVENTURE (BBC1 26/08/2000) Music
   score by The FRATELLI BROTHERS *unavailable*
LENNY (1974) including music by MILES DAVIS *-S/T-*
   RYKODISC (Vital): RCD 10707 (CD)
LEON (The Professional) (1994) Music score: ERIC SERRA
   -S/T- COLUMBIA (Ten): 478 323-2 (CD) -4 (MC)
LES DINER DES CONS - *see* 'DINNER GAME'

LES ENFANTS DU PARADIS (1945) Var.Music selections on
  AUVIDIS (Harmonia Mundi): K.1502 (CD)
LES MISERABLES (FILM 1997) Music sco: BASIL POLEDOURIS
  -S/T- EDEL-HOLLYWOOD (Vital) 012 147-2HWR (CD)
LES MISERABLES - songs by Alain Boublil-Claude Michel
  Schonberg with English lyrics by Herbert Kretzmer
  1.ORIG LONDON CAST 1985 *with:* PATTI LuPONE and Comp
    ENCORE CD1 (CD) ENCORE C1 (2MC)
  2.ORIG FRENCH CAST *FIRST NIGHT (Pinn):DOCRCD 1 (2CD)*
    COMPLETE SYMPHONIC RECORD LONDON PO.+ UK/USA Casts
    FIRST NIGHT (Pinn): MIZCD1 (3CDs) MIZC1 (3MC)
  3.FIVE OUTSTANDING PERFORMANCES From Les Miserables:
    FIRST NIGHT (Pinn): SCORCD 17 (CD) Highlights from
    Int.Cast *FIRST NIGHT (Pinn):CAST(C)(CD)20 (MC/CD)*
  4.MANCHESTER 1992 CAST RECORDING *FIRST NIGHT (Pinn):*
    SCORECD 34 (CDep)
  5.CARLTON SHOWS COLLECTION 1993 STUDIO RECORD *with:*
    DAVE WILLETTS-CLAIRE MOORE & West End Concert Orch
    CARLTON SHOWS: PWKS 4175 (CD) PWKMC 4175 (MC)
  6.ROYAL PHILHARMONIC ORCHESTRA *PLAY SUITES from*
    Miss Saigon and Les Miserables
    CARLTON Shows: PWKS(PWKMC) 4079 (CD/MC)
  7.10TH ANNIVERARY LONDON STAGE SHOW 1995
    FIRST NIGHT (Pinn):ENCORECD 8 (2CD) ENCOREC 8(2MC)
LES SILENCES DU PALAIS - *see* 'SILENCES OF THE PALACE'
LES VALSEUSES (1974 Fra) Music sco: STEPHANE GRAPPELLI
  -S/T- MUSIDISC (Discovery): 10870-2 (CD)
LESLEY GARRETT TONIGHT (BBC2 14/11/1998) SERIES SONGS
  BBC-BMG Con (BMG): 75605 51338-2 (CD) -4 (MC)(1999)
  BBC-BMG Con (BMG): 75605 51354-2 (CD) -4 (MC)(2000)
LET HIM HAVE JUSTICE (MUSICAL DRAMA 1999 based on the
  DEREK BENTLEY case) Music director: PHILLIP SUTTON
  Music,lyrics,book by the ORIGINAL LONDON CAST
  TER (Koch): CDTER 1257 (CD)
LET IT BE (1970) Songs: JOHN LENNON-PAUL McCARTNEY
  PARLOPHONE: CDP 746 447-2(CD) (TC)PCS 7096 (MC/LP)
LET NO MAN WRITE MY EPITAPH (1960) Music score by
  GEORGE DUNING and songs sung by ELLA FITZGERALD
  CLASSIC (Vivanti): VSCD 4043 (CD) VS 404345 (2LP)
LETHAL WEAPON *Coll on SILVA SCREEN: FILMCD 195 (CD)*
LEVIATHAN (1989) Music score: JERRY GOLDSMITH -S/T-
  VARESE (Pinn): VSD 5226 (CD)
LEXX: THE DARK ZONE STORIES (SKY1 8/97) Music score by
  MARTY SIMON -S/T- *COLOSS (Pinn): CST 348064 (CD)*
LIBERTY HEIGHTS (1999) Music score by ANDREA MORRICONE
  -S/T- (USA IMPORT) ATLANTIC (USA) 83271 (CD)
LIBERTY THE AMERICAN WAR OF INDEPENDENCE (C4 19/9/98)
  orig music by RICHARD EINHORN-MARK O'CONNOR
  -S/T- SONY CLASSICS: SK 63216 (CD)
LICENCE TO KILL - *see* COLL.46,47,
  see also JAMES BOND FILM INDEX p.346
LIDO LADY (O.LONDON CAST 1926) Songs (Rodgers- Hart)
  feat: CICELY COURTNEIDGE-BOBBY COMBER-PHYLLIS DARE
  JACK HULBERT *PEARL (Pavilion): GEMMCD 9105 (CD)*

LIEBESTRAUM (1991) Music score: MIKE FIGGIS and tracks
by Earl Bostic & His Orch and Bennie Moiseiwitsch
-S/T- *VIRGIN (EMI): CDV 2682 (CD) TCV 2682 (MC)*
LIFE (1999) V.ARTS -S/T- (music inspired by the film)
INTERSCOPE (Uni): 490 314-2 (CD)
LIFE AND DEATH OF RICHARD III (originally 1912,silent)
'Symphony For Richard III' comp.by ENNIO MORRICONE
SONY Classics: SK 60086 (CD)
LIFE AND LEGEND OF WYATT EARP (USA TV) *see COLL.245,*
LIFE AND TIMES OF DAVID LLOYD GEORGE (BBC2 4/3/1981)
theme mus 'Chi Mai' ENNIO MORRICONE *see COLL.177,*
LIFE AND TIMES OF GRIZZLY ADAMS (USA 78) theme "Maybe"
THOM PACE) instrumental version ('The Man From The
Mountains') *see COLL.246,*
LIFE IS BEAUTIFUL (La Vita E Bella) (1997) Music score
NICOLA PIOVANI -S/T- *VIRGIN (EMI): CDVIR 102 (CD)*
LIFE OF BIRDS The (BBC1 21/10/1998) Music score by
IAN BUTCHER and STEVEN FAUX -S/T-
BBC WORLD (Pinn): WMSF 60032 (CD)
LIFE OF GRIME, A (BBC1 20/04/1999) theme music "What A
Wonderful World" (Weiss-Douglas) from the album
'The Genius of LOUIS ARMSTRONG' on
LIFE LESS ORDINARY, A (1997) Music score: DAVID ARNOLD
-S/T-BECK-UNDERWORLD-REM-ELVIS PRESLEY-PRODIGY-ASH
DUSTED-BOBBY DARIN-CARDIGANS-FAITHLESS & others
A.& M.(Univ): 540 837-2 and LIFECD 1 (CD) -4 (MC)
LIFE WITH FATHER (1947) Mus: MAX STEINER *see COLL.239,*
LIFE WITH FRED (BBC2 10/3/94) theme music "Carnival Of
Venice" (Briccialdi) version by JAMES GALWAY on
RCA (BMG): PD 70260 (CD) PK 70260 (MC)
LIFEFORCE on 'SPACE & BEYOND' *S.SCR: FILMXCD 185 (CD)*
see COLL.232,
LIGHT OF EXPERIENCE The (BBC2 76-87) theme "Doina De
Jale" GHEORGE ZAMFIR *MCI (THE-DISC) MCCD 177 (CD)*
LIGHTHOUSE (1999) Music score by DEBBIE WISEMAN -S/T-
SILVA SCREEN (Koch): FILMCD 335 (CD)
LIKE SOLDIERS DO (BBC1 03/08/1999) title song composed
and sung by BILLY BRAGG from 'Back To Basics'
COOKING VINYL (Vital): COOKCD 060(CD)
LIKE WATER FOR CHOCOLATE (93) Music score: LEO BROWER
-S/T- *Milan (BMG): 887 797 (CD)*
LILAC TIME (O.LONDON CAST 1922) Mus (Franz SCHUBERT)
Lyr (Adrian ROSS) *feat:* CLARA BUTTERWORTH-DOROTHY
CLAYTON-EDMUND GWENN + *RIO RITA (1930) SOUTHERN
MAID (1920) PEARL (Pavilion): GEMMCD 9115 (CD)*
LILIES (1997) Music score: MYCHAEL DANNA -S/T- on
VARESE (Pinn): VSD 5868 (CD)
LILLIPUT IN ANTARCTICA (Cousteau Society/BBC1 2/8/93)
"Antarctica" VANGELIS *POLYD: 839 518-2(CD) -4(MC)*
LILY WAS HERE *see COLL.188,*
LIMELIGHT (1937) 4 songs on Coll 'LOUIS LEVY-MUSIC
FROM T.MOVIES' *EMPRESS (Koch): RAJCD 884*
LIMELIGHT (1952) Music score: CHARLES CHAPLIN *version*
by STANLEY BLACK ORCH *PRESIDENT: PLCD 527*

LIMEY The (1999) Music score by CLIFF MARTINEZ -S/T-
feat various 1960's/70's rock tracks
FLASH CUT-ARTISAN (Pinn-Sil.Sounds): 543 522 (CD)
LINGUINI INCIDENT The (1992) Music sco: THOMAS NEWMAN
-S/T- *VARESE (Pinn): VSD 5372 (CD)*
LION HAS WINGS (1939) *see COLL.9,*
LION IN WINTER The (1968) Music score by JOHN BARRY
-S/T- *LEGACY (TEN):502 388-2 (CD) also available :
SILVA SCREEN (KOCH): FILMCD 353 (CD) / see COLL.26,*
LION KING The (Original Broadway Cast Recording 1997)
Songs by ELTON JOHN and TIM RICE + addit.music by
LEBO M-MARK MANCINA-JAY RIFKIN-JULIE TAYMOR and
HANS ZIMMER *DISNEY-EDEL (Vital) 010 455-2DNY (CD)*
LION KING The (Original London Cast 1999) CORNELL JOHN
ROGER WRIGHT-LUKE YOUNGBLOOD-JOSETTE BUSHELL MINGO
ROB EDWARDS-SIMON GREGOR-MARTYN ELLIS and Company
ORIG LONDON CAST RECORDING CURRENTLY UNAVAILABLE
LION KING The (FILM 1994) Music score by HANS ZIMMER
Disney's Sounds & Stories *DISNEY WD 60802-2 (CD)*
LION KING 2 - *see* **SIMBA'S PRIDE** *see also* p.341
LION OF THE DESERT (1981) Music score: MAURICE JARRE
L.Symph Orch *SILVA SCREEN (Koch): FILMCD 060 (CD)*
LIONHEART (1987) Music score: JERRY GOLDSMITH -S/T-
VARESE (Pinn): VCD 47282 (CD-V1) VCD 47288 (CD-V2)
LISTEN TO THE WIND (MUSICAL 1996) songs: VIVIAN ELLIS
feat PAULA WILCOX-NAOMI BELL-CAMERON BLAKELY & Co
TER (Koch): CDTER 1251 (CD)
LITTLE BOY BLUE (1998) Music: STEWART COPELAND -S/T-
Sonic Images (Cargo-Greyhound): 7828 278810-2 (CD)
LITTLE FAUSS AND BIG HALSY (1970) Music by JOHNNY CASH
BOB DYLAN-CARL PERKINS -S/T- w 'I WALK THE LINE'
BEAR FAMILY (Rollercoaster): BCD 16130 (2CD)
LITTLE HOUSE ON THE PRAIRIE (USA 74 rpt C4-13/10/91)
theme: DAVID ROSE *see COLL.14,244,*
LITTLE ME - songs by Cy Coleman and Carolyn Leigh
 1.ORIG BROADWAY CAST 1962 *w* Sid Caesar-Virginia Mart
 in-Nancy Andrews *RCA Vic (BMG): 09026 61482-2 (CD)*
 2.ORIG LONDON CAST 1964 BRUCE FORSYTH-AVRIL ANGERS-
 JACK FRANCOIS-EILEEN GOURLAY-DAVID HENDERSON TATE-
 BERNARD SPEAR-SVEN SVENSON *DRG (Pin): CDSBL 13111*
 3.USA MUSICAL REVIVAL 1988 Songs: CY COLEMAN
 NEW BROADWAY CAST *VARESE (Pinn): VSD 6011 (CD)*
LITTLE MERMAID (1998) *see* WALT DISNEY FILM INDEX p.341
LITTLE NICKY (2000) Music score by TEDDY CASTELLUCCI
-S/T- *MAVERICK-WB (TEN): 9362 47856-2 (CD)*
LITTLE NIGHT MUSIC, A - songs by Stephen Sondheim
 1.NATIONAL THEATRE PROD 1996 JUDI DENCH-PATRICIA
 HODGE-SIAN PHILLIPS-SEAN MATHIAS & Com **ORIG.CAST**
 TRING: TRING 001 (CD) MCTRING 001 (MC) DELETED
 2.ORIG BROADWAY CAST 1973 *w:* GLYNIS JOHNS-LEN CARIOU
 H.GINGOLD-VICTORIA MALLORY-LAURENCE GUITTARD & Co.
 COLUMBIA (Ten): SMK 65284 (CD)
 3.ORIG LONDON CAST 1975 *with:* JEAN SIMMONS-HERMOINE
 GINGOLD-JOSS ACKLAND & Co *RCA (BMG) GD 5090 (CD)*

4.STUDIO RECORDING *w:* SIAN PHILLIPS-SUSAN HAMPSHIRE
ELISABETH WELCH arrang.& cond.by JOHN OWEN EDWARDS
TER (Koch): CDTER 1179 (CD)

5.STUDIO RECORDING *feat* TERRY TROTTER (solo piano)
VARESE (Pinn): VSD 5819 (CD)

LITTLE PRINCESS, A (1995) Music score: PATRICK DOYLE
-S/T- *VARESE (Pinn): VSD 5628 (CD)*

LITTLE RASCALS (USA TV) *see COLL.242,*

LITTLE SHOP OF HORRORS (FILM MUSICAL 1987) Songs (Alan
Menkin-Howard Ashman) Orig Film sco: MILES GOODMAN
-S/T- *GEFFEN-MCA (UNI): GFLD 19289 (CD)*

LITTLE SHOP OF HORRORS (CAST RECORDING)
UNIVERSAL-IMS: AAG EFD 2020 (CD)

LITTLE VOICE (1998) Music sc: JOHN ALTMAN -S/T- JANE
HORROCKS-JUDY GARLAND-BILLIE HOLIDAY-TOM JONES-
SHIRLEY BASSEY-ETHEL MERMAN-MARILYN MONROE on
EMI: 498 071-2 (CD) also: 'Further Adventures Of
Little Voice' (JANE HORROCKS) *EMI: 528 754-2 (CD)*

LITTLEST HOBO The (USA 1979) theme "Maybe Tomorrow"
composed & sung by TERRY BUSH *unavailable
version by* 'SCOOT' on collect 'BEST TV ADS...EVER'
VIRGIN (EMI): VTDCDX 306 (2CD) VTDMC 306 (MC)

LIVE A LITTLE LOVE A LITTLE (1968)
see ELVIS PRESLEY FILM INDEX p.348

LIVE AND LET DIE (1993) Music sco: GEORGE MARTIN title
song PAUL & LINDA McCARTNEY -S/T- *EMI CZ 553 (CD)*
see JAMES BOND INDEX p.346 *see COLL.46,222,251,*

LIVE FLESH (1998) Music score: ALBERTO IGLESIAS -S/T-
RCA VICTOR (BMG): 74321 54273-2 (CD)

LIVE FOR LIFE 'Vivre Pour Vivre' (1967) Music score:
FRANCIS LAI incl: 'A Man And A Woman' (1966) -S/T-
DRG (New Note-Pinn): DRGCD 12612 (CD)

LIVE FROM A QUARRY (1998) Music score: PAUL K.JOYCE
-S/T- *PKJ (Else): PKJCD 002 (CD)*

LIVER BIRDS The (BBC1 14/4/1969) "On A Mountain Stands
A Lady" (trad) by The SCAFFOLD *see COLL.3,283,*

LIVING BRITAIN (BBC2 31/10/1999) series music by
BRIAN BENNETT *unavailable*

LIVING DAYLIGHTS (1987) Title song "Living Daylights"
(John Barry-A.HA) "If There Was A Man" sung by The
PRETENDERS -S/T- *RYKODISC (Vital): RCD 10725 (CD)*
BOND FILM INDEX p.346 *also see COLL.26,47,204,*

LIVING OUT LOUD (1998) Music score by GEORGE FENTON
-S/T- *(V.Art) RCA VICTOR (BMG): 09026 63363-2 (CD)*

LIZA WITH A 'Z' (USA TV Concert 1972) -S/T- feat LIZA
MINNELLI reiss *SONY Coll: 982 994-2 (CD) -4 (MC)*

LOADED (1994) Music score: SIMON FISHER TURNER -S/T-
OCEAN DEEP (Grapev/Polyg): OCD 001 (CD)

LOCAL HERO (1982) Music: MARK KNOPFLER -S/T- *Vertigo
(Univ): 811038-2 (CD)*

LOCK STOCK AND TWO SMOKING BARRELS (FILM 1998) Music:
DAVID A.HUGHES-JOHN MURPHY -S/T- feat VARIOUS ARTS
-S/T- *ISLAND (Univ): CID 8077 (CD) also on
SIMPLY VINYL (Telstar): SVLP 89 (LP)*

LOCK STOCK AND...(TV SERIES C4 29/05/2000) Music from
and inspired by the series (Various Artists) on
VIRGIN (EMI): VTDCD 305 (2CD) VTDMC 305 (2MC)
LODGER The (1944) Music score: HUGO FRIEDHOFER / Suite
on Coll *with* 'RAINS OF RANCHIPUR'/'SEVEN CITIES OF
GOLD'/'ADV.OF MARCO POLO' The MOSCOW SYMPHONY ORCH
(W.T.Stromberg) *MARCO POLO (Select): 8.223857 (CD)*
LOGAN'S RUN (1976) Music score by JERRY GOLDSMITH -S/T-
inc: music from 'COMA' (1978) on
CHAPTER III (USA IMPT): CHA 0136 (CD)
LOIS AND CLARK *see* 'NEW ADVENTURES OF SUPERMAN'
LOLA MONTEZ (1955) *see* 'HUNCHBACK OF NOTRE DAME' 1956
LOLA RENNT - see 'RUN LOLA RUN'
LOLITA (1998) Music score: ENNIO MORRICONE conducting
the ACCADEMIA MUSICALE ITALIANA -S/T- on
MILAN (BMG): 74321 52318-2 (CD, 05.1998)
LOLITA (1961) Music sc: BOB HARRIS *feat:* NELSON RIDDLE
complete -S/T- *EMI GOLD SOUNDTRACK: 821 978-2 (CD)*
LONDON MARATHON The (BBC1 1984-2001) theme "The Trap"
by RON GOODWIN *see COLL.116,117,122,*
LONDON'S BURNING (LWT 1988-2001) or.theme "Blue Watch"
SIMON BRINT-RODDY MATTHEWS on 'LONDON'S BURNING'
-S/T- *EMI SOUNDTRACKS:521 944-2 (CD) DELETED 2001*
also available: "The Rose" sung by HEATHER PEACE
RCA: 74321 74289-2 (CDs) -4 (MC)
NEW SER.THEME MUSIC by WARREN BENNETT *unavailable*
LONE RANGER The (USA 1949 re-run C4 88) theme "William
Tell Overture" (ROSSINI) *see COLL.197,242,*
LONE STAR (1996) Music score: MASON DARING -S/T-
Daring (Direct): DARINGCD 3023 (CD)
LONELY ARE THE BRAVE (1962) Music sco: JERRY GOLDSMITH
Tsunami-Delphi (Greyhound): NR 9104 (CD)
LONELY PLANET (C4 from 28/9/94) theme mus: IAN RITCHIE
MICHAEL CONN sel.of World M. 'Music For The Lonely
Planet' *CINEPHILE-CASTLE (Pinn): CINCD 026 (2CD)*
also (VOL.2) 'MORE MUSIC FROM THE LONELY PLANET'
CINEPHILE-CASTLE (Pinn): CINCD 027 (2CD)
also available 'LISTEN TO THE PLANET' Var.Artists
MILAN (BMG): 74321 37243-2 (CD)
LONER The (USA TV 1965) themes by JERRY GOLDSMITH on
Coll 'Stagecoach' (Limited edition impt.) includes
score from 'STAGECOACH' (1966 J.GOLDSMITH) on
RETROGRADE (S.Screen/MFTM): FSMCD Vol.1 No.1 (CD)
LONESOME DOVE (USA TV/BBC1 30/8/93) music score: BASIL
POLEDOURIS -S/T- *SONIC IMAGES: SID 8816 (CD)*
LONG GOOD FRIDAY The (1980) Music sco: FRANCIS MONKMAN
feat KEVIN PEEK-TRISTRAM FRY-HERBIE FLOWERS (SKY)
-S/T- *SILVA SCREEN (Koch): FILMCD 020 (CD)*
LONG WAY HOME The (1997) Music score: LEE HOLDRIDGE
-S/T- *PROMETHEUS (Silva Screen): PCD 145 (CD)*
LONGEST DAY The (1962) Music score: PAUL ANKA
see COLL.61,123,265,
LONGITUDE (C4 03/01/2000) Music score composed by
GEOFFREY BURGON *unavailable*

LOOSE CHANGE VARIOUS ARTISTS -S/T-
SURFDOG (Cargo): SD 671172 (CD)
LOOSE WOMEN (ITV 06/09/1999-2001) series title music
by PATRICK DUFFIN *unavailable*
LOOT! (1970) Music score by KEITH MANSFIELD and vocals
by STEVE ELLIS -S/T- *RPM (Pinn): RPM 228 (CD)*
LORD JIM (1964) Music score: BRONISLAU KAPER
TARAN (Silver Sounds): W 9108 (CD)
LORD OF ILLUSIONS (1995) Music sc: SIMON BOSWELL -S/T-
IONIC/MUTE/RTM (Disc): IONIC 13CD (CD)
LORD OF THE DANCE 1996 SHOW Music: RONAN HARDIMAN feat
MICHAEL FLATLEY and Comp / Music cond and orch by
ANNE DUDLEY *POLYGRAM TV: 533 757-2 (CD) -4 (MC)*
LORD OF THE FLIES (1990) Music score: PHILIPPE SARDE
London Symphony Orch & The Trinity Boys Choir
-S/T- *SILVA SCREEN (Koch): FILMCD 067 (CD)*
LORD OF THE RINGS Trilogy (2000) Music by HOWARD SHORE
songs by ENYA -S/T- *WB (TEN): 9362 48238-2 (CD)*
LORD OF THE RINGS The (1978) Music: LEONARD ROSENMAN
-S/T- *FANTASY/INTRADA (S.Screen): FMTCD 8003 (CD)*
LORNA (1964 RUSS MEYER) V.ARTS -S/T- *with* 'VIXEN'/
'FASTER PUSSYCAT' *NORMAL/QDK (Pinn/Greyh/Dir):
QDKCD 008 (CD) QDKLP 008 (LP)*
LOST BOYS The (1987) Music score: THOMAS NEWMAN -S/T-
ATLANTIC (TEN): 781767-2 (CD) -4(MC)
LOST CHILD (BBC2 29/6/97) Violin Sonatas (FREDERICK
DELIUS) performed by TASMIN LITTLE and BOURNEMOUTH
SO (R.Hickox) *CON.CLASS (BMG): 75605 51315-2 (CD)*
LOST CONTINENT The (1968) Music score GERARD SCHURMANN
-S/T- on *GDI (ABM/Universal): GDICD 015 (CD)*
see also 'HORRORS OF THE BLACK MUSEUM'
LOST EMPIRE - see 'MONKEY KING'
LOST EMPIRES (Granada 24/10/86) music: DEREK HILTON
TER (Koch): CDTER 1119 (CD)
LOST HIGHWAY (1996) Music score: ANGELO BADALAMENTI
V.Arts -S/T- *INTERSCOPE-MCA (UNI): IND 90090 (CD)*
also on SIMPLY VINYL (Vital): SVLP 119 (2LP)
LOST HORIZON (1937) Music score by DIMITRI TIOMKIN
conducted by MAX STEINER
-S/T- *SOUND TRACK FACTORY (Discov) SFCD 33541 (CD)*
LOST IN SPACE (1998) Music score: BRUCE BROUGHTON
SINFONIA OF LONDON conducted by BRUCE BROUGHTON
*INTRADA (Silva Screen): MAF 7086 (CD) also on
TVT SOUNDTRAX: TVT 8180-2 (CD)* also on
EPIC Soundtracks: 491 303-2 (CD) -4(MC) -8(MD)
LOST IN SPACE (USA TV) *see COLL.38,84,218,242,246,*
LOST IN YONKERS (1993) ELMER BERNSTEIN *see COLL.40,*
LOST PATROL The (1934) Music: MAX STEINER *new record*
MOSCOW SO (Stromberg) + 'BEAST WITH 5 FINGERS'/
'VIRGINIA CITY' *MARCO POLO (Select): 8.223870 (CD)*
LOST SOULS (2000) Music score by JAN A.P.KACZMAREK
-S/T- *VARESE (Pinn): VSD 6191 (CD)*
LOST WEEKEND The (1945) Music sc: MIKLOS ROZSA / Suite
on Coll FILM NOIR CLASSICS *see* 'DOUBLE INDEMNITY'

LOST WORLD: Jurassic Park 2 (1997) Mus: JOHN WILLIAMS
-S/T- *MCA (UNI): MCAD 11628 (CD)*

LOTUS EATERS The (BBC 1971) series theme music
"Ta Trena Pou Fyghan" STAVROS XARAHAKOS
see COLL.200,

LOU GRANT (USA 77/C4 84) theme mus: PATRICK WILLIAMS
see COLL.14,

LOUIS L'ENFANT ROI (1993) Music by JEAN PIERRE FOUQUEY
AUVIDIS (Harmonia Mundi): K.1001 (CD)

LOVE AND DEATH (1975) theme on *NAXOS: 8551160 (CD)*

LOVE AND DEATH ON LONG ISLAND (1997) Music: INSECTS
-S/T- *OCEAN DEEP (Univ): OCD 014 (CD)*

LOVE AND SEX (2000) -S/T- EDDI READER-MARIE FRANK-LIVE
MERRYMAKERS-PHIL ROY-CHUCKLEHEAD-TODD THIBAUD-OVER
THE RHINE-TIM EASTON-HEITOR PEREIRA-VELVET BELLY
RCA VICTOR (BMG): 74321 77784-2 (CD)

LOVE BOAT (USA TV) *see COLL.244,*

LOVE HONOUR AND OBEY (2000) VARIOUS ARTISTS -S/T- inc:
"Avenues and Alleyways" sung by JONNY LEE MILLER
EMI SOUNDTRACKS: 526 313-2 (CD)

LOVE IS A MANY SPLENDORED THING - *see COLL.1,*

LOVE IS THE DEVIL (1997) Music sco: RYUICHI SAKAMOTO
ASPHODEL (Pinn): ASP 0987CD (CD)

LOVE JONES (1996) -S/T- featuring Various Artists on
COLUMBIA (Ten): 487 230-2 (CD) -4 (MC)

LOVE LETTER The (1999) Music score: LUIS BACALOV -S/T-
RCA VICTOR (BMG): 09026 63521-2 (CD)

LOVE ME TENDER (56) - *see* ELVIS PRESLEY INDEX p.348

LOVE STORY (1944) Music score: HUBERT BATH
see COLL.235,267,

LOVE STORY (1970) Music score: FRANCIS LAI -S/T-
MCA: MCLD 19157 (CD) see COLL.73,162,170,

LOVE STORY (TV 1970's) theme music: TONY HATCH
see COLL.24,131,

LOVE VALOUR COMPASSION (1997) Music sc: HAROLD WHEELER
-S/T- *DECCA (Univ): 455 644-2 (CD)*

LOVE YOU 'TIL TUESDAY (1969) C4 14/2/88 Music by
DAVID BOWIE -S/T- *CARLTON: PWKS 4131P(CD)*

LOVE'S LABOUR LOST (2000) Music score composed and dir
ected by PATRICK DOYLE *feat songs by* COLE PORTER-
GEORGE GERSHWIN and IRVING BERLIN -S/T- Cast Rec:
SONY CLASSICS (Ten): SK 89004 (CD)

LOVEJOY (BBC1 10/1/86-1994) theme music: DENIS KING
see COLL.4,20,

LOVERS PRAYER (2000) Music score by JOEL McNEELY
-S/T- *VARESE (Pinn): VSD 6173 (CD)*

LOVERS The (L'Amant) (1991) Music score: GABRIEL YARED
-S/T- *CIRCA / VIRGIN (EMI): CDVMM 9 (CD)*

LOVES OF JOANNA GODDEN The (1947) Music score: VAUGHAN
WILLIAMS *select.on* 'VAUGHAN WILLIAMS FILM MUSIC'on
PEARL Pavilion: GEMCD 0107 (CD)

LOVING YOU (1957) feat ELVIS PRESLEY remastered -S/T-
*RCA (BMG): 07863 67452-2 (CD) -4 (MC) / SANCTUARY
(Pinn):ELVIS 110 (LP) see also* PRESLEY INDEX p.348

LOW DOWN DIRTY SHAME (1994) Music: V.Arts -S/T- *JIVE*
(BMG): CHIPCD 156 (CD) HIPC 156 (MC) HIP 156 (LP)
LUCKY BREAK (2001) Music score by ANNE DUDLEY
-S/T- (music from and inspired by) VARIOUS ARTISTS
CHANNEL 4 MUSIC (UNIV): C4M 0014-2 (CD)
LULLABY OF BROADWAY (1950) *see COLL.196,,*

LUST FOR LIFE (1956) Music score: MIKLOS ROZSA -S/T-
VARESE (Pinn): VSD 5405 (CD)
LUZHIN DEFENCE The (2000) Music sco: ALEXANDRE DESPLAT
with The LONDON SYMPHONY ORCHESTRA -S/T- on
SILVA SCREEN (Koch): FILMCD 345 (CD)
M .BUTTERFLY (1993) Music score: HOWARD SHORE -S/T- on
VARESE (Pinn): VSD 5435 (CD)
M.SQUAD (USA TV 1957-60) theme mus: COUNT BASIE (ser.
2/3) STANLEY WILSON (1) 'Music From M.SQUAD' on
RCA (BMG): 74321 43397-2 (CD)   see COLL.245,
MA VIE EN ROSE (1998) Music score by DOMINIQUE DALCAN
-S/T- *MERCURY FRANCE (Discov): 536 026-2 (CD)*
McCALLUM (ITV 28/12/95) mus: DAEMION BARRY *unavailable*
"Cry Me A River" (A.Hamilton) sung by MARI WILSON
MANTRA (Import through Discovery): MANTRA 058 (CD)
MacGYVER (USA88)(BBC1 8/4/89) theme mus: RANDY EDELMAN
see COLL.14,247,
McVICAR (1980) Music score: JEFF WAYNE featuring ROGER
DALTREY-JEFF WAYNE-PETE TOWNSHEND -S/T- *re-issue:*
POLYDOR (Univ): 527 341-2 (CD)
MACK AND MABEL - songs by Jerry Herman
  1.ORIG BROADWAY CAST 1974 ROBERT PRESTON-BERNADETTE
  PETERS *MCA (UNI): MCLD 19089 (CD)*
  2.LIVE IN CONCERT RECORDING UK 1988 Various Artists
  First Night (Pinn): OCRCD 6015 (CD)
MAD CITY (1997) Music score: THOMAS NEWMAN -S/T-
VARESE (Pinn): VSD 5887 (CD)
MAD COWS (1998) Music score by MARK THOMAS -S/T- on
EAST WEST (Ten): 8573 80314-2 (CD)
MAD DOG AND GLORY (1992) Music score: ELMER BERNSTEIN
-S/T- *VARESE (Pinn): VSD 5415 (CD)*
MAD LOVE (1995) Music sco: ANDY ROBERTS -S/T- inc V/A:
DEDICATED (RTM/DISC):DEDCD 022 (CD)
MAD MAX (1979) Music score: BRIAN MAY -S/T- Import on
VARESE (Pinn): VCD 47144 (CD)
MAD MAX 2 (1981) Music score: BRIAN MAY -S/T- *VARESE*
(Pinn) VCD 47262 (CD)
MAD MAX 3 'Beyond Thunderdome' (1985) M: MAURICE JARRE
-S/T- *GNP (ZYX): GNPD 8037 (CD)*
see COLL.83,146,153,
MAD MONSTER PARTY (1966) Music by MAURY LAWS songs by
MAURY LAWS & JULES BASS.t.song sung by ETHEL ENNIS
PERCEPTO-RETROGRADE (S.Scr/MFTM): FSM 80125-2 (CD)
MADAME BOVARY (1949) Music score by MIKLOS ROSZA -S/T-
selection also incl.music from 'IVANHOE'/'MADAME
BOVARY'/'QUO VADIS'/'PLYMOUTH ADVENTURE'
TICKERTAPE USA (S.Scr): TT 3001 (CD) see COLL.214,

MADAME SOUSATZKA (1988) Music score: GERALD GOURIET
-S/T- *VARESE (Pinn): VSD 5204 (CD)*
theme also on NAXOS 8551157 (CD)
MADDIE ORIG LONDON CAST 1997 Songs by STEPHEN KEELING-
SHAUN McKENNA. O.L.C. *feat:* SUMMER ROGNLIE-GRAHAM
BICKLEY-KEVIN COLSON-LYNDA BARON *recording on*
DRESS CIRCLE (Silver Sounds): DRESSCD 003 (CD)
MADE IN HONG KONG (1999) Music score by LAM WAH CHUEN
IMPORT -S/T- on *LES DISQUES DU SOLEIL (Import*
through RER/Impetus): DSA 54066 (CD)
MADELINE (1998) Music score: MICHEL LEGRAND -S/T-
SONY WONDER: 493 409-2 (CD) -4 (MC)
MADNESS OF KING GEORGE The (94) Mus sco: GEORGE FENTON
adapt.HANDEL music) BAROQUE ORCH *see COLL.63,97,*
MAGIC PUDDING The (2000) Music by CHRIS HARRIOTT -S/T-
inc songs by WESTLIFE-TINA ARENA-N SYNC-MERRIL
BAINBRIDGE-HUMAN NATURE-KATE CEREBANO etc on
BMG IMPORTS: 74321 78430-2 (CD)
MAGIC ROUNDABOUT The (BBC1 64) theme: ALAIN LEGRAND
VID: *BBC: BBCV 4278 and 4494 see COLL.250,*
MAGICAL MYSTERY TOUR (1967) Feat music by The BEATLES
-S/T- *PARLOPHONE (EMI): PCTC 255 (LP) TC-PCS 3077*
(MC) CD-PCTC 255 (CD) SMMT 1 (2 x 7" singles)
MAGICIAN The (USA TV) *see COLL.246,*
MAGILLA GORILLA (USA TV) *see COLL.242,*
MAGNIFICENT AMBERSONS The (1942) Mus: BERNARD HERRMANN
-S/T- *5TH CONTINENT (HOT): PRCD 1783 (CD)*
MAGNIFICENT SEVEN The (1960) Music sc: ELMER BERNSTEIN
-S/T- inc 'RETURN OF THE MAGNIFICENT SEVEN' on
RYKODISC Vital: RCD 10741 (CD) see COLL.27,75,277,
MAGNOLIA (2000) Music score by JOHN BRION / "Save Me"
by AIMEE MANN -S/T- *WEA (TEN): 9362 47692-2 (CD)*
MAGNUM; P.I. (USA1980) theme: MIKE POST-PETE CARPENTER
see COLL.14,77,203,244,
MAHOGANY (1975) Music sc: MICHAEL MASSER theme "Do You
Know Where You're Going To" by DIANA ROSS -S/T-
MOTOWN (UNIV): 157 677-2 (CD)
MAHONEY'S LAST STAND (1975) *feat music by* RONNIE LANE
and RON WOOD *produced by* GLYN JOHNS -S/T- reissue
NEW MILLENNIUM (Pinn): PILOT 29 (CD)
MAIGRET (BBC1 1961) theme music: RON GRAINER
see COLL.2,8,24,77,261,
MAIGRET (Granada 9/2/1991) theme music by NIGEL HESS
vocal by OLIVE SIMPSON *see COLL.5,137,*
MAJOR BARBARA (1941) Music score by Sir WILLIAM WALTON
Academy Of St.Martin-In-The Fields (N.Marriner) +
'Richard III'/'Macbeth' *CHANDOS: CHAN 8841 (CD)*
MAJOR DAD (USA TV) *see COLL.248,*

MAJOR DUNDEE (1965) Music score: DANIELE AMFITHEATROF
-S/T- *TSUNAMI Germany (S.Screen): TSU 0111 (CD)*
MALCOLM (1986) Mus: SIMON JEFFES PENGUIN CAFE ORCH.
Penguin Cafe Orch *EG-VIRG: EGED 11(CD)* Music From
The PCO' *EGED 27* 'Broadcasting From Home' *EGED 38*

MALCOLM IN THE MIDDLE (BBC2 06/04/2001) music by THEY
  MIGHT BE GIANTS -S/T- *RESTLESS (Vital) 73743-2 (CD)*
MALENA (2001) Music score by ENNIO MORRICONE -S/T- on
  TRI-VIRGIN MUSIC (EMI): 72438 50811-2 (CD)
MALICE (1993) Music score: JERRY GOLDSMITH -S/T-
  VARESE (Pinn): VSD 5442 (CD)
MALICE AFORETHOUGHT (BBC2 15/3/79) *see COLL.6,*
MALTA GC - music by ARNOLD BAX *see COLL.49,*
MAMBO KINGS The (1992) Music by various artists -S/T-
  ELEKTRA (TEN): 7559 61240-2 (CD) -4 (MC)
MAME - songs by Jerry Herman
  1.ORIG BROADWAY CAST 1966) *with* ANGELA LANSBURY & Co
  CBS USA (Sil.Screen) CK 03000 (CD) JST 03000 (MC)
MAMMA MIA (SHOW 1999) Songs of ABBA (Benny ANDERSSON
  Bjorn ULVAEUS & others) ORIGINAL LONDON CAST 1999
  POLYDOR (Univ) 543 115-2 (CD) -4 (MC) / also avail
  LONDON STARS ORCH & SING. *WMO (BMG) WM 090367 (CD)*
MAN ABOUT THE HOUSE (Thames 1973) theme music
  "Up To Date" (JOHNNY HAWKESWORTH) *see COLL.3,125,*
MAN ALIVE (BBC2 1960s) TONY HATCH *see COLL.2,24,74,261,*
MAN AND A WOMAN A 'Un Homme Et Une Femme' (1966) Music
  by FRANCIS LAI incl: 'Live For Life' (67) -S/T-
  DRG (Pinn): DRGCD 12612 (CD) see COLL.162,
MAN CALLED HORSE, A (1970) Mus score: LEONARD ROSENMAN
  TICKERTAPE USA Impt.(S.Screen): TT 3004 (CD)
MAN CALLED IRONSIDE, A (USA) theme music: QUINCY JONES
  see COLL.83,124,200,242,261,
MAN FROM U.N.C.L.E. The (1966) music: HUGO MONTENEGRO
  (theme by JERRY GOLDSMITH) *imports via DISCOVERY*
  MAN FROM UNCLE *RCA VICT.EUROPE 74321 63819-2 (CD)*
  MORE MUSIC FROM T.MAN FROM UNCLE *74321 63706-2 CD*
  also on SIMPLY VIYNL (Telstar): SVLP 74 (2LP)
  ORIG TV -S/T- *RAZOR & TIE (Koch): RE 2133 (CD)*
  see COLL.14,75,77,175,242,250,
MAN IN A SUITCASE (ITC 27/9/67-68) theme: RON GRAINER
  see COLL.2,8,24,74,250,251,
MAN IN THE IRON MASK The (1997) Music s: NICK GLENNIE-
  SMITH -S/T- *MILAN (BMG): 74321 56495-2 (CD)*
MAN OF LA MANCHA - songs by Mitch Leigh and Joe Darion
  1.FILM (1972) -S/T- *RYKODISC (Vital): RCD 10730 (CD)*
  2.COMPLETE STUDIO RECORDING 1996 PLACIDO DOMINGO-
  MANDY PATINKIN-SAMUEL RAMEY-JERRY HADLEY & Company
  SONY Classical (Ten): SK 46436 (CD) ST 46436 (MC)
  3.SHOW (-) *TER (Koch): TER2 1263-2 (2CD)*
MAN ON THE MOON (1999) featuring music by REM
  -S/T- *WARNER (TEN): 9362 47483-2 (CD) -4 (MC)*
MAN WHO CRIED The (2000) Music score: OSVALDO GOLIJOV
  -S/T- *SONY CLASSICS (TEN): SK 61870 (CD)*
MAN WHO KNEW TOO LITTLE The (1997) Music: CHRISTOPHER
  YOUNG -S/T- *VARESE (Pinn): VSD 5886 (CD)*
MAN WHO WASN'T THERE (2001) Music score: CARTER BURWELL
  -S/T- (VAR.ARTISTS) *DECCA (UNIV): 016 019-2 (CD)*
MAN WITH THE GOLDEN ARM (1956) Music by ELMER BERNSTEIN
  -S/T- *SPECTRUM (UNIV): 544 627-2 (CD)*

MAN WITH THE GOLDEN GUN The (1974) Music: JOHN BARRY
   title song (John Barry-Don Black) sung by LULU
   -S/T- *reissue EMI PREMIER: CZ 552 (CD)*
   see JAMES BOND FILM INDEX p.346 see COLL.26,46,47,
MAN'S TRAGEDY, A (1981) Music score ENNIO MORRICONE on
   DRG (Pinn): DRGCD 32910 (CD)
MANCHURIAN CANDIDATE The (1962) Music sco: DAVID AMRAM
   -S/T- *PREAMBLE (Silver Sounds): PRCD 1059 (CD)*
MANDELA (1996) -S/T- featuring VARIOUS ARTISTS on
   MANGO-ISLAND (Univ): CIDM(MCT) 1116
MANGALA THE INDIAN GIRL Film Soundtrack -S/T-
   Club Du Disques Arabe (HARMONIA MUNDI): AAA121(CD)
MANHATTAN (1979) Music score: GEORGE GERSHWIN -S/T-
   SONY: MK 36020(CD) see COLL.64,73,
MANNIX (USA/1967-74) theme: LALO SCHIFRIN -S/T- SCORE
   ALEPH (Koch): ALEP 014 (CD) also on WB (TEN):
   8573 87363-2 (CD) also see COLL.124,142,242,
MANON DES SOURCES (1987) Music score: JEAN CLAUDE PETIT
   feat ORCHESTRE DE PARIS & TOOTS THIELMANS harmonica
   SILVA SCREEN (Koch): FILMCD 329 (CD)
   see COLL.64,
MANSFIELD PARK (1998) Music score by LESLEY BARBER and
   "Djonga" composed and performed by SALIF KEITA
   -S/T- *RCA (BMG): RCA 09026 63592-2 (CD)*
MAP OF THE WORLD, A (1999) Music score by PAT METHENY
   -S/T- *WARNER (TEN): WB 9362 47366-2 (CD)*
MARCUS WELBY, MD (USA TV) *see COLL.172,244,*
MARINE (2000) Music score by JOEL McNEELY score -S/T-
   VARESE (Pinn): VSD 6094 (CD)
MARK OF THE DEVIL 1 and 2 (1970/1972) Music score by
   MICHAEL HOLM -S/T- *WRASSE (UNIV): DIG 001 (CD)*
MARK OF THE VAMPIRE (1957) - see 'RETURN OF DRACULA'
MARK OF ZORRO (1940) *see COLL.61,240,*
MARK TWAIN (MUSICAL) songs by WILLIAM PERRY
   ORIG CAST *PREAMBLE (Silver Sounds) PRCD 1012 (CD)*
MARNIE (1964) Music by BERNARD HERRMANN *VARESE (Pinn):*
   VSD 6094 (CD) see COLL.136,141,142,143,144,
MARSEILLE CONTRACT (1974) Music sco: ROY BUDD -S/T-
   CINEPHILE (Pinn): CINCD 015 see COLL.54,
MARTHA MEET FRANK DANIEL AND LAURENCE (1998) Mus score
   by ED SHEARMUR -S/T- feat Various Artists on
   MERCURY (Univ): 558 396-2 (CD) -4 (MC)
MARTIN GUERRE songs: Alain Boublil-CLaude Michel
   Schonberg-Edward Hardy ORIGINAL LONDON CAST 1998
   FIRST NIGHT (Pinn): CASTCD 70 (CD)
   O.L.CAST 1996: *FIRST NIGHT (Pinn): CAST(CD)(C) 59*
MARVIN'S ROOM (1996) Music sco: RACHEL PORTMAN -S/T-
   EDEL-HOLLYWOOD (Vital) 012062-3 (CD) see COLL.202,
MARY POPPINS (1964) Songs: RICHARD & ROBERT SHERMAN
   DISNEY'S MUSIC AND STORIES *DISNEY (Technicolor):*
   WD 77572-2 (CD) -4(MC) see WALT DISNEY INDEX p.341
MARY QUEEN OF SCOTS (1971) Music: JOHN BARRY -S/T- inc
   'ANNE OF 1000 DAYS' (1969 GEORGES DELERUE)
   ARTEMIS (HOT): ARTF 005 (CD) / see COLL.26,28,32,

MARY TYLER MOORE SHOW (USA TV) *see COLL.243,*
M*A*S*H (FILM 1970) Mus sco: JOHNNY MANDEL-MIKE ALTMAN
  -S/T- *Columbia (Ten): CK 66804 (CD) see COLL.123,*
M*A*S*H (TVUSA 71-84 BBC2: 20/5/73) theme "Suicide Is
  Painless" (J.Mandel-M.Altman) *SONY: 983380-2(CD)*
  see COLL.84,172,182,200,244,
MASK OF ZORRO (1998) Music score: JAMES HORNER -S/T-
  SONY CLASSICS : SK 60627 (CD) ST 60627 (MC)
MASTERBLASTERS (BBC2 13/7/2000) Music by ANDY BLYTHE
  and MARTEN JOUSTRA *unavailable*
MASTERMIND (BBC 1972-97) theme "Approaching Menace"
  NEIL RICHARDSON *see COLL.5,*
MATCH OF THE DAY (BBC1 1970-) theme music "Offside" by
  BARRY STOLLER *see COLL.101,122,200,*
MATCH OF THE DAY (BBC1 1960s) theme "Drum Majorette"
  see COLL,100,122,
MATRIX The (1999) Music score by DON DAVIS
  -S/T- score: *VARESE (Pinn): VSD 6026 (CD)*
  -S/T- songs: *MAVERICK (Ten):9362 47419-2(CD)-4(MC)*
MATT HOUSTON (USA TV) *see COLL.247,*
MAVERICK (FILM 1994) *see COLL.279,*
MAVERICK (TV USA 57) title theme: PAUL FRANCIS WEBSTER
  and DAVID BUTTOLPH *see COLL.243,253,*
MAX HEADROOM (TV) *see COLL.221,229,248,*
MAYBE BABY (2000) Music score by COLIN TOWNS -S/T- on
  VIRGIN 9EMI): CDV 2916 (CD) TCV 2916 (MC)
MAY MORNING (1970) Music by The TREMELOES and others
  -S/T- *CASTLE MUSIC (Pinn): CMRCD 025 (CD)*
MAYERLING (1935) Music score: ARTHUR HONEGGER Suite on
  MARCO POLO (Select): 8.223467 (CD)
ME AND MY GIRL - songs by Noel Gay and Douglas Furber
  1.ORIG LONDON CAST 1985 ROBERT LINDSAY-EMMA THOMPSON
    FRANK THORNTON and Company *EMI: CDP 746393-2 (CD)*
  2.ORIG BROADWAY CAST 1987 *w* ROBERT LINDSAY-MARYANN
    PLUNKETT *TER: CDTER 1145 (CD) DELETED 98*
  3.CLASSIC MUSICALS SERIES *feat:* ROBERT LINDSAY
    MARYANN PLUNKETT-JANE SUMMERHAYS-GEORGE S.IRVING
    +songs from 'THE BOYFRIEND' *KOCH Int: 34080-2 (CD)*
ME MYSELF AND IRENE (2000) Music: PETER YORN-LEE SCOTT
  -S/T- V.ART. *EAST WEST (TEN): 7550 62512-2 (CD)*
ME WITHOUT YOU (2001) Music score by ADRIAN JOHNSTON
  -S/T- VARIOUS ARTISTS *SONYTV (TEN): 505 131-2 (CD)*
ME YOU THEM (2000) Music by GIL GILBERTO -S/T- V.ARTS.
  WARNER JAZZ (TEN): 8573 82768-2 (CD)
MECH WARRIOR 4: VENGEANCE (2000 Video Game) Mus score
  by DUANE DECKER -S/T- *VARESE (Pinn): VSD 6201 (CD)*
MEDIC (USA 1955)"Blue Star" VICTOR YOUNG *see COLL.245,*
MEDICAL CENTER (USA TV) *see COLL.243,277*
MEET JOE BLACK (1999) Music score: THOMAS NEWMAN -S/T-
  UNIVERSAL (BMG): UND 53229 (CD)
MEET ME IN ST.LOUIS (1944) VARIOUS ARTISTS SOUNDTRACK
  SOUNDTRACK FACTORY (Discov): SFCD 33526 (CD)
MEET THE PARENTS (2000) Music score by RANDY NEWMAN
  -S/T- *DREAMWORKS-UNIVERSAL: 450 286-2 (CD)*

MEETINGS WITH REMARKABLE MEN (1979) Music score by
LAURENCE ROSENTHAL and THOMAS DE HARTMANN
CITADEL (Pinn): STC 77123 (CD)
MELODY FOR TWO (1937) -S/T- V/A + 'GO INTO YOUR DANCE'
'YOU CAN'T HAVE EVERYTHING'/'YOU'LL NEVER GET RICH'
GREAT MOVIE THEMES (Target-BMG): CD 60014 (CD)
MELROSE PLACE (USA TV/SKY1 94) TV Soundtrack V/Arts
GIANT (BMG):74321 22608-2 (CD)   see COLL.14,248,
MEMPHIS BELLE (1990) Music score: GEORGE FENTON -S/T-
VARESE (Pinn): VSD(VSC) 5293 (CD/MC)
MEN BEHAVING BADLY (BBC1 1/7/94) theme by ALAN LISK on
'MEN BEHAVING BADLY' *REMEDIA (Pinn):REP 001CD (CD)*
MEN IN BLACK The (1996) M.sco: DANNY ELFMAN -S/T- V/A
-S/T- *COLUMBIA (SM): 488 122-2 (CD) -04 (MC)*
MEN OF TWO WORLDS (1946) Music sco: Sir ARTHUR BLISS
new recording by SLOVAK RADIO S.O. (Adriano) on
MARCO POLO (Select): 8.223315 (CD) see COLL.48,
MEN WITH GUNS (1998) Music sco: MASON DARING -S/T-
VARIOUS ARTS *RYKODISC (Vital): RCD 10437 (CD)*
MEPHISTO WALTZ The (1971) Music sco: JERRY GOLDSMITH
+ score 'The OTHER' *VARESE (Pinn): VSD 5851 (CD)*
MERCURY RISING (1998) Music score: JOHN BARRY -S/T-
VARESE (Pinn): VSD 5925 (CD) / see COLL.26,
MERLIN (1997,USA TV) Music score by TREVOR JONES with
LONDON SYMPHONY ORCH *VARESE (Pinn): VSD 5929 (CD)*
MERRILY WE ROLL ALONG (COMPLETE) Songs Stephen Sondheim
feat MARIA FRIEDMAN-MICHAEL CANTWELL-EVAN PAPPAS-
JACQUELINE DANKWORTH-LOUISE GOLD-GARETH SNOOK
JAY-TER (SSD): CDJAY2 1245 (2CD Complete Recording)
CDTER 1225 (Highlights CD)
MERRY CHRISTMAS MR.LAWRENCE (1983) M: RYUICHI SAKAMOTO
MILAN (BMG): 74321 22048-2 (CD) also VIRGIN (EMI):
CDV 2276 (CD) OVEDC 237 (MC) see COLL.84,188,216,
MERRY WIDOW The (operetta) - songs by Franz Lehar
  1.Studio Recording 1994 COMPLETE Operetta in German
    wit dialogue *feat:* BARBARA BONNEY-BRYN TERFEL
    DG (Univ): 439 911-2 (CD) -4 (MC)
  2.Studio Recording 1995 HIGHLIGHTS in English by
    SCOTTISH OPERA CHORUS & SCOTTISH NAT.ORCHESTRA
    (A.Gibson) *CFP (EMI): CDCFPSD 4742 (2CD)*
  3.NEW SADLERS WELLS 1986 CAST (2 versions)
    <u>Highlights</u> *TER (Koch): CDTEO 1003 (CD)*
    <u>Complete</u>: *TER (Koch): CDTER 1111 (CD)*
  4.Studio Recording HIGHLIGHTS + songs from 'Land Of
    Smiles' on *EMI BELLE EPOQUE: CZS 767 872-2 (2CD)*
MESSAGE The (MOHAMMED MESSENGER OF GOD)(1977) Music
    score: MAURICE JARRE Royal P.Orch on *SILVA SCREEN*
    (Koch): FILMCD 060 (CD) + mus 'Lion Of The Desert'
MESSAGE IN A BOTTLE (1999) Music score: GABRIEL YARED
    -S/T- (V.ARTISTS) *ELEKTRA (TEN) 7567 83163-2 (CD)*
MESSAGE TO LOVE: THE ISLE OF WIGHT FESTIVAL 1970 (BBC2
    26/8/95) *feat:* JIMI HENDRIX-FREE-BOB DYLAN-EMERSON
    LAKE & PALMER-JETHRO TULL-MILES DAVIS-THE DOORS-
    THE WHO-TINY TIM *ESSENTIAL (BMG): EDFCD 327 (CD)*

MESSENGER The: THE STORY OF JOAN OF ARC (1999) Music
score by ERIC SERRA -S/T- on
COLUMBIA-SONY CLASSICS (Ten): SK 66537 (CD)
METEMPSYCO (European Film) Music by ARMANDO SCIASCIA
-S/T- *DAGORED (Koch/Cargo): RED 134CD / RED134LP*
METROLAND (1997) Music score: MARK KNOPFLER -S/T- on
MERCURY (Univ): 536 912-2 (CD) -4 (MC)
METROPOLIS (O.LONDON CAST 1988) Music (Joe BROOKS) Lyr
ics (Joe BROOKS-Dusty HUGHES) *with* BRIAN BLESSED-
JUDY KUHN-GRAHAM BICKLEY-JONATHAN ADAMS & Company
TER (Koch): CDTER2 1168 (CDx2)
METROSEXUALITY (C4 2001) 'Metrosexuality - The Songs'
by MARK HAWKES and RIKKI BEADLE-BLAIR -S/T- on
CHANNEL 4 MUSIC (UNIV): C4M 0009-2 (CD)
MEXICAN The (2001) Music score: ALAN SILVERSTRI -S/T-
DECCA (UNIV): 013 757-2 (CD)
MIAMI 7 (S CLUB 7)(BBC1 08/04/1999) theme & incidental
music by PAUL HARDCASTLE and KEN BOLAM *unavailable*
S CLUB 7 "Bring It All Back" *POLY: 561 085-2 (CDs)*
"NATURAL" album *POLYDOR: 587 760-2 (CD) -4 (MC)*
"S CLUB 7" album *POLYDOR: 543 103-2 (CD) -4 (MC)*
"7" album *POLYDOR: 543 857-2 (CD) -4 (MC)*
MIAMI VICE (USA orig BBC1 4/2/85) theme: JAN HAMMER
'MIAMI VICE'/'MIAMI VICE 2'/MIAMI VICE 3' Collect
UNIVERSAL IMS: E.132 180-2 (3CDS)
'Best Of Miami Vice' *MCA: 241 746-2/-4/-1(CD/MC)*
'MIAMI VICE 1' *MCA (UNI): MCLD 19024 (CD)*
see *COLL.77,84,244,*
MICHAEL (1997) Mus score by RANDY NEWMAN -S/T- V.Arts
REVOLUTION (BMG): 74321 41880-2 (CD)
MICHAEL JORDAN: TO THE MAX (2000) V.ARTISTS SOUNDTRACK
CHAPTER III (Silver Sounds): 6760 31007-2 (CD)
MICKEY BLUE EYES (1999) Music score: BASIL POLEDOURIS
-S/T- *MILAN (BMG): 73421 69991-2 (CD)*
MICROCOSMOS (1996) Music score by BRUNO COULAIS and
featuring mezzo-soprano MARIE KOBAYASHI -S/T-
AUVIDIS (Harmonia Mundi): K.1028 (CD)
MIDAS RUN (1969) Music score by ELMER BERNSTEIN
selection with 'NIGHT VISITOR' and 'THE HOUSE' on
CITADEL (HOT): STC 77105 (CD)
MIDNIGHT CALLER (USA)(BBC 28/1/89) theme: BRAD FIEDEL
see *COLL.14,248,*
MIDNIGHT COWBOY (1969) Music score: JOHN BARRY t.song
"Everybody's Talkin'" (Fred Neil) by NILSSON -S/T-
EMI PREMIER: PRMCD 6 (CDP 748409-2) (CD)
SIMPLY VINYL (Vital): SVLP 150 (LP)
see *COLL.26,27,28,29,30,32,33,36,37,170,*
MIDNIGHT EXPRESS (1978) Music: GIORGIO MORODER -S/T-
CASABLANCA (Univ): 824 206-2 (CD) see *COLL.84,*
MIDNIGHT IN THE GARDEN OF GOOD AND EVIL (1997) Music
LENNIE NIEHAUS -S/T- *WB (TEN): 9362 46829-2 (CD)*
MIDSOMER MURDERS (ITVN 23/3/1997) Music by JIM PARKER
-S/T- *OCEAN DEEP (Grapevine/Poly): OCD 013 (CD)*

MIDSUMMER NIGHT'S DREAM,A (1999) Music: SIMON BOSWELL
   -S/T- *DECCA (Univ): 466 098-2 (CD)*
MIDSUMMER NIGHT'S SEX COMEDY (1982) music MENDELSSOHN
   on *COLL: NAXOS: 8551156 (CD) and 8551158 (CD)*
MIDWAY (1976) Music sco: JOHN WILLIAMS / new record
   VARESE (Pinn): VSD 5940 (CD)
MIGHTY APHRODITE (1996) Music arr/cond: DICK HYMAN
   -S/T- on *SONY Classics (SM): SK 62253 (CD)*
MIGHTY JOE YOUNG (1998) Music sco: JAMES HORNER -S/T-
   EDEL-HOLLYWOOD (Vital) 010090-2HWR (CD)
MIKADO The (operetta) - songs by Gilbert and Sullivan
   1.D'OYLY CARTE OPERA COMPANY 1989 (Jonathan Miller)
     featuring LESLIE GARRETT-ERIC IDLE-FELICITY PALMER
     <u>Highlights</u>: *E2 (MCI-THE): ETDCD 138 (CD reiss)*
     <u>Complete</u>: *TER: CDTER2 1178 (2CD) ZCTED 1178 (2MC)*
   2.SADLER'S WELLS OPERA ORCH & CHORUS (A.FARIS) JOHN
     HOLMES-JOHN WAKEFIELD-CLIVE REVILL-DENIS DOWLING
     JOHN HEDDLE NASH-MARION STUDHOLME-PATRICIA KERN-
     CFP (EMI): CDCFPD(TCCPFD) 4730 (2CDs/2MC)
   3.PRO-ARTE ORCHEST (Malcolm Sargent) GLYNDEBOURNE
     FESTIVAL CHOIR Solo: OWEN BRANNIGAN-RICHARD LEWIS
     GERAINT EVANS-IAN WALLACE *EMI:CMS 764403-2 (2CD)*
   4.HIGHLIGHTS feat National Opera Company
     TER (Koch): CDTER 1121 (CD)
   5.D'OYLY CARTE OPERA COMPANY - Royal Philharm Orch
     (R.Nash) - *LONDON (Univ): 425 190-2 (CDx2)*
   6.D'OYLY CARTE OPERA COMPANY CHORUS AND ORCHESTRA
     inc recording of 'YEOMAN OF THE GUARD' (1940's)
     PEARL (Harmonia Mundi): GEMS 0134 (3CDs)
MIKE BASSETT ENGLAND MANAGER (2001) VARIOUS ARTS -S/T-
   TELSTAR (BMG): TCD 3213 (CD)
MIKE HAMMER (USA 83 revival) theme "Harlem Nocturne"
   (E.Hagen) 'TV ACTION JAZZ' *BMG: 74321 59154-2 (CD)*
MILDRED PIERCE (1945) Music: MAX STEINER *see COLL.239,*
MILL ON THE FLOSS The (BBC1 1/1/1997) Music score by
   JOHN SCOTT -S/T- *JOS (Silva Screen): JSCD 124 (CD)*
MILLENNIUM (BBC2 UK/Canada Co-Prod 3/1/93) music score
   HANS ZIMMER arranged & performed by MARK MANCINA
   -S/T- *NARADA Cinema (Pinn): ND 66001 (CD)*
MILLENNIUM A 1000 YEARS OF HISTORY (BBC2 18/10/1999)
   Music score by RICHARD BLACKFORD and GLENN KEILES
   BBC CONCERT ORCHESTRA and BOURNEMOUTH SYMPH.CHORUS
   -S/T- *POINT (Pinn): MM 8969CD (CD) MM 8969MC (MC)*
MILLIENNIUM DOME SHOW (2000 MILLENNIUM DOME LONDON)
   Music by PETER GABRIEL 'OVO THE MILLENNIUM SHOW' on
   REAL WORLD (Univ): RWPG 01 (CD)
MILLION DOLLAR HOTEL The (2000) inc songs by U2 & BONO
   -S/T- *ISLAND-UNIVER: CID 8094 (CD) ICT 8094 (MC)*
MIMIC (1997) Music score: MARCO BELTRAMI -S/T- on
   VARESE (Pinn): VSD 5863 (CD)
MINTY (ITV Children 08/11/1998) MINTY TV series songs
   VIRGIN: VTCD 233 (CD) VTMC 233 (MC) VSCDT 1728 CDs
MINUS MAN (1999) Music score by CHRIS COVERT -S/T-
   VARESE (Pinn): VSD 6043 (CD)

MIRACLE ON 34TH STREET (1994) Music s: BRUCE BROUGHTON
-S/T- ARISTA (BMG): 07822 11022-2 (CD) -4 (MC)
MIRROR HAS TWO FACES The (96) Mus sco: MARVIN HAMLISCH
-S/T- V.ART *COLUMBIA (Ten): 485 395-2 (CD) -4 (MC)*
MISFITS The (1961) Music score: ALEX NORTH -S/T- reis
RYKODISC (Vital): RCD 10735 (CD, 1998)
MISHIMA 'A Life In Four Chapters' (1985) Music: PHILIP
GLASS -S/T- *ELEKTRA Nonesuch (TEN): 7559 79113-2*
MISS CONGENIALITY (2001) Music score: EDWARD SHEARMUR
-S/T- inc: BOSSON-TOM JONES-SALT'N'PEPA-GROOVE
ARMADA-LOS LOBOS-PYT-A.TEENS-BAHA MEN-RED VENOM etc
GUT RECORDS-TVT (Vital-Pinn): GUTCD 16 (CD)
MISS MARPLE (BBC1 from 26/12/84) theme: ALAN BLAIKLEY-
KEN HOWARD see *COLL.42,77,*
MISS SAIGON - songs by Alain Boublil - Claude Michel
Schonberg and Richard Maltby Jnr.
  1.ORIG LONDON CAST 1989 LEA SALONGA-JONATHAN PRYCE
SIMON BOWMAN-PETER POLYCARPOU & Company
Complete: *FIRST NIGHT (Pinn): ENCORE CD 5 (2CD)*
Highlights: *FIRST NIGHT (Pinn): CAST(C)(CD) 38*
  2.SYMPHONIC SUITES: *KIMCD1 (2CD) KIMC1 (MC) also on
CASTCD 39 (CD) CASTC 39 (MC)*
  3.INTERNATIONAL CAST RECORDING (HIGHLIGHTS)
FIRST NIGHT (Pinn): CASTCD 60 (CD) CASTMC 60 (MC)
MISSA LUBA (AFRICAN MASS) KENYAN FOLK MELODIES By The
MUUNGANO NATIONAL CHOIR, Boniface MGANGA (M.dir)
PHILIPS (Univ): 426 836-2 (CD) -4 (MC)
MISSING (1982) Music score: VANGELIS available vers:
VANGELIS on 'Themes' *POLYDOR: 839 518-2(CD) -4(MC)*
see *COLL.263,*
MISSION The (1986) Music score: ENNIO MORRICONE -S/T-
LONDON PHILHARMONIC ORCHESTRA (E.Morricone) *VIRGIN
EMI: SACDV 2402 (CD) MDV 2402 (MiniD) TCV (MC)*
see *COLL.73,97,176,177,178,188,266,*
MISSION IMPOSSIBLE (ORIG TV ser) theme: LALO SCHIFRIN
TV -S/T- *reissue: MCA (UNI): MCLD 19320 (CD)*
see *COLL.3,75,77,83,124,250,251,252,*
MISSION IMPOSSIBLE (1996) Music sco: DANNY ELFMAN orig
theme (Lalo Schifrin) version by Larry Mullen and
Adam Clayton (U2) -S/T- *feat* PULP-GARBAGE-BJORK-
MASSIVE ATTACK-CAST-GAVIN FRIDAY-MULLEN & CLAYTON
songs: MOTHER-ISLAND (Univ): MUMCD 9603 (CD)
score: POINT MUSIC (Univ): 454 525-2 (CD)
see *COLL.11,90,142,*
MISSION IMPOSSIBLE 2 (2000) Music score by HANS ZIMMER
-S/T- *inc:* FOO FIGHTERS-P.J.HARVEY-BRIAN MAY-
METALLICA-TORI AMOS-EVE 6-LIMP BIZKIT etc.
-S/T- (songs) *HOLLYWOOD-EDEL (Vital) 011 030-2HWR*
-S/T- (score) *HOLLYWOOD-EDEL (Vital) 010 969-2HWR*
MISSION IMPOSSIBLE (USA 60s re-r BBC2 87) theme: LALO
SCHIFRIN plus NEW 91 series music: JOHN E.DAVIS
-S/T- *GNP (ZYX): GNPD(GNP-5) 8029 (CD-MC)*
MISSION TO MARS (2000) Music score by ENNIO MORRICONE
-S/T- *HOLLYWOOD-EDEL (Vital) 010 888-2HWR (CD)*

MISSOURI BREAKS (1976) Music sco: JOHN WILLIAMS -S/T-
reissue *RYKODISC (Vital): RCD 10748 (CD)*
MISSISSIPPI: RIVER OF SONG (USA TV.1999) USA FOLK MUSIC
HISTORY *SMITHSONIAN FOLKWAYS (Koch):SFW 40086 (2CD)*
MISSISSIPPI BURNING (1988) Music sco: TREVOR JONES
-S/T- *re-iss.on Spectrum (Univ): 551 100-2 (CD)*
MOBO AWARDS 2001 (C4 10/2001) SELECTION VAR.ARTISTS
SONYTV (TEN): MOODCD 72 (2CD)
MOBY DICK (USA TV mini-s.1998) Music sco: CHRISTOPHER
GORDON -S/T- *VARESE (Pinn): VSD 5921 (CD)*
MOD SQUAD The (1999) Music score: B.C.SMITH -S/T- V/A
ELEKTRA (TEN): 7559 62364-2 (CD) -4 (MC)
MOD SQUAD (USA TV) *see COLL.242,*
MODERN TIMES (1936) Music by CHARLES CHAPLIN
SOUNDTRACK FACTORY (Discov): SFCD 33510 (CD) with
'CITY LIGHTS' *see COLL.66,69,*
MODERNS The (1988) Music score: MARK ISHAM Songs by
Charles Couture -S/T- *VIRGIN (EMI): CDV 2530 (CD)*
MODESTY BLAISE (1966) Music by JOHNNY DANKWORTH -S/T-
reissue *HARKIT! (Koch-BMG): HRKCD 8002 (CD)*
MOJO (1997) Music sco: MURRAY GOLD -S/T- V.ARTISTS
EMI Premier: 821 718-2 (CD)
MOLL FLANDERS (FILM 1996) Music score: MARK MANCINA
-S/T- *Import LONDON (Univ): 452 485-2 (CD)*
MOLL FLANDERS (O.LONDON CAST 1993) Songs (Geo.Stiles-
-Paul Leigh) *feat* JOSIE LAWRENCE-ANGELA RICHARDS
FIRST NIGHT (Pinn): OCRCD 6036 (CD)
MON ONCLE (Jacques Tati 1956) Music sco: ALAIN ROMAINS
-S/T- + 'JOUR DE FETE'/'MONSIEUR HULOT'S HOLIDAY'
POLY (Discov): 836 983-2 (CD)
MONA LISA (1986) *see COLL.170,*
MONARCH OF THE GLEN (BBC1 27/02/2000) Mus: SIMON BRINT
-S/T- on *BBC WORLDWIDE (Pinn): WMSF 6039-2 (CD)*
MONEY PROGRAMME (BBC2 1966-88 & 1995-2002) 'theme from
Carpetbaggers' (ELMER BERNSTEIN) by JIMMY SMITH on
'The Cat' *VERVE (Univ): 810 046-2 (CD)*
MONEY TALKS (1997) V/A *inc:* BARRY WHITE & FAITH EVANS-
LISA STANSFIELD-MARY J.BLIGE-SWV-ANGIE STONE-DEVOX
-S/T- *RCA (BMG): 07822 18975-2 (CD) -4 (MC) -1(LP)*
MONK DAWSON (1998) Music score: MARK JENSEN -S/T- V/A
De WARRENNE PICTURES (Koch): DWPCD 01 (CD)
MONKEES The (USA 1966) theme (Boyce-Hart) THE MONKEES
ARISTA: 257874 (CD) see COLL.243,
MONKEY BONE (2001) Music score by ANNE DUDLEY -S/T- on
VARESE (Pinn): VSD 6227 (CD)
MONKEY KING (The Lost Empire) (2001) Music score: JOHN
ALTMAN - -S/T- *WEA (TEN): 9274 2333-2 (CD)*
MONSIEUR HULOT'S HOLIDAY *see* 'MON ONCLE'
MONSOON WEDDING (2001) Music score by MYCHAEL DANNA
-S/T- *BMG IMPORTS: 74321 89824-2 (CD)*
MONSTERS INC. (2001) Music score by RANDY NEWMAN -S/T-
DISNEY (USA): 60712 (CD) see also DISNEY INDEX 341
MONTE WALSH (1970) Music score by JOHN BARRY
FSM CLASSICS FSMCD Vol 2.No.4 (CD) see COLL.26,

MONTY PYTHON 'ERIC IDLE SINGS MONTY PYTHON LIVE IN
   CONCERT' (songs from films and tv series)
   BMG IMPORTS: 74321 76082-2 (CD)
MONTY PYTHON AND THE HOLY GRAIL (1975) Mus: NEIL INNES
   -S/T- *VIRGIN (EMI): VCCCD 004 (CD) VCCMC 004 (MC)*
MONTY PYTHON'S FLYING CIRCUS (BBC2 5/10/69-1974) theme
   music "Liberty Bell March" (John Phillip SOUSA)
   "INSTANT MONTY PYTHON CD COLLECTION" (6CD Box set)
   VIRGIN: CDBOX 3 (CDx6) "Ultimate MONTY PYTHON Rip
   Off" *VIRGIN (EMI): CDV(TCV) 2748 (CD/MC)*
   see COLL.84,243,
MONTY PYTHON'S LIFE OF BRIAN (1979) Music score by
   GEOFFREY BURGON, Songs by ERIC IDLE
   EMI GOLD (reissue): 528 609-2 (CD) -4 (MC)
MONTY PYTHON'S MEANING OF LIFE (1983) M: JOHN DU PREZ
   ERIC IDLE *VIRGIN EMI: VCCD 010(CD) VCCMC 010(MC)*
   see COLL.240,
MOON OVER MIAMI (1941) -S/T- *featur:* BETTY GRABLE-DON
   AMECHE *incl.mus.from* 'Broadway Melody Of 1938'
   GREAT MOVIE THEMES (Target-BMG): CD 60030 (CD)
MOONLIGHTING (USA BBC2 29/5/86) t.theme (Al Jarreau-
   Lee Holdridge) by AL JARREAU *see COLL.247,*
MOONRAKER (1979) Music score: JOHN BARRY title song
   (John Barry-Hal David) sung by SHIRLEY BASSEY
   -S/T- *EMI: CZ 551 (CD) see COLL.26,46,197,222,*
MOONSTRUCK (1987) *see COLL.122,195,197,*
MORE (1969) Music score comp/performed by PINK FLOYD
   -S/T- *reiss: EMI: CDEMD 1084 (CD) TCEMD 1084 (MC)*
MORECAMBE & WISE SHOW The (BBC1 1966-1984) Var.themes
   "Bring Me Sunshine"/"Positive Thinkin'"/"We Get
   Along So Easily Don't You Agree" sung by MORECAMBE
   & WISE on 'Get Out Of That' *EMI: ECC 29 (MC only)*
   'Bring Me Sunshine' *see COLL.200,283,*
MORK AND MINDY (USA 78 / C4 16/3/93) theme music by
   PERRY BOTKIN JNR *see COLL.14,247,*
MORTAL KOMBAT (1995) Music sco: GEORGE S.CLINTON -S/T-
   + V.Arts *LONDON (Univ.): 828 715-2 (CD) -4 (MC)*
   'MORE KOMBAT' on *EDEL (Vital) 0022672CIN (CD)*
MORTAL KOMBAT: ANNIHILATION (1997) VARIOUS ARTS -S/T-
   LONDON (Univ): 828 999-2 (CD) -4 (MC)
MOST DANGEROUS GAME *see* 'HOUNDS OF ZAROFF'
MOST HAPPY FELLA The - songs by Frank Loesser
   1.FIRST COMPLETE STUDIO RECORDING (2000)
   NAT.SYMPH.ORCH.cond:JOHN OWEN EDWARDS *feat:* LOUIS
   QUILICO-EMILY LOESSER-RICHARD MUENZ-NANCY SHADE
   DON STEPHENSON-KAREN ZIEMBA & JO SULLIVAN LOESSER
   TER MASTER WORKS (Koch): CDTER3 1260 (3CDs)
MOTOR RACING *see* GRAND PRIX (BBC) 'F1' FORMULA 1 (ITV)
MOTORWAY LIFE (ITV 05/9/1998) theme "2-4-6-8 Motorway"
   TOM ROBINSON BAND *EMI GOLD (EMI): CDGOLD 1098 (CD)*
MOTOWN MANIA ITV 16/12/2000 VAR.ARTISTS COMPILATION
   BMG TV-UNIVERSAL: MCD 60075 (2CD) MCC 60075 (2MC)
MOULIN ROUGE (2000) Music score by CRAIG ARMSTRONG inc
   DAVID BOWIE -S/T- *POLYDOR (Univ): 493 035-2 (CD)*

MOUSE HUNT (1997) Music score: ALAN SILVESTRI -S/T-
  VARESE (Pinn): VSD 5892 (CD)
MR.& MRS.(Border 18/1/84) theme music "Be Nice To Each
  Other" TONY HATCH & JACKIE TRENT *see COLL.131,*
MR.BEAN (ITV 1/1/1990) theme "Ecce Homo Qui Est Faba"
  (Behold The Man Who Is A Bean) by HOWARD GOODALL
  on collection 'HOWARD GOODALL'S CHOIR WORKS'
  ASV (Select): CDDCA 1028 (CD)
MR.CINDERS (REVIVAL LONDON CAST 1983) Songs by
  Vivian Ellis-Richard Myers-Clifford Grey-Leo Robin
  TER (Koch): CDTER 1069 (CD)
MR.ED (USA 60s) *see COLL.242,*
MR.HOLLAND'S OPUS (1995) Mus sco: MICHAEL KAMEN + V/A:
  -S/T-(songs) *POLYDOR (Univ): 529 508-2 (CD)*
  -S/T-(score) *POLYDOR (Univ): 452 062-2 (CD) -4(MC)*
MR.LUCKY (USA) theme: HENRY MANCINI *see COLL.170,*
MR.MAGOO (USA TV) *see COLL.244,*
MR.MEN & LITTLE MISSES (BBC1 76) Arthur LOWE-Pauline
  COLLINS-J.ALDERTON *MSD: KIDM 9002/3 (MC)* also
  'BEST MR.MEN ALBUM IN THE WORLD..EVER' inc: THEME
  VIRGIN (EMI): VTCD 166 (CD) VTMC 166 (MC)
MR.ROSE (Granada 17/2/67-5/12/68) theme music "Mr.Rose
  Investigates" (Snow) *see COLL.24,*
MR.SKEFFINGTON (1944) Music by FRANZ WAXMAN. *NEW REC:*
  MOSCOW SYMPHONY ORCH. (William T.Stromberg,cond.)
  MARCO POLO (Select): 8225037 (CD) see COLL.272,
MR.WONDERFUL (O.BROADWAY CAST 1956) Songs (Jerry Bock-
  George Weiss-Larry Holfencor) *with* Sammy Davis Jnr
  MCA USA (S.Screen): MCAD 10303(CD) MCAC 10303(MC)
MRS.BRADLEY MYSTERIES (BBC1 31/8/1998)incidental score
  music by MATTHEW SCOTT *unavailable*
  period music arranged by GRAHAM DALBY,performed by
  GRAHAM DALBY & GRAHAMOPHONES / 'MUSIC FROM THE BBC
  SERIES 'MRS.BRADLEY MYSTERIES'on
  BBC WORLDWIDE (Pinn): WMSF 6021-2 (CD) also avail:
  'SWING CLASSICS' *EMI GOLD: 525 080-2 (CD)* and
  'MAD DOGS AND ENGLISHMEN' *PRESIDENT:PCOM 1097 (CD)*
  'TRANSATLANTIQUE' *PRESIDENT: PCOM 1128 (CD)*
MRS.BROWN (1997) Music score: STEPHEN WARBECK -S/T- on
  MILAN (BMG): 74321 51072-2 (CD)
MRS.DALLOWAY (1997) Music score: ILONA SEKACZ -S/T- on
  MILAN (BMG): 74321 57231-2 (CD)
MRS.DOUBTFIRE (1993) Music score: HOWARD SHORE -S/T-
  ARISTA BMG: 07822 11015-2 (CD) see COLL.64,197,
MRS.PARKER AND THE VICIOUS CIRCLE (1994) Music: MARK
  ISHAM -S/T- *VARESE (Pinn): VSD 5471 (CD)*
MRS.WINTERBOURNE (1996) Music sco: PATRICK DOYLE -S/T-
  VARESE (Pinn): VSD 5720 (CD)
MUDHONEY (1965 Russ Meyer) also inc 'FINDERS KEEPERS'
  'MOTOR PSYCHO' *QDK (Greyh/Pinn): QDKCD 011 (CD)*
MULAN (1998) Music: JERRY GOLDSMITH -S/T- *DISNEY-EDEL*
  (Pinn): 010 631-2 (CD) -4 (MC) see also p.341
MULHOLLAND FALLS (1996) Music score: DAVE GRUSIN -S/T-
  EDEL-CINERAMA (Vital) 002259-2CIN (CD)

MULHOLLAND DRIVE (2001) Music score ANGELO BADALAMENTI
-S/T- *BMG IMPORTS: 74321 89823-2 (CD)*
MUMFORD (2000) Music score by JAMES NEWTON HOWARD
-S/T- *HOLLYWOOD (USA): 62243-2 (CD)*
MUMMY The (1997) Music score by JERRY GOLDSMITH -S/T-
DECCA (Univ): 466 458-2 (CD)
MUMMY The (1959) Music score by FRANZ REIZENSTEIN
GDI (ABM): GDICD 006 (CD)
MUMMY RETURNS The (2000) Music score by ALAN SILVESTRI
-S/T- *UNIVERSAL MUSIC: 013 983-2 (CD)*
MUNSTERS The (USA 1963) *see COLL.14,242,*
MUPPET SHOW The (ITV 76/BBC1 86) *see COLL.244,*
MUPPET MOVIE The (1979) Music and songs: PAUL WILLIAMS
KENNY ASCHER *feat:* JIM HENSON-FRANK OZ-DAVE GOELZ
reiss: ARISTA (BMG): 74321 18247-2 (CD) -4 (MC)
MUPPETS FROM SPACE (1999) Music sco: JAMSHIED SHARIFI
score: *VARESE (Pinn): VSD 6060 (CD)*
songs: *COLUMBIA (TEE): 496 559-2 (CD)*
MURDER ON THE ORIENT EXPRESS (1974) Music score by
RICHARD RODNEY BENNETT new recording by the BBC
PHILHARMONIC ORCHESTRA on *CHANDOS: CHAN 9867 (CD)*
also see COLL.268,
MURDER SHE WROTE (USA) music:JOHN ADDISON *see COLL.14,*
MURDER WAS THE CASE (1994) Mus by SNOOP DOGGY DOGG+ VA
-S/T- *INTERSCOPE-MCA (UNI): IND 92484 (CD) also on*
DEATH ROW (RMG/UNIV): DROW 106 (CD)
MURIEL'S WEDDING (1994) Music score: PETER BEST -*S/T-*
POLYDOR (Univ): 527 493-2 (CD) 527 493-4 (MC)
MURPHY BROWN (USA TV) *see COLL.248,*
MUSE The (1999) Music score by ELTON JOHN -S/T- on
IMS MERCURY (Univ): AA 3145 46517-2 (CD)
MUSIC AND THE MIND (C4 5/5/96) feat The MEDICI STRING
QUARTET / PAUL ROBERTSON (speaker) music to accomp
any the series *KOCH SCHWANN (Koch): 36437-2 (CD)*
MUSIC IN MINIATURE (BBC) theme "Elizabethan Serenade"
RONALD BINGE *see COLL.44,92,94,100,*
MUSIC MACHINE (1979) Music: AARON HARRY feat PATTI
BOULAYE -S/T- *CASTLE MUSIC (Pinn): CMRCD 235 (CD)*
MUSIC MAN The - Songs by Meredith Willson
  1.FILM MUSICAL 1962 ROBERT PRESTON-SHIRLEY JONES
  -S/T- *WB USA IMPORT: 1459-2 (CD) M5 1459 (MC)*
  2.ORIG LONDON CAST 1961 *with* VAN JOHNSON-PATRICIA
    LAMBERT-RUTH KETTLEWELL-MICHAEL MALNICK and Comp
    LASERLIGHT POP-TARGET (BMG): 12447 (CD)
MUSIC OF THE HEART (1999) -S/T- *EPIC TEN 496 294-2 CD*
MUSIC TEACHER The (1990) -S/T- Operatic Classical Mus
PRESIDENT (BMG): PCOM(PTLC) 1109 (CD/MC)
MUSKETEER The (2001) Music score by DAVID ARNOLD -S/T-
DECCA LONDON (UNIV): 400 149-2 or 440 014 920 (CD)
MUTINY ON THE BOUNTY (1984) - *see* BOUNTY
MY BEST FRIEND'S WEDDING (1997) M: JAMES NEWTON HOWARD
-S/T- (V.Arts) *IMMORTAL-SONY (TEN): 488 115-2 (CD)*
VAR.ARTISTS VERSION *EXCEED (Technic): 50019-2 (CD)*
MY COUSIN RACHEL (1952) *see COLL.273,*

MY COUSIN VINNY (1991) Music sco: RANDY EDELMAN -S/T-
VARESE (Pinn): VSD 5364 (CD)
MY DINNER WITH ANDRE (1981) see *COLL.64,*
MY DOG SKIP (1999) Music score by WILLIAM ROSS
VARESE (Pinn): VSD 6106 (CD)
MY FAIR LADY - songs Alan Jay Lerner & Frederick Loewe
  1.ORIG LONDON CAST 2001 REVIVAL MARTINE McCUTCHEON-
    JONATHAN PRYCE-NICHOLAS LePREVOST-DENNIS WATERMAN-
    MARK UMBERS-PATSY ROWLANDS and Company
    FIRST NIGHT (Pinn): CASTCD 83 (CD) CASTC 83 (MC)
  2.FILM MUSICAL 1964 REX HARRISON-AUDREY HEPBURN
    sung by MARNI NIXON -S/T- *SONY: CD 70000 (CD) and
    also SK(ST) 66711 (CD/MC) also SONY: SS 89639 (CD)*
  3.O.BROADWAY CAST 1956 REX HARRISON-JULIE ANDREWS-
    STANLEY HOLLOWAY-ROBERT COOTE-ZENA DARE-AL.DUDLEY
    COLUMBIA (Ten): SMK 60539 (CD)
  4.STUDIO RECORD 1987 *w:* KIRI TE KANAWA-JEREMY IRONS-
    WARREN MITCHELL-JOHN GIELGUD *DECCA: 421 200-2 CD*
  5.CLASSIC MUSICALS SERIES *w:* ALEC McCOWEN and TINUKE
    OLAFIMIHAN-RON MOODY-HENRY WICKMAN & others
    + songs from 'CAMELOT' *KOCH INT: 34079-2 (CD)*
  6.ORIG MASTERWORKS EDIT. *w:* ALEC McCOWEN-BOB HOSKINS
    TINUKE OLAFIMIHAN-DUCLIE GRAY-HENRY WICKHAM-
    MICHAEL DENISON *TER (Koch): CDTER2 1211 (2CD)*
  7.STUDIO RECORDING (Highlights)
    TER (Koch): CDTEH 6005 (CD)
MY FAVOURITE HYMNS (ITV 05/07/1998-2000) CELEBRITY
  SELECTION OF HYMNS FROM TV SERIES - VARIOUS CHOIRS
  GLOBAL TV (BMG): 74321 78387-2 (CD) -4 (MC)
MY FELLOW AMERICANS (1996) -S/T- with VARIOUS ARTISTS
  -S/T- *SNAPPER (Pinn): SMMCD 616 (CD)*
MY GEISHA (1962) see *COLL.273,*
MY GIRL TISA - see under 'DISTANT DRUMS'
MY HERO (BBC1 04/02/2000) theme music composed and
  performed by PHILIP POPE *unavailable*
MY LEFT FOOT see *COLL.40,*
MY NAME IS JOE (1998) Music score: GEORGE FENTON -S/T-
  DEBONAIR (Pinn): CDDEB 1008 (CD)
MY NAME IS NOBODY (1973) Music score ENNIO MORRICONE
  ENNIO MORRICONE ORCH on *DRG USA (Pinn):
  DRGCD 32907 (CD) see COLL.177,*
MY SO CALLED LIFE (C4 26/7/95) mus: W.G.SNUFFY WALDEN
  -S/T- *WEA: 7567 82721-2 (CD) -4 (MC) see COLL.248,*
MY TWO DADS (USA C4 from 10/5/90) theme "You Can Count
  On Me" (GREG EVIGAN-Lenny Macallso-Michael Jacobs)
  see *COLL.248,*
MY UNCLE SILAS (ITV1 28/10/2001) Music: DEBBIE WISEMAN
  -S/T- *COLUMBIA (TEN): 472 087-2 (CD)*
MYSTERIES OF EDGAR WALLACE The (ITV 60s) Theme "Man Of
  Mystery" (Michael Carr) THE SHADOWS 'In The 60s'
  MFP (EMI): CDMFP 6076 (CD) (TC)MFP 5873 (MC/LP)
MYSTERIOUS ISLAND (1961) Music: BERNARD HERRMANN -S/T-
  see *COLL.135,174,*
MYSTERIOUS UNIVERSE - see ARTHUR C.CLARKE'S...

MYSTERY MEN (1999) Music score by STEPHEN WARBECK and
   SHIRLEY WALKER -S/T- *POLYD (Univ): 490 345-2 (CD)*
MYSTERY MOVIE (USA TV) *see COLL.243,*

MYSTERY OF MEN (BBC1 30/08/1999) incidental music by
   COLIN TOWNS *unavailable.* theme music "HI HO SILVER
   LINING" by JEFF BECK on 'Best Of of Jeff Beck'
   MFP (EMI): CDMFP 6177 (CD) TCMFP 6177 (MC)
MYTH OF FINGERPRINTS (1997) Music score: DAVID BRIDIE-
   and JOHN PHILLIPS -S/T- *featuring* VARIOUS ARTISTS
   VELVET (Pinn): VEL 797052 (CD)
N AKED BOYS SINGING (CELEBRATION THEATRE CAST 1998)
   DUCY LEE (Silver Sounds): 7042 771210-2 (CD)
NAKED CITY The (1948) Music sco: MIKLOS ROZSA select.
   on 'LUST FOR LIFE' *VARESE (Pinn): VSD 5405 (CD)*
NAKED CITY The (USA 1958-63) theme music by BILLY MAY
   versions by KEN MACKINTOSH 'Mac's Back' *PRESIDENT:
   PLCD 532 (CD) see COLL.24,131,274*
NAME OF THE ROSE (1986) Music sco: JAMES HORNER -S/T-
   VIRGIN France (Discovery): 88085-2 (CD)
NAPOLEON (1927) Contemporary score by CARL DAVIS
   see COLL.85, 'The SILENTS' *also on*
   FILMCD 149 (CD) and CFP (EMI): CDCFP 4542 (CD)
NAPOLEON: A NEW MUSICAL ORIGINAL LONDON CAST RECORDING
   FIRST NIGHT (Pinn): SCORECD 49 (CD)
NASA MARS MISSION (USA OFFICIAL MUSIC) 'MYTHODEA' by
   VANGELIS -S/T- *SONY CLASSICS 9TEN): SK 89191 (CD)*
NATIONAL LAMPOON LEMMINGS (USA SHOW) ORIGINAL CAST REC
   (Re-mastered) *UNIVERSAL IMS: AA.440014610-2 (CD)*
NATIONAL LAMPOON'S ANIMAL HOUSE (1978) Music: ELMER
   BERNSTEIN -S/T- *re-iss MCA (UNI): MCLD 19086 (CD)*
NATIONAL LOTTERY (BBC1 19/11/94-2001) theme music
   composed and arranged by ED WELCH *unavailable*
NATIONWIDE (BBC 70's) theme music "The Good Word" by
   JOHN SCOTT *see COLL.4,*
NATURAL The (1984) Music sco: RANDY NEWMAN -S/T- Imp
   W.BROS USA (Silva Screen) 925 116-2 -4 (CD/MC)
NATURAL BORN KILLERS (1994) music by VARIOUS ARTISTS
   INTERSCOPE (MCA/BMG): IND 92460-2 (CD)
   SIMPLY VINYL (Vital): SVLP 118 (2LP)
NATURE BOY (BBC2 14/02/2000) signature tune "Beautiful
   World" by BETH ORTON *unavailable.* incidental music
   score by SIMON FISHER TURNER *unavailable*
NAZIS: A WARNING FROM HISTORY (BBC2 10/9/97) open.mus:
   'German Requiem' Op.45 (BRAHMS) *version by* VIENNA
   PHIL.ORCH (Haitink) *Philips (Univ): 446 681-2 (CD)*
   also used: "Kline Dreigschenmusik" (arrangement of
   'Moritat'("Mack The Knife" 'The Threepenny Opera')
   (Weill-Brecht-Blitzstein) *BBC ARCHIVE unavailable*
NED KELLY (1970) Music score: SHEL SILVERSTEIN *feat*
   WAYLON JENNINGS "She Moved Through The Fair"
   -S/T- *RYKODISC (Vital): RCD 10708 (CD)*
NEEDFUL THINGS (1993) Music score: PATRICK DOYLE
   -S/T- *VARESE (Pinn): VSD 5438 (CD)*

NEIGHBOURS (BBC1 27/10/1986-2001)*theme* by JACKIE TRENT
  TONY HATCH *orig vers.*sung by BARRY CROCKER *DELETED*
NELL (1994) Music: MARK ISHAM. solo flute (Jim Walker)
  -S/T- *LONDON (IMS-Poly): E.444 818-2 (CD)*
NET The (1995) Music score: MARK ISHAM -S/T- on
  VARESE (Pinn): VSD 5662 (CD)
NEVADA SMITH (1966) Music score: ALFRED NEWMAN
  -S/T- *TSUNAMI Germ (Silva Screen): TSU 0113 (CD)*
NEVER BEEN KISSED (1999) Music score by DAVID NEWMAN
  -S/T- *feat:* BEACH BOYS/CARDIGANS/REM/JOHN LENNON
  and YOKO ONO/SMITHS/SEMISONIC/WILLIS etc.
  EMI SOUNDTRACKS: 498 505-2 (CD)
NEVER CRY WOLF (1983) Mus: MARK ISHAM *see* MRS.SOFFEL
NEVER MIND THE BUZZCOCKS (BBC2 12/11/96) title music:
  SWITCH AND THE GINGER GP *unavailable*
NEVER ON SUNDAY (1959) Music score: MANOS HADJIDAKIS
   -S/T- *RYKODISC (Vital): RCD 10722 (CD)*
NEVER SAY NEVER AGAIN - see JAMES BOND INDEX p.346
NEW ADVENTURES OF BLACK BEAUTY (BBC1 11/4/94) theme
  "Galloping Home" by DENIS KING *see COLL.3,*
NEW ADVENTURES OF SUPERMAN (USA/BBC1 8/1/1994) orig
  music: JAY GRUSKA *SONIC IMAGES (Cargo-Greyhound):*
  SI 8703 (CD) see COLL.221,248,
NEW AVENGERS The (ITV 22/10/76-78) theme mus: LAURIE
  JOHNSON *see COLL.3,156,158,250,*
NEW BRAIN (O.USA CAST REC) *RCA BMG: 09026 63298-2 (CD)*
NEW JACK CITY (91) Music score: MICHEL COLOMBIER
  -S/T- V.ARTISTS *GIANT (BMG): 74321 15104-2 (CD)*
NEW JERSEY DRIVE (1994) *feat:* Var.RAP & R.& B. -S/T-
  TOMMY BOY (Pinn): TB(CD)(C)(V) 1114 (CD/MC/2LP)
  TOMMY BOY (Pinn): (Volume 2) - 1130 (CD/MC/2LP)
NEW MOON - songs by Sigmund Romberg-Oscar Hammerstein
  1.ORIG LONDON CAST 1929   EVELYN LAYE-GENE GERRARD
    PEARL (Pavil): GEMMCD 9100(CD)
  2.STUDIO RECORDING   GORDON MacRAE-DOROTHY KIRSTEN
    see under 'DESERT SONG'
NEW ORLEANS (1947) *featur* LOUIS ARMSTRONG & ALL STARS
  BILLIE HOLIDAY-WOODY HERMAN ORCHESTRA and others
  -S/T- *JASMINE (BMG-Con): GOJCD 1025 (CD)*
  DEFINITIVE (Discovery): SFCD 33506 (CD)
NEW ROCKY HORROR SHOW (SHOW 1999) by RICHARD O'BRIEN
  feat JASON DONOVAN *DAMN IT JANET! (Pinn):DAMJAM 2*
  (CD) see also ROCKY HORROR SHOW
NEW YORK NEW YORK - songs by John Kander and Fred Ebb
  1.FILM MUSICAL 1977 *with:* LIZA MINNELLI -S/T-
    LIBERTY EMI Eur (Disc): 746 090-2 (CD)
NEW YORK ROCK (O.NEW YORK CAST RECORDING) *featuring*
  YOKO ONO *CAPITOL (EMI): CDP 829 843-2 (CD)*
NEWCOMERS The (BBC 1960's) - *see COLL.4,*
NEWS AT TEN (ITN 3/7/67-98) theme "Awakening" from
  '20th Century Portrait' by JOHNNY PEARSON o.vers:
  Coll 'SOUNDS VISUAL' *deleted see also* 'ITN NEWS'
NEWSNIGHT (BBC2 28/1/80-2001) theme music composed
  by GEORGE FENTON *unavailable*

NEXT BEST THING The (2000) *feat* MADONNA & V.ARTISTS
-S/T- *MAVERICK (TEN): 9362 47672-2 (CD) -4 (MC)*
NEXT FRIDAY (1999) Music by TERENCE BLANCHARD and
featuring ICE CUBE -S/T- with ICE CUBE & V.ARTS on
PRIORITY (EMI): CDPTY 185 (CD) PTYLP 185 (2LP)
NIAGARA NIAGARA (1997) Music score: MICHAEL TIMMINS &
JEFF BIRD -S/T- *VTW (Sil.Sounds):6381 27014-2 (CD)*
NICHOLAS NICKLEBY (1947) m: LORD BERNERS *see COLL.48,*

NICHOLAS NICKLEBY Life & Advent. ORIG LONDON CAST 1982
Songs: STEPHEN OLIVER *with* Royal Shakespeare Comp
JAY-TER (SSD): CDJAY 1338 (CD)
NIGHT AND DAY (ITV1 06/11/2001) Mus:DAVID ARCH & TODDY
theme sung by KYLLIE MINOGUE *recording unconfirmed*
NIGHT AND DAY (FILM 1946) VARIOUS ARTISTS SELECTIONS
SOUND TRACK FACTORY (Discov): SFCD 33529 (CD)
NIGHT AT THE OPERA (1935) *featuring* MARX BROTHERS
selection DEFINITIVE (Discov): SFCD 33502 (CD)
NIGHT AT THE ROXBURY,A (1997) Music score: DAVID KITAY
V.Artists -S/T- *DREAMWORKS (Univ): DRD 50033 (CD)*
NIGHT COURT (ITV 91) mus:JACK ELLIOTT *see COLL.14,247,*
NIGHT DIGGER The (1971) *see* BATTLE OF NERETVA
NIGHT GALLERY (USA TV) *see COLL.219,246,*
NIGHT MAIL (1936 Post Office) Mus s: BENJAMIN BRITTEN
score select.*HYPERION (Select): CDA 66845 (CD)*
NIGHT OF THE HUNTER MUSICAL *VARESE Pinn: VSD 5876 (CD)*
NIGHT PASSAGE (1957) Mus: DIMITRI TIOMKIN *see COLL.255,*
NIGHT VISITOR The (1970) Music score by HENRY MANCINI
selection with 'MIDAS RUN' and 'THE HOUSE' on
CITADEL (HOT): STC 77105 (CD)
NIGHTINGALE (O.LONDON CAST 1982) Songs Charles Strouse
w: SARAH BRIGHTMAN-GORDON SANDISON-SUSANNAH FELLOWS
JAY-TER (SSD): CDJAY 1327 (CD)
NIGHTMARE ON ELM STREET 1 (1984) Mus:CHARLES BERNSTEIN
NIGHTMARE ON ELM STREET 2: Freddy's Revenge (1985) Mus
CHRISTOPHER YOUNG *both S/T VARESE (Pinn) VSD 47255*
NIGHTMARE ON ELM STREET 3: Dream Warriors (1987) Mus:
ANGELO BADALAMENTI -S/T- *VARESE: VCD 47293 (CD)*
NIGHTMARE ON ELM STREET 4: Dream Master (1988) Music
CRAIG SAFAN -S/T- *VARESE (Pinn): VSD 5203 (CD)*
NIGHTMARE ON ELM STREET 5: Dream Child (1989) Music:
JAY FERGUSON -S/T- *VARESE (Pinn): VSD 5238 (CD)*
NIGHTMARE ON ELM STREET 6: Freddie's Dead (1991) Mus:
BRIAN MAY -S/T- *VARESE (Pinn): VSD 5333 (CD)*
see also 'FREDDIE'S DEAD - THE FINAL NIGHTMARE'
NIKITA (1989) Music score: ERIC SERRA -S/T-
VIRGIN (EMI): CDVMM 2 (CD) TCVMM 2 (MC)
NIKITA (TV series) - see 'LA FEMME NIKITA'
NIL BY MOUTH (1997) Music score: ERIC CLAPTON
-S/T- *unavailable.* song "PANDORA" by FRANCE on
SUPER VILLAIN WRECKUDS (Arabesque): SVP 001CDs
NINE - songs by Maury Yeston
ORIG LONDON CONCERT CAST 1992 *with:* JONATHAN PRYCE
ELAINE PAIGE *TER (Koch): CDTER2 1193 (2CD)*

NINTH GATE The (1999) Music score by WOJCIEK KILAR
performed by CITY OF PRAGUE PHILHARMONIC & CHORUS
and featuring Soprano SUMI JO. -S/T-
SILVA SCREEN (Koch): FILMCD 321 (CD)
NO BANANAS (BBC1 5/3/96) mus: JOHN ALTMAN -S/T- V.Arts
VIRGIN (EMI): CDVIP 176(CD) TCVIP 176(MC)
NO HIDING PLACE (ITV 16/9/59-67) theme: LAURIE JOHNSON
see *COLL.2,77,157,*
NO NO NANETTE - songs by Vincent Youmans-Otto Harbach
and Irving Caesar
  1.USA REVIVAL CAST 1971 RUBY KEELER *COLUMBIA Import*
  (Silva Screen): CK 30563 (CD) JST 30563 (MC)
  2.ORIG LONDON REVIVAL CAST 1973 *w:* ANNA NEAGLE-TONY
  BRITTON-ANNE ROGERS.*SONY West End: SMK 66173 (CD)*
NO WAY HOME (1997) Mus score: RICK GIOVINAZZO -S/T-
OCEAN DEEP (Grapev/Polyg): OCD 005 (CD)
NO WAY TO TREAT A LADY (ORIG USA CAST) songs by
DOUGLAS J.COHEN *VARESE (Pinn): VSD 5815 (CD)*
NOAH'S ARK (1998) Music score by PAUL GRABOWSKY -S/T-
VARESE (Pinn): VSD 6027 (CD)
NODDY IN TOYLAND (BBC1 16/4/1989) see *COLL.285,*
NOEL AND GERTIE (O.LONDON CAST 1986) Songs NOEL COWARD
with Lewis FIANDER-Patricia HODGE and Company
TER (Koch): CDTER 1117 (CD)
NOMADS OF THE WIND (BBC2 9/1/94) mus: BRIAN BENNETT
TV -S/T- *Karussell (Univ): IMS E.513 931-2 (CD)*
NORA (2000) Music score by STANISLAS SYREWICZ
VENTURE-VIRGIN (EMI): CDVE 950 (CD)
NORTH AND SOUTH (USA TV) see *COLL.14,*
NORTH BY NORTHWEST (1959) Music sco: BERNARD HERRMANN
-S/T- *re-issue EMI PREMIER (EMI): CDODEON 6 (CD)*
see *COLL.105,135,136,140,141,147,143,144,252,*
NORTH HOLLYWOOD HIGH (E4 07/2001) theme m "Bomb Diggy"
ANOTHER LEVEL on Coll 'TV 2000' *SONY: SONYTV82CD*
NORTH SQUARE (C4 18/10/2000) Incidental music score
by JOHN LUNN *unavailable*
NORTH STAR (1943) Music score by AARON COPLAND
new suite recording BY EOS ORCHESTRA & COLLEGIATE
CHORALE (Robert Bass) *TELARC (BMG): CD 80583 (CD)*
NORTH STAR (1996) Music score: JOHN SCOTT -S/T- on
JOHN SCOTT Records (Silva Screen): JSCD 120 (CD)
NORTHERN EXPOSURE (C4 16/3/1992) theme:DAVID SCHWARTZ
-S/T- *with Var.Art MCA (UNI): MCD 10685 (CD)*
-S/T- 'More Music' *MCA (UNI): MCLD 19350 (CD)*
see *COLL.14,*
NOSFERATU (1922) *RESTORED 1996 VERSION.* NEW SCORE BY
JAMES BERNARD. PRAGUE CITY PHILHARMONIC ORCH.cond:
NIC RAINE *SILVA SCREEN (Koch): FILMCD 192 (CD)*
NOSFERATU (1922) Music sco: HANS ERDMANN orchestral
version on **RCA** *(BMG): 09026 68143-2 (CD)*
NOTES OF LOVE (2000) Mus score: FRANCO PIERSANTI -S/T-
PACIFIC TIME ENT.(USA IMPT): PTE 8527-2 (CD)
NOTRE DAME DE PARIS (Musical 2000) Songs by RICHARD
COCCIANTE-LUC PLAMONDON with English Lyrics by

WILL JENNINGS. *feat* TINA ARENA-STEVE BALSAMO & Com
SONY CLASSICS: 497 764-2 (CD) -4 (MC) -8 (md)
also COLOSSEUM (Pinn): CST 8083-2 (CD)
NOTTING HILL (1999) -S/T- VARIOUS ARTISTS
ISLAND (Univ): 546 207-2 (CD) -4 (MC)
NOW AND THEN (95) Music sco: CLIFF EIDELMAN -S/T- (2)
score: *VARESE (Pinn): VSD 5675 (CD)*
songs: *COLUMBIA (Ten): 481 606-2 (CD) -4 (MC)*
NOW VOYAGER! (1942) see COLL.*69,239,*
NOWHERE (1997) Various Arts -S/T- including RADIOHEAD-
ELASTICA-CHEMICAL BROTHERS-MASSICE ATTACK etc.
MERCURY (Univ): 534 522-2 (CD)
NUNSENSE - songs by Dan Goggin
1.ORIG LONDON CAST 1987 HONOR BLACKMAN-ANNA SHARKEY
LOUISE GOLD *TER (Koch): CDTER 1132 (CD)*
2.ORIG OFF-BROADWAY CAST 1986 *w:* CHRISTINE ANDERSON
SEMINA de LAURENTIS *DRG (Pinn): CDSBL 12589 (CD)*
NUNSENSE 2: The Second Coming ORIG CAST RECORDING
DRG USA (Pinn): DRGMC 12608 (MC)
NURSE BETTY (2000) Music score by ROLFE KENT -S/T-
VARESE (Pinn): VSD 6184 (CD)
NUTTY PROFESSOR The (1995) Music score: DAVID NEWMAN
featuring various Rap Songs *(INSPIRED BY THE FILM)*
MERCURY-Def Jam (Univ): 531 911-2 /-4
NUTTY PROFESSOR II and 'The KLUMPS' (2000)(UK VERSION)
MERCURY (Univ): 560 809-2 (CD) / 542 885-2 (CD)
NYPD BLUE (USA1993) theme: MIKE POST on *SILVA TREASURY*
(Koch/S.Screen): SILVAD 3511 (CD) see COLL.*203,*
O (OTHELLO) (2001) Music score by JEFF DANNA -S/T-
VARESE (Pinn): VSD 6244 (CD)
O BROTHER WHERE ART THOU (2000) Music by T.BONE WALKER
V/A -S/T- *POLYDOR-MERCURY (Univ): 170 069-2 (CD)*
also POLYDOR (UNIV): 170 212-2 (CD)
O LUCKY MAN (1973) Music sco: ALAN PRICE -S/T- *reiss:*
WARNER BROS (TEN): 9362 46137-2 (CD)
O PIONEERS! (1991) Music score: BRUCE BROUGHTON -S/T-
INTRADA USA (Silva Screen) MAFCD 7023 (CD)
OBJECT OF MY AFFECTION (1998) Music sco: GEORGE FENTON
-S/T- *ARK 21 (Grapev/Poly): 61868 10027-2 (CD)*
OBJECTIVE BURMA! (1944) Music by FRANZ WAXMAN *new rec*
SLOVAK RADIO S.O.BRATISLAVA (WILLIAM T.STROMBERG)
MARCO POLO (Select): 8225148 (CD) / see COLL.270,
OBSESSION (1976) Music sco: BERNARD HERRMANN conduct:
NAT.PHILHARMONIC ORCHESTRA
UNICORN KANCHANA (Harmonia Mundi): UKCD 2065 (CD)
OCEANS ELEVEN (1960) songs sung by FRANK SINATRA-DEAN
MARTIN-SAMMY DAVIS JR. -S/T- Collection & others
CAPITOL-EMI: 536 452-2 (CD)
OCTOBER SKY (1999) Music score by MARK ISHAM -S/T- on
SONY CLASSICS: SK 61696 (CD)
OCTOPUSSY (1983) Music score: JOHN BARRY / theme song
"All Time High" sung by RITA COOLIDGE -S/T- *reiss*
+ addit.items RYKODISC (Vital): RCD 10705 (CD)
see JAMES BOND F.INDEX p.346 see COLL.*26,47,222,*

ODD COUPLE The (USA 70 BBC rerun 89) theme: NEAL HEFTI
see COLL.200,243,261,
ODD MAN OUT (1946) Music score by WILLIAM ALWYN
Suite LSO (Richard Hickox) CHANDOS: CHAN 9243 (CD)
OH KAY! (MUSICAL) songs by GEORGE and IRA GERSHWIN
COLUMBIA (Ten): SMK 60703 (CD)
OKLAHOMA! songs: Richard Rodgers-Oscar Hammerstein II

1. FILM MUSICAL 1955　GORDON MacRAE-SHIRLEY JONES-
GLORIA GRAHAM-ROD STEIGER-GENE NELSON- and Company
-S/T- re-mastered EMI ANGEL: CDC 527 350-2 (CD)
2. ORIG LONDON CAST 1998/99　HUGH JACKMAN-MAUREEN
LIPMAN-PETER POLYCARPOU-JOSEFINA GABRIELLE-VICKY
MON-JIMMY JOHNSTON-SHULER HENSLEY and Company
FIRST NIGHT (Pinn): CASTCD 69 (CD) CASTC 69 (MC)
3. ORIG LONDON CAST 1980 with: JOHN DIEDRICH-ROSAMUND
SHELLEY-MADGE RYAN-MARK WHITE-ALFRED MOLINA-
JILLIAN MACK-LINAL HAFT and Co.
Highlights: SHOWTIME (MCI-THE): SHOW(CD)(MC) 001
Complete: TER (Koch): (CD)(ZC)TEM 1208 (CD/MC)
FOR OTHER RECORDINGS SEE TELE-TUNES 1998 p.175/176
4. ORIG LONDON CAST 1947 with: HOWARD KEEL-BETTY JANE
WATSON-WALTER DONAHUE-ISABEL BIGLEY-HENRY CLARKE
LASERLIGHT (Target/BMG): 12 450 (CD)
5. STUDIO RECORD USA 1952 NELSON EDDY-KAYE BALLARD-
VIRGINIA HASKINS-PORTIA NELSON-LEE CASS-DAVID
ATKINSON-DAVID MORRIS SONY Broadway: SK 53326 (CD)
6. BROADWAY CAST RECORDING 1979　LAURENCE GUTTARD-
CHRISTINE ANDREAS-MARY WICKES RCA: RD 83572 (CD)
7. CLASSIC MUSICALS SERIES feat: JOHN DIEDRICH-MADGE
RYAN-ROSAMUND SHELLEY-MARK WHITE-ALFRED MOLINA
+ songs from 'THE KING & I' KOCH INT: 34077-2 (CD)
OLD GRINGO (89) Music score: LEE HOLDRIDGE Suite on
'LONESOME DOVE' SILVA SCREEN (Koch): FILMCD 176 CD
OLD HEIDELBERG (silent) Contemporary score by CARL
DAVIS see COLL.85, 'The SILENTS'
OLD HOUSE AT COATE (1948) Music score: MICHAEL HERBERT
-S/T- LUTTERWORTH-SILBERKLA (Ind) RJMC 1848-4 (MC)
OLD MAN AND THE SEA The (Yorkshire / 90) music: BRUCE
BROUGHTON -S/T- INTRADA (S.Screen): RVF 6008D (CD)
OLIVER! - songs by Lionel Bart
1. FILM MUSICAL 1968 w: HARRY SECOMBE-RON MOODY-SHANI
WALLIS-JACK WILD -S/T- RCA: ND(NK) 90311 (CD/MC)
2. NEW LONDON CAST 1994 JONATHAN PRYCE-SALLY DEXTER
FIRST NIGHT (Pinn): CASTCD 47 (CD) CASTC 47 (MC)
3. CARLTON SHOWS COLLECTION Studio 1994 w IAN WALLACE
BONNIE LANGFORD-GARETH STRINGER-VICTOR SPINETTI &
West End Concert Orch & Chorus (Matthew Freeman)
CARLTON SHOWS: PWKS(PWKMC) 4194 (CD/MC)
4. STUDIO RECORD 1991　JOSEPHINE BARSTOW-JULIAN FORS
YTHE-SHEILA HANCOCK-STUART KALE-RICHARD VAN ALLAN
National Symphony Orchestra (JOHN OWEN EDWARDS)
Highlights: SHOWTIME (MCI-THE): SHOW(CD)(MC) 004
Complete: TER (Koch): CDTER 1184 (CD)

5. LONDON STUDIO RECORD 1966 w: JON PERTWEE-JIM DALE
NICOLETTE ROEG-BLANCHE MOORE-TOMMY MANN-FRED LUCAS
CHARLES GRANVILLE and GEOFF LOVE & HIS ORCHESTRA
MFP (EMI):CC 8253 (CD) HR 8253 (MC)
6. ORIG BROADWAY CAST 1963 CLIVE REVILL-GEORGIA BROWN
RCA (BMG): GD 84113 (CD) GK 84113 (MC)
7. ORIG LONDON CAST 1960 w: RON MOODY-GEORGIA BROWN-
PAUL WHITSUN JONES-HOPE JACKMAN-DANNY SEWELL & Co
DERAM (Univ): 820 590-2 (CD)

OLIVER AND COMPANY (1989) Music score: J.A.C.REDFORD
-S/T- *DISNEY-EDEL (Vital) 010 890-2 (CD) -4 (MC)*

OLIVER TWIST (1948) Music score by ARNOLD BAX
see *COLL.48,120,*

OLIVIER OLIVIER (1991) Music: ZBIGNIEW PREISNER incl
'EUROPA EUROPA' -S/T- *DRG (Pinn): DRGCD 12606 (CD)*

OLYMPIC GAMES 2000 (SYDNEY AUSTRALIA)(BBC1 15/09/2000)
BBC theme music composed by MICHAEL CONN performed
by BBC CONCERT ORCHESTRA. Other specially composed
music by VANGELIS *unavailable.*

OLYMPUS ON MY MIND (USA CAST 96) Songs: **Grant Sturiale
Barry Harman)** *JAY-TER (SSD): CDJAY 1238 (CD)*

OMEGA MAN The (1971) Music score by RON GRAINER -S/T-
reissue *FSM (USA): VOL.3 NO.2 (CD)*

OMEN The (1976) M: JERRY GOLDSMITH -S/T- *VARESE (Pinn)
VSD 6288 (CD) and VSD 5281 (CD) VSC 5281 (MC)*
'O Fortuna' "Carmina Burana" (CARL ORFF)
see *COLL.62,83,115,138,150,219,*

OMEN II 'Damien' (1978) Music score: JERRY GOLDSMITH
-S/T- *VARESE (Pinn): VSD 6309 (CD)*

OMEN III 'Final Conflict' (1981) Mus: JERRY GOLDSMITH
-S/T- *VARESE (Pinn):VSD 6289 (CD) / VCD 47242 (CD)*

OMEN IV The Awakening' (1991) Music: JONATHAN SHEFFER
-S/T- *VARESE (Pinn): VSD(VSC) 5318 (CD/MC)*

ON DANGEROUS GROUND (1951) Music: BERNARD HERRMANN
-S/T- with 'HANGOVER SQUARE'/'A HATFUL OF RAIN'
TSUNAMI Imp (Silva Screen): TCI 0610 (CD)

ON DEADLY GROUND (1993) Music score: BASIL POLEDOURIS
-S/T- *VARESE (Pinn): VSD 5468 (CD)*

ON HER MAJESTY'S SECRET SERVICE (1969) Music sco: JOHN
BARRY t.song "We Have All The Time In The World"
(J.Barry-Hal David) sung by LOUIS ARMSTRONG -S/T-
EMI: CZ 549 (CD) see also JAMES BOND INDEX p.346
see *COLL.26,28,33,36,45,46,47,73,222,*

ON THE AVENUE (FILM CAST 1937) -S/T- *with* DICK POWELL-
SOUND TRACK FACTORY (Discov): SFCD 33537 (CD)
also available -S/T- including 'THANKS A MILLION'
SANDY HOOK (Silver Sounds): CDSH(CSH) 2012 (CD/MC)

ON THE BEACH (2000) Music score by CHRISTOPHER GORDON
-S/T- *VARESE (Pinn): VSD 6153 (CD)*

ON THE BUSES (ITV 28/2/69) theme music by TONY RUSSELL
see *COLL.5,125,*

ON THE RECORD (BBC1 1988-96) theme "Allegro" (Divertis
mento No.5 in C, K187)(MOZART) *vers:* Philharmonia
Orchestra (Wright) *NIMBUS: NI 5121 (CD)*

ON THE TOWN (FILM 1949) -S/T- *Imp* + 'ANCHORS AWEIGH'
BLUE MOON (Discovery): BMCD 7007 (CD)
ON THE TOWN (MUSICAL 1945) Music: LEONARD BERSTEIN and
1yr: ADOLPH GREEN-BETTY COMDEN.*ORIG BROADWAY CAST
COLUMBIA (Ten): SMK 60538 (CD)*
ON THE TOWN - songs by Leonard Bernstein-Betty Comden
and Adolph Green
1.STUDIO RECORD ST.LOUIS SYMPHONY ORCH Felix Slatkin
inc: CANDIDE/FANCY FREE.*EMI Eminence:CDEMX 2242 CD*
2.ORIG BROADWAY CAST 1944 VARIOUS ARTISTS
Columbia Masterworks (Ten): SK 60538 (CD)
3.ORIG LONDON CAST 1963 CAROL ARTHUR-ELLIOTT GOULD-
ROSAMUND GREENWOOD..*SONY BROADWAY:SMK 53497 (CD)*
4.ORIG MASTERWORKS EDIT (First Complete R) GREGG
EDELMAN-TIM FLAVIN-ETHAN FREEMAN-KIM CRISWELL-JUDY
KAYE-VALERIE MASTERSON *TER Koch:CDTER2 1217 (2CD)*
ON YOUR TOES (REVIV.BROADWAY CAST 1983) Mus R.RODGERS
L.HART *TER (Koch): CDTER 1063 (CD)*
ON YOUR TOES (CLASSIC MUSICALS SERIES) *feat:* EUGENE J.
ANTHONY-BETTY ANN GROVE-MARY C.ROBARE-LARA TEETER
+ songs from 'PAL JOEY' *KOCH INT: 34082-2 (CD)*
ONCE AND AGAIN (USA/SKY1 24/08/2000) music: W.G.SNUFFY
WALDEN on 'MUSIC BY..' *BMG IMP: 01934 11424-2 (CD)*
ONCE ON THIS ISLAND sgs: Lynn AHRENS-Stephen FLAHERTY
1.ORIG LONDON CAST 1994 VARIOUS ARTISTS
TER (Koch): CDTER 1224 (CD)
2.ORIG BROADWAY CAST 1990 VARIOUS ARTS *RCA IMPORT
(Silva Screen) 60595-2 (CD) 60595-4 (MC)*
ONCE UPON A TIME IN AMERICA (1984) Music score compos.
and conducted by ENNIO MORRICONE - *special edition
RESTLESS (BMG): 74321 61976-2 (CD)*
see *COLL.97,177,178,*
ONCE UPON A TIME IN THE WEST (1968) Music score by
ENNIO MORRICONE -S/T- complete with 'A FISTFUL OF
DOLLARS' (1964) /'FOR A FEW DOLLARS MORE' (1965)
RCA VICTOR (BMG): 74321 66040-2 (CD)
see *COLL.61,176,177,178,277,279,*
ONCE WERE WARRIORS (1994) Music sco: MURRAY GRINDLEY
and MURRAY McNABB -S/T- feat Various Artists on
MILAN (BMG): 74321 24902-2 (CD)
ONE EYED JACKS (1961) Music score: HUGO FRIEDHOFER
-S/T- *TSUNAMI Germ (Silva Screen): TSU 0114 (CD)*
ONE FINE DAY (1996) Mus sco: JAMES NEWTON HOWARD -S/T-
COLUMBIA (Ten): 486 910-2 (CD)
ONE FLEW OVER THE CUCKOO'S NEST (1975) Music sco: JACK
NITZSCHE -S/T- *FANTASY Imp FCD 4531 (CD) deleted
MOVING IMAGE (Cargo): MIE 001 (LP)*
ONE FOOT IN THE GRAVE (BBC1 4/1/1990-1995) theme song
by ERIC IDLE on Coll 'ERIC IDLE SINGS MONTY PYTHON'
BMG IMPORTS (BMG):74321 76082-2 (CD) final episode
song "End Of The Line" TRAVELING WILBURYS *deleted*
ONE FROM THE HEART (1982) Mus/Songs: TOM WAITS-CRYSTAL
GAYLE -S/T- re-iss *SONY MUSIC (SM):467 609-2 (CD)*

ONE GAME The (Central 4/6/88) theme mus "Saylon Dola"
NIGEL HESS sung CHAMELEON *see COLL.4,137,*
ONE MAN AND HIS DOG (BBC2 1976-1999) title theme music
composed by ALAN BENSON *unavailable*
ONE MAN'S HERO (1999) Music score: ERNEST TROOST -S/T-
CITADEL IMPRT (HOT): STC 77126 (CD)
ONE MILLION YEARS BC (1966) Music sc: MARIO NASCIMBENE
+ 'WHEN DINOSAURS RULED THE EARTH'/'CREATURES THE
WORLD FORGOT' *LEGEND (S.Screen): LEGEND CD13 (CD)*
ONE MORE KISS (1999) Music score: JOHN MURPHY-DAVID A.
HUGHES -S/T- *SILVA SCREEN (Koch): FILMCD 325 (CD)*
ONE NIGHT STAND (1997) Music score: MIKE FIGGIS -S/T-
VERVE (Univ): 539 025-2 (CD)
ONE TOUGH COP (1997) Music sco: BRUCE BROUGHTON -S/T-
INTRADA (S.Screen/Koch): MAF 7084CD (CD)
ONE TRICK PONY (1980) Music score: PAUL SIMON -S/T-
WB (TEN): K4-56846 (MC) K2-56846 (CD)
ONE TRUE THING (1998) Music sco: CLIFF EIDELMAN -S/T-
VARESE (Pinn): VSD 5972
ONEDIN LINE The (BBC1 15/10/1971) theme music "Adagio"
(love theme) from ballet 'SPARTACUS'(KHACHATURIAN)
see COLL.42,195,200,
ONEGIN (1999) Music score by MAGNUS FIENNES *feat* LOYKO
-S/T- on *MILAN (BMG IMPT): 74321 72987-2 (CD)*
ONLY FOOLS AND HORSES (BBC1 8/9/1981-) theme composed
& sung by JOHN SULLIVAN *unavailable*
ONLY THE LONELY: Roy Orbison Story (O.LONDON CAST 1995)
LARRY BRANSON *FIRST NIGHT (Pinn): ORCD 6054 (CD)*
OPERA (Terror At The Opera) (87) Music: ROGER & BRIAN
ENO-BILL WYMAN & extracts from var.Operas -S/T-
CINEVOX Italy Import (Silva Screen): CIA 5074 (CD)
OPERA SAUVAGE FRENCH TV Music score: VANGELIS -S/T- on
import: *POLYDOR (IMS-Poly): E.829 663.2 (CD)*
OPERATION DUMBO DROP (1995) Music by DAVID NEWMAN
-S/T- *EDEL-HOLLYWOOD (Vital) 012 032-2HWR (CD)*
OPERATION GOOD GUYS (BBC2 29/12/1997) series theme mus:
"Ready Or Not" performed by FEELYBOOTH -S/T- on
BBC WORLDWIDE (Pinn): WMSF 6027-2
OPPOSITE OF SEX The (1998) Music score: MASON DARING
-S/T- *DARING (Direct): DARINGCD 3034 (CD)*
OPRAH WINFREY SHOW The (USA/BBC2 96/97) end theme song
"Ten Years" composed/sung by PAUL SIMON on Coll:
'CARNIVAL!' *RCA Vict (BMG): 74321 44769-2 (CD)*
ORANGES ARE NOT THE ONLY FRUIT - *see COLL.202,*
ORCHESTRA! (C4 6/1/91) Sir GEORG SOLTI & DUDLEY MOORE
Orchestral Music -S/T- *DECCA:430 838-2(CD) -4(MC)*
ORCHESTRA WIVES (1942 MUSICAL) *with* GLENN MILLER BAND
RAY EBERLE *includ.songs from* 'SUN VALLEY SERENADE'
TARGET (BMG): CD 60002 (CD)
ORDINARY DECENT CRIMINAL (2000) Music by DAMON ALBARN
including tracks by BIS and SHACK -S/T- on
EAST WEST (TEN): 7567 83316-2 (CD) -4 (MC)
ORDINARY PEOPLE (1980) Theme 'Canon In D' (PACHELBEL)
on COLL.85,271,

ORIGINAL GANGSTAS (1996) RAP FILM -S/T- LUNIZ-ICE T-
SMOOTH-JUNIOR MAFIA *VIRGIN (EMI): CDVUS 104 (CD)*
ORIGINAL SIN (2001) Music score by TERENCE BLANCHARD
GOLD CIRCLE (PROPER): GC 3000-2 (CD)
ORLANDO (1992) Music: SALLY POTTER-DAVID MOTION-JIMMY
SOMERVILLE -S/T- *VARESE (Pinn): VSD 5413 (CD)*
ORPHEUS IN THE UNDERWORLD (MUSICAL OPERETTA) Music by
Jacques OFFENBACH / English text by S.Wilson- D.
Pountney - *English National Opera* (Mark Elder) on
TER (Koch):CDTER 1134 HIGHLIGHTS: *CDTEO 1008 (CD)*
OSCAR AND LUCINDA (1998) Mus score THOMAS NEWMAN -S/T-
SONY Classics: SK 60088 (CD)
OSCAR'S ORCHESTRA (ITV 12/9/95) var.classical music
Mozart-Glinka-Chopin-Tchaikovsky-Rimsky Korsakov-
-S/T- *ERATO (WEA Class): 0630 11865-2 (CD) -4 (MC)*
OSMOSIS JONES (2001) Music score by RANDY EDELMAN -S/T-
ATLANTIC (TEN): 7567 93034-2 (CD)
OSTERMAN WEEKEND The (1983) Music score: LALO SCHIFRIN
ALEPH (Koch): ALEP 010 (CD)
OTHELLO (1995-O.Parker) Music: CHARLIE MOLE -S/T-
VARESE (Pinn): VSD 5689 (CD)
OTHELLO Music score: ELLIOT GOLDENTHAL
VARESE (Pinn): VSD 5942 (CD)
OTHER PEOPLE'S CHILDREN (BBC2 10/09/2000) Music by ROB
LANE with CRYSTAL HAYES club singer
BBC WORLDWIDE (Pinn): WMSF 6032-2 (CD)
OTHER The (1972) Music score: JERRY GOLDSMITH score w:
'MEPHISTO WALTZ' *VARESE (Pinn): VSD 5851 (CD)*
OTHERS (Los Otros) (2001) Music by ALEJANDRO AMENABAR
-S/T- *SONY CLASSICS (TEN): SK 89705 (CD)*
OUR FRIENDS IN THE NORTH (BBC2 15/1/96 and 19/7/97)
theme/incidental score by COLIN TOWNS *unavailable*
-S/T- *(V.ARTS) TELSTAR TV (TEN): TTV(CD)(MC) 2922*
OUR MAN FLINT (1965) Music score: JERRY GOLDSMITH also
'IN LIKE FLINT' *VARESE: VSD 5935 (CD) see COLL.75,*
OUR TUNE (SIMON BATES, R1) "Romeo & Juliet Love Theme"
(NINO ROTA) *SILVA SCREEN (Koch): FILMCD 200 (CD)*
OUT OF AFRICA (1986) Music JOHN BARRY + Melissa Manche
ster-Al Jarreau -S/T- *MCA (UNI): MCLD(MCLC) 19092*
ROYAL SCOTT.NAT.ORCH *VARESE (Pinn): VSD 5816 (CD)*
see COLL.26,30,32,68,73,146,195,
OUT OF IRELAND (1995) *feat* SEAMUS EGAN-MICK MOLONEY-
EILEEN IVOR *SHANACHIE (Direct/Koch):*
SHANCD 79092 (CD) SHANMC 79092 (MC)
OUT OF SIGHT (1997) Music score: DAVID HOLMES -S/T-
MCA (UNI): MCD 11799 (CD)
OUT OF THE CLOUDS (1954) *see COLL.9,*
OUT OF THIS WORLD (1) songs: Cole Porter
1.ORIG NEW YORK CAST 1995 *featur:* ANDREA MARTIN-MARY
ANN LAMB *DRG (New Note-Pinn): DRGCD 94764 (CD)*
2.ORIG BROADWAY CAST 1950 *feat:* CHARLOTTE GREENWOOD-
WILLIAM REDFIELD-WILLIAM EYTHE-PRISCILLA GILLETTE-
BARBARA ASHLEY-DAVID BURNS *SONY: SK 48223 (CD)*
OUT OF THIS WORLD (2) (ITV 24/6/62) *see COLL.24,131,*

OUT OF TOWNERS (1999) Music score by MARC SHAIMAN
-S/T- *MILAN-RCA (BMG): 74321 67193-2 (CD)*
OUTBREAK (1995) Music score: JAMES NEWTON HOWARD
-S/T- *VARESE (Pinn): VSD 5599 (CD)*
OUTER LIMITS 1 (USA TV 1963) Music: DOMINIC FRONTIERE
see COLL.38,84,219,243,
OUTER LIMITS 2 (USA TV 1995) Music: MARK MANCINA-JOHN
VAN TONGREN *SONIC IMAGES (Greyhound):SI 8604 (CD)*
OUTLAND (1981) Music by JERRY GOLDSMITH -S/T- + music
from 'CAPRICORN ONE' *GNP USA (ZYX):GNPD 8035 (CD)*
GNP-5 8035 (MC) also *WB (TEN): 9362 47881-2 (CD)*
OVERLANDERS The (1946) Music sco: JOHN IRELAND / West
Australian S.O.(David MEASHAM) *UNICORN KANCHANA*
(Harmonia Mundi): UKCD 2062 (CD) see *COLL.48,*
OWEN MD (BBC1 1970) theme mus: "Sleepy Shores" by
JOHNNY PEARSON *see COLL.3,172,200,*
P ACIFIC BLUE (USA) Music by CHRISTOPHER FRANKE -S/T-
SONIC IMAGES (Silva Screen): SI 8700 (CD)
PACIFIC OVERTURES - songs by Stephen Sondheim
1.ENGLISH NATIONAL OPERA CAST *TER (Koch): CDTER*
1151 (CD Highlights) CDTER2 1152 (2CD Complete)
PADDINGTON GREEN (BBC1 28/12/1998) music by GUY DAGUL
version by JACKIE McAULIFFE on 'Forgotten Dreams'
DECCA (Univ): 466 566-2 (CD) -4 (MC)
PAINT YOUR WAGON *sgs:* Alan Jay Lerner-Frederick Loewe
1. Film Soundtrack 1969 *w:* LEE MARVIN-CLINT EASTWOOD
-S/T- *reissued on MCA (UNI): MCLD 19310 (CD)*
2. Orig Broadway Cast 1951 JAMES BARTON-OLGA ST.JOHN
-TONY BAVAAR *RCA (BMG): GD 60243 (CD)*
PAJAMA GAME The - Songs by RICHARD ADLER-JERRY ROSS
1.HIGHLIGHTS STUDIO RECORDING 1998
NATIONAL SYMPHONY ORCH (JOHN OWEN EDWARDS) *feat:*
JUDY KAYE-RON RAINES-KIM CRISWELL-AVERY SALTZMAN
TER (Koch): CDTEH 6004 (CD)
2.First Complete Recording JUDY KAYE-RON RAINES-KIM
CRISWELL-AVERY SALTZMAN-BROOKE ALMY-DAVID GREEN-
NAT.S.O.JOHN OWEN EDWARDS *TER: CDTER2 1232 (2CD)*
3.**FILM MUSICAL 1957** *with:* DORIS DAY -S/T- inc.songs
from 'CALAMITY JANE' *COLUMBIA (TEN):501 871-2 (CD)*
4.**ORIG BROADWAY CAST 1954** *w:* John Raitt-JANIS PAIGE-
EDDIE FOY JNR-CAROL HANEY-RETA SHAW-RALPH DUNN
SONY CLASSICS (TEN): SMK 89253 (CD)
PAL JOEY - songs by Richard Rodgers and Lorenz Hart
1.REVIVAL LONDON CAST 1980 *with:* SIAN PHILLIPS-DENIS
LAWSON and Company
<u>Highlights</u>: *SHOWTIME (MCI-THE): SHOW(CD)(MC) 008*
<u>Complete</u>: *TER (Koch): (CD)(ZC)TER 1005 (CD/MC)*
2.BROADWAY CAST OF 1952   HAROLD LANG-VIVIENNE SEGAL
HELEN GALLAGHER-LIONEL STANDER-PATRICIA NORTHROP-
ELAINE STRITCH *EMI ANGEL ZDM 764696-2 (CD)*
3.CLASSIC MUSICALS SERIES *feat:* DENIS LAWSON-
SIAN PHILLIPS-DANIELLE CARSON-DARLENE JOHNSON etc
+songs from 'ON YOUR TOES' *KOCH INT: 34082-2 (CD)*
PALLISERS (BBC1 19/1/74) HERBERT CHAPPELL *see COLL.42,*

PALOOKAVILLE - see *COLL.202*,
PAN TADEUSZ (1999 Poland) Music score by WOJCIECH
   KILAR -S/T- on *POMATON (EMI): 72434 99949-2 (CD)*
PANAMA HATTIE (1942) inc.songs by COLE PORTER
   recording also incl.extracts from 'ANYTHING GOES'
   *SANDY HOOK (Silver Sounds): CDSH 2043 (CD) also
   available* with 'BLOOD AND SAND' (1941,A.Newman)
   GREAT MOVIE THEMES (BMG): CD 60047 (CD)
PANORAMA (BBC1 1953-2001) Various Themes including
   1980-2000 Theme "Aujourd Hui C'est Toi" from
   'A MAN AND A WOMAN' (66-FRANCIS LAI) available
   -S/T- MUSIDISC (Pinn): 10129-2 (CD) -4 (MC)
PAPER CHASE (1973) Music score: JOHN WILLIAMS on
   'POSEIDON ADVENTURE' *(Ltd edition import) on
   RETROGRADE (S.Screen/MFTM): FSMCD Vol.1 No.2 (CD)*
PAPER CHASE (USA TV) see *COLL.247*,
PAPER TIGER (1974) Music score: ROY BUDD -S/T- on
   CINEPHILE-CASTLE (Pinn): CINCD 012 (CD)
PAPILLON (1973) Music score: JERRY GOLDSMITH -S/T-
   SILVA SCREEN (Koch): FILMCD 029 (CD) see *COLL.61*,
PARADE (ORIGINAL BROADWAY CAST 1998)
   Songs by JASON ROBERT BROWN / ORIG CAST RECORDING
   RCA VICTOR (BMG): 09026 633780-2 (CD)
PARADINE CASE The (1947) Music score: FRANZ WAXMAN sel
   'Hollywood Piano Concertos' *Koch Int: 37225-2 (CD)*
PARADISE HAWAIIAN STYLE see PRESLEY FILM INDEX p.348
PARADISE ROAD (1996) Music: DVORAK and other classics
   -S/T- SONY CLASSICS: SK 63026 (CD)
PARENT TRAP The (1998) Music sco: ALAN SILVESTRI -S/T-
   -S/T- (songs) HOLLYWOOD (Univ): 162 167-2 (CD)
PARIS BLUES (1961) Music by DUKE ELLINGTON and others
   -S/T- re-issue RYKODISC (Vital): RCD 10713 (CD)
PARIS TEXAS (1984) Original Songs by RY COODER -S/T-
   WB (TEN): 9362 48089-2 (CD) also 925 270-2 (CD)
PARKINSON (BBC1 1970-81 & 1997-2001) see *COLL.283*,
PARRISH (1961) Music score: MAX STEINER see *COLL.239*,
PART OF YOUR WORLD (2000) Music score by
   -S/T- VARESE (Pinn): VSD 6146 (CD)
PARTRIDGE FAMILY The (USA TV 70s) see *COLL.243*,
PARTY The (1968) Music score: HENRY MANCINI -S/T-
   reissue with score from 'THE GREAT RACE' (1965) on
   RCA CAMDEN (BMG): 74321 82238-2 (CD)
PARTY OF 5 (1997) Music sco: STEVEN CAHILL -S/T- V/A
   WEA: 9362 46431-2(CD) -S/T- EMI UK: PRMDCD 32(CD)
PARTY PARTY (1983) Music by Various Arts -S/T- *reiss:
   SPECTRUM (Univ): 551 440-2 (CD)*
PASSAGE TO INDIA (1985) MAURICE JARRE see *COLL.153,154*,
PASSION - Songs by STEPHEN SONDHEIM
   (1) O.LONDON CAST 1996-MICHAEL BALL-MARIA FRIEDMAN
   FIRST NIGHT (Pinn): CASTCD 61 (CD) CASTC 61 (MC)
   (2) O.BROADWAY CAST 1994 *w:* DONNA MURPHY & Company
   EMI CLASSICS: CDQ 555 251-2 (CD)
PASSION FISH (1993) Music score: MASON DARING -S/T-
   DARING (Project-CMD-ADA):DRCD 3008 (CD)

PASSION OF MIND (1999) Music score by RANDY EDELMAN
-S/T- *MILAN (BMG IMPORTS): 74321 75917-2 (CD)*
PASSIONATE FRIENDS (1948) *see COLL.9,*
PASSPORT TO PIMLICO (1949) *see COLL.22,161,*
PAT GARRETT & BILLY THE KID (1973) Songs: BOB DYLAN
-S/T- reiss *SONY M: CD 32098 (CD) 40-32098 (MC)*
PATCH OF BLUE, A (1965) Music score: JERRY GOLDSMITH
-S/T- *INTRADA (Koch/S.Screen): MAF 7076CD (CD)*
PATIENCE (operetta) - songs by Gilbert and Sullivan
   1.D'OYLE CARTE OPERA CHORUS AND ORCHESTRA 1994
    TER (Koch): CDTER2 1213 (2CD)
   2.D'OYLY CARTE OPERA COMPANY New Symph.Or.Of London
    (Is.Godfrey) *LONDON (Univ): 425 193-2 (CDx2)*
PATRIOT The (2000) Music score by JOHN WILLIAMS -S/T-
   HOLLYWOOD-EDEL (Vital): 011 244-2HWR (CD)
PATTON (1970) Music score: JERRY GOLDSMITH
   1. *with* 'FLIGHT OF THE PHOENIX' (De VOL, 1966) on
    RETROGRADE (S.Screen/MFTM): FSMCD Vol.2 No.2 (CD)
   2. *with* 'TORA TORA TORA'(GOLDSMITH, 1970) on
    VARESE (Pinn): VSD 5796 (CD) see COLL.1,115,265,
PAUL TEMPLE (BBC1 23/11/69) theme music: RON GRAINER
   see COLL.6,100,119,
PAULIE: A PARROT'S TALE (1998) Music sco: JOHN DEBNEY
   feat LOS LOBOS -S/T- *VARESE (Pinn): VSD 5936 (CD)*
PAVILION OF WOMEN (2000) Music score by CONRAD POPE
   VARESE (Pinn): VSD 6245 (CD)
PAY IT FORWARD (2000) Music score by THOMAS NEWMAN
   -S/T- (score) *VARESE (Pinn): VSD 6195 (CD)*
PAYBACK (1998) Music score: CHRIS BOARDMAN -S/T- on
   VARESE (Pinn): VSD 6003 (CD)
PEACEMAKER The (1997) Music score: HANS ZIMMER
   -S/T- *DREAMWORKS (BMG): DRD 50027 (CD)*
PEAK PRACTICE (NEW SERIES ITV1 25/10/2001) orig music
   by CRAIG PRUESS and theme by JOHN ALTMAN new -S/T-
   NEWSOUND (Pinn): N 2K 038 (CD)
PEAK PRACTICE (ORIG SER.ITV 10/5/1993) mus:JOHN ALTMAN
   -S/T- *SOUNDTRACKS EMI GOLD: 521 943-2 (CD)*
   see COLL.42,172,
PEANUTS (USA TV) *see COLL.243,*
PEANUTS BANK FOOTS THE BILL (1995) -S/T- Import on
   COLOSSEUM (Pinn): CST 348053 (CD)
PEARL HARBOUR (2001) Musi score by HANS ZIMMER -S/T-
   WB (TEN): 9362 48113-2 (CD) -4 (MC)
PECKER (1998) Music score by STEWART COPELAND -S/T- on
   RCA VICTOR (BMG): 09026 63339-2 (CD)
PEG (O.LONDON CAST 1984) Songs: DAVID HENEKER *featur:*
   SIAN PHILLIPS *TER (Koch): CDTER 1024 (CD)*
PENDRAGON composed by PETER ALLWOOD / Recording by the
   NATIONAL YOUTH MUSIC THEATRE COMPANY on
   TER (Koch): CDTER 21282 (2CD)
PENNIES FROM HEAVEN (BBC2 7/2/90 prev.shown 1/12/1978)
   1930's music re-recorded from orig 78's / 65 songs
   CONNOISS (Pinn): POTTCD 300 (2CD) POTTMC 300 (2MC)
   see also entry 'SINGING DETECTIVE'

PEOPLE'S CENTURY (BBC2 13/9/95) t.music by ZBIGNIEW
 PRIESNER other mus by ORLANDO GOUGH-FIACHRA TRENCH
 DEBBIE WISEMAN -S/T- *VIRGIN (EMI): CD(TC)VIP 177*
PEPE (1960)SHIRLEY JONES-MAURICE CHEVALIER-SAMMY DAVIS
 JNR-ANDRE PREVIN-BING CROSBY-BOBBY DARIN-JUDY
 GARLAND *COLL CHOICE (Sil.Sounds) WSCCM 0113-2 (CD)*
PERCY (1971) Music: RAY DAVIES Songs sung by The KINKS
 -S/T- *CASTLE Classics (Pinn): ESMCD 510 (CD)*
PERDITA DURANGO (1998) Music score by SIMON BOSWELL
 -S/T- (Var.Arts) *ARISTA (BMG): 74321 54116-2 (CD)*
PERFECT MURDER,A (1997) Music sco: JAMES NEWTON HOWARD
 -S/T- *VARESE (Pinn): VSD 5946 (CD)*
PERFECT SCOUNDRELS (TVS from 22/4/90) mus (2nd ser) by
 NIGEL HESS see *COLL.137,*
PERFECT STORM The (2000) Music score by JAMES HORNER
 -S/T- *SONY CLASS (TEN) SK 89282 (CD) SM 89282 (MC)*
PERFECT STRANGERS (BBC2 10/05/2001) Music by ADRIAN
 JOHNSTON -S/T- *BBC WORLDWIDE (Pinn):WMSF 6051-2 CD*
PERFECT STRANGERS (USA TV) see *COLL.247,*
PERFORMANCE (1970) Music score: JACK NITZSCHE Songs by
 RANDY NEWMAN-RY COODER-MERRY CLAYTON-BUFFY SAINTE
 MARIE-LAST POETS -S/T- *WB (TEN): 7599 26400-2 (CD)*
PERILS OF PENELOPE PITSTOP see *COLL.259,*
PERRY MASON (USA TV) Music theme by FRED STEINER
 see *COLL.24,77,83,124,242,261,*
PERSONALS ORIG.LONDON CAST (1998) *feat* DAVID BARDSLEY-
 MARTIN CALLAGHAN-MARCUS ALLEN COOPER-CHRISTINA FRY
 RIA JONES-SUMMER ROGNLIE *TER (Koch): CDTER 1254 CD*
PERSUADERS The (ITV 17/9/71-72) theme mus: JOHN BARRY
 see *COLL.3,26,30,36,83,200,250,*
PERVIRELLA (1997) Music score: FRANCOIS EVANS -S/T-
 DIONYSUS (Cargo): ID 123369CD (CD) ID 123369 (LP)
PETE KELLY'S BLUES (USA TV) see *COLL.245,*
PETE'S DRAGON - see WALT DISNEY INDEX p.341
PETER AND THE WOLF (1996) SERGEI PROKOFIEV *feat.voices*
 KIRSTIE ALLEY-ROSS MALINDER-LLOYD BRIDGES *with the*
 RCA SYMPHONY ORCHESTRA (cond;Daughterty)
 RCA VICTOR Gold Seal (BMG): 74321 31869-2 (CD)
PETER GUNN (USA TV 1959) Music score by HENRY MANCINI
 TV -S/T- *BUDDAH-RCA (BMG): 74321 69203-2 (CD)*
 also on FRESH SOUNDS (Disc): FSCD 2009 (CD)
 'MORE MUSIC FROM PETER GUNN' Henry Mancini on *RCA*
 (BMG): 74321 29857-2 (CD) see *COLL.170,243,*
PETER PAN (FILM 1953) Music: OLIVER WALLACE-PAUL SMITH
 DISNEY-EDEL (Vital) 017 582-2 (CD) -4 (MC)
PETER PAN - songs by MOOSE CHARLAP and CAROLYN LEIGH +
 add.material: JULE STYNE-BETTY COMDEN-ADOLPH GREEN
 1.*TER* STUDIO REC.1998 CATHY RIGBY-PAUL SCHOEFFLER-
 JENNY AGUTTER-HELEN HOBSON-LISA SAGARDIA
 JAY-TER (SSD): CDJAY 1352 (CD)
 2.O.LONDON CAST 1994 *feat* RON MOODY-NICOLA STAPLETON
 & Co *FIRST NIGHT (Pinn): CASTCD 46 (CD)*
PETER'S FRIENDS (1992) The Album (Various Artists)
 EPIC (Ten): MOODCD 27 (CD)

PETTICOAT JUNCTION (USA TV) *see COLL.242,*
PEYTON PLACE (USATV 1957) Music score: FRANZ WAXMAN
  new rec by ROYAL NATIONAL SCOTTISH ORCH conducted
  by FREDERIC TALGORN *VARESE (Pinn): VSD 6070 (CD)*
  see COLL.24,74,246,253,270,
PHANTOM OF THE OPERA (1) songs by Andrew Lloyd Webber
  Charles Hart-Richard Stilgoe see LONDON STAGE SHOWS
  1.ORIG LONDON CAST 1986 *with:* MICHAEL CRAWFORD-SARAH
    BRIGHTMAN *POLYDOR: 543 928-2 (2CD) 831 273-2 (2CD)*
  2.HIGHLIGHTS *831 563-2(CD) -5(DCC) POLH(C)33 (MC/LP)*
  3.STUDIO RECORD 1993   GRAHAM BICKLEY-JOHN BARROWMAN
    CLAIRE MOORE-ETHAN FREEMAN cond: John Owen Edwards
    Complete: *JAY-TER (SSD): CDJAY 1235 (CD)*
    Highlights: *CURTAIN CALL-MCI (DISC): CURTCD 011 CD*
  4.CARLTON SHOWS COLL.1993 Studio Record w:PAUL JONES
    STEPHANIE LAWRENCE-CARL WAYNE-FIONA HENDLEY & Comp
    CARLTON: PWKS 4164 (CD) PWKMC 4164 (MC)
    also contains songs from 'ASPECTS OF LOVE'
  5.CLASSIC MUSICALS SERIES *feat:*GRAHAM BICKLEY-CLAIRE
    MOORE-JOHN BARROWMAN-MUNICH SYMPH.ORCH+ *songs from*
    'CATS' *KOCH Int: 34078-2 (CD)*
PHANTOM OF THE OPERA (2) (1925 FILM *featur.*LON CHANEY)
  1.(1996 restoration) Music by Carl Davis conducting
    The CITY of PRAGUE PHILHARMONIC, organ: JOHN BIRCH
    SILVA SCREEN (Koch): FILMCD 193 (CD) + FILMXCD 326
  2.(Studio Recording 1995) music by Rick Wakeman on
    'Phantom Power' *AMBIENT (AMT): A1OM2 (CD)*
  3.(1977 version) Music: Gaylord Carter organ 'Mighty
    Wurlitzer' *NEW WORLD (Conifer): NW 227 (LP) delet.*
PHANTOM OF THE OPERA (1998) Music sco: ENNIO MORRICONE
  DRG IMPRT (Pinn): DRGCD 12620 (CD)
PHANTOM OF THE OPERA (1989) FILM feat: Robert Englund)
  Symphonic music score by Mischa Segal -S/T- on
  SILVA SCREEN (Koch): FILMCD 069 (CD)
PHANTOM OF THE OPERA ON ICE (1996) Mus: ROBERTO DANOVA
  -S/T- *Roberto Danova-PLAZA (Pinn): PZA 008(CD(MC)*
PHAR LAP (1983) Music score: BRUCE ROWLAND -S/T- *IMPORT*
  inc:'ZEUS & ROXANNE' *PERCEPTO USA:PERCEPTO 004 (CD)*
PHAT BEACH (1996) -S/T- *EDEL (Vital) 0022622CIN (CD)*
PHILADELPHIA (1994) Music score: HOWARD SHORE opening
  song by BRUCE SPRINGSTEEN 2 Soundtracks available
  -S/T- Songs *EPIC (SM): 474 998-2(CD) -8 (MD)*
  -S/T- Score deleted *EPIC: 475 800-2 (CD) -4 (MC)*
  see COLL.182,
PHILADELPHIA EXPERIMENT The (1984) Mus: KEN WANNBERG
  -S/T- *also contains score from* 'MOTHER LODE' on
  PROMETHEUS (S.Screen): PCD 121(CD)
PHILADELPHIA STORY The (1940) Music sco: FRANZ WAXMAN
  theme on RCA: GD 80708 (CD)
PI THE MOVIE (1998) Music score: CLINT MANSELL -S/T-
  songs by MASSIVE ATTACK-APHEX TWIN-ORBITAL-GUSGUS
  SILVA SCREEN (Koch): FILMCD 312 (CD)
PIAF (ORIG LONDON CAST 1994) *featuring* ELAINE PAIGE
  WB (TEN): 4509 94641-2 (CD) -4 (MC)

PIANO The (1993) Music score: MICHAEL NYMAN -S/T- on
VENTURE-VIRGIN (EMI): CD(TC)VE 919 (CD/MC)
see COLL.73,188,
PICASSO'S WOMEN (2000) Music score by TOT TAYLOR
-S/T- *TWEED COUTURE (Pinn): TWEEDCD 11 (CD)*
PICKWICK THE MUSICAL CHICHESTER FESTIVAL THEATRE 1993
Songs (Cyril ORNADEL-Leslie BRICUSSE) *featuring:*
HARRY SECOMBE-ALEXANDRA BASTEDO-ROY CASTLE-RUTH
MADOC-GLYN HOUSTON-DAVID CARDY-MICHAEL HOWE & Comp
Highlights: *SHOWTIME (MCI-THE): SHOWCD 023 (CD)*
Complete: *TER (Koch): CDTER 1205 (CD)*
Classic Musicals series *feat:* HARRY SECOMBE
RUTH MADOC-ROY CASTLE-DAVID CARDY-ROBERT MEADMORE
+ *songs from* 'SCROOGE' *KOCH INT: 34081-2 (CD)*
PICNIC (1956) Music sco: GEORGE DUNING -S/T- *MCA USA*
Import (Silva Screen): MCAD 31357 (CD)
PICNIC AT HANGING ROCK *theme on NAXOS: 8551159 (CD)*
PILLOW BOOK The (1996) Music score: BRIAN ENO -S/T-
XIII BIS (Discovery): LBS 197101 (CD)
PINK PANTHER The (1963) Music score by HENRY MANCINI
-S/T- complete with 'RETURN OF THE PINK PANTHER'
RCA CAMDEN (BMG): 74321 66047-2 (CD)
see COLL.83,155,170,200,204,243,
PINK PANTHER The (TV-USA 1970s Cartoon) "Panther Pink
From Head To Toes" by DOUG GOODWIN *unavailable*
PINK PANTHER STRIKES AGAIN (1976) Music: HENRY MANCINI
"Come To Me" sung by TOM JONES -S/T- on
RYKODISC (Vital): RCD 10739 (CD)
PINOCCHIO (1939) M: LEIGH HARLINE-P.SMITH-N.WASHINGTON
-S/T- *DISNEY (B.Vista): WD 75430-2 (CD) -4 (MC)*
see also WALT DISNEY INDEX p.341
PINOCCHIO (1996) Music sco: RACHEL PORTMAN -S/T- *feat*
STEVIE WONDER-JERRY HADLEY & SISSEL and BRIAN MAY
DECCA (Univ.): 452 740-2 (CD) -4 (MC)
PIRATES OF PENZANCE operetta by W.S.Gilbert-A.Sullivan
  1.D'OYLY CARTE OPERA COMPANY 1989 STUDIO RECORDING
  with: MARILYN HILL SMITH and Company
  TER (Koch): CDTER2 1177 (2CD)
  2.O.BROADWAY CAST 1983 : KEVIN KLINE-LINDA RONSTADT
  IMPRT (Silva Screen): WA 601 (CD)
  3.PRO-ARTE ORCHEST (Malcolm Sargent) GLYNDEBOURNE
  FESTIVAL CHOIR Solo: George Baker-James Milligan-
  John Cameron-Richard Lewis *EMI:CMS 764409-2 (2CD)*
  4.D'OYLY CARTE OPERA COMP with RPO cond: I.Godfrey
  LONDON (Univ): 425 196-2 (CDx2) 425 196-4 (MC)
PJ'S The (USA) -S/T- from and inspired by TV series
EDEL-HOLLYWOOD (Vital) 010 089-2HWR
PLAN 9 FROM OUTER SPACE (1956) mus.sup: GORDON ZAHLER
-S/T- *Impt. PERFORMANCE (Greyhound):PERF 391 (LP)*
PLANET OF THE APES (2001) Music score: DANNY ELFMAN
-S/T- *SONY CLASSICS (TEN): SK 89666 (CD)*
PLANET OF THE APES (1968) Music score: JERRY GOLDSMITH
score on *VARESE (Pinn): VSD 5848 (CD)*
see COLL.218,

PLANETS The (BBC) Orig music score by JIM MEACOCK and music from 'The Planets' (Gustav HOLST) -S/T- on *BBC (Pinn): WMSF 60102 (CD)*

PLATOON 1.(1986) Mus: GEORGES DELERUE (rejected orig score) *PROMETHEUS (Silva Screen): PCD 136 (CD)* + complete score 'SALVADOR' see *COLL.87,204,*

PLATOON 2. (1986) Music: GEORGES DELERUE Main theme 'Adagio For Strings' (Samuel BARBER) Vancouver SO -S/T- *ATLANTIC (TEN): 781 742-2 (CD) WX 95 (MC)*

PLAY AWAY / PLAY SCHOOL (BBC1-2 / 1964-88) *MFP:TC-DL 1114 (2MC) see COLL.132,*

PLAY IT TO THE BONE (1999) Music sc: ALEX WURMAN -S/T- (V.ART) *EDEL-HOLLYWOOD (Vital): 010 806-2HWR (CD)*

PLAY ON! (ORIG BROADWAY CAST RECORDING) featuring the songs of DUKE ELLINGTON in 'TWELFTH NIGHT' setting ORIG BROADWAY CAST *VARESE (Pinn): VSD 5837 (CD)*

PLAYER The (1991) Music score: THOMAS NEWMAN -S/T- *VARESE USA (Pinn): VSD 5366 (CD)*

PLAYING BY HEART (1998) Music by JOHN BARRY with CHET BAKER-CHRIS BOTTI -S/T- MOBY/NENEH CHERRY/GOMEZ -S/T- score: *DECCA (Univ): 466 275-2 (CD) -4 (MC)* -S/T- songs: *EMI Soundtracks: 520 510-2 (CD)*

PLAYING THE FIELD (BBC1 8/3/1998-2001) series title song sung by ALISON MOYET *unavailable*

PLEASANTVILLE (1998) Music score by RANDY NEWMAN -S/T- score: *VARESE (Pinn): VSD 5988 (CD)* -S/T- songs: *COLUMBIA (Ten): 492 594-2 (CD)*

PLEASE SIR (LWT 68) theme by SAM FONTEYN see *COLL.2,*

PLEASURE ISLAND (ITV 09/05/2000) theme by ONE LOVE -S/T- *GLOBAL TV (BMG): RADCD(RADMC) 165 (2CD/2MC)* -S/T- PLEASURE ISLAND 2001 *JETSTAR:JSCD 1015 (CD)*

PLEDGE The (2000) Music by HANS ZIMMER-CLAUS BADELT -S/T- VAR.ARTISTS *BMG IMPORTS: 74321 89822-2 (CD)*

PLUNKETT & MACLEANE (1997) Music sco: CRAIG ARMSTRONG "Houses In Motion" sung by LEWIS PARKER-HELEN WHITE -S/T- *MELANKOLIC-VIRGIN: CDSAD 7 (CD)*

PLYMOUTH ADVENTURE (1952) Mus.sco by MIKLOS ROSZA -S/T select.inc.'MADAME BOVARY'/'QUO VADIS'/'IVANHOE' *TICKERTAPE USA Impt.(S.Screen): TT 3001 (CD)*

POCAHONTAS (1995) Music score: ALAN MENKEN Songs (Alan MENKEN-Stephen SCHWARTZ) "Colours Of The Wind" by VANESSA WILLIAMS -S/T- *DISNEY-EDEL: 015462-2 (CD)* SEE ALSO DISNEY INDEX p.341

POINT The (1970) Music by HARRY NILSSON -S/T- includ: 'SKIDOO' on *RCA (BMG): 74321 75743-2 (CD)*

POINT BREAK (1991) Music: MARK ISHAM + VARIOUS ARTISTS re-iss: *MCA GEFFEN (BMG): MCLD 19327 (CD)*

POIROT see 'AGATHA CHRISTIE'S POIROT' see *COLL.4,*

POKEMON (SKY1/GMTV 1999) MUSIC FROM THE HIT TV SERIES inc.theme "PokeRap" V.Arts + POKERAP MUSIC VIDEO *KOCH INT: 33362-2 (CD) 33362-4 (MC)*

POKEMON THE FIRST MOVIE (1999) Theme by BILLY CRAWFORD -S/T- inc BRITNEY SPEARS-CHRISTINA AGUILERA-BILLIE EMMA BUNTON etc. *ATLANTIC (Ten): 7567 83261-2 (CD)*

POKEMON 2: THE POWER OF ONE (2000) VARIOUS ARTS -S/T-
ATLANTIC (TEN): 7567 83370-2 (CD)
POKEMON 3: The Ultimate Soundtrack VAR.ARTS.including
INNOSENSE "To Know The Unknown" + TV series music
-S/T- *KOCH INT (KOCH): KOCCD 8296 (CD)*
POLA X (1999) Music composed by SCOTT WALKER -S/T- on
BARCLAY France: 547 608-2 (CD)
POLDARK (BBC1 5/10/1975) *see COLL.42,*
POLICE SQUAD (USA) *see COLL.84,247,*
POLICE STORY (USA) *see COLL.14,246,*
POLICE WOMAN (USA) *see COLL.77,246,*
POLLOCK (2000) Music score by JEFF BEAL -S/T- on
UNITONE (Proper): UTON 5301 (CD)
POLTERGEIST (1982) Music score: JERRY GOLDSMITH -S/T-
EMI GOLD: 821 957-2 (CD) see COLL.121,138,219,
POLTERGEIST: THE LEGACY (1997) mus: MARK MANCINA-JOHN
VAN TONGREN sco: JOHN VAN TONGREN-CHRISTOPHER WARD
SONIC IMAGES (Greyhound-Cargo): SI 8701 (CD)
POPEYE (USACart.40s) theme "I'm Popeye The Sailor Man"
(Sammy Lerner) *see COLL.242,*
POPPIE NON GENA (MUSICAL 83) JOE BOYD / ORIG S.AFRICAN
CAST *reissued May 96 HANNIBAL-RYKODISK (Vital):
HNCD 1351 (CD) HNBC 1351 (MC)*
PORGY AND BESS - songs by George and Ira Gershwin
with DuBose Heyward
  1.FILM MUSICAL 1959 DOROTHY DANDRIDGE-SIDNEY POITIER
-S/T- *SONY Europe (Discovery): CD 70007 (CD)*
  2.Studio HIGHLIGHTS LEONTYNE PRICE-WILLIAM WARFIELD
JOHN W.BUBBLES-McHENRY BOATWRIGHT+Symphonic Dances
to WEST SIDE STORY *RCA (BMG): 74321 24218-2 (CD)*
  3.ORIG BROADWAY CAST 1942 *w:* Todd Duncan-Anne Brown-
Edward Matthews-Helen Dowdy *MCA (UNI):MCLD 19158*
  4.GLYNDEBOURNE FESTIVAL OPERA 1988 WILLARD WHITE-
CYNTHIA HAYMON-DAMON EVANS-BRUCE HUBBARD-LPO(Simon
Rattle) *EMI ANGEL: CDS 556 220-2 (3CDs-Compl) orig
LDB 491 131-2 (2CDs) or CDC 754 325-2 Highlights*
  5.Houston Grand Opera: DONNIE RAY ALBERT-CLAMMA DALE
ANDREW SMITH-WILMA SHAKESNIDER-BETTY LANE and Comp
Complete Rec: *RCA Red Seal (BMG): RD 82109 (3 CDs)*
Highlights Only: *RCA Red Seal (BMG): RD 84680 (CD)*
  6.STUDIO HIGHLIGHTS (1975) WILLARD WHITE-BARBARA
HENDRICKS & Comp with CLEVELAND ORCH & CHOIR cond
LORIN MAAZEL *DECCA (Univ): 436 306-2DH (CD)*
  7.STUDIO RECORDING 'Great Scenes From PORGY & BESS'
LEONTYNE PRICE/WILLIAM WARFIELD/RCA VICTOR ORCHEST
McHENRY BOATWRIGHT/JOHN W.BUBBLES/BARBARA WEBB etc
RCA HIGH PERFORMANCE (BMG): 09026 63312-2 (CD)
PORTERHOUSE BLUE (C4 3/6/87) Title theme by Rick Lloyd
sung by FLYING PICKETTS *see COLL.5,*
PORTRAIT OF A LADY (1996) Music score: WOJCIECH KILAR
plus additional music by FRANZ SCHUBERT -S/T- on
DECCA (Univ): 455 011-2 (CD) -4 (MC)
PORTRAIT OF TERROR (1998) Music score: JOHN OTTMAN
-S/T- *VARESE (Pinn): VSD 5986 (CD)*

POSEIDON ADVENTURE The (1972) Music sco: JOHN WILLIAMS
complete score *(Ltd edit.imp) with* 'PAPER CHASE'
RETROGRADE (S.Screen/MFTM): FSMCD Vol.1 No.2 (CD)
POSTMAN The (1997) Music score: JAMES NEWTON HOWARD
theme song sung by KEVIN COSTNER -S/T- on
WARNER SUNSET (TEN) 9362 46842-2 (CD)
POSTMAN The (Il Postino) (1994) Music sc: LUIS BACALOV
-S/T- *EDEL-HOLLYWOOD (Vital) 012 029-2HWR (CD) and*
-S/T- MILAN (Pinn): 162 209-2 (CD)
POSTMAN PAT (BBC1 1982-2002) music: BRYAN DALY sung by
KEN BARRIE *POST MUSIC (Pinn): PPCD 101 (CD) PMC*
101 (MC) also available '100 RHYMES AND SONGS'
REDROCK (Univ): RKCD 27 (CD) see COLL.132,285,
POT BLACK/JUNIOR P.BLACK (BBC2 1972-86) "Black & White
Rag" (George Botsford) WINIFRED ATWELL *PRESIDENT:*
PLCD 531 (CD) see COLL.101,
POTTER'S WHEEL (BBC 1950's) *see COLL.100,119,*

POWAQQATSI (1988) Music score: PHILIP GLASS -S/T- on
ELEKTRA NONESUCH (TEN): 7559 79192-2 (CD) -4(MC)
POWER The (1967) Music score: MIKLOS ROZSA Suite + mus
ic from 'BEN HUR'/'KING OF KINGS' 12 choral pieces
PROMETHEUS (Silva Screen): PCD 122 (CD)
POWER GAME The (ITV 65) theme music: CYRIL STAPLETON
see COLL.2,24,74,
PRACTICAL MAGIC (1998) Music sco: ALAN SILVESTRI -S/T-
VARIOUS ARTISTS *WARNER: 9362 47253-2 (CD)*
PRAYER FOR THE DYING, A (1988) Orig score: JOHN SCOTT
(replaced by BILL CONTI score) - John Scott vers
available on *JOS (Silva Screen): JSCD 102*
(CD) inc John Scott's score 'WINTER PEOPLE' (1989)
PREACHER'S WIFE The (1996) Music sc: HANS ZIMMER songs
comp/produced by Annie LENNOX/David FOSTER/Trevor
HORN/BABYFACE and performed by WHITNEY HOUSTON
-S/T- *ARISTA (BMG): 74321 44125-2 (CD) -4 (MC)*
-S/T- special ltd ed: *07822 18951-2 (CD) -4 (MC)*
PREACHING TO THE PEVERTED (1997) Various Arts -S/T- on
NAKED (Pinn): PERVCDLP 001 (CD) PERVMCLP 001 (MC)
PRELUDE TO A KISS (1992) Music sco: HOWARD SHORE -S/T-
MILAN (BMG): 11125-2 (CD) 11125-4 (MC)
PRESIDENT'S COUNTRY - *see COLL.254,*
PRESIDENT'S LADY The - *see COLL.1,*
PRESUMED INNOCENT (1990) Music score: JOHN WILLIAMS
-S/T- *VARESE (Pinn): VSD 5280 (CD)*
PRET-A-PORTER (1994) INA KAMOZE-TERENCE TRENT D'ARBY-
CRANBERRIES-M.PEOPLE *COLUMB (Ten): 478 226-2 (CD)*
PRETTY WOMAN (1989) Music by JAMES NEWTON HOWARD -S/T-
EMI USA (EMI): CDP 793492-2 (CD) see COLL.11,
PRICE OF MILK The (2001) Music: RIMSKY KORSAKOV-LIADOV
RACHMANINOV-TCHAIKOVSKY-TCHEREPNIN performed by
MOSCOW SYMPHONY ORCHESTRA cond.by VALERY POLYANSKY
-S/T- *BMG IMPORTS: 74321 84321-2 (CD)*
PRICKLY HEAT (SKY1 11/10/1998) theme mus "Oooie Oooie
Oooie" PRICKLY HEAT *VIRGIN (EMI):VSCDT 1727(CDs)*

PRIDE AND PREJUDICE (BBC1 24/9/95) orig mus.composed
and conducted by CARL DAVIS -S/T- *featuring*
MELVYN TAN (fortepiano) on *EMI: CDEMC 3726 (CD)*

PRIDE AND THE PASSION The (1957) Music: GEORGE ANTHEIL
with 'AGONY & THE ECSTASY' (ALEX NORTH) 75m
CLOUD NINE (BMG-Con): CNS 5001 (CD)

PRIMARY COLORS (1998) Music score: RY COODER -S/T- on
MCA (UNI): MCD 11775 (CD)

PRINCE AMONG ISLANDS, A (ITV 10/5/92) mus CAPERCAILLIE
"Coisich A Ruin" featuring KAREN MATHIESON -*S/T*-
selection on SURVIVAL (BMG): ZT 45394 (MC)

PRINCE AND THE PAUPER (1937) Music sco: ERICH WOLFGANG
KORNGOLD perform.by BRANDENBURG PHILHARMONIC ORCH
(William T.Stromberg) *with* 'ADVENTURES OF MARK
TWAIN' (MAX STEINER) *RCA (BMG): 09026 62660-2 (CD)*
also on VARESE (Pinn): VSD 5207 (CD)

PRINCE AND THE SHOWGIRL 1957 see COLL.7,

PRINCE OF DARKNESS (1988) Music: JOHN CARPENTER & ALAN
HOWARTH -S/T- *COLOSSEUM (Pinn): CST348031 (CD)*
VARESE (Pinn): VCD 47310 (CD)

PRINCE OF EGYPT (1996) Music score: HANS ZIMMER
-S/T- (music sco) *DREAMWORKS (BMG): DRD 50041 (CD)*
-S/T- (nashville) *DREAMWORKS (BMG): DRD 50045 (CD)*
-S/T- (inspirational) *"   (BMG): DRD 50050 (CD)*
see COLL.3,

PRINCE OF FOXES (1949) Music score by ALFRED NEWMAN
FSM CLASSICS (USA Ltd Ed.): FSMCD Vol 2.No.5 (CD)

PRINCE OF PLAYERS (1955) Music score: BERNARD HERRMANN
new recording: MOSCOW SYMPHONY ORCH. (W.Stromberg)
also features music from 'GARDEN OF EVIL' (1954)
MARCO POLO (Select): 8.223841 (CD) see COLL.1,

PRINCE VALIANT (1954) Music score by FRANZ WAXMAN
FSM CLASSICS: FSMCD Vol 2.No.3 (CD) see COLL.1,

PRINCESS BRIDE The (1987) Music score: MARK KNOPFLER
-S/T- *VERTIGO: VERH 53C (MC) 832864-2 (CD)*

PRINCESS DIARIES The (2001) Music score JOHN DEBNEY
-S/T- V.Artists *HOLLYWOOD 9TEN): 0927 43082-2 (CD)*

PRINCESS IDA (GILBERT & SULLIVAN) ORIG 1932 SHOW CAST
GEM-PEARL (Harmonia Mundi): GEM 0144 (CD)

PRINCESS MONONOKE (1999) Music score by JOE HISAISHI
-S/T- *BMG IMPORTS: 74321 71668-2 (CD)*

PRIORY The (C4 09/11/1999) series theme music by
MINT ROYALE *Faith & Hope (Pinn): FHCD 016 (CDs)*

PRISCILLA: QUEEN OF THE DESERT (1994) Mus: GUY CROSS
-S/T- *MOTHER (Univ): 516 937-2 (CD) -4 (MC)*

PRISONER The (ITV 29/9/1967) Theme music: RON GRAINER
score by RON GRAINER-ALBERT ELMS etc.*SILVA SCREEN*
(Koch): FILMCD 042 (V1) FILMCD 084 (V2) FILMCD 126
(Vol.3) see COLL.6,38,83,219,250,

PRISONER CELL BLOCK H (Australia 79-87)(UK 84) theme
"On The Inside" (A.Caswell) LYNNE HAMILTON *DELETED*

PRISONERS OF CONSCIENCE (BBC2 27/11/89) theme music
"Fragile" (G.Sumner) STING 'Nothing Like The Sun'
A.& M. CDA 6402 (CD) AMA 6402 (LP) AMC 6402 (MC)

PRIVATE FILES OF J.EDGAR HOOVER The (1978) Mus score:
MIKLOS ROZSA -S/T- *CITADEL (Hot): STC 77118 (CD)*
PRIVATE LIVES OF ELIZABETH AND ESSEX (1939) Music sco
ERICH WOLFGANG KORNGOLD. *NEW COMPLETE RECORDING on
VARESE (Pinn): VSD 5696 (CD). Selections available
on KOCH: 37302-2 (CD)* with 'JAUREZ'/'The SEA WOLF'
also *SILVA SCREEN: FILMXCD 188* see *COLL.160,240,*
PRIVATE PARTS (1996) Score: VAN DYKE PARKS -S/T- V.Art
W.BROS (TEN): 9362 46477-2 (CD)
PRIZZI'S HONOR (1987) Music score: ALEX NORTH
see *COLL.197,*
PRODUCERS The (1968,Mel Brooks) music sco: JOHN MORRIS
-S/T- + dialogue *RAZOR & TIE (Koch): RE 2147 (CD)*
-S/T- also *SONY CLASSICS: SK 89646 (CD)*
PROOF OF LIFE (2000) Music score: DANNY ELFMAN -S/T-
VARESE (Pinn): VSD 6208 (CD)
PROFESSIONAL The - see 'LEON'
PROFESSIONAL The (1981) Music score by ENNIO MORRICONE
DRG (Pinn): DRGCD 32927 (2CD)
PROFESSIONALS The (LWT 1977-1983) theme LAURIE JOHNSON
LJ'S LONDON BIG BAND *VIRGIN (EMI):VSCDT 1643 (CDs)
VST 1643 (12")* see *COLL.4,153,156,158,250,279,*
PROFESSIONALS The (1966) Music sc: MAURICE JARRE -S/T-
SILVA TREASURY (Koch): SSD 5002 (CD)
PROMENADE (MUSICAL) Music by AL CARMINES Lyrics by
MARIA IRENE FORNES. *ORIG 1969 OFF BROADWAY CAST
RCA (BMG): 09026 63333-2 (CD)*
PROMISES PROMISES songs: Burt Bacharach-Hal David
O.BROADWAY CAST 1968 *feat* JERRY ORBACH-JILL O'HARA
EDWARD WINTER *RYKODISC (Vital): RCD 10750 (CD)*
PROPOSITION The (1998) Music score: STEPHEN ENDELMAN
-S/T- *PHILIPS (Univ): 462 504-2 (CD)*
PROSPERO'S BOOKS (1991) Music: MICHAEL NYMAN -S/T-
PHILIPS (Univ.): 425 224-2 (CD) -4 (MC)
PROTECTORS The (ITC orig 29/9/72) theme mus "Avenues
& Alleyways" sung by TONY CHRISTIE *MCA (UNI):
MCA: MCLD (MCLC) 19204 (CD/MC)* see *COLL.250,*
PROUD REBEL The (1958) M: JEROME MOROSS see 'CARDINAL'

PSYCHO (1960) Music score by BERNARD HERRMANN
new record.by ROYAL SCOTTISH NATIONAL ORCH cond,
Joel McNEELY *VARESE (Pinn): VSD 5765 (CD)*
see *COLL.105,135,136,140,141,142,143,144,*
PSYCHO (1998) Music adapted by DANNY ELFMAN from orig
BERNARD HERRMANN score *VIRGIN IMP: 72438 4765729*
PSYCHO BEACH PARTY (2000) Music score by BEN VAUGHN
-S/T- *NETTWERK (Pinn/Greyh): 62428 40013-2 (CD)*
PSYCHODERELICT (Rock Opera 93) Songs: PETER TOWNSHEND
ATLANTIC/EAST WEST (TEN): 7567 82494-2(CD) -4(MC)
PSYCHOS (C4 06/05/1999) recordings used included
"Pearl's Girls" and "Cherry Pie" by UNDERWORLD on
JUNIOR-TVT (Cargo-Greyhound): TVT 87482 (CD)
PUBLIC EYE (1992) Music score: MARK ISHAM -S/T-
VARESE (Pinn): VSD 5374 (CD)

PULP FICTION (1993) Music by V.Arts -S/T- *REISSUE with*
'RESERVOIR DOGS' *MCA (Univ): MCD 11188 (2CDs)*
MCA (UNI): MCD 11103 (CD) also on SIMPLY VINYL
(Telstar): SVLP 27 (LP) see COLL.90,95,

PUMP UP THE VOLUME (C4 13/11/2001) 'HISTORY OF HOUSE'
COLLECTION *CHANNEL 4 MUS (Univ): C4M 0015-2 (2CD)*

PUMP UP THE VOLUME (FILM 1990) -S/T- feat VAR.ARTISTS
MCA (UNI): MCD 06121 (CD)

PUPPET ON A CHAIN (1970) Music score by PIERO PICCIONE
-S/T- *DC RECORDS (Vit) DC 039CD (CD) DC039LP (LP)*

PURE COUNTRY (1992) Music comp/perf. by GEORGE STRAIT
-S/T- *MCA (UNI): MCD 10651 (CD) MCC 10651 (MC)*

PURE WICKEDNESS (BBC1 14/09/1999) Music by JOHN KEANE
Songs included "Sexy Boy" by AIR on 'MOON SAFARI'
SOURCE-VIRGIN (EMI): CDV(TCV)(MDV) 2848 (CD/MC/md)
also VSCDT 1672 (CDs) VSC 1672 (MC) VST 1672 (12")
end song "Blood Red River" BETH ORTON on 'Central
Reservation' *HEAVENLY (BMG): HVNLP 22 (CD)*

PURELY BELTER (2000) Music: IAN BROUDIE-MICHAEL GIBBS
V.ARTS -S/T- *BOILER HOUSE (BMG): 74321 80248-2 CD*

PURPLE RAIN (1984) Music: PRINCE & REVOLUTION -S/T-
WB (TEN): 759 925 110-2 (CD) -4 (MC) -5 (DCC)

PUSHER (1997) Music score: PETER PETER-POVI KRISTIAN
-S/T- VARIOUS ARTISTS *MCA (UNI): MCD 85013 (CD)*

PUSHING TIN (1999) Music score by ANNE DUDLEY -S/T-
RESTLESS (BMG): 73421 67253-2 (CD)

PUTTING IT TOGETHER (O.USA CAST 1993) Songs (Stephen
SONDHEIM) *featuring* JULIE ANDREWS-STEPHEN COLLINS
RCA (BMG): 09026 61729-2 (CD) -4 (MC)

PYROMANIAC'S LOVE STORY, A (1994) Music score: RACHEL
PORTMAN -S/T- *VARESE (Pinn): VSD 5620 (CD)*

Q MILLIGAN (BBC2 5/9/93) "Q Theme": SPIKE MILLIGAN on
'BRITISH COMEDY CLASSICS' *EMI: ECC 7 (2MC)*

Q THE WINGED SERPENT (1982) Music sc: ROBERT O.RAGLAND
-S/T- *reiss: CAM (SSD): CSE 800128 (CD)*

QB VII (74 Mini-series) Music by JERRY GOLDSMITH -S/T-
INTRADA (S.Screen): MAF 7061D (CD)

QUADROPHENIA (1979) Songs: PETE TOWNSHEND feat WHO
POLYDOR (Univ): 531 971-2 (Complete 2CDs) also on
813 074-2 (2CD's) also: 519 999-2 (CD)
Re-mastered edit.2000 on *POLY-UNIV: 543 691-2 (CD)*

QUANTUM LEAP (USA 89)(BBC2 13/2/90) theme: MIKE POST
-S/T- *GNP (ZYX) GNPD 8036(CD) GNP-5 8036(MC)*
see *COLL.14,38,203,221,248,*

QUATERMASS / QUATERMASS II(1957) see *COLL.5,127,215*

QUATERMASS AND THE PIT see *COLL.126,207,*

QUATERMASS EXPERIMENT The (1955) Music: JAMES BERNARD
see *COLL.207,* BBC TV theme "Mars"'Planets' (HOLST)

QUEER AS FOLK (C4 23/02/1999) score mus.by MURRAY GOLD
unavailable / 32 trk.V.ARTS.select.incl: BLONDIE/
RUFF DRIVERZS/ALEXIA/ULTRA NATE/WEATHER GIRLS etc.
Volume 1 orig.ser. *ALMIGHTY (BMG): ALMYCD 28 (2CD)*
Volume 2 2nd series (music from & inspired by) on
CHANNEL 4 MUSIC (C4): C4M 40001-2 (2CD)

QUEER AS FOLK (USA 2001 series) -S/T- VARIOUS ARTISTS
  BMG IMPORTS: 09026 63769-2 (CD)
QUEST (1996) Music score: RANDY EDELMAN -S/T- on
  VARESE (Pinn): VSD 5716 (CD)
QUESTION OF SPORT, A (BBC1 1970-2001) theme music by
  RICHIE CLOSE *see COLL.101,*
QUESTION TIME (BBC1 1979-2001) theme music composed
  by STANLEY MYERS *unavailable*
QUICK AND THE DEAD The (1994) Mus sco: ALAN SILVESTRI
  -S/T- *VARESE (Pinn): VSD 5595 (CD)*
QUICKSILVER (1986) Music sco: TONY BANKS + 'Lorca
  & The Outlaws' *Charisma (VIRGIN): CASCD 1173 (CD)*
QUIDAM (SHOW 2000 by CIRQUE DU SOLEIL) Music by BENOIT
  JUTRAS -S/T- *RCA VICTOR (BMG): 09026 68601-2 (CD)*
QUIET AMERICAN The (1958) Music sco: MARIO NASCIMBENE
  -S/T- *'ROOM AT THE TOP'/'BAREFOOT CONTESSA'*
  DRG (Pinn): DRGCD 32961 (CD)
QUIET MAN The (1952) Music sco: VICTOR YOUNG *complete*
  orig score DUBLIN SCREEN ORCH (Kenneth Alwyn)
  SILVA CLASSICS (Koch): SSD 1118 / also on SCANNAN
  (Koch): SFC 1501 (CD) includes 'SAMSON & DELILAH'
  VARESE (Pinn): VSD 5497 (CD) see COLL.69,258,284,
QUILLER MEMORANDUM The (1966) Music score: JOHN BARRY
  see COLL.26,
QUILLS (2000) Music score by STEPHEN WARBECK -S/T- on
  BMG IMPORTS: 09026 63737-2 (CD)
QUINCY (USA 76) theme mus: GLEN A.LARSON-STU PHILLIPS
  see COLL.172,244,
QUIZ SHOW (1994) Music score: MARK ISHAM -S/T- *reissue*
  EDEL-HOLLYWOOD (Vital) 012000-2HWR (CD)
QUO VADIS (1951) Music by MIKLOS ROSZA -S/T- sel.incl:
  'MADAME BOVARY'/'IVANHOE'/'PLYMOUTH ADVENTURE'
  TICKERTAPE USA Impt.(S.Screen): TT 3001 (CD)
  also SILVA SCREEN: FILMCD 180 (3CD) see COLL.214,
R AB C.NESBITT (BBC2 27/9/90) series theme music by
  DAVID McNIVEN *unavailable*
RAD (C5 1999/2000) theme (2000 ser) "Drop The Bomb" by
  SONA FARIQ *WEA (TEN): WEA 278CD (CDs) 278T (12"s)*
  theme (1999 s) "Get Up 52" by KANE / selection on
  RAD (Pinn): LJCD 012 (CD)
RAGE IN HARLEM, A - *see COLL.40,*

RAGE OF THE HEART (ORIG CONCEPT ALBUM) Songs (Enrico
  Garzilli) *feat* MICHAEL BALL and JANET MOONEY
  FIRST NIGHT (Pinn): OCRCD 6025 (CD)
RAGING BULL (1980) "Intermezzo" 'Cavalleria Rusticana'
  (MASCAGNI) *see COLL.97,195,*
RAGTIME (BBC CHILDREN'S TV 1970s) *see COLL.132,*

RAGTIME (MUSICAL: ORIGINAL BROADWAY CAST RECORDING)
  RCA VICTOR (BMG): 09026 63167-2 (2CDs)
RAIDERS OF THE LOST ARK (1981) Music: JOHN WILLIAMS
  SILVA SCREEN (Koch): RAIDERS 001 (CD) 821 583-4 MC
  see COLL.121,146,281,

RAILWAY CHILDREN The (1970) Music sco: JOHNNY DOUGLAS
  also feat LIONEL JEFFRIES *-S/T- reiss: MFP (EMI):*
  CDMFP 6373 (CD and 7243 857005-2) TCMFP 6383 (MC)
  also 'On Screen' *DULCIMA: DLCD 110* 'Dancing Feet'
  Andy ROSS ORCH *PRESIDENT: PCOM 1107 (CD)*

RAIN MAN (1989) Music score by HANS ZIMMER -S/T- with
  VAR.ARTISTS *-S/T-CAPITOL EMI: CDP 791 866-2 (CD)*

RAINMAKER The (1997) Music sco: ELMER BERNSTEIN -S/T-
  HOLLYWOOD-PHILIPS CLASS (Univ): 162 141-2PH (CD)

RAINS OF RANCHIPUR (1955) Music score: HUGO FRIEDHOFER
  Suite on Coll *inc* 'ADV.OF MARCO POLO'/'THE LODGER'
  'SEVEN CITIES OF GOLD' by MOSCOW SYMPHONY ORCH.
  MARCO POLO (Select): 8.223857 (CD) see COLL.1,

RAINTREE COUNTY (58) Music score: JOHNNY GREEN -S/T-
  USA Import (Hot): 2PRCD 1781 (CDx2)

RAISE THE TITANIC (1980) Music score by JOHN BARRY
  SILVA SCREEN Koch: FILMCD 319 (CD) **see COLL.26,30,**

RALLY REPORT (BBC2 22/11/96) theme "Duel" - PROPAGANDA
  from 'Secret Wish' *ZTT (Pinn): ZTT 118CD (CD)*

RAMBO 'FIRST BLOOD PART 1' (1982) Mus: JERRY GOLDSMITH
  VARESE (Pinn): VSD 6155 (CD) also FMT 8001D (CD)

RAMBO 'FIRST BLOOD PART 2' (1985) Mus: JERRY GOLDSMITH
  -S/T- SILVA SCREEN (Koch): FILMCD 307 (CD) also
  COLOSS.(Pinn):CST 348005 (CD)   see COLL.115,

RANCHO DE LUXE (1974) Music score: JIMMY BUFFETT -S/T-
  RYKODISC (Vital): RCD 10709 (CD)

RANDALL AND HOPKIRK (DECEASED) (2000)(BBC1 18/03/2000)
  Music score by MURRAY GOLD *unavailable* theme music
  by DAVID ARNOLD-NINA PERSSON *ISLAND: CID 762 (CDs)*
  -S/T- inc PULP-BASEMENT JAXX-CHARLATANS-JAMES-PULP
  & SWINGLE SINGERS-TALVIN SINGH-GAY DAD-WITNESS etc
  ISLAND-UNIVERSAL: CID 8096 (CD)

RANDALL AND HOPKIRK (DECEASED) (1969)(ITV 26/9/1969)
  theme music by EDWIN ASTLEY *see COLL.5,83,250,*

RANDOM HEARTS (1999) Music score by DAVE GRUSIN -S/T-
  SONY CLASSICAL (TEN): SK 51336-2 (CD)

RAPA NUI: The Centre Of The World (1993) Mus: STEWART
  COPELAND -S/T- *MILAN (BMG): 214 402 (CD)*

RAPID FIRE (1992) Music score: CHRISTOPHER YOUNG
  -S/T- *VARESE (Pinn): VSD 5388 (CD)*

RAT PATROL (USA TV) *see COLL.243,*

RAT RACE (2001) Music score by JOHN POWELL -S/T-
  IMPORT BEYOND USA: 578 216-2 (CD)

RAT RACE (1960) Music score by ELMER BERNSTEIN
  feat SAM BUTERA & THE WITNESSES -S/T-
  JASMINE (Koch): JASCD 356 (CD)

RAVENOUS (1998) Music by MICHAEL NYMAN-DAMON ALBARN &
  WILLIAM ORBIT -S/T- *EMI SOUNDTRACK: 522 370-2 (CD)*

RAWHIDE (USA 57) title song (D.Tiomkin-Ned Washington)
  FRANKIE LAINE 'Round-Up' *TELARC (BMG): CD 80141 CD*
  see Coll 'MY RIFLE MY PONY & ME' *see COLL.243,*

RAZOR'S EDGE (1984) Music score by JACK NITZSCHE feat
  LONDON STUDIO SYMPHONY ORCHESTRA (Stanley Black)
  PREAMBLE (HOT): PRCD 1794 (CD)

RAZOR'S EDGE (1946) Music score by ALFRED NEWMAN -S/T-
   TSUNAMI IMP (Discov): TSI 0622 (CD)- see COLL.1,
REACH THE ROCK (1997) Music score: JOHN McENTIRE -S/T-
   HEFTY (Pinn-Greyhound): HEFTY 014 / 005 (CD)
READY STEADY COOK (BBC2 24/10/94-2001) theme music by
   KEN BOLAM *unavailable*
READY TO RUMBLE (2000) Music score by GEORGE S.CLINTON
   -S/T- V.ARTISTS *ATLANTIC (TEN): 7567 83334-2 (CD)*
REAL McCOY (1993) Music score: BRAD FIEDEL -S/T-
   VARESE (Pinn): VSD 5450 (CD)
REAL WOMEN (BBC1 26/2/1998) Music (98 ser.) CARL DAVIS
   ROBERT LOCKHART (99 ser) song "She's A Good Girl"
   composed and sung by EDDI READER *unavailable*
REALITY BITES (1993) -S/T- incl LENNY KRAVITZ & V.Arts
   -S/T- *RCA (BMG): 07863 66364-2 (CD) -4 (MC)*
REBECCA (1940) Music score: FRANZ WAXMAN -S/T- reissue
   SOUNDTRACK FACTORY (Discovery): SFCD 33561 (CD)
   see COLL.141,142,144,
REBECCA (BBC2 17/1/79) music: DEBUSSY *see COLL.6,*
REBEL HEART (BBC1 07/01/2001) title song "Rebel Heart"
   sung by The CORRS from the album 'IN BLUE'
   ATLANTIC (TEN): 7567 83352-2 (CD) -4 (MC) -8 (MD)
   Music score composed/conducted by DEBBIE WISEMAN
   and performed by the BBC CONCERT ORCH *unavailable*
REBEL WITHOUT A CAUSE (1955) Music: LEONARD ROSENMAN
   new Recording LONDON SINFONIETTA (J.ADAMS) *with*
   'EAST OF EDEN' (1954 Leonard Rosenman) *NONESUCH*
   (TEN): 7559 79402-2 (CD) + 'GIANT'/'EAST OF EDEN'
   CINERAMA-EDEL (Vital) CIN 2206-2 (CD) -4 (MC)
RECESS (SCHOOL'S OUT) (2000) Music DENNIS M.HANNIGAN
   -S/T- *HOLLYWOOD-EDEL (Vital): 012 979-2HWR (CD)*
RECORD BREAKERS (BBC TV) *see COLL.132,*
RECORD OF THE YEAR (ITV 09/12/2000) V/A COMPILATION
   TELSTAR (BMG): TTVCD 3154 (2CD) TTVMC 3154 (2MC)
RED CORNER (1998) Music score: THOMAS NEWMAN -S/T-
   EDEL-CINERAMA (Vital) 0022882CIN (CD)
RED DWARF (BBC2 15/2/88-1997) music and theme song by
   HOWARD GOODALL *see COLL.38,83,*
RED PLANET (2000) Music score by GRAEME REVELL -S/T-
   incl.songs by PETER GABRIEL-STING-STRANGE CARGO
   ARK 21-UNIVERSAL: 520 055-2 (CD) and
   PANGAEA: 1867 810 063-2 (CD)
RED RIVER (1948) Music: DIMITRI TIOMKIN *see COLL.255,*

RED SHOE DIARIES (Films) Music GEORGE S.CLINTON on
   WIENERWORLD/GRAPEVINE (Discov): WNRCD 6001 (CD)
RED SHOES The (1948) Music score: BRIAN EASDALE
   PEARL (Harm.Mundi): GEMMCD 0100 (CD) see COLL.48,
RED TENT The (1970) Music score ENNIO MORRICONE -S/T-
   LEGEND ITALIAN IMPORT: LEGEND CD 5 (CD)
RED VIOLIN The (1997) Music sco: JOHN CORIGLIANO -S/T-
   SONY CLASSICS: SK 63010 (CD) SM 63010 (MC)
REDS (1981) Music: STEPHEN SONDHEIM-DAVE GRUSIN -S/T-
   RAZOR & TIE (Koch): RE 82203-2 (CD)

REF The (1998) Music: DAVID A.STEWART -S/T- on
   IMAGO (Direct): 7278 723014-2 (CD)
REGENERATION (1998) Music score by MYCHAEL DANNA -S/T-
   VARESE (Pinn): VSD 6005 (CD)
REILLY-ACE OF SPIES (Thames 9/83) theme from 'Romance'
   (SHOSTAKOVICH) *tv version arr.by* HARRY RABINOWITZ
RELATIVE VALUES (2000) Music score: JOHN DEBNEY -S/T-
   SILVA SCREEN (Koch): FILMCD 337 (CD)
REMEMBER THE TITANS (2000) Music score by TREVOR RABIN
   -S/T- (V/A) *DISNEY-EDEL (Vital): 012 143-2DNY (CD)*
REMINGTON STEELE (USA)(BBC1 3/9/1983) *see COLL.14,*
REN AND STIMPY SHOW (USA/BBC1 10/1/1994) **see COLL.248,**
RENAISSANCE (BBC2 21/11/1999) (various period CHORAL
   WORKS) -S/T- *BBC RECORDS: to be confirmed*
RENAISSANCE MAN (1993) Music score HANS ZIMMER -S/T-
   VARESE (Pinn): VSD 5502 (CD)
RENT - songs: Jonathan Larson / Orig 1996 Broadway
   Cast *DREAMWORKS-MCA (UNI): DRD 50003 (CD)*
REPLACEMENT KILLERS The (1997) Music sc: HARRY GREGSON
   WILLIAMS -S/T- *VARESE (Pinn): VSD 5915 (CD)*
REPLACEMENTS (2000) Music score by JOHN DEBNEY
   -S/T- *VARESE (Pinn): VSD 6180 (CD)*
REQUIEM (ROCK REQUIEM 1985) Music: ANDREW LLOYD WEBBER
   Placido DOMINGO-Sarah BRIGHTMAN-Paul M.KINGSTON
   ENGLISH CHAMBER ORCH *EMI: EL 270 242-2 (CD)*
REQUIEM FOR A DREAM (2000) Music score: CLINT MANSELL
   with the KRONOS QUARTET -S/T- on
   NONESUCH-WARNER (TEN): 755 979611-2 (CD)
RESCUERS The / RESCUERS DOWN UNDER - see DISNEY p.341
RESERVOIR DOGS (1992) -S/T- feat VAR.ARTISTS *REISSUE*
   with 'PULP FICTION': *MCA (UNIV): MCD 11188 (2CDs)*
   also: MCA (UNI): MCD 10793 (CD) MCC 10793 (MC)
   S.VINYL (Telstar): SVLP 28 (LP) see COLL.95,
RESORT TO MURDER (BBC1 27/7/95) Music sco: BILL CONNOR
   -S/T- *Debonair (Pinn): CDDEB 1002 see COLL.5,17*
RESPECTABLE TRADE, A (BBC1 19/4/1998) Music score by
   JULIAN NOTT with the CITY OF PRAGUE PHILHARMONIC
   WARNER ESP (TEN): 3984 23248-2 (CD) -4 (MC)
RETURN OF DRACULA The (1958) Music score: GERALD FRIED
   Ltd Ed.Import COLL incl: 'MARK OF THE VAMPIRE',
   'I BURY THE LIVING' and 'THE CABINET OF CALIGARI'
   RETROGRADE (S.Screen/MFTM): FSMCD Vol.1 No.4 (2CD)
RETURN OF THE JEDI (Star Wars 3) Music: JOHN WILLIAMS
   Special-Edition ORIG SOUNDTRACK Recording (1997)
   RCA (BMG): 09026 68748-2 (Deluxe 2CD)
   RCA (BMG): 09026 68774-2 (Slimline 2CD) -4 (2MC)
   see COLL.218,238,281,
RETURN OF THE PINK PANTHER The (1974) Music score by
   HENRY MANCINI -S/T- complete + 'THE PINK PANTHER'
   RCA CAMDEN (BMG): 74321 66047-2 (CD)
RETURN OF THE SAINT The (ITV 78) theme: IRVING MARTIN-
   BRIAN DEE *see COLL.2,200,*
RETURN OF THE SEVEN (1966) Music sco: ELMER BERNSTEIN
   -S/T- *RYKODISC (Vital):RCD 10714 (CD)*

RETURN TO PARADISE (1998) Music sc: MARK MANCINA -S/T-
VARESE (Pinn): VSD 5964 (CD)
RETURN TO THE FORBIDDEN PLANET (ORIG LONDON CAST 1989)
Bob CARLTON'S Sci-Fi Musical *VIRGIN: CDV(TCV) 2631*
REVOLVER (Italian Western) Music score: ENNIO MORRICONE
-S/T- *DAGORED (Koch): RED 112CD (CD) RED 112LP (LP)*
REX (MUSICAL 1976) Songs: RICHARD RODGERS and SHELDON
HARNICK *feat:* NICOL WILLIAMSON and Company
Broadway Cast Rec. *RCA (BMG): 09026 68933-2 (CD)*
RHAPSODY IN BLUE (1945) VARIOUS -S/T- SELECTIONS on
GREAT MOVIE THEMES: (Targ-BMG): CD 60028 (CD)
RHONA (BBC2 25/07/2000) music by ALASTAIR COLLINGWOOD
title song sung by RHONA CAMERON *unavailable*
RHYTHM ON THE RIVER (1940) VARIOUS -S/T- SELECTIONS on
GREAT MOVIE THEMES: (Targ-BMG): CD 60025 (CD)
RICHARD III (1955) Music: WILLIAM WALTON / Academy Of
St.Martin-In-The-Fields,Neville MARRINER with Sir
John GIELGUD *CHANDOS: CHAN 8841 (CD)*
RICHARD BOONE SHOW (USA) *see COLL.24,*
RICHIE RICH (1994) Music score: ALAN SILVESTRI -S/T-
VARESE (Pinn): VSD 5582 (CD)
RICK STEIN'S... (BBC2 from 1995) *see COLL.241,*
RICKY 6 (2000) Music score by JOE DELIA -S/T- (USA) on
PACIFIC TIME ENTERPRISES (USA): PTE - (CD)
RIDE WITH THE DEVIL (1999) Music score: MYCHAEL DANNA
-S/T- *ATLANTIC (TEN): 7567 83262-2 (CD) -4 (MC)*
RIDGE RIDERS Music by ASHLEY HUTCHINGS-PHIL BEER-
CHRIS WHITE -S/T- *TALKING ELEPHANT (Pinn): TECD 018
(CD) also on HTD (Pinn): HTDCD 103 (CD)*
RIDING IN CARS WITH BOYS (2001) Music by HANS ZIMMER
-S/T- *506 014-2 (CD)*
RIFLEMAN The (USA TV 60s) *see COLL.242,*
RIGHT STUFF The (1983) Mus: BILL CONTI+ 'NORTH & SOUTH'
-S/T- *VARESE: VCD 47250 (CD) see COLL.61,232,*
RIN TIN TIN (USA TV) *see COLL.242,*
RING OF BRIGHT WATER (1969) Music score: FRANK CORDELL
-S/T- inc.'KHARTOUM' *ARTEMIS (HOT): ARTF 003 (CD)*
RINK The - songs by John Kander and Fred Ebb
1.ORIG LONDON CAST 1987/88) DIANE LANGTON-JOSEPHINE
BLAKE & COMP *TER (Koch): CDTERS 1155 (CD)*
2.ORIG BROADWAY CAST 1983 *with* LIZA MINNELLI and CO
TER (Koch): CDTER 1091 (CD)
RIO BRAVO (1959) Music score: DIMITRI TIOMKIN
Title theme (D.Tiomkin-P.F.Webster) by DEAN MARTIN
MFP EMI: CDMFP 6032 (CD) see COLL.255,
RIO CONCHOS (1964) Music score: JERRY GOLDSMITH -S/T-
FSM SILVER AGE (USA): FSM VOLUME 2 NUMBER 8 (CD)
also INTRADA (USA): RVF 6007D(CD) / see COLL.1,
RIO GRANDE (1950) Music score: VICTOR YOUNG -S/T-
VARESE (Pinn): VSD 5378 (CD)
RIO RITA (OLC 1930) Songs (Harry Tierney-Joe McCarthy)
EDITH DAY-MARIA DE PIETRO *PEARL: GEMMCD 9115 (CD)*
RISING DAMP (ITV orig 1974) ORIG TV CAST RECORDING on
MAGMASTERS (Koch): MSE 011 (MC) see COLL.125,

RISKY BUSINESS (1983) Mus: TANGERINE DREAM-BOB SEGER
   -S/T- *VIRGIN (EMI): CDV 2302 (CD) OVEDC 240 (MC)*
RIVER OF SOUND, A (BBC2 27/12/95) featuring:
   MICHEAL O'SUILLEABHAIN + various artists -S/T-
   VIRGIN (EMI): CDV 2776 (CD) TCV 2776 (MC)
RIVERDANCE SHOW The (1995) music by BILL WHELAN *reis*
   CELTIC HEARTBEAT (BMG): UND(UMC) 53076 / 53106
   New Version (Oct 95) *WEA 7567 82816-2(CD) -4(MC)*
   see *COLL.108,188,*
   RIVERDANCE (TRIBUTE TO) 'THIS LAND' Various Arts
   MFP (EMI): CDMFP 6237 (CD) TCMFP 6237 (MC)
RIVERDANCE / LORD OF THE DANCE (Highlights from both)
   VOICES OF IRELAND *K-TEL: ECD 3396 (CD)*
ROAD HOUSE (1989) Music: MICHAEL KAMEN + JEFF HEALEY
   BAND-BOB SEGER-OTIS REDDING-LITTLE FEAT-PATRICK
   SWAYZEE-KRIS McKAY -S/T- *ARISTA BMG: 259.948 (CD)*
ROAD RUNNER (USA TV) *see COLL.243,*
ROAD TO ELDORADO The (2000) Animated feature
   Music by ELTON JOHN, Lyrics by TIM RICE
   MERCURY-UNIVERSAL: 450 219-2 (CD) -4 (MC)
ROAD TO MOROCCO (1942) *feat* BING CROSBY-BOB HOPE and
   DOROTHY LAMOUR + 'TWO FOR TONIGHT' & 'HOLIDAY INN'
   GREAT MOVIE THEMES (Target-BMG): CD 60027 (CD)
ROAD TO WELLVILLE The (1994) Music sco: RACHEL PORTMAN
   -S/T- *VARESE (Pinn): VSD 5512 (CD)*
ROAD TRIP (2000) Music score by MIKE SIMPSON
   -S/T- *INTERSCOPE-POLYDOR (UNIV): 450 262-2 (CD)*
ROB ROY (1995) Music: CARTER BURWELL Songs performed
   by CAPERCAILLIE feat KAREN MATHIESON -S/T- on
   VIRGIN: CDVMM 18 (CD) TCVMM 18 (MC) see *COLL.3,*
ROBE The (1953) Mus: ALFRED NEWMAN -S/T- *FOX-ARISTA*
   (BMG): 07822 11011-2 (CD) and Import version on
   VARESE (Pinn): VARESE: VSD 5295 (CD)
ROBERT AND ELIZABETH songs: Ron Grainer-Ronald Miller
  1.ORIG CHICHESTER THEATRE CAST 1987 MARK WYNTER-
   GAYNOR MILES-JOHN SAVIDENT and Company
   FIRST NIGHT (Pinn): OCRCD 6032 (CD)
ROBIN AND MARIAN (1976) Music score by JOHN BARRY
   New Record CITY OF PRAGUE PHILH.ORCH.(Nic Raine)
   SILVA SCREEN (Koch): FILMXCD 354 (CD) also
   see *COLL.26,30,146,240,*
ROBIN HOOD (1973 Cartoon) *see* WALT DISNEY INDEX p.341

ROBIN HOOD (1991) (w: Patrick Bergin) Music: GEOFFREY
   BURGON -S/T- *SILVA SCREEN (Koch): FILMCD 083 CD*
ROBIN HOOD 'The Adventures Of' *see* ADVENTURES OF ROBIN

ROBIN HOOD: PRINCE OF THIEVES (1991) Music score by
   MICHAEL KAMEN "(Everything I Do) I Do It For You"
   sung by BRYAN ADAMS *AMCD 789 -S/T-MORGAN CREEK*
   (Univ): 002249-2 MCM (CD) see *COLL.73,159,240,*
ROBIN OF SHERWOOD (HTV 28/4/84) theme music "Robin The
   Hooded Man)" CLANNAD on 'The Ultimate Collection'
   RCA (BMG): 74321 48674-2 (CD)

ROBINSON CRUSOE (Adventures of) (BBC1 12/10/65) Music
score: ROBERT MELLIN-GIAN PIERO REVERBERI Original
TV S/TRACK *reissued w.ADDITIONAL unreleased music*
SILVA SCREEN (Koch): FILMCD 705 (CD)
ROBOCOP (1987) Music score: BASIL POLEDOURIS -S/T-
VARESE: (Pinn) VSD 47298 (CD) reissue / also on
ESSENTIAL (BMG):ESSCD 285(CD) ESSMC 285(MC)
-S/T- TER (Koch):CDTER 1146 (CD) see COLL.221,
ROBOCOP 2 (1990) Music score: LEONARD ROSENMAN -S/T-
VARESE USA (Pinn): VSD 5271 (CD)
ROBOCOP 3 (1993) Music score: BASIL POLEDOURIS -S/T-
VARESE USA (Pinn): VSD 5416 (CD)
ROBOCOP: PRIME DETECTIVES (2000) Mus: NORMAN ORENSTEIN
GNP USA (ZXY): GNPD - (CD)
ROBOCOP: TV SERIES (ITV 7/9/96) -S/T- feat JOE WALSH-
LITA FORD-THE BAND-DAVE EDMUNDS-TODD RUNDGREN
ESSENTIAL (Pinn): ESMCD 491 (CD) see COLL.221,
ROBOT WARS (BBC2 20/2/1998)"Robot Wars" (Android Love)
music by JOHN WADDELL-WILLIAM PARNELL
POLYDOR (UNIV): 587 935-2 / 587 936-2 (CDs) -4(MC)
ROCK The (1996) Music: NICK GLENNIE SMITH-HANS ZIMMER
-S/T- EDEL-HOLLYWOOD (Vital) 010 262-2HWR (CD)
ROCK FOLLIES (ITV 1976-77) Music by ANDY MACKAY *reiss:*
VIRGIN (EMI): CDV 2914 (CD) also CDVIR 2915 (CD)
ROCK STAR (2001) Music score TREVOR RABIN -S/T- V.ARTS
PRIORITY-VIRGIN (EMI): CDPTY 222 (CD)
ROCKERS (1978) Music score (Reggae) featur PETER TOSH
GREGORY ISAACS-THE MIGHTY DIAMONDS & others -S/T-
REGGAE REFRESHERS-ISLAND (Univ): RRCD 45 (CD)
ROCKETEER The (1991) Music score: JAMES HORNER -S/T-
HOLLYWOOD Imp: HWD 161117 (CD) see COLL.83,148,
ROCKFORD (2000) VARIOUS ARTISTS SOUNDTRACK on
BLUE ELEPHANT (TEN): 495 418-2 (CD)
ROCKFORD FILES (USA75) theme: MIKE POST-PETE CARPENTER
see COLL.14,77,124,203,244,
ROCKY (1976) Music: BILL CONTI Song "Gonna Fly Now"
performed by Frank Stallone -S/T- *re-issue*
EMI EUROPE (Discov): 746 081-2 (CD)
ROCKY STORY The - Various Artists (From Soundtracks)
POLYDOR (UNIVERSAL): 848 242-2 (CD)   *1991*
ROCKY HORROR SHOW The - songs by Richard O'Brien
  1.25TH ANNIVERSARY 'ROCKY HORROR PICTURE SHOW'
    CASTLE MUSIC (Pinn): CMRCD 296 (CD)
  2.FILM MUSICAL 1975 (<u>Rocky Horror Picture Show</u>) *with*
    TIM CURRY-LITTLE NELL-MEATLOAF-SUSAN SARANDON
    ESSENTIAL (Pinn): ESDCD 908 (2CD) reiss.07,2000
    also ESMCD 932 (CD) (ORIGINAL ROXY CAST)
    Castle Comm (Pinn): ROCKY1 (4CD inc.O.LONDON Cast)
  3.ORIG LONDON CAST 1973 TIM CURRY-RICHARD O'BRIEN-
    LITTLE NELL- *First Night (Pinn): OCRCD 6040 (CD)*
  4.REVIVAL LONDON CAST 1990 TIM McINNERNY-ADRIAN
    EDMONDSON-GINA BELLMAN and Company / *reissued on*
    MFP (EMI): CD(TC)MFP 5977 (CD/MC)

5.CARLTON SHOWS COLLECTION 1995 CHERYL BAKER-ROBIN
  COUSINS-TRACEY MILLER-NICK CURTIS *pr* Gordon Lorenz
  CARLTON SHOWS Collect: 30362 0016-2 (CD) -4 (MC)
6.STUDIO R.1995 ANITA DOBSON-TIM FLAVIN-KIM CRISWELL
  HOWARD SAMUELS-AIDAN BELL-ISSY VAN RANDWYCK-
  CHRISTOPHER LEE Complete: *TER (Koch): CDTER 1221*
  Highlights: *CURTAIN CALL-MCI (DISC): CURTCD 002 CD*
7.NEW BROADWAY CAST 2000 *BMG IMP: 09026 63801-2 (CD)*
  see also NEW ROCKY HORROR SHOW

ROGUE TRADER (1999) Music score by IAIN JAMES -S/T-
  COLUMBIA (Ten): 495 051-2 (CD)

ROLLERCOASTER (1977) Music score: LALO SCHIFRIN -S/T-
  ALEPH USA (Koch): ALEP 021 (CD)

ROMANCE ROMANCE (O.BROADWAY CAST 1988) Songs: KEITH
  HERRMANN-BARRY HARMON *TER (Koch): CDTER 1161 (CD)*

ROMEO AND JULIET (1996) Music score: CLIFF EIDELMAN
  -S/T- songs (vol.1) *CAPITOL EMI: PRMDCD 28 (CD)*
  -S/T- songs (vol.2) *CAPITOL EMI: PRMDCD 34 (CD)*

ROMEO AND JULIET (1968) Music score by NINO ROTA
  SILVA SCREEN (Koch): FILMCD 200 (CD)
  see COLL.61,67,170,

ROMEO MUST DIE (1999) Music score: STANLEY CLARKE and
  TIMBERLAND -S/T- *VIRGIN (EMI): CDVUS 169 (CD)*

ROMPER STOMPER (1992) Music score: JOHN CLIFFORD WHITE
  "Pearl Fishers Duet" (Bizet) ERNEST BLANC-NICOLAI
  GEDDA -S/T- *PICTURE THIS (Greyhound): PTR 002 (CD)*

RONIN (1998) Music score: ELIA CMIRAL -S/T- on
  VARESE (Pinn): VSD 5977

ROOBARB (BBC1 70's) music: JOHNNY HAWKSWORTH
  orig theme see COLL.132,

ROOM 43 - *see COLL.75,*

ROOM AT THE TOP (1958) Music score: MARIO NASCIMBENE
  -S/T- inc.'BAREFOOT CONTESSA'/'THE QUIET AMERICAN'
  DRG (Pinn): DRGCD 32961 (CD)

ROOM WITH A VIEW, A (1986) Music sco: RICHARD ROBBINS
  -S/T- *DRG (Pinn): CDSBL 12588 (CD)*
  see COLL.81,82,122,195,204,

ROOTS (USA TV) *see COLL.247,*

ROOTS OF HEAVEN (1958) Music score by MALCOLM ARNOLD
  new score recording by MOSCOW SYMPHONY ORCHESTRA
  (W.Stromberg, cond) *inc* 'DAVID COPPERFIELD' score
  MARCO POLO (Select): 8225167 (CD)

ROSE The (1979) *featuring* BETTE MIDLER -S/T- on
  ATLANTIC (TEN): 7567 82778-2 (CD)

ROSE OF WASHINGTON SQUARE (1939 MUSICAL) ALICE FAYE-
  AL JOLSON-TYRONE POWER *inc.songs* 'DOLLY SISTERS'
  'GOLD DIGGERS OF 1933' *TARGET (BMG): CD 60009*

ROSE OF WASHINGTON SQUARE *VARESE (Pinn): VSD 6089 (CD)*

ROSEANNE (USA C4 from 27/1/89) theme mus: DAN FOLIART
  HOWARD PEARL *see COLL.14,248,*

ROSEMARY'S BABY (1968) Music score: CHRISTOPHER KOMEDA
  reiss POLONIA (Silva Screen): POLONIA CD 160 (CD)
  also includes music of 'FEARLESS VAMPIRE KILLERS'
  DISCMEDI (Silver Sounds): PIG 02 (CD)

ROSIE & JIM (CITV 1990) see COLL.285,
ROSWELL HIGH (USA 1999/SKY1 2000) theme mus "Here With
Me" sung by DIDO from the album 'No Angel' on
CHEEKY RECORDS (BMG): 74321 80268-2 (CD) -4 (MC)
ROTHSCHILD'S VIOLIN (Film Score) Music: FLEISCHMANN m
comleted & orches. by SHOSTAKOVICH. The ROTTERDAM
PHILHARMONIC ORCH *RCA V (BMG): 09026 68434-2 (CD)*
ROTTENTROLLS The (ITV 23/09/1998) theme ROTTENTROLLS
HIT LABEL (Univ): HLC 14 (CDs)
ROUND MIDNIGHT (1986) Mus sc: HERBIE HANCOCK w: DEXTER
GORDON -S/T- reiss *(SM): 486799-2 (CD) also* 'OTHER
SIDE OF ROUND MIDNIGHT' *BLUENOTE: CDP 746386-2 CD*
ROUNDERS (1998) Music score: CHRISTOPHER YOUNG -S/T-
VARESE (Pinn): VSD 5980 (CD)
ROUSTABOUT see ELVIS PRESLEY INDEX p.348
ROUTE 66 (USA) see COLL.75,124,243,
ROYAL ASCOT (BBC1 20/6/95) theme "Odissea" (Reverberi-
Farina) by RONDO VENEZIANO on 'Odissea' *BMG Italy
(Select): 610 529 (CD) also used* 'Regata Dei Dogi'
RONDO VENEZIANO *BMG ITALY (Select): 610 535 (CD)*
ROYLE FAMILY (BBC2 14/9/1998) theme "Half The World
Away" by OASIS *CREATION (Vital): CRESCD 195 (CDs)
also on COLL.260,* 'TV 2000' *SONY: SONTV82CD (CD)*
RUBY CAIRO (1992) Music score by JOHN BARRY -S/T-
PROMETHEUS (USA Import): PCD 150 (CD)
RUDDIGORE (operetta) W.S.Gilbert & A.Sullivan
1.NEW SADLERS WELLS OPERA COMPANY *KOCH Int (Koch):
340342 (CD) 240344 (MC) / TER: CDTER2 1128 (2CD)*
RUGBY SPECIAL (BBC2 78-1990) "Holy Mackerel" by BRIAN
BENNETT see COLL.3,101,122,
RUGBY UNION 5 NATIONS CUP (BBC1 20/1/96) trailer music
"Adiemus" (KARL JENKINS) from 'Songs Of Sanctuary'
VIRGIN EMI: CD(TC)VE 925 (CD/MC) also see COLL.10,
RUGBY WORLD CUP 1999 (ITV 01/10/1999) ser.theme music
"World in Union" (C.Skarbek-G.Holst) BRYN TERFEL &
SHIRLEY BASSEY *DECCA (Univ): 466 940-2 (CDs)*
WORLD CUP 99 ALBUM *'LAND OF MY FATHERS'* feat: BRYN
TERFEL-SHIRLEY BASSEY-MICHAEL BALL-BLACK MOUNTAIN
CHORUS-THE LADYSMITH BLACK MAMBAZO-RUSSELL WATSON
DECCA (Univ): 466 567-2 (CD)
RUGRATS THE MOVIE (1998) Music sco: MARK MOTHERSBAUGH
songs *INTERSCOPE (BMG): IND(INTC) 90181 (CD/MC)*
score *CASUAL TONALITIES (Pinn): XOCD 9943 (CD)*
RUGRATS IN PARIS (1999) M: MARK MOTHERSBAUGH & V.ARTS.
-S/T- *WEA INT (TEN): 9362 48034-2 (CD) -4 (MC)*
RULES OF ENGAGEMENT (2000) Music score by MARK ISHAM
-S/T- *MILAN (BMG): 74321 76481-2 (CD)*
RUMBLE FISH (1983) Music score: STEWART COPELAND -S/T-
A.& M. (IMS-Polyg): AA 750 214983-2 (CD) reissue
RUN LOLA RUN (LOLA RENNT) (1999) Music sco: TOM TYKWER
-JOHNNY KLIMEK-REINHOLD HEIL -S/T- inc.songs by
FRANKA POTENTE etc.*BMG ARIOLA: 74321 60477-2 (CD)*
RUNAWAY BRIDE (1999) Music score by
-S/T- *COLUMBIA (Ten): 494 873-2 (CD) -4 (MC)*

RUNNING FREE (1999) Music score by NICOLA PIOVANNI
  -S/T- *VARESE (Pinn): VSD 6152 (CD)*
RUNNING MAN The (1988) Music score: HAROLD FALTERMEYER
  -S/T- reissue *COLOSSEUM (Pinn): CST 348032 (CD)*
RUPERT THE BEAR (ITV) see *COLL.285,*
RUSH HOUR (1998) Music score by LALO SCHIFRIN score on
  ALEPH (Koch): ALEP 005 + WB TEN 8573 87367-2 (CDs)
  songs on *MERCURY (Univ): 558 663-2 (CD) -1 (2LP)*
RUSH HOUR 2 (2001) Music score by LALO SCHIFRIN
  songs on *MERCURY (Univ): 586 216-2 (CD)*
  score on *VARESE (Pinn): VSD 6279 (CD)*
RUSHMORE (1998) Music score: MARK MOTHERSBAUGH -S/T-
  -S/T- (score) *LONDON (Univ): 556 074-2 (CD)*
  -S/T- (songs) *LONDON (Ten): 3984 263691-2 (CD)*
RUTH RENDELL MYSTERIES (TVS 19/6/1988) m.BRIAN BENNETT
  -S/T- *EMI SOUNDTRACKS: 520 687-2 (CD) DELETED 2001*
  also see *COLL.4,42,*
RUTLES The (1978 'All You Need Is Cash' seq) 'ARCHAE
  OLOGY' *VIRGIN (EMI): CDVUS 119 (CD) VUSMC 119 (MC)*
S.CLUB 7: MIAMI 7 (BBC1 08/04/1999) theme & incidental
  music by PAUL HARDCASTLE and KEN BOLAM *unavailable*
  S CLUB 7 "Bring It All Back" *POLYD: 561 085-2 (CDs)*
  "NATURAL" album *POLYDOR: 587 760-2 (CD) -4 (MC)*
  "S CLUB 7" album *POLYDOR: 543 103-2 (CD) -4 (MC)*
  "7"   album *POLYDOR: 543 857-2 (CD) -4 (MC)*
S.W.A.T. (USA) see *COLL.124,244,*
SABRINA THE TEENAGE WITCH (Disney 1995) song "Walk Of
  Life" by SPICE GIRLS on 'TV 2000' *SONYTV82CD (CD)*
SAFE (1994) Music score: ED TOMNEY -S/T- issued on
  MUTE-Fine Line (RTM-Pinn): IONIC 14CD (CD)
SAIL AWAY MUSICAL by NOEL COWARD
  EMI Catalogue: 520 726-2 (CD)
SAIL THE WORLD WHITBREAD ROUND THE WORLD YACHT RACE 94
  (ITV 19/3/94) music score: ANTHONY PHILLIPS -S/T-
  RESURGENCE-BLUEPRINT (Pinn): RES 102CD (CD)
SAINT The (1997) Music score: GRAEME REVELL -S/T-
  V.Arts: ORBITAL-CHEMICAL BROTHERS-UNDERWORLD-
  DAVID BOWIE-DAFT PUNK *VIRGIN (EMI): CDVUS 126 (CD)*
  VUSMC 126 (MC) ORBITAL *Fffr (Univ): FCD 296 (CDs)*
SAINT The (ITC 4/10/62-69) theme music: EDWIN ASTLEY
  TV -S/T- *RAZOR & TIE (Koch): RE 21562 (CD)*
  see *COLL.2,24,64,74,83,95,172,243,250,251,253,261,*
SAINT ELMO'S FIRE (1985) Music sco: DAVID FOSTER *feat*
  JOHN PARR -S/T- *ATLANTIC (TEN): 7567 81261-2 (CD)*
SAINT ELSEWHERE (USA) theme music by DAVE GRUSIN
  see *COLL.14,244,*
SAINT PATRICK...THE IRISH LEGEND (1999) Music score by
  INON ZUR perf by TEL AVIV SYMPHONY & EBLANA CHAMBER
  CHOIR -S/T- *SHANACHIE (Proper): SHANCD 78037 (CD)*
SAINT SHE AIN'T, A! (MUSICAL SHOW) Music by DENIS KING
  Lyrics & book by DICK VOSBURGH / ORIG LONDON CAST
  FIRST NIGHT (Pinn): CASTCD 73 (CD)
SALAAM BOMBAY! (1988) Music score: L.SUBRAMANIAM -S/T-
  DRG (Pinn): CDSBL 12595 (CD)

SALAD DAYS songs by Julian Slade and Dorothy Reynolds
  1.REVIVAL LONDON CAST *with:* ELIZABETH SEAL-SHEILA
    STEAFEL-CHRISTIINA MATTHEWS-ADAM BAREHAM & Company
    TER (Koch): CDTER 1018 (CD)
  2.40th Anniv.STUDIO Record 1994 SIMON GREEN-JANIE
    DEE-TIMOTHY WEST-JOSEPHINE TEWSON-PRUNELLA SCALES-
    VALERIE MASTERSON-JOHN WARNER-TONY SLATTERY *and Co*
    EMI: CDC 555200-2 (CD) EL 555200-4 (MC)
  3.5TH ANNIVERSARY PROD *FIRST NIGHT: SCORECD 43 (CD)*
SALLY HEMMINGS: AN AMERICAN SCANDAL (2000) Music score
  JOEL McNEELY -S/T- *PROMETHEUS IMPORT: PCD 149 (CD)*
SALSA (1988) VARIOUS ARTISTS -S/T- (Import)
  MERCURY France (Discov): 542 331-2 (CD)
SALTIMBANCO (1996) Music by RENE DUPERE performed by
  CIRQUE DU SOLEIL (Circus Of The Sun) ORIG CAST REC
  RCA VICTOR (BMG): 74321 25707-2 (CD) -4 (MC)
SALVADOR (1986) Music score: GEORGES DELERUE -S/T- and
  'WALL STREET' *TER (Koch): CDTER 1154 (CD)*
SAMSON AND DELILAH (1949) Music: VICTOR YOUNG -S/T-
  incl. 'THE QUIET MAN' *VARESE (Pinn): VSD 5497 (CD)*
  see COLL.284,
SAN FRANCISCO (1936) *COLLECTION with* 'DAMES'/'SUZY' on
  GREAT MOVIE THEMES (Targ-BMG): CD 60022 (CD)
SAND PEBBLES The (1966) Music score: JERRY GOLDSMITH
  new recording incl.previously unreleased material
  VARESE (Pinn): VSD 5795 (CD)
SANDPIPER The (1965) Music sc: JOHNNY MANDEL song "The
  Shadow Of Your Smile"(J.Mandel-P.F.Webster) -*S/T-*
  VERVE (Univ): 531 229-2 (CD) see COLL.61,
SAPPHIRE AND STEEL (ITV 10/7/79) theme music: CYRIL
  ORNADEL *see COLL.250,*
SARAFINA: THE SOUND OF FREEDOM (1992) Mus: STANLEY
  MYERS -S/T- V.Ars *WB (TEN) 9362 45060-2 (CD)*
SATURDAY NIGHT Songs by STEPHEN SONDHEIM - V.ARTISTS
  FIRST NIGHT (Pinn): CASTCD 65 (CD)
SATURDAY NIGHT FEVER (ORIGINAL LONDON CAST 1998) *feat:*
  ADAM GARCIA-TARA WILKINSON-ANITA LOUISE COMBE-
  SIMON GRIEFF *O.CAST REC. POLYDOR: 557 932-2 (CD)*
SATURDAY NIGHT FEVER (FILM 1978) -S/T- Music: BEE GEES
  RSO (Univ): 825 389-2 (CD)
SATURDAY NIGHT LIVE (USA TV) *see COLL.244,*
SAVE THE LAST DANCE (2001) Music score by MARK ISHAM
  -S/T- inc FREDRO STARR-SNOOP DOGG-X2C-CHAKA DEMUS
  Vol.1 *HOLLYWOOD-EDEL (Vital): 012 542-2HWR (CD)*
  Vol.2 *HOLLYWOOD-EDEL (Vital): 011 739-2HWR (CD)*
  More Music *"   " (Vital): 012 998-2HWR (CD)*
SAVED BY THE BELL (NBC USA/C4 1/1/95) theme music by
  SCOTT GALE and RICH EAMES *see COLL.248,*
SAVING GRACE (1999) Music score by MARK RUSSELL
  -S/T- *WEA INT (TEN): 8573 83095-2 (CD) -4 (MC)*
SAVING PRIVATE RYAN (1997) Music score: JOHN WILLIAMS
  -S/T- *DREAMWORKS (BMG): DRD 50046 (CD, 07.1998)*
  song "Tu Es Partout" by EDITH PIAF *(not on -S/T-)*
  ON FLAPPER (Pinn): PASTCD 7820 (CD)

SAYONARA (1957) Music sco: FRANZ WAXMAN orch.suite
  RCA Red Seal (BMG): 09026 62657-2 (CD)
SCANNERS (1980) - see DEAD RINGERS / see COLL 219,
SCARAMOUCHE (1952) Music: VICTOR YOUNG new recording
  BRANDENBURG S.ORCH.(KAUFMAN) with other items on
  MARCO POLO (Select): 8.223607 (CD)
SCARFACE (1983) Music sco: GIORGIO MORODER / songs V/A
  -S/T- reissue MCA (UNI): MCD 06126 (CD)
SCARFIES (2000) -S/T-
  FLYING NUN (Pinn/Cargo): DFN 425 (CD)
SCARLET LETTER (1995) Music sco JOHN BARRY see COLL.26,
SCARLET PIMPERNEL The (BBC1 24/01/1999) Music score by
  MICHAL PAVLICEK conducted by MARIO &d ADAM KLEMENS
  and performed by PRAGUE PHILHARMONICS
  -S/T- *BBC WORLDWIDE (Pinn): WMSF 60022 (CD)*
SCARLET PIMPERNEL The (ORIG.BROADWAY CAST RECORDING)
  FIRST NIGHT (Pinn): CASTCD 72 (CD)
SCARLET TUNIC The (1997) Music score: JOHN SCOTT -S/T-
  JOHN SCOTT Records (Silva Screen): JSCD 125 (CD)
SCARS OF DRACULA (1970) Music score: JAMES BERNARD
  -S/T- *GDI (ABM/Univ): GDICD 014 (CD) see COLL.126,*
SCARY MOVIE (1999) Music score by DAVID KITAY -S/T-
  EPIC (TEN): 501 045-2 (CD)
SCHINDLER'S LIST (1993) Music: JOHN WILLIAMS / Violin
  Itzhak PERLMAN -S/T- MCA (UNI): MCD 10969 (CD)
  see COLL.3,68,121,188,204,280,281,
SCOOBY DOO (USA TV) see COLL.244,259,
SCOOBY DOO AND THE WITCHES GHOST (1999) Music score by
  BODIE CHANDLER-GLENN LEOPOLD featuring vocals by
  JANE WEIDLIN & The HEX GIRLS. theme adapated by
  BILLY RAY CYRUS -S/T- *RHINO USA IMP: R2 75709 (CD)*
SCORE The (2001) Music score by HOWARD SHORE -S/T-
  VARESE (Pinn): VSD 6267 (CD)
SCOTT OF THE ANTARCTIC (1948) see COLL.42
SCREAM (1997) Music sco: MARCO BELTRAMI -S/T- **V.Arts**
  EDEL (Vital) 0022822CIN (CD)
SCREAM / SCREAM 2 (1997/1998) Music sc: MARCO BELTRAMI
  scores only *VARESE (Pinn): VSD 5959*
SCREAM 2 (1998) -S/T- Music score: MARCO BELTRAMI
  EMI PREMIER: 821 911-2 (CD) -4 (MC)
SCREAM 3 (2000) Music score by MARCO BELTRAMI
  -S/T- score: *VARESE (Pinn): VSD 6116 (CD)*
  -S/T- songs: *EPIC (TEN): 497 611-2 (CD) -4 (MC)*
SCROOGE (O.LONDON CAST 1992) Songs: LESLIE BRICUSSE w:
  ALBERT FINNEY *TER (Koch): CDTER 1194 (CD)*
SCROOGE (Classic Musicals series) feat: ANTHONY NEWLEY
  TOM WATT-GEORGE ASPREY-TANYA COOKE-JON PERTWEE etc
  + songs from 'PICKWICK' *KOCH INT: 34081-2 (CD)*
SEA DEVILS The (1953) see COLL.9,
SEA HAWK The (1940) Music sco: ERICH WOLFGANG KORNGOLD
  NEW RECORDING with OREGON SYMPHONY ORCH (James De
  Priest) *DELOS (Nimbus): DE 3234 (CD) also availab:*
  VARESE (Pinn): VSD 47304 (CD) see COLL.61,160,240,
SEA HUNT (USA TV) theme by RAY LLEWELLYN see COLL.243,

SEA OF LOVE (1989) Music score: TREVOR JONES -S/T-
SPECTRUM (Univ): 550 130-2 (CD) -4 (MC)
SEA WOLF The (1941) Mus score: ERICH WOLFGANG KORNGOLD
+ *mus.from* 'PRIVATE LIVES OF ELIZABETH AND ESSEX'/
'JAUREZ' new record.by NEW ZEALAND SYMPH.ORCHESTRA
(cond: James Sedares) *KOCH: 37302-2 (CD)*
SEA WOLVES The (1980) Music score by ROY BUDD with the
NAT.PHILHARM.ORCH *CINEPHILE (Pinn): CINCD 023 (CD)*
SEAFORTH (BBC1 9/10/94) Music sco: JEAN-CLAUDE PETIT
-S/T- *D.SHARP-JADEAN (Pinn): DSCHCD(DSHMC) 7016*
SEAQUEST DSV (USA/ITV 16/10/93) Mus: JOHN DEBNEY -S/T-
VARESE (Pinn): VSD 5565 (CD) see COLL.38,83,
SEARCHERS (1956) m: MAX STEINER *see COLL.239,258,279,*
SECOND JUNGLE BOOK The (1997) Music score: JOHN SCOTT
-S/T- *JOHN SCOTT Rec (Silva Screen): JSCD 123 (CD)*
SECRET GARDEN The (ROYAL SHAKESPEARE CAST 2001) Songs:
LUCY SIMON (music) MARTHA NORMAN (lyrics)
FIRST NIGHT (Pinn): CASTCD 82 (CD)
SECRET GARDEN The (1992) Music sco: ZBIGNIEW PREISNER
"Winter Light" (Z.Preisner-L.Ronstadt-E.Kaz) by
LINDA RONSTADT -S/T- *VARESE (Pinn):VSD 5443 (CD)*
SECRET GARDEN The (BBC1 75 & 85) theme "The Watermill"
see COLL.44,
SECRET OF NIMH The (1982) Mus: JERRY GOLDSMITH Songs:
PAUL WILLIAMS -S/T- *VARESE (Pinn): VSD 5541 (CD)*
also on TER (Koch): CDTER 1026 (CD)
SECRET OF NIMH 2: Timmy To The Rescue (1998) Music sc:
LEE HOLDRIDGE, lyrics by RICHARD SPARKS -S/T- on
SONIC IMAGES (Cargo): SID 8820 (CD)
SECRET OF THE SAHARA (RAI/ZDF/TFI Co.Prod ITV 12/9/93)
music score: ENNIO MORRICONE vocal by AMII STEWART
-S/T- *RCA (BMG): 74321 34226-2 (CD) also on COLL*
TV FILM MUSIC (COLL) RCA (BMG): 74321 31552-2 (CD)
SECRET SQUIRREL (USA TV) *see COLL.246,259,*
SEINFELD (BBC2 6/10/93) m:JONATHAN WOLFF *see COLL.248,*
SELFISH GIANT The (O.CAST RECORD 1993) Songs: MICHAEL
JENKINS-NIGEL WILLIAMS *featur:* GRAHAM TREW-ALISON
CAIN-RICHARD TILEY *TER (Koch): CDTER 1206 (CD)*
SENSE AND SENSIBILITY (1996) Music sco: PATRICK DOYLE
-S/T- *SONY CLASSICS: SK 62258 (CD) ST 62258 (MC)*
SENTINEL The (USA DRAMA S) theme: JAMES NEWTON HOWARD
score by JOHN KEANE, songs by STEVE POCORO (Toto)
-S/T- *SONIC IMAGES (Cargo-Grehound): SI 8802 (CD)*
SERGEANT YORK (1941) Music: MAX STEINER *see COLL.239,*
SERIES 7 CONTENDERS (2000) Music: GIRLS AGAINST BOYS
-S/T- *KOCH INTERNATIONAL: KOCCD 8298 (CD)*
SERPICO (1973) Mus score: MIKIS THEODARAKIS
theme on COLL on NAXOS: 8551171 (CD)
SESAME STREET (USA 70's) theme music: JOE RAPOSO
see COLL.200,244,
SESSION 9 (2001) Music by CLIMAX GOLDEN TWINS -S/T-
IMPORT MILAN USA: MILAN 35957 (CD)
SEVEN (1994) Music score: HOWARD SHORE -S/T- VAR.ARTS.
CINERAMA/TVT/EDEL UK (Vital): 002243-2(CD)

SEVEN BRIDES FOR SEVEN BROTHERS - songs: Johnny Mercer
Gene De Paul + additional music by Adolph Deutsch
1. ORIG FILM -S/T- 1954 *with* HOWARD KEEL-JANE POWELL-
JEFF RICHARDS-RUSS TAMBLYN-TOMMY RALL -S/T- *27trks*
EMI PREMIER (EMI): CDODEON 17 (CD)
2. ORIG LONDON CAST 1986 *with new songs by* Al Kasha-
Joel Hirschhorn w: RONI PAGE-STEVE DEVEREAUX-GEOFF
STEER-PETER BISHOP-JACKIE CRAWFORD and Company
FIRST NIGHT (Pinn): OCRCD 6008 (CD)
SEVEN CITIES OF GOLD (1955) Mus score: HUGO FRIEDHOFER
Suite on Coll *with* 'THE RAINS OF RANCHIPUR' + 'THE
LODGER' by The MOSCOW SYPHONY ORCH (W.T.Stromberg)
MARCO POLO (Select): 8.223857 (CD)
SEVEN DEADLY SINS (SHOW) / SONGS by KURT WEILL sung by
MARIANNE FAITHFULL and conducted by RUSSELL DAVIS
RCA VICTOR (BMG): 74321 60119-2 (CD, 10.1998)
SEVEN MOONS (Sieben Monde)
-S/T- *COLOSSEUM (Pinn): CST 348072 (CD)*
SEVEN WAVES AWAY (1956) Music score: Sir ARTHUR BLISS
new recording by SLOVAK RADIO S.O. (Adriano) on
MARCO POLO (Select): 8.223315 (CD)
SEVEN YEAR ITCH The (1955) *see COLL.1,269,*
SEVEN YEARS IN TIBET (1997) Music score: JOHN WILLIAMS
-S/T- *SONY CLASSICS: SK 60271 (CD)*
SEVEN WONDERS OF THE WORLD (1956) *see* 'CARDINAL The'
SEVENTH VICTIM (1943) music: ROY WEBB *see COLL.275,*
SEVENTH VOYAGE OF SINBAD (1958) Mus: BERNARD HERRMANN
New ed: ROYAL SCOTTISH NAT.ORCH (John Debney cond)
VARESE (Pinn):VSD 5961 (CD) see COLLS.135,240,
SEVENTIES MANIA (ITV 16/6/2001) 1970s VARIOUS ARTISTS
COMPILATION *BMG: 74321 85219-2 (CD)*
SEVENTY GIRLS 70 - songs by John Kander and Fred Ebb
1. ORIG LONDON CAST 1991 *with* DORA BRYAN and Company
TER (Koch): CDTER 1186 (CD)
SEX CHIPS AND ROCK'N'ROLL (BBC1 05/09/1999) orig music
by MIKE MORAN,songs by MIKE MORAN-DEBBIE HORSFIELD
-S/T- feat: 'The ICE CUBES' + VAR.60's CHART HITS
VIRGIN (EMI): VTDCD 264 (2CD) VTDMC 264(2MC) other
music: "Rhapsody in G.minor Op.79 No.2" (J.BRAHMS)
SEX LIES & VIDEOTAPE (1989) Music sco: CLIFF MARTINEZ
-S/T- *VIRGIN (EMI): CDV 2604 (CD)*
SEXTON BLAKE (BBC 1967) theme music: FRANK CHACKSFIELD
see COLL.4,
SEXY BEAST (2001) Music score by ROQUE BANOS -S/T- inc
DEAN MARTIN-STRANGLERS-GIBSON BROS-UNKLE & SOUTH
EDEL (Vital): 012 578-2ERE (CD)
SHADOW The (1993) Music score: JERRY GOLDSMITH -S/T-
ARISTA (BMG): 0782218763-2 (CD) 0782218763-4 (MC)
SHADOW OF THE NOOSE (BBC2 1/3/89) *see COLL.5,20,*

SHADOW OF THE VAMPIRE (2000) Music score by DAN JONES
-S/T- *PACIFIC TIME (USA Import): PTE 8531 (CD)*
SHADOWLANDS (1993) Music score: GEORGE FENTON -S/T-
EMI: CDQ 555093-2 (CD) -4 (MC)

SHAFT (1971) Music score by ISAAC HAYES -S/T- reissue
STAX (Pinn): CDSXE 021 (CD) and *SCD 24880-2 (CD)*
MOVING IMAGE ENT (Silver Sounds): MIE 0022 (2LP)
see *COLL.13,75,90,95,104,223,*
SHAFT 2000 (2000) Music score: DAVID ARNOLD
-S/T- SONGS V.Arts *(music from and 'inspired' by)*
ARISTA-LaFACE (BMG): 073008 260802-2 (CD) -4 (MC)
-S/T- SCORE Arnold *HOLLYWOOD (Vital): 011 589-2ERE*
SHAKA ZULU *featuring* LADYSMITH BLACK MAMBEZO -S/T- on
WB (TEN): 7599 25582-2 (CD) WX 94C (MC)
SHAKA ZULU (ITV 22/6/91) music composed & performed by
DAVE POLLECUTT TV-S/T- *Imp: CDC 1002 (CD) deleted*
SHAKESPEARE IN LOVE (1998) Music sco: STEPHEN WARBECK
-S/T- *SONY CLASSICS: SK 63387 (CD)*
SHAKESPEARE REVUE (CHRISTOPHER LUSCOMBE-MALCOLM McKEE)
feat: SUSIE BLAKE-MARTIN CONNOR-JANIE DEE-C.LUS
COMBE-MALCOLM McKEE *TER (Koch): CDTEM2 1237 (CD)*
SHALL WE DANCE (1937) FILM MUSICAL *feat* FRED ASTAIRE
& GINGER ROGERS -S/T- *inc.songs from 'SWINGTIME'*
SANDY HOOK (Silver Sounds): CSH 177 178 (MC) also
+ 'TOP HAT' *GREAT MOVIE THEMES (BMG):CD 60042 (CD)*
SHALLOW HAL (2001) VARIOUS ARTISTS -S/T- with IVY on
ISLAND-UNIVERSAL: 586 569-2 (CD)
SHANE (Film 1953/TV 1966) "Call Of The Faraway Hills"
(Victor YOUNG-Mac DAVID) *see COLL.284,*
SHANGHAI NOON (2000) Music score: RANDY EDELMAN -S/T-
VARESE (Pinn): VSD 6154 (CD)
SHANGHAI VICE (C4 28/02/1999) Music sco: GEORGE FENTON
-S/T- *DEBONAIR (Pinn): CDDEB 1009 see COLL.20,*
SHARPE (ITV 05/5/93-1996) Music: JOHN TAMS and DOMINIC
MULDOWNEY *Collection* 'Music from Sharpe' (Various)
VIRGIN (EMI): VTCD 81 (CD) VTMC 81 (MC)
SHATTERER The (1999) Music score: TOT TAYLOR -S/T- on
TWEED COUTURE (Pinn): TWEEDCD 06 (CD)
SHE (1965) Music by JAMES BERNARD -S/T-+ 'VENGEANCE OF
SHE' *GDI (ABM/UNIV): GDICD 018 (CD) see COLL.126,*
SHE WORE A YELLOW RIBBON (1949) Music score: RICHARD
HAGEMAN and others *see COLL.258,279,*
SHE'S THE ONE (1995) Music by TOM PETTY -S/T- on
WEA (TEN): 9362 46285-2 (CD) -4 (MC)
SHELTERING SKY The (1990) Music sco: RYIUCHI SAKAMOTO
-S/T- *VIRGIN (EMI): CDV 2652 (CD)*
SHERLOCK HOLMES (Granada) 'Adventures'/'Return'/'Sign'
music: PATRICK GOWERS St.Paul's Cathedral Choir &
Gabrieli String Quartet and The Wren Orchestra
JAY-TER (SSD): CDJAY 1334 (CD)
SHERLOCK HOLMES AND THE VOICE OF TERROR (1942) Music:
FRANK SKINNER *new rec:* SLOVAK RADIO S.O. (William
Stromberg) *MARCO POLO (Select): 8.225124 (CD)*
SHERLOCK HOLMES The Musical (O.LONDON CAST 92) Songs
(L.BRICUSSE) *feat:* ROBERT POWELL-ROY BARRACLOUGH-
LOUISE ENGLISH *TER (Koch):CDTER 1198 (CD)*
SHILOH (1997) Music score: JOEL GOLDSMITH -S/T- on
VARESE (Pinn): VSD 5893 (CD)

SHINE (1996) Mus score: DAVID HIRSCHFELDER *piano music*
p: DAVID HIRSCHFELDER-DAVID HELFGOTT-RICKY EDWARDS
WILHELM KEMPF -S/T- *PHILIPS (Univ): 454 710-2 CD*
454 710-4 (MC) / also : 'BRILLIANTISSIMO' feat
DAVID HELFGOTT *RCA: 74321 46725-2 (CD) -4(MC)*
see *COLL.64,67,*

SHINER (2000) Music score by PAUL GRABOWSKI with -S/T-
VARIOUS ARTISTS *DECCA (UNIV): 470 183-2 (CD)*

SHIP OF FOOLS (1965) Music score by ERNEST GOLD -S/T-
ARTEMIS (HOT): ARTF 002 (CD)

SHIPWRECKED! (C4 12/01/2000) theme "The Sea" MORCHEEBA
from 'Big Calm' *INDOCHINA (TEN): 3984 22244-2(CD)*
also on *COLL.260,* 'TV 2000' *SONY: SONTV82CD (CD)*

SHIRLEY VALENTINE (1989) Music: WILLY RUSSELL-GEORGE
HATZINASSIOS "The Girl Who Used To Be Me" (Marvin
HAMLISCH) sung by PATTI AUSTIN -S/T- on
Silva Screen (Koch): FILMCD 062 (CD)

SHIRLEY'S WORLD (ATV 1971) "Shirley's Theme"/"Rickshaw
Ride" by LAURIE JOHNSON see *COLL.156,158,*

SHOCKHEADED PETER (MUSICAL based on HEINRICH HOFFMANN's
'Junk Opera' "STRUWWELPETER") feat: TIGER LILLIES
-S/T- *NVC ARTS-WARNER (TEN): 3984 26522-2 (CD)*

SHOESTRING (BBC1 30/9/1979) theme music GEORGE FENTON
see *COLL.4,42,*

SHOOTERS (2000) Music score: JOHN MURPHY -S/T- on
SANCTUARY (Pinn):SANCD 080 (CD)

SHOOTING FISH (1997) Music: STANISLAS SYREWICZ -S/T-
EMI: PRMDCD 35 (CD) PRMDTC 35 (MC) DELETED 2001

SHOOTING PARTY The (1985) Music sco: JOHN SCOTT Royal
Phil Orch (J.Scott) *JS (limited ed) JSCD 113 (CD)*

SHOOTIST The (1976) Music sco: ELMER BERNSTEIN suite
VARESE (Pinn): VCD 47264 (CD) see *COLL.40,*

SHORT CUTS (1993) VARIOUS ARTISTS -S/T- (Import) on
IMAGO (Direct): IMACD 23013 (CD)

SHORT EYES (1977) Music by CURTIS MAYFIELD -S/T-
with 'SUPERFLY' on *SEQUEL (BMG): NEMCD 964 (2CD)*
song "BreakIt Down" performed by FREDDY FENDER
-S/T- also on **CHARLY (Koch): CPCD 8183 (CD)**

SHORTLAND STREET (ITV 6/12/93) theme by GRAEME BOLLARD
sung by TINA CROSS *unavailable* see *COLL.172,*

SHOT AT GLORY, A (2000) Music score by MARK KNOPFLER
-S/T- *UNIVERSAL MUSIC: 548 127-2 (CD)*

SHOW BOAT - songs by Jerome Kern-Oscar Hammerstein II

1. FILM SOUNDTRACK 1951 *feat:* HOWARD KEEL-AVA GARDNER
KATHRYN GRAYSON -S/T- *29tks EMI PREM.CDODEON 5*
2. STUDIO RECORDING 1993 National Symphony Orchestra
w: BRIAN GREENE-FRAN LANDESMAN-JASON HOWARD-JANIS
KELLY-WILLARD WHITE-SALLY BURGESS-SHEZWAE POWELL-
CAROLINE O'CONONOR-SIMON GREEN and Company
Highlights: *SHOWTIME (MCI-THE): SHOWCD 011 (CD)*
Complete: *TER (Koch): CDTER2 1199 (2CD)*
3. REVIVAL USA CAST 1991 LINCOLN CENTER THEATRE
RCA (BMG): 09026 61182-23 (CD)

4. STUDIO RECORDING 1988 *1st complete* FREDERICA VON
STADE-JERRY HADLEY-TERESA STRATAS-BRUCE HUBBARD-
KARLA BURNS-DAVID GARRISON-PAIGE O'HARA-ROBERT
NICHOLS-NANCY KULP-LILLIAN GISH with the AMBROSIAN
CHORUS and LONDON SINFONIETTA (John McGlinn)
EMI HMV: TCRIVER 1 (3MC) CDRIVER 1 (3CD)
HIGHLIGHTS: *EMI CDC 749847-2(CD) EL 749847-4(MC)*
5. ORIG BROADWAY REVIVAL CAST 1946 *with:* JAN CLAYTON-
Carol Bruce-Charles Fredericks-Kenneth Spencer-Col
ette Lyons *SONY BROADWAY: SMK 61877 (CD)*
6. O.LONDON CAST 1928 MARIE BURKE-COLIN CLIVE-VIOLA
COMPTON-EDITH DAY-CEDRIC HARDWICKE-PAUL ROBESON
LESLIE SARONY-HOWETT WORSTER *+ mus 'LIDO LADY'* &
'SUNNY' (1926) PEARL *(Pavilion):* GEMMCD 9105 *(CD)*
O.USA CAST REC.1928-1947 VARIOUS ARTISTS
PEARL (Pavilion): GEMMCD 0060
7. ORIG LONDON CAST 1971 *with* CLEO LAINE-ANDRE
JOBIN-LORNA DALLAS-THOMAS CAREY-ENA CABAYO & Co.
LASERLIGHT POP-TARGET (BMG): 12446 (CD)
8. *GREAT MOVIE THEMES (Proper): CD 60054 (CD)*
SHOW GOES ON The (ORIGINAL CAST RECORDING)
DRG USA (New Note-Pinn): DRGCD 19008 (CD)
SHOW PEOPLE (1928 silent) Contemporary score by CARL
DAVIS *see COLL.85,* 'The SILENTS'
SHREK (2001) Music score HARRY GREGSON WILLIAMS-JOHN
POWELL -S/T- *DREAMWORKS UNIV: 450 305-2 (CD) also*
'MORE MUSIC FROM SHREK' *VARESE Pinn: VSD 6308 (CD)*
SID AND NANCY (1986) Music by JOE STRUMMER-THE POGUES
-S/T- *reissue UNIVERSAL: 088 112 413-2 (CD)*
SIEGE (1998) Music score: GRAEME REVELL -S/T- on
VARESE (Pinn): VSD 5989 (CD)
SIESTA (1988) Music sco: MARCUS MILLER-MILES DAVIS
-S/T- *WB (TEN) K925655-4 (MC) -2 (CD)*
SILENCE OF THE LAMBS The (1991) Music: HOWARD SHORE
see COLL.64,97,
SILENCERS The (1966) Songs performed by DEAN MARTIN
on collect. 'TV Shows & Songs from The Silencers'
COLLECTORS CHOICE (Koch/BMG): CCM 0256-2 (CD)
SILENCES OF THE PALACE (Les Silence Du Palais) (1994)
Music sc: ANOUR BRAHEM -S/T- *VIRGIN: CDVIR 35 (CD)*
SILENT FALL (1995) Music score: STEWART COPELAND -S/T-
MORGAN CREEK (Pinn): 002250-2 MCM (CD)
SILENT WITNESS (BBC1 21/2/96) theme mus (series 2 & 3)
by JOHN HARLE with vocal by SARAH LEONARD on
'SILENCIUM' *see COLL.130,*
orig.series theme by GEOFFREY BURGON *unavailable*
SILK ROAD The (ITV 23/6/87) 'Silk Road Suite' KITARO
+ LSO 'Silk Road 1' *Domo (Pinn): DOMO 71050-2 (CD)*
-4 (MC) 'Silk Road 2' *Domo: 71051-2 (CD) -4 (MC)*
SILKWOOD (1983) Music sco: GEORGES DELERUE -S/T- *reiss*
DRG (Pinn): DRGCD 6107 (CD)
SIMBA'S PRIDE (LION KING 2)(1998) Music: MARK MANCINA
'The LION KING Collection' (Various Artists) on
EDEL-DISNEY (Vital) 010150-2DNY (CD) -4(MC)

SIMON BATES OUR TUNE - see OUR TUNE
SIMON BIRCH (1999) Music score by MARC SHAIMAN -S/T-
   EPIC (Ten): 491 826-2 (CD) -4 (MC)
SIMPLE MAN, A (BBC2 1987) Music by CARL DAVIS (Ballet)
   about L.S.LOWRY *FIRST NIGHT (Pinn): OCRCD 6039 CD*
SIMPLE PLAN, A (1998) Music score: DANNY ELFMAN -S/T-
   SILVA SCREEN (Koch): FILMCD 310 (CD) also on imp:
   CMP USA (Silva Screen-Koch): 6676 03015-2 (CD)
SIMPLE TWIST OF FATE, A (1994) Music: CLIFF EIDELMAN
   -S/T- VARESE (Pinn): VSD 5538 (CD)
SIMPLY BARBRA ORIG.CAST REC. *feat:* STEVEN BRINBERG as
   BARBRA STREISAND.RECORDED 'LIVE' ABBEY RD STUDIOS
   TER (Koch): CDTER 1256 (CD)
SIMPLY IRRESTIBLE (1999) Music score by GIL GOLDSTEIN
   V.ARTS.-S/T- *RESTLESS (USA IMP):01877 72993-2 (CD)*
SIMPSONS The (Sky90/BBC1 23/11/96) theme: DANNY ELFMAN
   score: RICHARD GIBBS /'Simpsons Sing The Blues' +
   "Do The Bartman" *GEFFEN (BMG): GED 24308 (CD)*
   'SIMPSONS-THE YELLOW ALBUM' *GEFFEN: GED 24480 (CD)*
   'SONGS IN THE KEY OF SPRINGFIELD' Various Artists
   RHINO (TEN): 8122 72723-2 (CD) / 8122 75985-2 CD
   'GO SIMPSONIC WITH..' *(TEN): 8122 75480-2 (CD)*
   above 2 albums now on 1CD: (TEN) 8122 73529-2 (CD)
   also see COLL.248,
SINBAD AND THE EYE OF THE TIGER (1977) Music: ROY BUDD
   -S/T- CINEPHILE-CASTLE (Pinn): CINCD 005 (CD)
SINGIN' IN THE RAIN (FILM 1952) Songs: ARTHUR FREED-
   NACIO HERB BROWN *-S/T- reiss EMI ODEON: CDODEON 14*
   (CD) also: Impt.sco.+ *-S/T- 'AN AMERICAN IN PARIS'*
   BLUE MOON (Discovery): BMCD 7008 (CD)
SINGIN' IN THE RAIN (STUDIO RECORDING 1998) *featuring:*
   MICHAEL GRUBER-NANCY RINGHAM-RANDY ROGEL-CHRISTINA
   SAFFRAN & NATIONAL SYMPHONY ORCHEST (CRAIG BARNA)
   TER (Koch): CDTER 1240 (CD)
SINGIN' IN THE RAIN (O.LONDON CAST 1983) TOMMY STEELE-
   ROY CASTLE-SARAH PAYNE-DANIELLE CARSON & Company
   MD:Michael Reed *FIRST NIGHT (Pinn):OCRCD 6013 (CD)*
SINGLES (1992) Music by PAUL WESTERBERG-RICHARD GIBBS-
   CHRIS CORNELL *-S/T-reiss EPIC (TEN):471 438-2 (CD)*
SINS The (BBC1 24/10/2000) incident.music by ROB LANE
   "What Is A Man" sung by The TINDERSTICKS + others
   -S/T- BBC WORLDWIDE (Pinn): WMSF 6035-2 (CD)
SIR FRANCIS DRAKE (ABC/ATV 12/11/61-29/4/62) theme m:
   (Ventura) *see COLL.24,*
SIR HENRY AT RAWLINSON END (1980) M: VIVIAN STANSHALL
   featur: TREVOR HOWARD-PATRICK MAGEE-DENISE COFFEY-
   J.G.DEVLIN and VIVIAN STANSHALL *-S/T- re-issued on*
   VIRGIN (EMI): VCCCD 18 (CD) VCCMC 18 (MC)
SISTER ACT (1992) Music sco: MARC SHAIMAN *-S/T- reiss:*
   EDEL-HOLLYWOOD (Vital) 011334-2 (CD)
SISTER ACT 2: BACK IN THE HABIT (1993) Music score by
   MILES GOODMAN *-S/T-* with VARIOUS ARTISTS - *REISSUE*
   EDEL-HOLLYWOOD (Vital) 011 562-2HWR (CD)

SISTER MARY EXPLAINS IT ALL (2001) Music score:
-S/T- *VARESE (Pinn): VSD 6268 (CD)*
SISTERS (1973) - *see* BATTLE OF NERETVA
SIX DAYS SEVEN NIGHTS (1998) Music sco: RANDY EDELMAN
-S/T- *HOLLYWOOD (Univ): 162 163-2 (CD)*
SIX MILLION $ MAN (USA 1970's) *see COLL.124,221,246,*
SIX WEEKS (1982) Music score by DUDLEY MOORE on
GRP (BMG): GRP 96612 (CD) GRP 96614 (MC)
SIXTH DAY (2000) Music score by TREVOR RABIN -S/T-
VARESE (Pinn): VSD 6196 (CD)
SIXTH SENSE (1999) Music score by JAMES NEWTON HOWARD
-S/T- *VARESE (Pinn): VSD 6061 (CD)*
SKI SUNDAY (BBC2 1972-2002) theme mus "Pop Goes Bach"
SAM FONTEYN *see COLL.4,122,*
SKIDOO (1968) Music by HARRY NILSSON -S/T- *including*
'THE POINT' on *RCA (BMG): 74321 75743-2 (CD)*
SKIN The (LA PELLE/LA PEAU)(81) Mus sco: LALO SCHIFRIN
-S/T- *CINEVOX Ita (Silva Screen): CDCIA 5095 (CD)*
SKIPPY THE BUSH KANGAROO (Austral.TV 1966-68) theme by
ERIC JUPP *see COLL.246,*
SKULLS (2000) Music score by RANDY EDELMAN -S/T- on
LONDON (Univ): 466 989-2 (CD)
SKY AT NIGHT The (BBC1 1957-2002) theme "At The Castle
Gate" from 'Pelleas et Melisande' Op.46 (SIBELIUS)
SKY'S THE LIMIT (1943 MUSICAL) *feat:* FRED ASTAIRE and
JOAN LESLIE *inc.songs from* 'DUBARRY WAS A LADY' +
'42ND STREET' *TARGET (BMG):CD 60010 (CD)*
SLAB BOYS The (1997) Mus.arr.by JACK BRUCE *feat:* EDWYN
COLLINS-PAT KANE-PROCLAIMERS-LULU-EDDI READER
-S/T- *OCEAN DEEP (Grapevine-Poly): OCD 006 (CD)*
SLAUGHTER'S BIG RIP-OFF (1973) Music by JAMES BROWN
-S/T- *POLYDOR: 517 136-2 (CD)*
SLC PUNK (2000) V.Art: SUICIDE MACHINES/EXPLOITED/FEAR
STOOGES/SPECIALS/BLONDIE/GENERATION X/MOONDOGS/
VELVET UNDERGROUND/FIFI/ADOLESCENTS/DEAD KENNEDYS
HOLLYWOOD-EDEL (Vital) 010 255-2HWR (CD)
SLEDGEHAMMER (ITV 12/1/89)m: DANNY ELFMAN *see COLL.14,*
SLEEPING BEAUTY (1959) Mus d: GEORGE BRUNS -S/T- songs
EDEL-DISNEY (Vit) WDR 75622 (CD) see DISNEY P.341
SLEEPING WITH THE ENEMY *see COLL.64,*
SLEEPLESS IN SEATTLE (1993) Music: MARC SHAIMAN -S/T-
EPIC (Ten): 473 594-2 (CD) -4 (MC) -8 (MD)
see COLL.182,
SLEEPY HOLLOW (1999) Music score by DANNY ELFMAN -S/T-
HOLLYWOOD-EDEL (Vital) 012 262-2HWR (CD)
SLICE OF SATURDAY NIGHT, A (O.LONDON CAST 1989) Arts
Theatre Club / *with* BINKY BAKER-DAVID EASTER-
CLAIRE PARKER-MITCH JOHNSON-ROY SMILES
reissue: FIRST NIGHT (Pinn): OCRCD 6041 (CD)
SLIDING DOORS (1998) Music score: DAVID HIRSCHFELDER
-S/T- *MCA (UNI): MCD 11715 (CD)*
SLOW DRAG The (SHOW 1997) by CARSON KREITZER *featur:*
KIM CRISWELL-LIZA SADOVY-CHRISTOPHER COLQUHOUN
1940's Jazz Standards *TER (Koch): CDTER 1249 (CD)*

SLUMS OF BEVERLY HILLS (1998) Music sco: ROLFE KENT
-S/T- with VAR.ARTS *RCA (BMG): 09026 63269-2 (CD)*
SMACK THE PONY (C4 19/02/1999) mus: JONATHAN WHITEHEAD
theme "In The Middle Of Nowhere" (Kaye-Verdi) sung
by JACKIE CLUNE *unavailable*.orig DUSTY SPRINGFIELD
on 'Goin' Back' *PHILIPS: 848 789-2 (CD) -4 (MC)*
SMALL SOLDIERS (1998) Music sco: JERRY GOLDSMITH
-S/T- (score) *VARESE (Pinn): VSD 5963*
-S/T- (songs) *Dreamworks (BMG): DRD 50051 (CD)*
SMILLA'S FEELING FOR SNOW (1997) Music by HANS ZIMMER-
HARRY GREGSON WILLIAMS + "Stabat Mater"(PERGOLESI)
-S/T- *TELDEC (TEN): 0630 17872-2 (CD)*
SMOKEY JOE'S CAFE (Songs JERRY LEIBER & MIKE STOLLER)
O.LONDON CAST *FIRST NIGHT (Pinn) ENCORECD10 (2CD)*
O.BROADWAY CAST *ATLANTIC (TEN) 7567 82765-2 (CD)*
SMURFS The (1974) *see COLL.244,*

SNAGGLEPUSS - *see COLL.259,*

SNAKE EYES (1998) Music score: RYUICHI SAKAMOTO -S/T-
EDEL-HOLLYWOOD (Vital) 012 155-2HWR (CD)
SNAKE PIT The (1948) Music score by ALFRED NEWMAN
-S/T- incl.music from 'CAPTAIN FROM CASTILE'(1947)
TSUNAMI IMPORT (Discovery): TCI 0620/21 (2CD)
SNATCH (2000) Music score by JOHN MURPHY -S/T- (V.Art)
UNIVERSAL MUSIC: 524 999-2 (CD)
SNOOKER (BBC Sport) theme mus "Drag Racer" by DOUGLAS
WOOD GROUP *see COLL.101,122,see also* WORLD SNOOKER
SNOOPY THE MUSICAL (ORIG USA CAST RECORDING 1981) on
DRG USA (Pinn): CDRG 6103 (CD)
SNOW DAY (2000) Music score by STEVE BARTEK -S/T- on
POLYDOR (Univ): 490 598-2 (CD)
SNOW FALLING ON CEDARS (1998) Music sco: JAMES NEWTON
HOWARD -S/T- *DECCA (UNIV): 466 818-2 (CD)*
SNOW WHITE & T.SEVEN DWARFS (1937) S: FRANK CHURCHILL-
LEIGH HARLINE-PAUL SMITH feat: ADRIANA CASELOTTI
-S/T- *WEA-LONDON (TEN): 0927 42514-2 (CD) -4 (MC)*
see also WALT DISNEY FILM INDEX p.341
SNOW WHITE: A TALE OF TERROR (1996) Music score by
JOHN OTTMAN -S/T- *CITADEL (import) STC 77116 (CD)*
SNOWMAN The (C4 Cartoon 24/12/85) music: HOWARD BLAKE
Narr: Bernard Cribbins with The Sinfonia Of LONDON
Song *"Walking In The Air"* sung by PETER AUTY -S/T-
COL Ten CDX 71116 (CD) 40-71116 *(MC) see* COLL.285,
SNOWS OF KILIMANJARO The (1952) Mus: BERNARD HERRMANN
new score recording MOSCOW SYMPHONY ORCH conducted
by WILLIAM STROMBERG (incl: 'FIVE FINGERS' score)
MARCO POLO (Select): 8225168 (CD)
score select SILVA SCREEN (Koch): FILMCD 162 (CD)
also on 'Citizen Kane' *DECCA 417852-2 (CD)-4 (MC)*
SO GRAHAM NORTON (C4 24/01/2000) theme music "History
Repeating" by The PROPELLERHEADS with SHIRLEY
BASSEY *WALL OF SOUND (Vital): WALLD 036 (CDs)*

SOAP (USA 1980's) *see COLL.200,247,*
SOFTLY SOFTLY (BBC1 1970-80s) - *see COLL.124,*
SOLDIER BLUE (1970) Music score: ROY BUDD -S/T-Collect
   also feat 'CATLOW' (1971) and 'ZEPPELIN' (1971) on
   CINEPHILE (Pinn): CINCD 022 (CD)
SOLDIER SOLDIER (ITV from 10/6/1991) music: JIM PARKER
   -S/T- *SOUNDTRACK EMI GOLD: 520 686-2 (CD)*
SOLDIER'S DAUGHTER NEVER CRIES (1998) Music score by
   RICHARD ROBBINS -S/T- *EMI PREMIER: 497 060-2 (CD)*
SOLDIERS TO BE (BBC1 03/08/1999) theme "Like Soldiers
   Do" from 'Back To Basics' comp/sung by BILLY BRAGG
   COOKING VINYL (Vital) COOK(CD)(C) 060 (CD/MC)
SOLOMON AND SHEBA (1959) Music score: MARIO NASCIMBENE
   DRG-New Note (Pinn): DRGCD 32963 (CD) + 'VIKINGS'
SOME KIND OF WONDERFUL (1987) Music by Var.Arts -S/T-
   Beat Goes On (Pinn): BGO(CD)(MC) 178 (CD/MC)
SOME LIKE IT HOT (FILM 1959) music: ADOLPH DEUTSCH
   -S/T- *CD de-luxe RYKODISC (Vital): RCD 10715 (CD)*
SOME LIKE IT HOT (O.LONDON CAST 1992) Songs Jule STYNE
   BoB MERRILL *w.*TOMMY STEELE-BILLY BOYCE-ROYCE MILLS
   MANDY PERRYMENT *First Night (Pinn): OCRCD 6028 CD*
SOMEONE TO WATCH OVER ME (1987) *see COLL.123,227,*
SOMETHING TO BELEIVE IN (1997) Music sc: LALO SCHIFRIN
   -S/T- *ALEPH (Koch): ALEP 008 or 6517 926329-2 (CD)*
SOMETHING TO HIDE (1971) Music score by ROY BUDD
   -S/T- + music from INTERNECINE PROJECT (1974)
   CINEPHILE (Pinn): CINCD 019 (CD)
SOMEWHERE IN TIME (1980) Music: JOHN BARRY -S/T- on
   BEAT GOES ON (Pinn): BGO(CD)(MC) 222.new recording
   ROYAL SCOTTISH NATIONAL ORCHEST (John Debney,cond)
   VARESE (Pinn): VSD 5911 (CD) see COLL.26,30,64,
SON DE MAR Sound Of The Sea (2001) music by PIANO MAGIC
   -S/T- *4AD RECORDS: MAD 2105 (CD)*
SON OF FRANKENSTEIN (1939) Music score: FRANK SKINNER
   new r MOSCOW S.O. (Stromberg) *MARCO POLO (Select)*
   8.223748 (CD) + INVISIBLE MAN RETURNS-THE WOLF MAN
SON OF KONG (1933) Music: MAX STEINER *new recording by*
   MOSCOW S.O.conducted by WILLIAM T.STROMBERG / also
   incl.score to 'HOUNDS OF ZAROFF' (MOST DANGEROUS
   GAME) (1932) *MARCO POLO (Select): 8225166 (CD)*
SONDHEIM: A MUSICAL TRIBUTE ORIG BROADWAY CAST *with*
   DOROTHY COLLINS-CHITA RIVERA-ANGELA LANSBURY etc.
   RCA Vict: RD 60515 (2CDs)
SONG AND DANCE - songs: Andrew Lloyd Webber-Don Black
   1.ORIG LONDON CAST 1982 *with:* MARTI WEBB & Company
      POLYDOR: 843 619-2 (CD) PODVC 4 (2Cas)
   2.SONG AND DANCE / TELL ME ON A SUNDAY (STUDIO 1984)
      with SARAH BRIGHTMAN and WAYNE SLEEP and Company
      RCA (BMG) BD 70480 (CD) BK 70480 (MC)
SONG OF BERNADETTE The (1943) Music sco: ALFRED NEWMAN
   NEW REC: VARESE (Pinn): VSD 26025 (2CD) see COLL.1,
SONG OF NORWAY (STUDIO MUSICAL) Songs (Robert Wright-
   George Forrest adapt.from music by GRIEG) *featur:*
   VALERIE MASTERSON *TER (Koch) CDTER2 1173 (2CD)*

SONG OF THE SOUTH - *see also* WALT DISNEY INDEX p.341
SONGBOOK (ORIG LONDON CAST 1979) Songs by Monty Norman
    & Julian More *feat:* GEMMA CRAVEN-DAVID HEALY-DIANE
    LANGTON-ANTON RODGERS-ANDREW C.WADSWORTH *reissue:*
    DRG (New Note-Pinn): DRGCD 13117 (CD)
SONGCATCHER (2001)(V.Arts) -S/T- Music from & inspired
    by *VANGUARD (Proper): VCD 79586 (CD)*
SONGS OF PRAISE (BBC1 12/9/93) Organ theme by ROBERT
    PRIZEMAN recorded by STEPHEN CLEOBURY on Coll
    'Splendour Of Kings' *COLLINS (Koch): 14012 (CD)*
    'HARRY SECOMBE - SONGS OF PRAISE' (Collection) *on*
    RECOGNITION-WORD (UNIV): INCLD 001 (CD)
    'SONGS FROM THE HOLY LAND' VARIOUS ARTISTS *on*
    BBC WORLDWIDE (Pinn): WMEF 00562 (CD) 00564 (MC)
    Collection of hymns recorded at Old Trafford (BBC)
    EMI ALLIANCE (EMI): ALD 026 (CD) ALC 026 (MC)
    CHRISTMAS SONGS OF PRAISE *BBC WORLDWIDE (Pinn):*
    WMEF 0049-2 (CD) WMEF 0049-4 (MC)
    CELBRATION OF FAVOURITE HYMNS *BBC:WMEF 0069-2(CD)*
SONS AND DAUGHTERS (Australia ITV 19/10/83) title song
    (Peter Pinne-D.Battye) KERRI & MICK *DELETED*
SONS AND LOVERS (1960) Music: MARIO NASCIMBENE -S/T- +
    'A FAREWELL TO ARMS' *DRG (Pinn): DRGCSD 32962 (CD)*
SOOTY (CITV) music by MATTHEW CORBETT *see COLL.285,*
SOPHIA LOREN IN ROME (-S/T-) Music by JOHN BARRY
    PENDULUM (Hot): PEG 023 (CD)
SOPHIE'S CHOICE (1983) Orig mus: MARVIN HAMLISCH -S/T-
    SOUTHERN CROSS (Hot/S.Screen) SCCD 902 (CD)
SOPRANOS The (USA 1998/C4 15/07/1999) ser.theme music
    "Woke Up This Morning" by ALABAMA 3 on *ELM 41CDS1*
    SOPRANOS -S/T- *COLUMB (Ten): 497 403-2 (CD) -4(MC)*
    SOPRANOS -S/T- 'Peppers and Eggs' *502 188-2 (CD)*
    also on COLL.260, 'TV 2000' *SONY: SONTV82CD (CD)*
SORCERER The - *see under* 'Wages Of Fear' (1978)
SORDID LIVES (2001) Music score by GEORGE S.CLINTON
    -S/T- *VARESE (Pinn): VSD 6257 (CD)*
SOUL FOOD (1997) -S/T- featuring VARIOUS ARTISTS on
    LaFACE-RCA (BMG): 73008 26041-2 (CD) -4 (MC)
    also on (BMG): 74321 52307-2 (CD)
SOUL IN THE HOLE (1997) Basketball Drama-Documentary
    ORIG.MUSIC FROM AND INSPIRED BY MOTION PICTURE
    -S/T- (V.ARTISTS) *CLOUD (BMG): 07863 67531-2 (CD)*
SOUL MAN (1986) Music sco: TOM SCOTT + V.Arts -S/T-
    re-issued on SPECTRUM (Univ): 551 431-2 (CD)
SOUL MUSIC (TERRY PRATCHETT'S) - *see* DISCWORLD
SOUL SURVIVORS (1999) Music score by DANIEL LICHT
    -S/T- *IMPORT BEYOND (USA): 578 220-2 (CD)*
SOUND BARRIER The (1952) M: MALCOLM ARNOLD "Rhapsody"
    'Film Music' LSO (R.Hickox) *CHANDOS: CHAN 9100 CD*
    see COLL.120,
SOUND OF MUSIC - Richard Rodgers-Oscar Hammerstein II
    1.FILM MUSICAL 1965 JULIE ANDREWS-CHRISTOPER PLUMMER
    (a): -S/T- 35th anniversary edit.+ *prev.UNRELEASED*
    tracks RCA (BMG): 07863 67972-2 (CD)

(b): -S/T- *ORIGINAL (RE-MASTERED EDITION)*
RCA (BMG): 07863 67965-2 (CD.09/2000)
2.ORIG BROADWAY CAST 1959 MARY MARTIN-THEODORE BIKEL
PATRICIA NEWAY-KURT KASZNAR-MARION MARLOWE-LAURIE
PETERS-BRIAN DAVIES *SONY BROADWAY: SK 60583 (CD)*
3.ORIG LONDON CAST 1961 *with* JEAN BAYLESS-CONSTANCE
SHACKLOCK-OLIVE GILBERT-SYLVIA BEAMISH-LYNN KENNIN
GTON *LASERLIGHT (BMG): 12448 (CD) also on*
FIRST NIGHT (Pinn): OCRC 2 (MC)
SOUNDS OF THE SUBURBS - see John Peel's Sounds Of...
SOUTH BANK SHOW (LWT 1978-2000) theme "Caprice In A.
Minor No.24" 'Themes & Variations 1-4' (PAGANINI)
ANDREW & JULIAN LLOYD WEBBER *MCA: MCLD 19126 (CD)*
SOUTH PACIFIC - songs by Richard Rodgers and Oscar
Hammerstein II
1.FILM MUSICAL 1958 MITZI GAYNOR-ROSSANO BRAZZI*-
JOHN KERR*-JUANITA HALL* *re-mastered edit -S/T- on*
RCA (BMG): 07863 67977-2 (CD, 11/2000)
2.REVIVAL LONDON CAST 1988 *w:* GEMMA CRAVEN-BEATRICE
READING *FIRST NIGHT (Pinn): OCRCD 6023 (CD)*
3.STUDIO RECORDING 1986 KIRI TE KANAWA-JOSE CARRERAS
Sarah Vaughan-Mandy Patinkin-Ambrosia Singers
L.S.O.(Jonathan Tunick) *SONY: CBSCD 42205 (CD)*
4.ORIG BROADWAY CAST 1949 MARY MARTIN-EZIO PINZA-
JUANITA HALL-BARBARA LUNA-MICHAEL DeLEON-MYRON
McCORMICK-WILLIAM TABBERT-BETTA St.JOHN and Comp
COLUMBIA (Ten): SMK 60722 (CD)
5.STUDIO RECORDING 1996) *feat* PAIGE O'HARA
JUSTINO DIAZ-SHEZWAE POWELL-SEAN McDERMOTT with
NATIONAL SYPHONY ORCH conduct: JOHN OWEN EDWARDS
TER (Koch):CDTER 1242 (2CD) Highlights CDTEH 6009
6.**REPRISE MUSICAL REPERTORY COMPANY** *including* 'KISS
ME KATE'/'FINIAN'S RAINBOW'/'GUYS & DOLLS'
REPRISE (TEN): 9362 47775-2 (4CD set)
SOUTH PARK - Bigger Longer and Uncut VARIOUS ARTISTS
ATLANTIC (TEN): 7567 83199-2 (CD) -4 (MC)
SOUTH PARK (USA 97/C4 10/7/1998) "South Park Theme"
PRIMUS. 'SOUTH PARK CHEF AID' V.Arts compilation
COLUMBIA (Ten): 491 700-2 (CD) 491 700-4 (MC)
'MR.HANKY POO'S CHRISTMAS CLASSICS' EXPLICIT
(explicit: COLUMBIA (Ten): 496 714-2 (CD) -4 (MC)
(edited v: COLUMBIA (Ten): 496 714-9 (CD) -3 (MC)
see COLL 'HIT TV' on ***VARESE (Pinn): VSD 5957 (CD)***
SOUTH RIDING (ITV 1974) m: RON GRAINER *see COLL.6,8,*

SOUTHERN MAID (O.LONDON CAST 1920) Songs: H.FRASER
SIMPSON-DION CLAYTON CALTHROP-HARRY GRAHAM with
addit.songs by IVOR NOVELLO-DOUGLAS FURBER *feat:*
GWENDOLINE BROGDEN-ERNEST BERTRAM-JOSE COLLINS
Pearl (Pavilion): GEMMCD 9115 (CD)
SOUVENIR DE VOYAGE Music score: BERNARD HERRMANN
VARESE (Pinn): VSD 5559 (CD)
SPACE 1999 (ITC 4/9/75-77) music by BARRY GRAY
see COLL.38,84,218,237,250,

SPACE...ABOVE AND BEYOND (USA) *see COLL.218,*

SPACE COWBOYS (2000) Music score LENNIE NIEHAUS -S/T-
(V.ARTS) *WARNER (TEN) 9362 47848-2 (CD) -4 (MC)*
SPACE IS THE PLACE featuring music by SU RA -S/T- on
EVIDENCE (Harmonia Mundi): ECD 22070-2 (CD)
SPACE JAM (1996) Music score: JAMES NEWTON HOWARD
-S/T- songs: *ATLANTIC (TEN): 7567 82961-2 (CD)*
-S/T- score: *ATLANTIC (TEN): 7567 82979-2 (CD)*
SPACED (C4 24/09/1999) Orig music by GUY PRATT -S/T-
CHANNEL 4 MUSIC (Univ): C4M 0010-2 (CD)
SPARTACUS (USA-60/renovated 91) Music sco: ALEX NORTH
-S/T- *MCA (S.Screen): MCAD 10256 (CD)* addit.mus.
IMPORT TSUNAMI (S.Screen): TSI 0603 (CD)
SPARTACUS (Jeff Wayne's Musical Version 1992)
Columbia (Ten): 472030-4 (2 MC) 472030-2 (2CD)
SPAWN (1997) Music sco: GRAEME REVELL -S/T- V.Artists
IMMORTAL-SONY (TEN): 488 188-2 (CD) 488 118-0 3LPs
SPECIALIST The (1994) Music: JOHN BARRY *see COLL.26,*
SPEED (94) Music score: MARK MANCINA V.Arts -S/T-
Songs: *ARISTA (BMG): 07822 11018-2 (CD)*
Score: *MILAN (BMG): 234 652 (CD)*
SPEED 2: CRUISE CONTROL (1997) Music sco: MARK MANCINA
VIRGIN (EMI): CDVUS 129 (CD)
SPEEDWAY *see* ELVIS PRESLEY INDEX p.348
SPELLBOUND (1945) Music score: MIKLOS ROSZA -S/T- incl
'JUNGLE BOOK' (ROSZA) *FLAPPER (Pinn): PASTCD 7093
(CD) see COLL.50,144,191,214,235,267,268,*
SPENCER'S MOUNTAIN (1963) m: MAX STEINER *see COLL.239,*
SPEND SPEND SPEND! (MUSICAL 1999) *not available*
SPENSER FOR HIRE (USA 85)(BBC1 12/9/89) theme: STEVE
DORFF-LARRY HERBSTRITT *see COLL.14,*
SPHERE (1997) Music score: ELLIOT GOLDENTHAL -S/T- on
VARESE (Pinn): VSD 5913 (CD)
SPIDER The (TV THRILLER DENMARK) Music score by SOREN
HYLDEGAARD -S/T- *REC-ART IMPORT: 527 050-2 (CD)*
SPIDERMAN (USA TV) *see COLL.243,*
SPINAL TAP - *see* THIS IS SPINAL TAP
SPINOUT *see* ELVIS PRESLEY INDEX p.348
SPIRITS GHOSTS AND DEMONS (C4 27/9/94) orig music by
GEORGE FENTON - *see* 'BEYOND THE CLOUDS' entry
SPITTING IMAGE (Central 6/86) 'Spit In Your Ear' V/A
VIRGIN (EMI) CDVIP 110 (CD) TCVIP 110 (MC)
SPORTSMASTER *see COLL.100,122,*
SPORTSNIGHT (BBC1 1970-1997) *see COLL.2,122,131,200,*
SPORTSVIEW (BBC 1954-68) theme music "Saturday Sports"
by WILFRED BURNS *see COLL.5,122,*
SPRINGTIME IN THE ROCKIES (1942 FILM CAST) *feat:* BETTY
GRABLE-CARMEN MIRANDA inc.sel.from 'SWEET ROSIE O'
GRADY' *SANDY HOOK (Silver Sounds): CDSH 2090 (CD)*
SPY KIDS (2000) Music by DANNY ELMAN with JOHN DEBNEY-
GAVIN GREENAWAY-HEITOR PEREIRA-ROBERT RODRIGUEZ &
LOS LOBOS -S/T- *GOLD CIRCLE (Prop) GC 30002-2 (CD)
CHAPTER III (USA Import (-) (CD)*

SPY WHO LOVED ME The (1977) Music sco: MARVIN HAMLISCH title song (M.Hamlisch-Carole Bayer Sager) sung by CARLY SIMON -S/T- *reissue EMI PREMIER: CZ 555 (CD)* JAMES BOND FILM INDEX p.346 *see COLL.47,222,*

SPYSHIP (BBC1 9/11/83) theme "A Cold Wind" by RICHARD HARVEY vocal by JUNE TABOR *K-TEL: ONCD 3435 (CD)*

ST. - *see under* 'SAINT...'

STAGE DOOR CANTEEN (1943) ORIGINAL FILM CAST RECORDING *SANDY HOOK (Silver Sounds): CDSH 2093 (CD)*

STAGECOACH (1965) Music score: JERRY GOLDSMITH -S/T- inc music to 'THE LONER' *Ltd Edition Import on RETROGRADE (S.Screen/MFTM): FSMCD Vol.1 No.1 (CD) see COLL.258,*

STAND The (1993) Music score: W.G.SNUFFY WALDEN -S/T- *VARESE (Pinn): VSD 5496 (CD)*

STAND BY ME (1987) Mus sco: JACK NITZSCHE -S/T- V.ARTS *ATLANTIC (TEN): CD 7567 81677-2 (CD) WX 92C (MC)*

STAND BY YOUR MAN (MUSICAL) *feat* HELEN HOBSON & Comp. *SILVA SCREEN (Koch): SONGCD 913 (CD) SONGC 913(MC)*

STAR! (1968) feat JULIE ANDREWS as Gertrude Lawrence -S/T- *FOX-ARISTA (BMG): 07822 11009-2 (CD)*

STAR DUST (1940) VARIOUS -S/T- SELECTIONS on *GREAT MOVIE THEMES: (Targ-BMG): CD 60032 (CD)*

STAR FOR A NIGHT (BBC1 26/06/1999-2000) COLLECTION OF PARTICIPATING ARTISTS FROM 1999/2000 SERIES on *BBC WORLDWIDE (Pinn): WMEF 0065-2 (CD)*

STAR IS BORN,A (54) JUDY GARLAND-JAMES MASON -S/T- *CBS USA (S.Screen): CK 44389 (CD) JST 44389 (MC)*

STAR IS BORN,A (76)BARBRA STREISAND-KRIS KRISTOFFERSON -S/T- *COLUMBIA Sony: 474905-2 (CD) -4 (MC)*

STAR KID (1997) Music score: NICHOLAS PIKE -S/T- on *SONIC IMAGES (Cargo-Greyhound): SCI 8800 (CD)*

STAR SPANGLED RHYTHM (1942 MUSICAL) *feat:* BETTY HUTTON BING CROSBY-DICK POWELL *incl.songs from* 'FOOTLIGHT PARADE' *TARGET (BMG): CD 60013 (CD)*

STAR TREK (TV) (USA1966) theme: ALEXANDER COURAGE *note* 30TH BIRTHDAY EDITION (Coll) Music taken from best STAR TREK 1966-1968 ROYAL PHILHARMONIC ORCHESTRA orch: FRED STEINER *VARESE (Pinn): VSD 25762 (2CD)* *also* VOLS 1/2 *VARESE (Pinn): VSD 47235 / 457240* CLASSIC SERIES V.1 *GNPD 8006 (CD) GNP-5 8006 (MC)* CLASSIC SERIES V.2 *GNPD 8025 (CD) GNP-5 8025 (MC)* CLASSIC SERIES V.3 *GNPD 8030 (CD) GNP-5 8030 (MC)* SOUND EFFECTS (60) *GNPD 8010 (CD) GNP-5 8010 (MC)* STAR TREK *GNP (Vivanti): GNP 8006 (LP Audio Qual)* TV SCORES 1/2 (R.P.O.) *CBS (HOT): LXE 703/704 (CD) see COLL.38,61,65,115,117,218,237,242,*

STAR TREK (TV): THE NEXT GENERATION (88)(BBC2-26/9/90) New theme: JERRY GOLDSMITH-ALEXANDER COURAGE plus music by DENNIS McCARTHY *all distributed by ZYX* Volume 1 - *GNPD 8012 (CD) GNP-5 8012 (MC)* Volume 2 - *GNPD 8026 (CD) GNP-5 8026 (MC)* Volume 3 - *GNPD 8031 (CD) GNP-5 8031 (MC) see COLL.14,218,248,*

STAR TREK (TV): DEEP SPACE NINE (BBC2 28/9/95) music:
DENNIS McCARTHY-JAY CHATTAWAY -S/T- *GNP (ZYX)*
GNPD 8034 (CD) GNP-5 8034 (MC)
STAR TREK (TV): VOYAGER (USA 94/BBC 6/95) theme JERRY
GOLDSMITH score: JAY CHATTAWAY -S/T- *GNPD 8041*
(CD) GNP-5 8041 (MC) see COLL.114,115,
STAR TREK: THE MOTION PICTURE (1979) Music score JERRY
GOLDSMITH. *reiss:* GENE RODDENBERRY'S 'INSIDE STAR
TREK' *SONY: SK 66134 (2CD) / 489 929-2 (CD) -4(MC)*
STAR TREK (2) The Wrath Of Khan (1982) Mus sco: JAMES
HORNER) -S/T- *GNP USA IMPT (ZYX): GNPD 8022*
(CD) GNP-5 8022 (MC) with orig Alex.Courage theme
STAR TREK (3) Search For Spock (1984) M: JAMES HORNER
-S/T- *GNP-58023 (MC)*
STAR TREK (4) The Voyage Home (1987) Mus sco: LEONARD
ROSENMAN -S/T- *MCA (UNI): MCLD 19349 (CD deleted)*
STAR TREK (5) The Final Frontier (1989) Mus sc: JERRY
GOLDSMITH -S/T- *EPIC: 465925-2(CD) -4(MC) deleted*
STAR TREK (6) The Undiscovered Country (1991) Mus sco
CLIFF EIDELMAN -S/T- *MCA (UNI): MCLD 19348 (CD)*
STAR TREK (7) Generations (1994) Mus sc: DENNIS McCAR
THY -S/T- *GNP (ZYX): GNPD(GNP5) 8040 (CD/MC)*
STAR TREK (8) First Contact (Generations 2) (1996) Mus
JERRY GOLDSMITH *GNP (ZYX): GNPD 8052 (CD) COLL.118*
STAR TREK (9) Insurrection (1998) Mus: JERRY GOLDMITH
-S/T- *GNP CRESCENDO (ZYX): GNPD 8059 (CD)*

STAR WARS EPISODE 1: THE PHANTOM MENACE (1998) Music:
JOHN WILLIAMS conducting LONDON SYMPHONY ORCHESTRA
SONY CLASSICAL: SK 61816 (CD) ST 61816 (MC) also
VARESE (Pinn): VSD 6086 (CD)(COLL.WITH OTHER HITS)
'THE ULTIMATE EDITION' with unreleased material on
SONY CLASSICS (TEN): S2K 89460 (2CD)
STAR WARS (1) (1977) Music score: JOHN WILLIAMS -S/T-
RSO 2679 092 (LP) 800 096-2 (CD) also available
on *RCA RCD 13650 (CD)* c/w 'Close Encounters..'
see *COLL.73,171,218,232,237,238,280,281,*
STAR WARS (2) The Empire Strikes Back (1981) Mus sco
JOHN WILLIAMS -S/T-*Imp (S.Screen): 827580-4 (MC)*
Special Edit: *RCA (BMG): 09026 68773-2 (CD) -4(MC)*
STAR WARS (3) Return Of The Jedi (1983) Music score:
JOHN WILLIAMS - National Philharmonic Orchestra
(Charles Gerhardt) *-RCA Vict (BMG): GD 60767 (CD)*
-S/T- *RCA: RK 14748 (MC) RCD 14748 (CD)*
Special Edit. *RCA (BMG): 09026 68774-2 (CD) -4(MC)*
STAR WARS (A NEW HOPE) Music score: JOHN WILLIAMS
Special Edition ORIG SOUNDTRACK RECORDING (1997)
RCA (BMG): 09026 68746-2 (Deluxe 2CD)
Special Ed: *RCA (BMG): 09026 68772-2 (2CD) -4(2MC)*
also available -S/T- *VARESE (Pinn): VSD 5794 (CD)*
STAR WARS: SHADOWS OF THE EMPIRE Music by JOEL McNEELY
VARESE (Pinn): VSDE 5700 (CD)
STAR WARS TRILOGY - The ORIGINAL SOUNDTRACK ANTHOLOGY
Music score by JOHN WILLIAMS / also containing the

20th Cent.Fox Fanfare with Cinemascope Extention
(Alfred Newman) *this collect. contains previously
UNRELEASED m. FOX-Arista (BMG): 07822 11012-2 4CDs*
STAR WARS TRILOGY Sel.mus.from 3 films + 'Close Encou
nters' UTAH SYMPH OR *VARESE (Pinn): VCD 47201(CD)*
STARGATE (1994) Music score: DAVID ARNOLD -S/T- reiss:
MILAN BMG: 74321 24901-2(CD) see COLL.218,233,
STARLIGHT EXPRESS - songs by Andrew Lloyd Webber and
Richard Stilgoe
    1.ORIG LONDON CAST 1993 *Apollo Victoria Cast
    POLYDOR 519 041-2 (CD) 4 (MC) -1 (LP) -5 (Mini-D)*
STARMAN (1985) Music score: JACK NITZSCHE -S/T-
VARESE (Pinn):VCD 47220 (CD) see COLL.220,
STARS IN THEIR EYES (ITV 1990-2000) ARTISTS COLLECTION
*BMG TV (BMG): 74321 78966-2 (CD) -4 (MC) also
available 2000 winner* NICOLA KIRSCH (MARIA CALLAS)
'VOICE OF A STAR' *BMG: 74321 82266-2 (CD)*
STARSHIP TROOPERS (1997) Music score: BASIL POLEDOURIS
-S/T- *VARESE (Pinn): VSD 5877 (CD) see COLL.233,*
STARSKY & HUTCH (USA 75) theme "Gotcha" TOM SCOTT
see COLL.244,
STARTING HERE STARTING NOW songs: David Shire-Richard
Maltby Jr O.LONDON CAST *TER (Koch): CDTER 1200*
STATE AND MAIN (2000) Music score by THEODORE SHAPIRO
-S/T- *BMG IMPORTS: 09026 63740-2 (CD)*
STATE FAIR songs: Richard Rodgers-Oscar Hammerstein II
BROADWAY CAST 1996 JOHN DAVIDSON-DONNA McKECHNIE
DRG (Pinn): DRG(CD)(MC) 94765 (CD/MC)
STATE FAIR 2 *VARESE (Pinn): VSD 6090 (CD)*
STAY AWAY JOE *see* ELVIS PRESLEY INDEX p.348
STAY TUNED (1992) Music sc: BRUCE BROUGHTON + Various
Arts -S/T- *MORGAN CREEK (Pinn): 002251-2 MCM (CD)*
STAYING ALIVE (1983) Music score: JOHNNY MANDEL feat:
BEE GEES *reissued* -S/T- *RSO (Univ): 813269-2 (CD)*
STEAL THIS MOVIE! (2000) Music score by MADER
-S/T- (songs) *EPIC (TEN): 498 574-2 (CD)*
-S/T- (score) *VARESE (Pinn): VSD 6177 (CD)*
STEALING HEAVEN (1989) Music score: NICK BICAT -S/T-
TER (Koch): CDTER 1166 (CD)
STENDHAL SYNDROME The (1996) Music sc: ENNIO MORRICONE
-S/T- *DRG (Pinn): DRGCD 12621 (CD)*
STEP LIVELY (1944 MUSICAL) *feat* FRANK SINATRA-ADOLPHE
MENJOU-GLORIA DE HAVEN *inc.songs from* 'HIGHER AND
HIGHER' *TARGET (BMG): CD 60004 (CD)*
STEPPING OUT (ORIGINAL LONDON CAST 1997)
FIRST NIGHT (Pinn): SCENECD 24 (CD)
STEPTOE & SON (BBC 5/1/62) theme "Old Ned" RON GRAINER
see COLL.2,8,24,74,253,261,
STEVEN BRINBERG IS SIMPLY BARBARA (ORIG LONDON CAST)
TER (Koch): CDTER 1256 (CD)
STIFF UPPER LIPS (1998) VARIOUS CLASSICAL MUSIC -S/T-
EMI PREMIER Soundtracks: 495 529-2 (CD)
STIGMATA (1999) Music score by ELIA CMIRAL -S/T- on
VIRGIN (EMI): CDVUS 161 (CD)

STILL BREATHING (1998) -S/T- on
WILL (Silver Sands): 7801 633649-2 (CD)
STILL CRAZY (1998) Music: CLIVE LANGER-ALAN WINSTANLEY
feat JIMMY NAIL and STRANGE FRUIT & BILLY CONNOLLY
-S/T- (10/1999) *LONDON (Ten): 3984 28235-2 (CD)*
-S/T- (10/1998) *LONDON (Univ): 556 055-2 (CD)*
STING The (1973) Music: MARVIN HAMLISCH-SCOTT JOPLIN
-S/T-*MCA (UNI): MCLD 19027(CD)*
STINGRAY (ATV/ITC 6/10/64 reshown BBC2 11/9/92) music
BARRY GRAY (vocal: *GARRY MILLER)*
see *COLL.2,24,38,74,84,118,246,250,253,*
STIR OF ECHOES (1999) Music score: JAMES NEWTON HOWARD
-S/T- *NETTWERK (Pinn): 30145-2 (CD)*
STOLEN HEARTS (1996) Mus: NICK GLENNIE SMITH-PADDY MOL
ONEY / "Haunted" by SHANE MacGOWAN-SINEAD O'CONNOR
-S/T- *M.CREEK-CINERAMA (Vital): 002253-2 MCM*
STONE KILLER The (1973) Music score: ROY BUDD -S/T- on
CINEPHILE (Pinn): CINCD 006 (CD) see COLL.54,
STOP IN THE NAME OF LOVE (ORIG LONDON CAST 1990) *with*
Fabulous Singlettes Live From The Piccadilly on
FIRST NIGHT (Pinn): OCRCD 6017 (CD)
STOP MAKING SENSE (LIVE CONCERT FILM 1984) Music by
DAVID BYRNE and TALKING HEADS *remixed, remastered,*
re-edited by DAVID BYRNE and containing 7 extra
tracks not on original *EMI: 522 453-2 (CD) -4 (MC)*
STOP THE WORLD I WANT TO GET OFF (ORIG LONDON CAST 61)
1.*with* MIKE HOLOWAY-LOUISE GOLD and The NSO ENSEMBLE
(Martin Yates, MD) *TER (Koch): CDTER 1226 (CD)*
STOREFRONT HITCHCOCK (1998) Music sco: ROBYN HITCHCOCK
-S/T- *WARNER: 9362 46848-2 (CD)*
STORMY WEATHER (1943 FILM CAST) *feat* LENA HORNE-BENNY
CARTER-CAB CALLOWAY AND HIS BAND-FATS WALLER etc.
SANDY HOOK (Silver Sounds): CDSH 2037 (CD) also on
DEFINITIVE (Discovery): SFCD 33505 (CD) and
STORY OF THREE LOVES The (1953) 'Rhapsody On A Theme
Of Paganini' (RACHMANINOV) on 'CLASSIC EXPERIENCE'
EMI PREMIER (EMI): CDCLEXP 1 (2CD) TCLEXP 1 (2MC)
-S/T- on *TICKERTAPE (USA): TT 3015 (CD)*
STORY OF US The (2000) Mus: ERIC CLAPTON-MARC SHAIMAN
-S/T- *REPRISE (TEN): 9362 47608-2 (CD)*
STRADIVARI (1989) -S/T- Class Mus: TELEMANN-H.PURCELL
VIVALDI-PACHELBEL-HANDEL -S/T-*PHIL: 422 849-2 (CD)*
STRAIGHT STORY The (1999) Music sc: ANGELO BADALAMENTI
-S/T- *WINDHAM HILL-RCA (BMG): 01934 11513-2 (CD)*
STRAIGHT TO HELL (1987) Mus: POGUES-JOE STRUMMER-ELVIS
COSTELLO-PRAY FOR RAIN-ZANDER SCHLOSS -S/T- on
RERERTOIRE (Pinn): REP 4224WY (CD)
STRANGE REPORT (ITV 21/9/68) ROGER WEBB *see COLL.250,*

STRANGER THAN PARADISE (1986) + 'The Resurrection of
Albert Ayler' Music sco: JOHN LURIE -S/T- score
MADE TO MEASURE (New Note-Pinn): MTM 7 (CD)
STRANGERERS The (SKY1 02/2000) Music by PETER BREWIS
unavailable

STREET SCENE (SHOW 1989) Songs: KURT WEILL-LANGSTON HUGHES / O.LONDON CAST *feat* KRISTINE CIESINSKI-JANIS KELLY-RICHARD VAN ALLAN-CATHERINE ZETA JONES BONAVENTURA BOTTONE *TER (Koch): CDTER2 1185 (2CD)*

STREETCAR NAMED DESIRE A (1951) Music sco: ALEX NORTH Orchestral score: NATIONAL PHILHARMONIC ORCH cond. by JERRY GOLDSMITH *VARESE (Pinn): VSD 5500 (CD)*

STREETCAR NAMED DESIRE A (1951) Music sco: ALEX NORTH Orchestral score: NATIONAL PHILHARMONIC ORCH cond. by JERRY GOLDSMITH *VARESE (Pinn): VSD 5500 (CD) also avail.on CLOUD NINE (S.Screen): CNS 5003 (CD) with* symphonic suites from 'The INFORMER' (35-Max Steiner) 'NOW VOYAGER' (42-Max STEINER) & 'SINCE YOU WENT AWAY' (44-Max STEINER) *Archive Series*

STREETFIGHTER (1994) Music sco: GRAEME REVELL 2 -S/T- Songs: *VIRGIN: CDPTY(PTYMC)(PTYLP) 114 (CD/MC/LP)* Score: *VARESE (Pinn): VSD 5560 (CD)*

STREETHAWK (USA84 ITV) m: TANGERINE DREAM *see COLL.14,*

STREETS APART (BBC1 1988) mus:DAVE MACKAY *see COLL.20,*

STREETS OF FIRE (1984) Songs: JIM STEINMAN -S/T- *reiss Beat Goes On (Pinn): BGO(CD)(MC) 220 (CD/MC) also*

STREETS OF SAN FRANCISCO (USA) Music by PAT WILLIAMS *see COLL.84,124,244,*

STRESSED ERIC (BBC2 30/08/2000) 2nd series music by PETE BAIKIE-JASON McDERMID-MAT CLARK *unavailable*

STRICTLY BALLROOM (1992) Music sco: DAVID HIRSCHFELDER -S/T- reissue *COLUMBIA (Ten): 472300-2*

STRIPPER The (1963) Music score: JERRY GOLDSMITH *see COLL.1,*

STUART LITTLE (1999) Music score by ALAN SILVESTRI -S/T- *MOTOWN (Univ): 542 083-2 (CD)*

STUDENT PRINCE The - songs by Sigmund Romberg
  1.FILM MUSICAL 1954 *with:* MARIO LANZA *RCA Red Seal (BMG): GD(GK) 60048 (CD/MC) with:* The DESERT SONG
  2.STUDIO REC.1990 *with:* NORMAN BAILEY-MARILYN HILL SMITH-DIANA MONTAGUE-DAVID RENDALL-ROSEMARY ASHE Highlights: *TER (Koch): CDTEO 1005 (CD)*
    Complete: *TER (Koch): CDTER2 1172 (2CDs)*
  3.STUDIO RECORDING *with:* GORDON MacRAE and Company *see under* 'DESERT SONG The'

SUCH A LONG JOURNEY (1999) Music by JONATHAN GOLDSMITH -S/T-*UNFORSCENE-NETTWERK (Pinn):6242 840008-2 (CD)*

SUDDEN DEATH (1995) Music score: JOHN DEBNEY -S/T- on *VARESE (Pinn): VSD 5663 (CD)*

SUESSICAL
  UNIVERSAL MUSIC: AA 12159792-2 (CD)

SUGAR (songs: Jule Styne-Bob Merrill)
  ORIG BROADWAY CAST (1972) *feat:* ROBERT MORSE-TONY ROBERTS-CYRIL RITCHARD-ELAINE JOYCE-SHEILA SMITH *RYKODISC (Vital): RCD 10760 (CD)*

SUMMER HOLIDAY (FILM MUSIC.1963) CLIFF RICHARD-Shadows -S/T- *MFP (EMI): TCMFP 5824 (MC) CDMFP 6021 (CD) see COLL.210,*

SUMMER MAGIC - *see* WALT DISNEY INDEX p.341
SUMMER OF '42 (1971) Music score: MICHEL LEGRAND
  -S/T- reissue *WB (TEN): 9362 48087-2 (CD)*
SUMMER OF LOVE (umbrella title for C4 series beginning
  14 AUG 1999) Collection of music (inspired by the
  series) on *EMI-VIRGIN-C4: VTDCD 280 (2CD)*
SUMMER OF SAM (1999) Music sc: TERENCE BLANCHARD -S/T-
  V/A MARVIN GAYE/ABBA/WHO/ROY AYERS/GRACE JONES etc
  EDEL-HOLLYWOOD (Vital) 012 190-2HWR (CD)
SUMMER PLACE,A (1960) Music: MAX STEINER *see COLL.239,*
SUMMER'S LEASE (BBC2 1/11/89) theme "Carmina Valles"
  NIGEL HESS sung CHAMELEON *see COLL.137,*
SUN VALLEY SERENADE (1941 MUSICAL) *w* GLENN MILLER BAND
  and TEX BENEKE *includ.songs from* 'ORCHESTRA WIVES'
  TARGET (BMG): CD 60002 (CD) also on
  JASMINE (Koch-Cadillac): JASMCD 2570 (CD)
SUNBURN (BBC1 16/01/1999) mus: JULIAN NOTT *unavailable*
  songs: "Sunburn" sung by MICHELLE COLLINS on
  BBC AUDIO INT (Pinn): WMSS 6008-2 (CDs) -4 (MC)
  "Can't Smile Without You" sung by JAMES BULLER on
  BBC AUDIO INT (Pinn): WMSS 6009-2 (CDs) -4 (MC)
SUNDAY BLOODY SUNDAY (71) *see COLL.197,*
SUNDAY IN THE PARK WITH GEORGE (O.BROADWAY CAST 1984)
  Songs: STEPHEN SONDHEIM Mandy PATINKIN-Bernadette
  PETERS *RCA (BMG): RD 85042 (CD) RK 85042 (MC)*
SUNNY (ORIG LONDON CAST 1926) Songs (Jerome Kern-Oscar
  Hammerstein II) *feat:* JACK BUCHANAN-BINNIE HALE-
  PEARL (Pavilion): GEMMCD 9105 (CD)
SUNSET (O.OFF-BROADWAY CAST 1984) Music: GARY WILLIAM
  FRIEDMAN Words: WILL HOLT *feat* TAMMY GRIMES-RONEE
  BLAKELY-KIM MILFORD   *TER (Koch): CDTER 1180 (CD)*
SUNSET BOULEVARD - songs by Andrew Lloyd Webber
 1a ORIG LONDON CAST 1993   PATTI LuPONE-KEVIN ANDERSON
  REALLY USEFUL (Univ): 519 767-2 (2CD) -4 (2MC)
 1b Highlights *POLYDOR (Univ): 527 241-2 (CD) -4 (MC)*
 2. USA STAGE CAST 1994 *with:* GLENN CLOSE and Company
  REALLY USEFUL (Univ): 523 507-2 (2CD) -4 (2MC)
SUNSHINE (2000) Music score by MAURICE JARRE -S/T- on
  MILAN-RCA (BMG): 74321 729 862-2 (CD)
SUPERCAR (ITV 9/61) music: BARRY GRAY *see COLL.3,250,*
SUPERFLY (1972) Music by CURTIS MAYFIELD -S/T- reiss.
  with 'SHORT EYES' *SEQUEL (BMG): NEMCD 964 (2CD) +*
  NEMLP 964 (LP) / also on CHARLY: CDNEW 1302 (2CDs)
  CHARLY: SNAP 005 (CD)
SUPERGIRL (1984) Music score by JERRY GOLDSMITH *NEW*
  RECORDING: SILVA SCREEN (Koch): FILMCD 132 (CD)
SUPERHUMAN (BBC1 15/10/2000) Original music score by
  CHRIS WHITTEN *unavailable*
SUPERMAN THE MOVIE (1978) Music score: JOHN WILLIAMS
  LONDON SYMPHONY ORCHESTRA cond.by JOHN WILLIAMS
  RHINO (TEN): 8122 75874-2 (2CD)
  new recording by SCOTTISH NATIONAL ORCHESTRA cond.
  JOHN WILLIAMS *VARESE (Pinn): VSD 25981 (2CD)*
  see COLL.83,84,221,242,280,281,

SUPERMAN (LOIS AND CLARK) - see 'New Adventures of
Superman' see COLL.221,248,
SUPERMAN THE ULTIMATE COLLECTION VARIOUS ARTISTS
VARESE (Pinn): VSD 5998 (CD)
SUPERSTARS (BBC 80s) see COLL.122,
SUPERTED! - see COLL.132,
SURVIVOR (ITV 21/05/2001) Music by RUSS LANDAU & DAVID
VANNACORE -S/T- UNIVERSAL TV MUSIC: 014 650-2 (CD)
SUSPIRIA (1976) Music score: DARIO ARGENTO by GOBLIN
-S/T- CINEVOX Ita (Silva Screen): CDCIA 5005 (CD)
also on DAGORED (Koch): RED 1271LP (CD)
SUTHERLAND'S LAW (UKGO 18/2/95 orig BBC1 6/6/73) theme
music (Hamish MacCunn) SCOTTISH NATIONAL ORCHESTRA
conduct: Alexander Gibson CHANDOS: CHAN 8379 (CD)
SUZY (1936) COLLECTION with 'SAN FRANCISCO'/'DAMES' on
GREAT MOVIE THEMES (Targ-BMG): CD 60022 (CD)
SWAN PRINCESS The (1994) Songs: LEX DE AVEZEDO & DAVID
ZIPPEL feat LIZ CALLOWAY SONY WOND: 483772-2 (CD)
SWAP SHOP - see COLL.132,
S.W.A.T. (USA TV) see COLL.124,244,
SWEENEY The (Thames 2/1/75) theme music: HARRY SOUTH
'SHUT IT - THE MUSIC OF THE SWEENEY) Various Arts
SANCTUARY (PINN): SANCD 092 (CD) SANDV 092 (2LP)
see COLL.4,77,124,250,
SWEENEY TODD (O.BROADWAY CAST 1979) Songs: STEPHEN
SONDHEIM feat: ANGELA LANSBURY-LEN CARIOU RCA Imp
(S.Screen): 3379-2 (2CD) HIGHLIGHTS RCD1 5033 (CD)
SWEET AND LOWDOWN (2000) Mus: DICK HYMAN -S/T- V.ARTS.
SONY CLASSICS (TEN): SK 89019 (CD)
SWEET CHARITY - songs by Cy Coleman & Dorothy Fields
1.FILM MUSICAL 1969 SHIRLEY MacLAINE-SAMMY DAVIS JR.
CHITA RIVERA -S/T- EMI AMERICA: ZDM 746562-2 (CD)
2.STUDIO RECORD 1995 JACQUELINE DANKWORTH-GREGG EDEL
MAN-JOSPEHINE BLAKE-SHEZWAE POWELL-DAVID HEALEY
TER (Koch): CDTER2 1222 (2CD, 09.1998)
3.ORIG BROADWAY CAST 1966 with: GWEN VERDON & Comp.
CBS USA (S.Screen): CK 02900 (CD) JST 02900 (MC)
4.ORIG LONDON CAST 1967 JULIET PROWSE-ROD MacLENNAN
JOSEPHINE BLAKE-ROGER FINCH-PAULA KELLY-JOHN
KESTON etc.SONY WEST END (TEN): SMK 66172 (CD)
SWEET HEREAFTER (1997) Music score: MYCHAEL DANNA
-S/T- (VAR.ARTS) VIRGIN (EMI): CDVIR 68 (CD)
SWEET NOVEMBER (2001) Music score: CHRISTOPHER YOUNG
"Only Time" composed and sung by ENYA -S/T- on
REPRISE (TEN): 9362 48061-2 (CD) -4 (MC)
SWEET ROSIE O'GRADY (1943 FILM CAST)feat BETTY GRABLE
inc.selection from 'SPRINGTIME IN THE ROCKIES'
SANDY HOOK (Silver Sounds): CDSH 2090 (CD)
SWEET SMELL OF SUCCESS The (1957) Music score: ELMER
BERNSTEIN and songs by CHICO HAMILTON & FRED KATZ
-S/T- incl. 'WALK ON THE WILD SIDE' (1962 -S/T-)
TICKERTAPE USA Impt.(S.Screen): TT 3002 (CD)
SWEPT FROM THE SEA (1998) Music sco: JOHN BARRY -S/T-
DECCA (Univ): 458 793-2 (CD)

SWING (1998) VARIOUS ARTISTS inc LISA STANSFIELD -S/T-
  BMG SOUNDTRACKS: 74321 66923-2 (CD)
SWING TIME (1936) *with* FRED ASTAIRE-GINGER ROGERS
  -S/T- *selection + songs from* 'FOLLOW THE FLEET'/
  'TOP HAT'/'CAREFREE' *GREAT MOVIE THEMES (Targ-BMG)*
  CD 60015 (CD) +'FOLLOW THE FLEET'*IRIS Mus-Chansons*
  Cin (Discov):CIN 006 (CD) see COLL.21,182,
SWINGERS (1996) Music score: JUSTIN REINHARDT -S/T-
  Various Artists *POLYDOR (Univ): 162 091-2 (CD)*
  'SWINGERS TOO' (more music from and inspired by)
  HOLLYWOOD-EDEL (Vital) 012 235-2HWR (CD)
SWISS FAMILY ROBINSON 2 (1999) Music score: JOHN SCOTT
  -S/T- *JOHN SCOTT REC (Silva Screen): JSCD 126 (CD)*
SWORD IN THE STONE - *see* WALT DISNEY INDEX p.341
SWORDFISH (2001) Music by PAUL OAKENFIELD-CHRIS YOUNG
  -S/T- *FFFR (TEN): 6434 431169-2 (CD)*
SWORDSMAN OF SIENNA (1962) *see COLL.240,*

T AFFETAS The (OFF-BROADWAY CAST 1988) by RICK LEWIS
  with Jody ABRAHAMS-Karen CURLEE-Melanie MITCHELL-
  Tia SPEROS *TER (Koch): CDTER 1167 (CD)*
TAGGART (Scottish TV began 2/7/85) music: MIKE MORAN
  theme song "No Mean City" sung by MAGGIE BELL
  SOUNDTRACKS EMI: 521 942-2 (CD) *DELETED 02/2001*
TAILOR OF PANAMA The (2001) Music score by SHAUN DAVEY
  -S/T- *VARESE (Pinn): VSD 6243 (CD)*
TAKE A GIRL LIKE YOU (BBC1 26/11/2000) VARIOUS ARTISTS
  BBC WORLDWIDE MUSIC (Pinn): WMSF 6041-2 (CD)
TAKE A HARD RIDE (1975) Music score by JERRY GOLDSMITH
  -S/T- *RETROGRADE (FSM): FSMCD VOL.3 NO.1 (CD)*
TAKE ME HIGH (1973) songs TONY COLE *feat* CLIFF RICHARD
  EMI: CDEMC 3641 (CD) with 'HELP IT ALONG' album
  see COLL 'CLIFF RICHARD: AT THE MOVIES'
TAKE THREE GIRLS (BBC2 1971) theme "Light Flight" by
  PENTANGLE from 'Basket Of Light' *Transatlantic-*
  Essential (BMG): ESMCD 406 (CD) see COLL.24,74,
TAKING MY TURN (MUSICAL) GARY WILLIAM FRIEDMAN (music)
  WILL HOLT (lyrics) ORIGINAL USA CAST RECORDING on
  DRG USA (Pinn): DRGCD 19012 (CD)
TAKING OF PELHAM 1,2,3 (1974) Music score: DAVID SHIRE
  -S/T- *RETROGRADE (Hot/Sil.S) FSMDS 80123-2 (CD)*
TALENTED MR.RIPLEY The (1999) Music sco: GABRIEL YARED
  -S/T- *SONY (TEN): SK 51337 (CD) SM 51337 (MC)*
TALE OF TWO CITIES (1958) *see COLL.7,*
TALES FROM THE CRYPT (USA TV) *see COLL.219,248,*
TALES FROM THE DARKSIDE-THE MOVIE (90) Music (Donald B
  Rubinstein-Pat Regan-Jim Manzie-Chaz Jankel) -S/T-
  GNP (ZYX): GNPD 8021(CD) GNP-5 8021 (MC)
TALES OF BEATRIX POTTER (1971) Music: JOHN LANCHBERRY
  ROYAL OPERA HOUSE ORCHESTRA (John Lanchbery) -S/T-
  re-issued on *CFP (EMI): CDCFP 6074 (CD)*
TALES OF THE UNEXPECTED Mus: RON GRAINER *see COLL.3,8,*
TALL MEN The - *see COLL.1,*
TAMARIND SEED (1974) Music by JOHN BARRY *see COLL.26,*

TAMING OF THE SHREW The (1967) Music score: NINO ROTA
NEW RECORDING *DRG (Pinn): DRGCD 32928 (CD)*
TANGO (1997) Music score by LALO SCHIFRIN -S/T- on
DG (Universal): 459 145-2 (CD)
TARAS BULBA (1962) Music score: FRANZ WAXMAN -S/T-
*RYKODISC (Vital): RCD 10736 (CD) / also on Import
TARAN (Silver Sounds): W 9107 (CD)* see *COLL.266,*
TARRANT ON TV (ITV 08/11/1996) theme music "Penthouse
Suite" by SYD DALE ORCHESTRA on 'SOUND GALLERY 1'
EMI RECORDS: CDTWO 2001 (CD)
TARZAN (1999) Music: MARK MANCINA songs: PHIL COLLINS
*DISNEY-EDEL (Vital) 010247-2DNY (CD) -4DNY (MC)
DISNEY-EDEL: 010248-2DNY (CD) 010249-4DNY (MC)*
see *COLL.243,* see also WALT DISNEY INDEX p.341
TASTE THE BLOOD OF DRACULA (1969) Music: JAMES BERNARD
GDI (ABM): GDICD 010 (CD) see *COLL.126,138,150,*
TAXI (USA1979/BBC1 17/4/80) Mus: BOB JAMES 'The Genie:
Themes & Variations from TV Series TAXI'+ "Angela"
(theme m) *ESSENTIAL-CASTLE (Pinn): ESMCD 465 (CD)*
see *COLL.14,200,244,*
TAXI (1999) Music score: IAM -S/T- + VARIOUS ARTISTS
COLUMBIA (TEN/Sony Eur-Discovery): 489 990-2 (CD)
TAXI DRIVER (1976) Music score BERNARD HERRMANN
SIMPLY VINYL (Telstar): SVLP 60 (LP)
also *ARISTA (BMG): 78221 9005-1 (LP)*
previously unreleased tracks and new dialogue on
ARISTA (BMG): 07822 19005-2 (CD) also 258 774 (CD)
see *COLL.83,105,135,*
TEA WITH MUSSOLINI (1998) Music score composed by
ALESSIO VLAD and STEFANO ARNALDI -S/T- on
*FIRST NIGHT (Pinn): REELCD 101 (CD) / also import
DRG (New Note/Pinn): DRGCD 12618 (CD) / also on
IMAGE (Silver Sounds): IMG 1379-2 (CD)*
TEACHERS (C4 21/03/2001) VAR.ARTS.SOUNDTRACK including
"Insomnia" by FAITHLESS, "Catch The Sun" The DOVES
"Buck Rogers" by FEEDER & others / COMPILATION on
CHANNEL 4 MUSIC (UNIV): C4M 0011-2 (CD)
TEACHING MRS.TINGLE (1999) Music score: JOHN FRIZZELL
-S/T- *VARESE (Pinn): VSD 6064 ()CD)*
TEENAGE OPERA, A (1967 musical) songs by MARK WIRTZ
feat KEITH WEST & others. *RPM (Pinn): RPM 165 (CD)*
TELETUBBIES (BBC1 31/3/97) m.dir: ANDREW McCRORY-SHAND
'TELETUBBIES' *BBC (BMG): WMXU 0014-2 (CD) -4 (MC)*
'Fun With' *BBC: YBBC 2063 (MC)* also see *COLL.285,*
TELEVISION NEWSREEL (BBC 1950's) theme "Girls in Grey"
CHARLES WILLIAMS see *COLL.45,119,*
TELL ME ON A SUNDAY (STUDIO RECORDING 1979) Songs by
DON BLACK-ANDREW LLOYD WEBBER *with* MARTI WEBB
POLY: 833 447-2 (CD) see *COLL.274,*
TEMPEST The (2000) Music score by TOT TAYLOR -S/T-
TWEED COUTURE (Pinn): TWEEDCD 13 (CD)
TEN COMMANDMENTS (1956) ELMER BERNSTEIN see *COLL.36*
TEN THINGS I HATE ABOUT YOU (1998) Mus: RICHARD GIBBS
-S/T- *HOLLYWOOD-EDEL (Vital) 010254-2HWR (CD)*

TENDER IS THE NIGHT (BBC2 23/09/1985) Music score by
RICHARD RODNEY BENNETT / "Nicole's Theme" on new
rec.by BBC PHILHARMONIC ORCH *CHANDOS: CHAN 9867 CD*
TENDERLOIN (ORIG BROADWAY CAST 1960) Songs: JERRY BOCK
SHELDON HARNICK *feat:* MAURICE EVANS and Company
EMI Angel: ZDM 565 022-2 (CD)
DRG USA (Pinn): DRGCD 94770-2 (CD)
TENEBRAE (1982) Music score composed and performed by
GOBLIN -S/T- *DAGORED (Koch): RED 131 (CD) also imp*
CINEVOX (S.Screen): CDCIA 5035 (CD)
TENTH KINGDOM (2000) Music score by ANNE DUDLEY
-S/T- *VARESE (Pinn): VSD 6115 (CD)*
TERMINATOR The (1984) Music sc: BRAD FIEDEL definitive
edition *EDEL-CINERAMA (Vital) 0022082CIN (CD) also*
SILVA SCREEN (Koch): FILM(C)(CD) 101 (LP/MC/CD)
see COLL.,217,221,
TERMINATOR 2 (1991) Music sco: BRAD FIEDEL -S/T- score
VARESE (Pinn): VSD(VSC) 5335 (CD/MC) see COLL.217,
special edition VARESE (Pinn): VSD 5861 (CD)
TERROR AFTER MIDNIGHT (Neunzig Minuten Nacht...1961)
Music score by BERT KAEMPFERT -S/T- reissued on
BEAR FAMILY (Roller) BCD 16571 (CD)
TERROR FIRMER (1999) V.ARTISTS / TROMA Soundtrack Imp.
GOLF (Plastic Head): CD HOLE 032 (CD)
TERRY PRATCHETT'S DISCWORLD *see* DISCWORLD / SOUL MUSIC
TEST CRICKET (C4 22/07/1999) "Mambo No.5" (P.Prado) by
LOU BEGA *RCA: 74321 69672-2 (CDs) -4 (MC) -1 (12")*
'A LITTLE BIT OF MAMBO' *RCA: 74321 68861-2 (CD)*
TEST CRICKET (BBC 'til 1998) "Soul Limbo" by BOOKER T.
& The MG's.'Great Sporting Experience' Collection
EMI: CDGOAL 1 (2CD) see COLL.122,
TESTAMENT (C4 6/11/88) theme: NIGEL HESS *see COLL.137,*
TESTAMENT OF YOUTH (BBC2 4/11/79 also BBC2 3/10/92)
theme music: GEOFFREY BURGON *see COLL.55,*
TESTAMENT: THE BIBLE IN ANIMATION (BBC2 16/10/96)
mus "Adiemus" by KARL JENKINS from 'ADIEMUS-SONGS
OF SANCTUARY' *VIRGIN (EMI): CD(TC)VE 925 (CD/MC)*
see COLL.10,
TFI FRIDAY (Ginger/C4 9/2/96) opening mus "Man In A
Suitcase" by RON GRAINER *see* 'MAN IN A SUITCASE'
see COLL.2,8,24,74,250,251,
THANK YOUR LUCKY STARS (1943 FILM CAST) -S/T- select:
SANDY HOOK (Silver Sounds): CDSH 2012 (CD)
THANK YOUR LUCKY STARS (ATV 1960's) theme music: PETER
KNIGHT *see COLL.2,24,274*
THANKS A MILLION (FILM CAST 1935) -S/T- *w:* DICK POWELL
PAUL WHITEMAN BAND incl. -S/T- to 'ON THE AVENUE'
SANDY HOOK (Silver Sounds): CDSH(CSH) 2012 (CD/MC)
THAT DARN PUNK 2001) VARIOUS ARTISTS SOUNDTRACK on
KUNG FU (CARGO-PINN): 78780-2 (CD)
THAT 70's SHOW (C5 2001) theme based on "In The Street"
(A.Chilton-C.Bell) sung by TODD GRIFFIN / 2 albums:
'THAT 70's ALBUM-JAMMIN' *VOLCANO (Pinn): 921 006-2*
'THAT 70's ALBUM-ROCKIN' *VOLCANO (Pinn): 921 007-2*

THAT'S THE WAY IT IS *see* ELVIS PRESLEY INDEX p.348
THELMA & LOUISE (1991) Music score: HANS ZIMMER -S/T-
    reissue MCA (UNI): MCLD 19313 (CD)
THERE'S NO BUSINESS LIKE SHOW BUSINESS (1954) Songs by
    IRVING BERLIN *feat* MARILYN MONROE-ETHEL MERMAN-DAN
    DAILEY-DONALD O'CONNOR. *DIGITALLY RE-MIXED -S/T-
    FOX CLASSICS-VARESE (Pinn): VSD 5912 (CD)*
THERE'S ONLY ONE JIMMY GRIMBLE (2000) Music score by
    SIMON BOSWELL-ALEX JAMES *-S/T- VAR.ARTISTS includ:*
    CHARLATANS-HAPPY MONDAYS-MOBY-FAT BOY SLIM-STONE
    ROSES-IAN McCULLOCH-ECHO & BUNNYMEN etc.
    WRASSE RECORDS: WRASS 023 (CD)
THERE'S SOMETHING ABOUT MARY (1998) music VAR.ARTISTS
    -S/T- *EMI PREMIER: 495 737-2 (CD)*
THEY CALL ME MR.TIBBS! (1970) Music sco: QUINCY JONES
    -S/T- inc.mus.from 'IN THE HEAT OF THE NIGHT (67)
    RYKODISC (Vital): RCD 10712 (CD)
THEY DIED WITH THEIR BOOTS ON (1941) Music score: MAX
    STEINER orchestrated by HUGO FRIEDHOFER.*new record*
    MOSCOW SYMPHONY ORCH conductor: Willam T.STROMBERG
    MARCO POLO Select: 8225079 (CD)
THEY MIGHT BE GIANTS (1972) Music score by JOHN BARRY
    NEW VERSION inc 'WALKABOUT'/'CORN IS GREEN' and
    other themes *SILVA SCREEN (Koch): FILMCD 339 (CD)*
THEY THINK IT'S ALL OVER (BBC1 14/9/95-2000) theme
    music by STEVE BROWN *unavailable*
THEY'RE PLAYING OUR SONG - songs by Marvin Hamlisch
    and Carole Bayer Sager
    1.ORIG LONDON CAST 1980 *with:* GEMMA CRAVEN-TOM CONTI
    Complete: *TER (Koch): CDTER 1035 (CD)*
    2.ORIG BROADWAY CAST 1979 *with:* LUCIE ARNAZ-ROBERT
    KLEIN *CASABLANCA (IMS-Poly):AA826 240-2 (CD)*
THIEF (aka Violent Streets)(1981) Mus: TANGERINE DREAM
    -S/T- TANGERINE DREAM *VIRGIN (EMI): TAND 12 (CD)*
THIEF OF BAGHDAD The (1924 silent Contemporary score
    by CARL DAVIS *see COLL.61,85,266*, 'The SILENTS'
THIEF OF BAGHDAD The (1940) Music: MIKLOS ROZSA -S/T-
    with 'JUNGLE BOOK' *COLOSS (Pinn):CST 348044 (CD)*
    see COLL.214,
THIN BLUE LINE The (1989) Music score: PHILIP GLASS
    -S/T- *ELEKTRA NONESUCH (TEN): 7559 79209-2 (CD)*
THIN LINE BETWEEN LOVE AND HATE, A (1995) VAR.ARTISTS
    -S/T- *WB (TEN): 9362 46134-2 (CD) -4 (MC)*
THIN RED LINE The (1997) Music score: HANS ZIMMER
    -S/T- score: *RCA VICTOR (BMG): 09026 63382-2 (CD)*
    chants: Melanesian Choirs *RCA: 09026 63470-2 (CD)*
THING The (1982) Music score ENNIO MORRICONE -S/T-
    VARESE (Pinn): VSD 5278 (CD) VSC 5278 (MC)
THING ABOUT VINCE The (ITV 24/07/2000) original music
    by DEBORAH MOLLISON *unavailable*
THINGS TO COME *see COLL.49,237,*

THINNER (1996) Music score by DANIEL LICHT -S/T-
    VARESE (Pinn): VSD 5761 (CD)

THIRD MAN The (1949) Music score by ANTON KARAS -S/T-
DEFINITIVE (Disc):SFCD 33538 see COLL.75,235,253,
THIRD MIRACLE The (1999) Music sco: JAN A.P.KACZMAREK
-S/T- *(USA IMPORT) MILAN: 35899 (CD)*
THIRD WORLD COP (2000) Music by WALLY BADAROU with SLY
& ROBBIE and other artists -S/T- on
PALM PICTURES (3MV-TEN): PALMCD 2034-2 (CD) -1(LP)
THIRTEENTH FLOOR The (1999) Music score: HARALD KLOSER
-S/T- *MILAN (BMG): 73138 35882-2 (CD)*
THIRTEENTH WARRIOR The (1999) Music by JERRY GOLDSMITH
-S/T- *VARESE (Pinn): VSD 6038 (CD)*
THIRTYSOMETHING (USA)(C4 18/1/89) theme: W.G.SNUFFY
WALDEN-STEWART LEVIN theme on coll 'MUSIC BY..'
BMG IMPORTS: 01934 11424-2 (CD) also see COLL.248,
THIS EARTH IS MINE (1959) Music score: HUGO FRIEDHOFER
+ 'THE YOUNG LIONS' *VARESE (Pinn): VSD 25403 (2CD)*
THIS GUN FOR HIRE (1942) MUSICAL *feat* VERONICA LAKE-
ALAN LADD *incl.songs from* 'BATHING BEAUTY' & 'HERE
COMES THE WAVES' *TARGET (BMG): CD 60001 (CD)*
THIS IS SPINAL TAP (1984) Mus comp/sung by SPINAL TAP
-S/T- *POLYDOR (UNIVERSAL): 549 075-2 (CD)*
-S/T- *RAZOR-Castle (Pinn): LUSLP(MC)2 (LP/MC)*
THIS IS THE ARMY (1943 FILM CAST) -S/T- selection on
SANDY HOOK (Silver Sounds): CDSH 2035 (CD)
THIS IS YOUR LIFE (BBC1 1994-2002/ITV 1968-93) series
theme music "Gala Performance" by LAURIE JOHNSON
PLAY IT AGAIN (Koch):PLAY 010 (CD) see COLL.4,156,
THIS LIFE (BBC1 BBC2 18/3/1996) t.music by The WAY OUT
V.Art.-S/T- *BBC WORLDWIDE (Pinn): WMSF 6026-2 (CD)*
THIS MORNING (ITV 3/10/1988-2001) theme music by DAVID
PRINGLE and RAY MONK *unavailable*
THIS WEEK (ITV) theme "Alla Marcia 3 - Karelia Suite"
(SIBELIUS) *version: PHILIPS (Univ): 412 727-2 (CD)*
THIS WORLD THEN THE FIREWORKS (1997) Orig.Jazz score
PETE RUGOLO -S/T- *VARESE (Pinn): VSD 5860 (CD)*
THIS YEARS LOVE (1998) Music score: SIMON BOSWELL
-S/T- *V2 (3MV-Pinn): VVR 100636-2 (CD)*
THOMAS AND THE KING Songs: John Williams-James Harbert
O.LONDON CAST 1975: JAMES SMILLIE-DILYS HAMLETT-
LEWIS FIANDER-RICHARD JOHNSON-CAROLINE VILLIERS
TER (Koch): CDTER 1009 (CD, reiss 09.1998)
THOMAS AND THE MAGIC RAILROAD (2000) VAR.ARTISTS -S/T-
NETTWERK PRODUCTIONS (Pinn): 34011-2 (CD) -4 (MC)
THOMAS CROWN AFFAIR The (1999) Music score: BILL CONTI
"Windmills Of Your Mind" (Legrand-Bergman) STING
-S/T- *ARK 21 (UNIV): 153 986-2 (CD)*
THOMAS CROWN AFFAIR The (1968) Music by MICHEL LEGRAND
"Windmills Of Your Mind" sung by NOEL HARRISON
RYKODISC (Vital): RCD 10719 (CD) see COLL.61,
THOMAS THE TANK ENGINE & FRIENDS (ITV 25/2/92) theme
JUNIOR CAMPBELL-MIKE O'DONNELL *MFP: TCMFP 6104 MC*
THORN BIRDS The (USA BBC1 8/1/84) music: HENRY MANCINI
see COLL.108,

THOUSAND ACRES, A (1997) Music score: RICHARD HARTLEY
-S/T- *VARESE (Pinn): VSD 5870 (CD)*
THREE COINS IN THE FOUNTAIN (1954) t.song (Sammy CAHN-
Jule STYNE) sung by FRANK SINATRA 'Screen Sinatra'
MFP (EMI): CD(TC)MFP 6052 (CD/MC) see COLL.92,227,
THREE COLEURS: BLEU-BLANC-ROUGE (1993-94) M: ZBIGNIEW
PREISNER *VIRGIN Fra (EMI): CDVMM 15 (3 CDbox set)*
THREE COLOURS: BLUE (1993) Music sc: ZBIGNIEW PREISNER
VIRGIN France (EMI): CDVMM 12 (CD)
THREE COLOURS: RED (1994) Music sc: ZBIGNIEW PREISNER
VIRGIN Fra (EMI): CDVMM 14 (CD) or 839 784-2 (CD)
THREE COLOURS: WHITE (1993) Music s: ZBIGNIEW PREISNER
VIRGIN France (EMI): 839 472-2 (CD)
THREE MUSKETEERS The (1935) Music sco: MAX STEINER new
record BRANDENBURG S.ORCH. (Kaufman) + other items
MARCO POLO (Select): 8.223607 (CD)
THREE MUSKETEERS The (1993) Music score: MICHAEL KAMEN
-S/T- *A.& M. (IMS-Poly): E.540 190-2 (CD)*
THREE O'CLOCK HIGH (1987) Music score: TANGERINE DREAM
-S/T- *VARESE (Pinn): VCD 47307 (CD)*
THREE SISTERS (1970) Music sco: Sir WILLIAM WALTON New
Recording by Academy of St.Martin-in-the-Fields
(Neville Marriner) *CHANDOS: CHAN 8870 (CD)*
THREE STOOGES The (USA) *see COLL.243,*
THREE THE HARD WAY (1974) Music: The IMPRESSIONS -S/T-
reissue GET BACK (Cargo-Greyhound): GET 8007 (CD)
THREE WORLDS OF GULLIVER (1959) Music BERNARD HERRMANN
new recording (score) *VARESE (Pinn): VSD 6162 (CD)*
also see COLL.135,
THREEPENNY OPERA 1.(ORIG DONMAR WAREHOUSE CAST 1994/5)
Songs: KURT WEILL-MARC BLITZSTEIN *w:* TARA HUGO-TOM
MANNION-SHARON SMALL-TOM HOLLANDER-SIMON DORMANDY
TER (Koch): CDTER 1227 (CD)
THREEPENNY OPERA 2.(ORIG BROADWAY CAST 1954) Songs by:
KURT WEILL-MARC BLITZSTEIN *feat* LOTTE LENYA & Comp
TER (Koch): CDTER 1101 (CD)
THREEPENNY OPERA 3.feat: MAX RAABE-H.K.GRUBER-NINA
HAGEN-SONA MacDONALD-HANNES HELLMAN (ENSEMBLE
MODERN) *RCA RED SEAL (BMG): 74321 66133-2 (CD)*
THUNDERBALL (1965) Music: JOHN BARRY t.song (J.Barry-
Don Black) TOM JONES -S/T- *EMI:CZ556 (CD) see COLL*
26,28,36,45,46,47,75,175,222, BOND FILM INDEX p.346
THUNDERBIRDS! (ATV/ITC 30/9/1965-66 / BBC2 20/9/1991)
theme: BARRY GRAY *see COLL.2,15,24,38,74,84,118,*
210,221,246,250,253,261,
TIC CODE The (2000) Music score by MICHAEL WOLFF
-S/T- *RAZOR & TIE (Koch): RE 82859-2 (CD)*
TICK TICK BOOM (MUSICAL 2000) Songs by JONATHAN LARSON
ORIG USA CAST *RCA VICTOR BMG: 09026 63862-2 (CD)*
TICKLE ME *see* ELVIS PRESLEY INDEX p.348
TIGER BAY (1959) Mus: LAURIE JOHNSON *see COLL.156,158,*
TIGGER MOVIE The (2000) Music: HARRY GREGSON WILLIAMS
music and songs arranged by MARTIN ERSKINE
-S/T- *DISNEY-EDEL (Vital) 010 874-2DNY (CD)*

TILL THE CLOUDS ROLL BY (FILM MUS.1946,JEROME KERN)
FRANK SINATRA-JUDY GARLAND-TONY MARTIN-LENA HORNE
SANDY HOOK (Silver Sounds): CDSH 2080 (CD)
TIME AFTER TIME (1979) Music score by MIKLOS ROZSA
-S/T- *SOUTHERN CROSS Import (HOT): SCCD 1014 (CD)*
TIME MACHINE The (1960) Music (Russell Garcia) -S/T-
GNP (ZYX): GNPD (GNP5) 8008 (CD/MC)
TIME REGAINED (Le Temps Retrouve) (1999) Music score:
JORGE ARRIAGADA -S/T- *VIRGIN FRANCE: 45355-2 (CD)*
TIME TUNNEL (USA 66) theme music: JOHN WILLIAMS
see COLL.38,84,218,243,
TIMECOP (1993) Music score: MARK ISHAM -S/T- on
VARESE (Pinn): VSD 5532 (CD)
TIMEWATCH (BBC2 6/11/94) opening t.music "In Trutina"
from 'Carmina Burana' CARL ORFF *vers.by* LUCIA POPP
EMI Studio Plus: CDM 764328-2 (CD)
TINKER TAILOR SOLDIER SPY (BBC1 10/9/79) theme "Nunc
Dimittis" GEOFFREY BURGON Seaford Col.Chapel Choir
see COLL.5,55,121,
TINSEL TOWN (BBC2 07/08/2000) theme music by BLUE NILE
-S/T- *BBC WORLD (Pinn): WMSF 6030-2 (2CD) -1 (2LP)*
TIP ON A DEAD JOCKEY (1957) Music score: MIKLOS ROZSA
TICKERTAPE USA Impt.(S.Screen): TT 3011 (CD)
TISWAS (ATV 1970s) *see COLL.250,*
TITAN A.E. (2000) Music score by GRAEME REVELL -S/T-on
EMI SOUNDTRACKS: 525 275-2 (CD)
TITANIC (FILM 1997) Music score: JAMES HORNER "Love
Theme" from 'The TITANIC' performed by CELINE DION
-S/T- *SONY CLASSICS: SK(ST)(SM) 63213 (CD/MC/MD)* +
'Back To Titanic' *SONY CLASS: SK(ST) 60691 (CD/MC)*
also on *SONY CLASSICAL: SS 63213 (CD)*
a) 'THE LAST DANCE: MUSIC FOR A VANISHING ERA'
by I SALONISTI *CONIFER (BMG): 05472 77377-2 (CD)*
b) 'TITANIC: MELODIES FROM THE WHITE STAR MUSIC book
on The TITANIC' *FLAPPER (Pinn): PASTCD 7822 (CD)*
c) 'TITANIC: THE ULTIMATE COLLECTION' (from 5
'TITANIC' productions) 1.CURRENT 1997 film 2.The
1953 version. 3.1958 'A Night To Remember' 4.The
1996 Mini-series 5. The BROADWAY Musical. V.Arts
VARESE (Pinn): VSD 5926 (CD)
TITANIC THE MUSICAL (MUSICAL 1997) Songs: MAURY YESTON
ORIG.BROADWAY CAST *RCA (BMG): 09026 68834-2 (CD)*
TITANIC TOWN (1998) Music score by TREVOR JONES -S/T-
ISLAND (Univ) CID 8081 (CD)
TITFIELD THUNDERBOLT The (1952) *see COLL.22,161,*

TITUS (1999) Music score by ELLIOT GOLDENTHAL -S/T-
SONY CLASSICS (TEN): SK 89171 (CD)
TJ HOOKER (USA) *see COLL.247,*
TO HAVE AND HAVE NOT (1945) Music score: FRANZ WAXMAN
also VARIOUS -S/T- SELECTIONS *GREAT MOVIE THEMES:
(Targ-BMG): CD 60032 (CD) see also* CASABLANCA
TO HAVE AND TO HOLD (1995) M: NICK CAVE-BLIXA BARGOED
MICK HARVEY-S/T- *MUTE-RTM (Vit): IONIC 015CD (CD)*

TO INFINITY AND BEYOND (MUSIC FROM TOY STORY 1.& 2)
DISNEY-EDEL (Vital) 010 753-2DNY (CD)
TO KILL A MOCKINGBIRD (1962) Music sc: ELMER BERNSTEIN
rec.by ROYAL SCOTTISH NATIONAL ORCH (E.Bernstein)
VARESE (Pinn): VSD 5754 (CD) see COLL.40,
TO LIVE AND DIE IN L.A. (1986) Music: WANG CHUNG -S/T-
GEFFEN-MCA Goldline (BMG): GED 24081 (CD)
TO SIR WITH LOVE (1967) Music: RON GRAINER / t.song
by LULU -S/T- also featuring The MINDBENDERS
-S/T- RETROACTIVE (Greyhound): RECD 9004 (CD)
TOM BROWN'S SCHOOLDAYS (1951) *see COLL.7,*
TOM JONES (BBC1 9/11/97) Music score: JIM PARKER -S/T-
OCEAN DEEP (Univ): OCD 012 (CD)
TOMB RAIDER (2001) Music score by GRAEME REVELL
SONGS V.ARTS.-S/T- *ELEKTRA (TEN) 7559 62665-2 (CD)*
SCORE GRAEME REVELL *ELEKTRA (USA): EA 62681-2 (CD)*
TOM'S MIDNIGHT GARDEN (2000) Musaic score composed and
conducted by DEBBIE WISEMAN "After Always" sung by
BARBARA DICKSON-MIRIAM STOCKLEY -S/T- on
FIRST NIGHT (Pinn): REELCD 103 (CD)
TOMMY (FILM ROCK OPERA 1975) Music by PETE TOWNSHEND
The WHO-ELTON JOHN etc.
-S/T- RE-MASTERED EDITION: POLYDOR 841 121-2 (CD)
RE-MASTERED VERSION (1996) POLYDOR 531 043-2 (CD)
TOMMY (ROCK OPERA) LONDON SYMPH ORCH / PETE TOWNSHEND
Roger DALTREY-Maggie BELL-Rod STEWART-Sandy DENNY-
Ringo STARR-John ENTWISTLE-Steve WINWOOD-R.HAVENS
ESSENTIAL-CASTLE (Pinn): ESMCD 404 CD)
TOMMY (ORIG BROADWAY CAST 1993) Songs: PETE TOWNSHEND
RCA VICTOR (BMG): 09026 6187402 (CD)
TOMMY AND THE WILDCAT (1999) Music sc: SOREN HYLDGAARD
-S/T- BMG Finland (Import): 74321 65553-2 (CD)
TOMORROW NEVER COMES (1977) Music score by ROY BUDD
"Alone am I" (title song) sung by MATT MONRO
-S/T- CINEPHILE (Pinn): CINCD 020 (CD)
TOMORROW NEVER DIES (1997) Music score: DAVID ARNOLD
title song by SHERYL CROW with end song by k.d.lang
-S/T- A.& M: 540 830-2 (CD) -4 (MC) see COLL.3,46,
see also JAMES BOND FILM INDEX p.346
TOMORROW PEOPLE The (Thames 30/4/73-79) music: DUDLEY
SIMPSON and BRIAN HODSON *deleted*
TOMORROW'S WORLD (BBC2 1997/2001) theme "In Pursuit
of Happiness" (Neil Hannon) DIVINE COMEDY 'Short
Album About Love" *SETANTA (Vital): SET(CD)(MC) 036*
and on 'SHOOTING FISH' -S/T- *EMI: 7243 821495-2 CD*
TONIGHT WITH TREVOR McDONALD (ITV 08/04/1999-2002)
theme music by MIKE WOOLMANS *unavailable*
TONITE LET'S ALL MAKE LOVE IN LONDON (FILM MUSIC.1967)
SEE FOR MILES (Pinn): SEECD 258 (CD)
TOP CAT (USA 62/BBC UKtitle 'Boss Cat') md HOYT CURTIN
"Top Cat" theme *see COLL.259,*
TOP GEAR (BBC2 70's-99) *Opening theme* "Jessica" ALLMAN
BROTHERS BAND on 'Brothers and Sisters' album
CAPRICORN (Univ.): 825 092-2 (CD)

TOP GEAR RALLY REPORT (BBC2 22/11/96) theme "Duel" by
    PROPAGANDA from the album 'Secret Wish' on
    ZTT (Pinn): ZTT 118CD (CD)
TOP GUN (1986) Music score by HAROLD FALTERMEYER
    "Take My Breath Away" by BERLIN -S/T- on
    COLUMBIA (TEN): CD 70296 and 498 207-2 (CD)
    see COLL.73,
TOP HAT (1935) FILM MUSICAL *feat* FRED ASTAIRE-GINGER
    ROGERS -S/T- *sel.on* 'Let's Swing and Dance'+ songs
    from 'FOLLOW THE FLEET'/'SWING TIME'/'CAREFREE'
    GREAT MOVIE THEMES (Target-BMG): CD 60015 (CD)
    also available a recording with 'THE GAY DIVORCEE'
    IRIS-Mus-Chansons Cinema (Discovery): CIN 005 (CD)
    also available with 'SHALL WE DANCE'
    GREAT MOVIE THEMES (Target-BMG): CD 60042 (CD)
    also on SOUNDTRACK FACTORY (Disc): SFCD 33557 (CD)
    see COLL.21,
TOP OF THE FORM (BBC2 1960's) theme "Marching Strings"
    (Ross) *see COLL.283,*
TOP OF THE POPS (BBC1 1/1/64-2002) various theme mus:
    (from 1/5/98) "Whole Lotta Love" *re-arrangement by*
    BAD MAN BAD and LED ZEPPELIN *unavailable*
    (from 2/2/95) theme: VINCE CLARKE *unavailable*
    (from 3/10/91) "Get Out Of That" by TONY GIBBER
    (from 1986-91) "The Wizard" PAUL HARDCASTLE *delet.*
    (from 1981-85) "Yellow Pearl" (M.URE-PHIL LYNOTT)
    VERTIGO (Univ): PRICE(PRIMC) 88 (LP/MC)
    (from 1974-80) "Whole Lotta Love" CCS *see COLL*
    (orig by *LED ZEPPELIN ATLANTIC (TEN): K(2)(4)40037*
    (from 1969-74) theme arrangement by JOHNNY PEARSON
    (from 1965-69 o.theme: JOHNNIE STEWART-HARRY RABIN
    OWITZ version by BOBBY MIDGLEY (2 versions)
TOP OF THE POPS 2 (BBC2 17/9/94) m:BILL PADLEY *unavail.*
TOP SECRET (ITV 11/8/61-62) "Sucu Sucu" LAURIE JOHNSON
    see COLL.2,24,157,261,
TOPAZ (1969) music by MAURICE JARRE *see COLL.141,*
TOPLESS WOMEN TALK ABOUT THEIR LIVES (1998) Music by
    FLYING NUN -S/T- *CURVEBALL (3M-Pin): FNCD 402 (CD)*
TOPSY TURVY (2000) Original Music by CARL DAVIS conduc
    ting the songs & music of GILBERT & SULLIVAN -S/T-
    SONY CLASSICAL (TEN): SK 61834 (CD) MD 61834 (MD)
TORA! TORA! TORA! (1970) music score: JERRY GOLDSMITH
    score + 'PATTON' new rec: ROYAL SCOTTISH NAT.ORCH.
    (Jerry Goldsmith) *VARESE (Pinn): VSD 5796 (CD)*
TORN CURTAIN (1966) *original score:* JOHN ADDISON
    VARESE (Pinn): VSD 5817 (CD)
TORN CURTAIN (1966) *rejected score:* BERNARD HERRMANN
    SILVA SCREEN (Koch): FILMCD 162 (CD) -S/T- reissue
    see COLL.135,136,144,146,
TOSCA THE MOVIE (2001) Music by PUCCINI *feat* ANGELA
    GHEORGHIU-ROBERTO ALAGNA-RUGGERO RAIMONDI -S/T- on
    EMI CLASSICS (CD cat.number to be confirmed
TOTAL ECLIPSE (1995) Music: JAN A.P.KACZMAREK -S/T-
    Var.Arts *SONY Classics (SM): SK 62037 (CD)*

TOTAL RECALL (1989) Music score: JERRY GOLDSMITH -S/T-
VARESE (Pinn): VSD 6197 (CD) and VSD 5267 (CD)
see *COLL.114,115,217,218,*
TOUCH (1998) Music score: DAVID GROHL (FOO FIGHTERS)
-S/T- *CAPITOL-ROSWELL (EMI): 855 632-2 (CD)*
TOUCH OF CLASS, A (1973) Music score by JOHN CAMERON
"All That Love Went To Waste" (Sammy Cahn-George
Barrie) sung by MADELINE BELL -S/T- *reissue on
DRG-NEW NOTE (Pinn): DRGCD 13115 (CD)*
TOUCH OF EVIL, A (1958) Music score by HENRY MANCINI
UNIVERSAL INTERNATIONAL ORCH (Joseph Gershenson)
-S/T- *BLUE MOON (Discovery): BMCD 7050 (CD)*
VARESE (Pinn): VSD 5414 (CD) + DISCOVERY: MSCD 401
TOUCH OF FROST,A (YTV 6/12/92-2000) music composed and
perf.by BARBARA THOMPSON & JON HISEMAN *unavailable*
TOUR DE FRANCE (TSL/C4 1991-1998) theme music composed
& peformed by PETER SHELLEY *(p.Virgin) unavailable*
note: earlier theme (series 1987-91) see *COLL.122,*
TOUS LE MATINS DU MONDE (France 1992) Music sco: JORDI
SAVALL -S/T- *AUVIDIS Valoir (H.Mundi): AUV 4640 CD
AUV 54640 (MC)* also on *NAXOS: 8551156 (CD)*
TOWER OF DEATH (-) Music score by KIRTH MORRISON -S/T-
YX (CARGO): YX 28022 (LP)
TOWERING INFERNO The (1974) Music score: JOHN WILLIAMS
see *COLL.257,280,*
TOWN AND COUNTRY (2001) Music score: ROLFE KENT -S/T-
NLR USA IMPORT: NLR 39007 (CD)
TOY STORY (1996) Mus.songs: RANDY NEWMAN "You've Got A
Friend In Me" (Newman) sung by RANDY NEWMAN -S/T-
DISNEY MUS (Vital): 017130-2DNY (CD) WD 771304(MC)
TOY STORY 2 (1999) Music score and songs: RANDY NEWMAN
song "When She Loved Me" sung by SARAH McLACHLAN
-S/T- (1) *DISNEY-EDEL (Vital) 010 724-2DNY (CD)*
-S/T- (2) Songs from & inspired by TOY STORY 1/2)
DISNEY-EDEL (Vital) 010 753-2DNY (CD)
see also DISNEY FILM INDEX p.341
TRACEY ULLMAN SHOW The (USA TV) see *COLL.248,*
TRACKS (BBC2 18/5/94) music 'DREAMCATCHER' composed
and performed by DAVID LOWE *unavailable*
TRADING PLACES *Classical music on NAXOS: 8551159 (CD)*

TRAFFIC (2001) Music score by CLIFF MARTINEZ -S/T- inc
FATBOY SLIM-MORCHEEBA-BRIAN ENO-KRUDER & DORFMEIST
TVT RECORDS USA (Silver Sounds): 6960-2 (CD)
TRAINING DAY (2001) Music score by MARK MANCINA -S/T-
V.ARTS *VIRGIN (EMI): CDPTY 220 (CD) PRI 46671 (LP)*
TRAINSPOTTING (1995) -S/T- VARIOUS ARTISTS
EMI:CDEMC 3739 (CD) TCEMC 3739 (MC) EMC 3739 (2LP)
VOL.2 *EMI SOUNDTRACK: PRMDCD 36 (CD) PRMDTC 36(MC)*
TRAP The (1966) Music sco: RON GOODWIN *theme also used
for* BBCTV 'LONDON MARATHON' coverage / Film -S/T-
(S.Screen): LXE 708 (CD) see *COLL.116,117,122,*
TRAVELLING MAN (Granada 3/9/85) theme: DUNCAN BROWNE &
SEBASTION GRAHAM JONES see *COLL.5,20,*

TREASURE ISLAND (ORIG LONDON CAST 1973)
   Music: CYRIL ORNADEL Lyrics: HAL SHAPER
   PRESTIGE (THE-DISC): CDSGP 9801 (CD)
TREASURE OF THE SIERRA MADRE (1948) Music score: MAX
   STEINER *new recording by* MOSCOW SYMPHONY ORCHESTRA
   & CHORUS conducted by WILLIAM T.STROMBERG on
   MARCO POLO (Sel) 8225149 CD also see COLL.61,239,
   see also 'CHARGE OF THE LIGHT BRIGADE'
TRIAL BY JURY (Operetta) *D'Oyly Carte Opera Company*
   (GILBERT & SULLIVAN) also 'Yeomen Of The Guard'
   London (Univ): 417 358-2CD EARLY VERS.inc 'PIRATES
   OF PENZANCE' on *PEARL (Pavilion): GEMS 0097 (CD)*
TRIALS OF LIFE (BBC1 3/10/1990) mus sco: GEORGE FENTON
   PRESTIGE (BMG): CDSGP 030 (CD) see *COLL.4,20,*
TRIBE The (C5 24/04/1999) theme "The Dream Must Stay
   Alive" sung by MERYL CASSIE / Music by SIMON MAY
   "ABE MESSIAH" Music inspired by 'THE TRIBE' with
   ORIGINAL CAST on *SANCTUARY (Pinn): SANCD 009 (CD)*
TRIBUTE TO THE BLUES BROTHERS (ORIG.LONDON CAST 1991)
   feat Con O'Neill-Warwick Evans & Company
   FIRST NIGHT (Pinn): CASTCD 25 (CD) CASTC 25 (MC)
TRIGGER HAPPY TV (C4 14/01/2000) theme "Connection" by
   ELASTICA *DECEPTIVE (Vit): BLUFF 014(CD)(MC)*
   -S/T- Vol 1 *CHANNEL 4 MUS (Univ):C4M 00082 (CD)*
   -S/T- Vol 2 *CHANNEL 4 MUS (Univ):C4M 00122 (CD)*
   "Someone Speak To Me" GENE *UNIV: 553 975-2 (2CD)*
   "If You Could Read My Mind" GORDON LIGHTFOOT *WEA*
   "Just Looking" STEREOPHONICS on'TV2000'*SONYTV82CD*
TRIP The (1967) Music score by THE ELECTRIC FLAG -S/T-
   CURB USA (Greyhound/Silver Sounds): D.277836 (CD)
TRIPPIN' (1999) VARIOUS ARTISTS -S/T-
   EPIC (Ten): 494 391-2 (CD) -4 (MC)
TRIUMPH OF LOVE (ORIGINAL BROADWAY CAST 1997) *Songs by*
   JEFFREY STOCK-SUSAN BIRKHENHEAD *O.BROADWAY CAST:*
   BETTY BUCKLEY-CHRIS.SIEBER-ROGER BART-F.MURRAY
   ABRAHAM-SUSAN EGAN *TER (Koch): CDTER 1253 (CD)*
TROMEO AND JULIET (1996) Music score: WILLIE WISELY
   -S/T- *TROMA (Greyhound): 42907 (CD)*
TROUBLE EVERY DAY (2001) Music by TINDERSTICKS -S/T-
   BEGGARS BANQUET (Vit): BBQCD 225(CD) BBQLP 225(LP)
TROUBLE MAN (1972) Music & songs by MARVIN GAYE -S/T-
   MOTOWN (Univ): 530 884-2 (CD)
TROUBLE WITH GIRLS The *see* ELVIS PRESLEY INDEX p.348

TROUBLE WITH HARRY The (1955) Music: BERNARD HERRMANN
   VARESE: VSD 5971 (CD) see *COLL.135,136,143,144,*
TROUBLESHOOTERS (BBC 60's) "Mogul" by TOM SPRINGFIELD
   on Coll by HARRY STONEHAM *EMI: 495 618-2 (CD)*
TROUBLESOME CREEK: A MID-WESTERN (1995) Music score
   by SHELDON MIROWITZ and DUKE LEVENE -S/T-
   Daring Rec.(Pinn/Topic): DARINGCD 3024 (CD)
TRUCK TURNER (1974) Music sco: ISAAC HAYES -S/T-
   reissue STAX (Pinn): SXD 129 (LP) also with
   'THREE TOUGH GUYS' (1974) *STAX: CDSXE 2095 (2CD)*

TRUE BLUE (1996) Music: STANISLAS SYREWICZ -S/T- V/A
DECCA (Univers.): 455 012-2 (CD) -4 (MC)
TRUE GRIT (1969) Music sco: ELMER BERNSTEIN title song
(Bernstein-Black) GLEN CAMPBELL on 'Country Boy'
MFP EMI:CDMFP 6034 (CD) see *COLL.40,258,277,279,*
TRUE LIES (1994) Mus: BRAD FIEDEL see *COLL.68,217,*
TRUE ROMANCE (1993) Music: HANS ZIMMER & MARK MANCINA
-S/T- reiss: *MORGAN CREEK (Univ): 002242-2MCM (CD)*
TRUE STORIES (1986) Music: DAVID BYRNE / TALKING HEADS
-S/T- *EMI: TC-EMC 3520 (MC) CDP 746345-2 (CD)*
TRUE WOMEN (TVM) Music score: BRUCE BROUGHTON -S/T- on
INTRADA (Koch): MAFD 7077 (CD)
TRUMAN SHOW The (1998) Music score: BURKHARD DALLWITZ
-S/T- VAR.ARTISTS *RCA (BMG): 74321 60822-2 (CD)*
TRUMPTON (BBC 1967) Music & songs by FREDDIE PHILLIPS
sung by BRIAN CANT see *COLL.132,*
TRUSTING BEATRICE (Film) Music score: STANLEY MYERS
with Suite from 'COLD HEAVEN' (Stanley MYERS) on
INTRADA Imprt (Silva Screen): MAF 7048D (CD)
TUBE The (C4/Tyne Tees 82-84) theme "Star Cycle" (JEFF
BECK) 'Best Of Beckology' *EPIC: 471 348-2 (CD)*
TUMBLEWEEDS (1999) Music score: DAVID MANSFIELD -S/T-
RCA (BMG): 09026 63580-2 (CD)
TURBULENCE 2: FEAR OF FLYING (2000) Music by DON DAVIS
-S/T- *PACIFIC TIME ENT (USA IMPT): PTE 8526 (CD)*
TURKISH BATH (1997) Music: HAMAM TRANSCENDENTAL (PIVIO,
ALDO DE SCALZI) -S/T- *CNI (Discov): MDL 978 (CD)*
TV NEWSREEL (BBC 50's) Theme "Girls In Grey" CHARLES
WILLIAMS see *COLL.45,119,*
TWEENIES (BBC1 06/09/1999-2000) Music and songs by
LIZ KITCHEN and GRAHAM PIKE / 'TWEENIES-THE ALBUM'
BBC WORLDWIDE (Pinn): WMSF 6036-2 (CD) -4(MC) also
AVAILABLE 'BEST FRIENDS FOREVER' (TWEENIES) on
BBC WORLDWIDE (Pinn): WMSS 6038-2 (CDs) -4 (MCs)
'TWEENIES CHRISTMAS' *BBC WORLD: WMSF 6049-2 (CD)*
also see *COLL.285,*
TWELFTH NIGHT (1996) Music score by SHAUN DAVEY
SILVA SCREEN (Koch): FILMCD 186 (CD)
TWILIGHT (1998) Music score: ELMER BERNSTEIN -S/T- on
EDEL-CINERAMA (Vital) 0022902CIN (CD)
TWILIGHT ZONE The (TV USA 60s) theme: BERNARD HERRMANN
BEST O.TWILIGHT ZONE *VARESE (Pinn): VCD 47233 (CD)*
V2' *VCD 47247 (CD) VSD 26087 (2CD)* 'TWILIGHT ZONE'
/ 1986 *theme by* GRATEFUL DEAD & MERL SAUNDERS
SILVA SCREEN (Koch): FILMCD 203 (CD)
40th ANNIVERSARY COLL *SILVA SCREEN (Koch) STD 2000*
TWIN FALLS IDAHO (2000) Music sco: STEWART MATTHEWMAN
-S/T- *EPIC (TEN): 499 679-2 (CD)*
TWIN PEAKS (BBC2-23/10/90) Music: ANGELO BADALMENTI
"Falling" v: JULEE CRUISE 'Music From Twin Peaks'
WEA: 7599 26316-2 (CD) -4 (MC) / for theme see
COLL.20,137,138,250,259,
TWIN PEAKS: FIRE WALK WITH ME (1992) Music: ANGELO
BADALAMENTI) -S/T- *WB (TEN): 9362 45019-2 (CD) -4*

TWIN TOWN (1997) Music sco MARK THOMAS / Var.Artists
   -S/T- on *A.& M. (Univ): 540 718-2 (CD)*
TWINS OF EVIL (1971) Music score by HARRY ROBINSON
   GDI (ABM/Univ): GDICD 012 (CD)
TWO CAN PLAY THAT GAME (2001) Music by MARCUS MILLER
   -S/T- *UNIVERSAL MUSIC: AA.88112711-2 (CD)*
TWO DAYS IN THE VALLEY (1996) Music: ANTHONY MARINELLI
   -S/T- *EDEL (Vital) 0029772EDL (CD)*
TWO FAMILY HOUSE (2001) Music score: STEPHEN ENDELEMAN
   -S/T- feat JOHN PIZZARELLI TRIO and other artists
   BMG IMPORTS: 09026 63733-2 (CD)
TWO FOR THE ROAD (1966) Music score: HENRY MANCINI
   -S/T- reissue *RCA (BMG): 74321 62997-2 (CD)*
TWO FOR TONIGHT (1935) *feat* BING CROSBY-JOAN BENNETT
   with 'HOLIDAY INN' & 'ROAD TO MOROCCO'
   GREAT MOVIE THEMES (Target-BMG): CD 60027 (CD)
TWO GIRLS AND A SAILOR (1944) -S/T- JUNE ALLYSON-JIMMY
   DURANTE-GLORIA DE HAVEN-VAN JOHNSON-TOM DRAKE
   GREAT MOVIE THEMES (Target-BMG): CD 60023 (CD)
TWO MOON JUNCTION (1988) Music: JONATHAN ELIAS -S/T-
   VARESE (Pinn): VSD 5518 (CD)
TWO ON THE AISLE (SHOW 1951) Songs by JULE STYNE-BETTY
   COMDEN-ADOLPH GREEN *UNIVER-IMS:AA.440014583-2 (CD)*
TWO RONNIES The (BBC1 1970s-80s) ('The DETECTIVES'
   'Charley Farley and Piggy Malone') *see COLL.231,*
TWO THOUSAND YEARS (ITV 18/04/1999) title music by
   ROBERT HARTSHORNE -S/T- *feat Various Classics on*
   CONIFER CLASSICS (BMG): 75605 51353-2 (2CD)
U.F.O. (ATV/ITC 16/9/70-73) music: BARRY GRAY
   see COLL.84,220,237,250,
U.S.MARSHALLS (1997) Music sco: JERRY GOLDSMITH -S/T-
   VARESE (Pinn): VSD 5914 (CD)
ULEE'S GOLD (1997) Music score: CHARLES ENGSTROM -S/T-
   RYKODISC (Vital): RCD 10731 (CD)
ULYSSES GAZE (1995) Music sco: ELENI KARAINDROU -S/T-
   ECM NEW NOTE (Pinn): 449 153-2 (CD) -4 (MC)
UMBRELLAS OF CHERBOURG (1964) Music sc: MICHEL LEGRAND
   -S/T- *ACCORD (Discovery): 10326-2 (CD) also*
   SILVA SCREEN: 834 139-2 (CD) see COLL.68,
UN COEUR EN HIVER - see HEART IN WINTER, A
UN HOMME ET UNE FEMME - see MAN AND A WOMAN, A
UNA SULL'ALTRA (1969) Music score: RIZ ORTOLANI -S/T-
   DAGORED (Koch/Cargo): RED 128-2 (CD) RED 1281 LP
UNBREAKABLE (2000) Music score by JAMES NEWTON HOWARD
   -S/T- *EDEL-HOLLYWOOD (Vital): 012 285-2HWR (CD)*
UNCLE TOM'S CABIN - Music composed by PETER THOMAS
   BEAR FAMILY (Rollercoaster): BCD 16238(CD)
UNDER CAPRICORN (1949) see *COLL.9,141,*
UNDER FIRE (1983) Music score: JERRY GOLDSMITH -S/T-
   WEA (TEN): 7599 23965-2 (CD) reissue
UNDER SIEGE (1992) Music score: GARY CHANG -S/T-
   VARESE (Pinn): VSD 5409 (CD) VSC 5409 (MC)
UNDER SUSPICION (1999) Music by BRIAN TRANSAU -S/T-
   EMI SOUNDTRACKS: 523 642-2 (CD)

UNDER THE CHERRY MOON (1986) Music: PRINCE -S/T- on
WB (TEN): 925 395-2 (CD)
UNDERNEATH THE ARCHES (O.LONDON CAST 1982) Songs of
FLANAGAN & ALLEN *feat* ROY HUDD-CHRISTOPHER TIMOTHY
TER (Koch): CDTER 1015 (CD)
UNFORGIVEN (1992) Music score: LENNIE NIEHAUS -S/T-
VARESE (Pinn): VSD 5380 (CD)
UNINVITED The (FILM 1944) Music score by VICTOR YOUNG
+ *suites from* 'GULLIVER'S TRAVELS'/'GREATEST SHOW
ON EARTH' *MARCO POLO (Select): 8225063 (CD)*
UNINVITED The (ITV 25/9/97) Music score: MARTIN KISZKO
-S/T- *OCEAN DEEP (Univ): OCD 007 (CD)*
UNIVERSAL SOLDIER (1992) Music sco: CHRISTOPHER FRANKE
-S/T- *VARESE (Pinn): VSD 5373 (CD*
UNIVERSAL SOLDIER: THE RETURN (1999) Music: DON DAVIS
-S/T- *VARESE (Pinn): VSD 6068 (CD)*
UNIVERSITY CHALLENGE (BBC2 21/9/1994-2001) theme music
"College Boy" DEREK NEW *unavailable*
UNSINKABLE MOLLY BROWN The (1964) -S/T- reissue on
RHINO RECORDS (USA) cat.number to be confirmed
UNTAMED HEART (1992) Music score: CLIFF EIDELMAN
-S/T- *VARESE (Pinn): VSD 5404 (CD) VSC 5404 (MC)*
UNTOUCHABLES The (1987) Music score ENNIO MORRICONE
-S/T- *A.& M.(IMS-Poly): E.393 909-2 (CD)*
see COLL.75,124,178,245,252,
UP 'N' UNDER (1997) Music score: MARK THOMAS -S/T- V/A
EDEL UK (Vital): 0022872CIN (CD)
UP AT THE VILLA (2000) Music score by PINO DONAGGIO
-S/T- *VARESE (Pinn): VSD 6128 (CD)*
UP CLOSE AND PERSONAL (1995) Music sco: THOMAS NEWMAN
V/A -S/T- *EDEL-HOLLYWOOD (Vital) 012 053-2HWR (CD)*
UP ON THE ROOF (1997) Music score: ALAN PARKER -S/T-
OCEAN DEEP (Univ): OCD 009 (CD)
UP THE JUNCTION (1967) Music by MIKE HUGG-MANFRED MANN
-S/T- reissued on *RPM (Pinn): RPM 189 (CD)*
UPSTAIRS DOWNSTAIRS (LWT 70 rep C4-13/11/82) theme mus
"The Edwardians" by ALEXANDER FARIS
see COLL.3,200,
URBAN LEGEND (1998) Music score: CHRISTOPHER YOUNG
-S/T- *RCA (BMG): 74321 63477-2 (CD)*
URBAN LEGENDS FINAL CUT (aka UL2)(2000) Music score:
JOHN OTTMAN -S/T- *VARESE (Pinn): VSD 6179 (CD)*
URGA (1990) Music score: EDWARD ARTEYMEV -S/T- *Import
PHILIPS (Discovery): 510 608-2 (CD)*
URINETOWN: THE MUSICAL (2001) Songs: MARK HOLLMAN and
GREG KOTIS - ORIG CAST *BMG IMP: 09026 63821-2 (CD)*
US GIRLS (BBC1 27/2/92) theme music: NIGEL HESS
see COLL.137,
USUAL SUSPECTS The (1995) Music score: JOHN OTTMAN
-S/T- *MILAN (BMG): 30107-2 (CD)*
UTILIZER The (USA TV Sci-fi) Music sc: DENNIS McCARTHY
-S/T- *INTRADA (Silva Screen): MAF 7067 (CD)*
UTU (1983) Music score by JOHN CHARLES -S/T- on
LEGEND-LABEL X (Hot): LXCD 6 (CD reissue)

V : THE SERIES (USA 84 ITV 2/1/89) theme music: DENNIS
McCARTHY Orchestral score JOE HARNELL *see COLL.14,*
VALENTINE (2001) Music score: DON DAVIS -S/T- V.ARTS
WB (TEN): 9362 479 43-2 (CD) -4 (MC)
VALLEY OF THE DOLLS (1967) Music score: ANDRE PREVIN
PHILIPS (Univ.): 3145 36876-2 (CD)
VALLEY OF THE KINGS (1954) Music score: MIKLOS ROZSA
TICKERTAPE USA Impt.(S.Screen): TT 3010 (CD)
VALMOUTH (O.LONDON CAST 1958) Songs: SANDY WILSON *feat*
MARCIA ASHTON-CLEO LAINE-FENELLA FIELDING-PETER
GILMORE-IAN BURFORD *DRG (Pinn): CDSBL 13109 (CD)*
VALMOUTH (O.CHICHESTER CAST) BERTICE READING-FENELLA
FIELDING-DORIS HARE *TER (Koch): CDTER 1019 (CD)*
VAMPIRE LOVERS The (1970) Music score: HARRY ROBINSON
-S/T- *GDI (UNIV): GDICD 009 (CD)*
VAMPIRES (John Carpenter's) (1998) Music score by
JOHN CARPENTER -S/T- *MILAN (USA) IMPORT*
VAMPYROS LESBOS (1970) Music: MANFRED HUBLER-SIEGFRIED
SCHWAB -S/T- *MOTEL (Greyhound): ROOM 1CD (CD)*
VAN DER VALK (ITV 73) theme "Eye Level" (JACK TROMBEY)
SIMON PARK ORCHESTRA *see COLL.3,200,250,*
VANAPRASTHAM: THE LAST DANCE (1999) Original Music by
ZAKIR HUSSEIN -S/T- *EmArCy (Univ): 546 501-2 (CD)*
VANITY FAIR (BBC1 01/11/1998) Music score: MURRAY GOLD
-S/T- *BBC AUDIO INT (Pinn): WMSF 60042 (CD)*
VANITY FAIR (BBC1 6/09/1987) music by NIGEL HESS
see COLL.44,92,94,137,
VARIETY GIRL (1947) -S/T- + 'IT HAPPENED IN BROOKLYN'
selections *GREAT MOVIE THEMES (BMG): CD 60034 (CD)*
VARSITY BLUES (1998) Music score: MARK ISHAM -S/T- inc
FOO FIGHTERS/THIRD EYE BLIND/LOUDMOUTH/VAN HALEN
EDEL-HOLLYWOOD (Vital) 010 205-2HWR (CD)
VATEL (2001) Music score by ENNIO MORRICONE -S/T- on
VIRGIN IMPORTS (CD)
VELVET GOLDMINE (1998) Music score: CARTER BURWELL
VARIOUS ARTS -S/T- *LONDON (Univ): 556 035-2 (CD)*
VENGEANCE OF SHE(1967) Music score:JAMES BERNARD -S/T-
with 'SHE' *GDI (ABM/UNIV): GDICD 018 (CD)*
VERONICA'S CLOSET (USA 1997/SKY1 2000) theme music
"Body Rock" BY MOBY from album 'Play'
MUTE (Vital): CDSTUMM 172 (CD) CSTUMM 172 (MC)
VERSACE MURDER The (1999) Music sco: CLAUDIO SIMONETTI
-S/T- *TSUNAMI (Discovery): TOS 0308 (CD)*
VERTICAL LIMIT (2000) Music score: JAMES NEWTON HOWARD
-S/T- *VARESE (Pinn): VSD 6207 (CD)*
VERTIGO (1958) Mus sc: BERNARD HERRMANN -S/T- original
restored 1958 score conducted by Muir Mathieson
VARESE (Pinn): VSD 5759 (CD) / ALSO AVAILABLE:
1995 recording by Royal Scottish National Orch
(Joel McNeely) on *VARESE (Pinn): VSD 5600 (CD)*
see COLL.97,105,135,136,140,141,142,143,144,
VERY ANNIE MARY (2000) Music score by STEPHEN WARBECK
-S/T- VARIOUS ARTISTS music from and inspired by
UNIVERSAL MUSIC: 461 877-2 (CD)

VERY GOOD EDDIE (REV.BROADWAY CAST 1975) Songs: JEROME
KERN-SCHUYLER GREENE *DRG (Pinn): CDRG 6100 (CD)*
VETS IN PRACTICE (BBC1 26/8/97-2001) and **VET'S SCHOOL**
(BBC1 14/10/96) mus.by DEBBIE WISEMAN *unavailable*
VETS IN THE WILD (BBC2 00/00/2000) Music by TY UNWIN
-S/T- BBC WORLDWIDE (Pinn): WMSF 6018-2 (CD)
VICAR OF DIBLEY The (BBC1 10/11/1994) theme m. (Psalm
23) on collection 'HOWARD GOODALL'S CHOIR WORKS'
ASV (Select): CDDCA 1028 (CD)
VICE The (ITV 04/01/1999) series music by JULIAN NOTT
unavailable. theme song "Sour Times" by PORTISHEAD
from 'Dummy' *GO DISCS (Univ): 828 522-2(CD) -4(MC)*
VICTOR VICTORIA O.BROADWAY CAST RECORDING *with* JULIE
ANDREWS-TONY ROBERTS-MICHAEL NOURI-RACHEL YORK
PHILIPS (Univ): 446 919-2 (CD) 446 919-4(MC)
VICTOR VICTORIA (1982) Music: HENRY MANCINI Lyrics by
LESLIE BRICUSSE *feat* JULIE ANDREWS-ROBERT PRESTON
-S/T- GNP CRESCENDO (ZYX/Greyh): GNPD 8038 (CD)
VICTORIAN KITCHEN GARDEN The (BBC2 8/5/1998 orig 1987)
theme by PAUL READE perf.by EMMA JOHNSON (flute)
'ENCORES' *ASV (Select): CDDCA 800 (CD)*
VICTORY AT SEA (USA 50's) music score: RICHARD RODGERS
arr/cond: Robert Russell BENNETT *version on*
TELARC USA (BMG): CD 80175 see COLL.123,
VIDEODROME (1982) Music score by HOWARD SHORE
-S/T- VARESE (Pinn): VSD 5975 (CD)
VIETNAM A TV HISTORY (USA TV) *see COLL.247,*

VIEW TO A KILL A - *see* JAMES BOND FILM INDEX p.346
see COLL.26,46,47,
VIKINGS The (1958) Music score: MARIO NASCIMBENE new
recording of score with 'Solomon and Sheba' music
DRG-NEW NOTE (Pinn): DRGCD 32963 (CD)
see COLL.61,62,266,
VILLAGE OF THE DAMNED (1994) Music sco: JOHN CARPENTER
VARESE (Pinn): VSD 5629 (CD)
VIOLATOR (2000)
MERCURY (Univ): 558 941-2 (CD) -4 (MC) -1 (LP)
VIOLENT SATURDAY - *see COLL.1,*

VIOLENT STREETS ('THIEF') (1981) Mus: TANGERINE DREAM
VIRGIN (EMI): CDV 2198 (CD)
VIRGIN SUICIDES (1999) Music by AIR -S/T- on
SOURCE-VIRGIN (EMI): CDV(TCV)(MDV) 2910 (CD/MC/md)
EMPEROR NORTON (Pinn): EMN 7029(CD)(LP) (CD/LP)
VIRGINIA CITY (1940) Mus sco: MAX STEINER *new record:*
MOSCOW SO (Stromberg) *inc:* 'BEAST WITH 5 FINGERS'
'LOST PATROL' *MARCO POLO (Select) 8.223870 (CD)*
VIRGINIAN The (USATV)(rpt.BBC2 128/4/1998) theme music
PERCY FAITH on 'TELEVISION'S G.HITS VOL.2' *EDEL-
CINERAMA (Vital): 0022712CIN (CD) see COLL.243,*
VISION ON (BBC1 1964-76) pict.gallery "Left Bank Two"
(WAYNE HILL) The NOVELTONES *see COLL.3,*
VISIT The USA (S/T) *CONCORD JAZZ (Pinn):CCD 49662 (CD)*

VISITOR The (USA 1997/ITV 25/4/1998) Main theme by
DAVID ARNOLD / score by KEVIN KINER *unavailable*
VIVA LAS VEGAS *see* ELVIS PRESLEY INDEX p.348

VIVA ZAPATA! (1952) Music sco: ALEX NORTH. new record
ing by SCOTTISH NATIONAL ORCHESTRA conducted by
JERRY GOLDSMITH on *VARESE (Pinn): VSD 5900 (CD)*
see COLL.1,
VIVRE POUR VIVRE - *see* 'LIVE FOR LIFE' + 'UN HOMME ET
UNE FEMME' (MAN AND A WOMAN, A) *see COLL.190,*
VIXEN (1968 RUSS MEYER) Mus: WILLIAM LOOSE -S/T- *reiss*
LASERLIGHT (Greyhound): 12922 (CD) ALSO ON QD with
'LORNA'/'FASTER PUSSYCAT' - *NORMAL/QDK MEDIA*
(Pinn/Greyhound/Direct) QDK(CD)(LP) 008
VOICES *BBC WORLDWIDE (Pinn): WMEF 0066-2 (CD)*
VOLCANO (1997) Music score: ALAN SILVESTRI -S/T- score
VARESE (Pinn): VSD 5833 (CD)
VOYAGE OF THE DAMNED (1976) Music score: LALO SCHIFRIN
suite on 'CONTINUUM JOURNEY'S VOYAGE' Lalo Shifrin
LEGEND IMPT. (Hot): LXCD 11 (CD)
VOYAGE TO THE BOTTOM OF THE SEA (USA TV)
GNP CRESCENDO (Greyhound): GNPD 8046 (CD)
see COLL.38,84,218,243,
WACKY RACES (USA68/BBC 70's) theme music (Hoyt Curtin
W.Hanna-J.Barbera) (USA TV) *see COLL.246,259,*
WAG THE DOG (1997) Music score: MARK KNOPFLER -S/T-
MERCURY (Univ): 536 864-2 (CD) -4 (MC)
WAGES OF FEAR (1978)'The Sorcerer' M: TANGERINE DREAM
MCA Imp (Silva Screen): MCAD 10842 (CD)
WAGON TRAIN (USA1957) Theme 1 "Roll Along Wagon Train"
(Fain-Brooks) *vocal version by* ROBERT HORTON on
'TV CLASSICS 4' *CASTLE (Pinn): MBSCD 412 (4CDset)*
Theme 2 "Wagons Ho!"JEROME MOROSS *MFP: HR418109-4*
Theme 3 "Wagon Train" (Rene-Russell)
see COLL.243,253,279,
WAITING FOR GOD (BBC1 28/6/90) theme 'Piano Quintet
in A'("Trout") D.667 (SCHUBERT) *HMV:CDC 747 448-2*
(CD) -4 (MC) TV vers unavailable
WAITING TO EXHALE (1995) *featuring* WHITNEY HOUSTON
-S/T- *ARISTA (BMG): 07822 18796-2 (CD) -4 (MC)*
WAKING NED (1998) Music score by SHAUN DAVEY -S/T-
featuring "Fisherman's Blues" by The WATERBOYS
LONDON (Univ): 460 939-2 (CD)
WALDEN ON HEROES (BBC2 6/1/1998) t.music "Brandenburg
Concerto No.5 in D.Major" (BACH) recording used:
NAXOS (Select): 8.550048 (CD)
WALK IN THE CLOUDS, A (1995) Music sco: MAURICE JARRE
-S/T- *MILAN (BMG): 28666-2 (CD)*
WALK ON THE MOON, A (1999) Music score: MASON DARING
-S/T- (VARIOUS ARTS) *SIRE (TEN): 4344 31041-2 (CD)*
WALKABOUT (1970) Music score: JOHN BARRY / *NEW VERSION*
inc 'THEY MIGHT BE GIANTS'/'THE CORN IS GREEN' and
other themes *SILVA SCREEN (Koch): FILMCD 339 (CD)*
see COLL.26,28,32,

WALKING THUNDER (1996) Music sco: JOHN SCOTT -S/T- on
JS (Silva Screen): JSCD 117 (CD)
WALKING WITH BEASTS (BBC1 15/11/2001) Music by BEN
BARTLETT performed by the BBC CONCERT ORCHESTRA
-S/T- *BBC WORLDWIDE (Pinn): WMSF 6046-2 (CD)*
WALKING WITH DINOSAURS (BBC1 10/1999) Music score by
BEN BARTLETT -S/T- *BBC (Pinn): WMSF 6013-2 (CD)*
WALL The (1981) Music: PINK FLOYD -S/T-
Harvest (EMI): CDS 746036-8(2CD) TC2SHDW 411(2MC)
WALTONS The (USA 1972-81) theme mus: JERRY GOLDSMITH
see COLL.14,244,
WALTZ OF THE TORREADORS (1962) *see COLL.8,*
WANDERERS The (1979) VARIOUS ARTISTS -S/T- *reiss on*
CINEPHILE (Pinn): CINCD 029 (CD)
WAR OF THE BUTTONS (1994) Music score: RACHEL PORTMAN
-S/T- *VARESE (Pinn): VSD 5554 (CD) see COLL.202,*
WAR OF THE WORLDS (JEFF WAYNE Musical Concept Album)
COLUMBIA (Ten): CDX 96000 (2CD) 4096000 (2MC)
Highlights on SONY: CDX 32356 (CD)
WAR REQUIEM (1988) Music: BENJAMIN BRITTEN based on
'War Requiem Op.66' C.B.S.O.(Simon RATTLE) *EMI:*
CDS 747 034-8 (2CDs) LONDON SYMPH.ORCH (B.BRITTEN)
DECCA (Univ): 414 383-2DH2 (2CD) K27K22 (MC)
WARRIORS (BBC1 21/11/1999) Music by DEBBIE WISEMAN
-S/T- *BBC WORLDWIDE (Pinn): WMSF 6019-2 (CD)*
WARRIORS The (1979) Music sco: BARRY DE VORZON + V/A
-S/T- *re-iss on SPECTRUM (Univ): 551 169-2 (CD)*
WARRIORS OF VIRTUE (1997) Music score: DON DAVIS
-S/T- *PROMETHEUS (Silva Screen): PCD 144 (CD)*
also on KID RHINO (TEN): 8122 72640-2 (CD)
WASH The (2001) VAR.ARTISTS inc DR.DRE-SNOOP DOGGY DOG
-S/T- *POLYDOR (UNIV): 493 128-2 (CD) -1 (LP)*
WASHINGTON SQUARE (1997) Music sco: JAN A.P.KACZMAREK
-S/T- *VARESE (Pinn): VSD 5869 (CD)*
WATCHER (2000) Music score by MARCO BELTRAMI
-S/T- *VARESE (Pinn): VSD 6181 (CD)*
WATCHING AND WAITING (-) Music by GERRY MULLIGAN -S/T-
DRG USA (New Note-Pinn): DRGCD 8475 (CD)
WATERBOY The (1998) Music score: ALAN PASQUA -S/T- inc
LENNY KRAVITZ/CANDYSKINS/DOORS/RUSH/CCR/MELLENCAMP
EDEL-HOLLYWOOD (Vital) 010 092-2HWR (CD)
WATERCOLOUR CHALLENGE (C4 14/7/1998-2001) original
music by DAVID ARNOLD and PAUL HART *unavailable*
WATERLOO BRIDGE (1940) VARIOUS -S/T- SELECTIONS on
GREAT MOVIE THEMES: (Targ-BMG): CD 60032 (CD)
WATERSHIP DOWN (FILM 1978) Music score by ANGELA MORLEY
"Bright Eyes" (Mike Batt) sung by ART GARFUNKEL
ORIG SOUNDTRACK: COLUMBIA: CBS 70161 (LP deleted)
WATERSHIP DOWN (TV SERIES 1999) Music Graham Walker
"Bright Eyes" sung by STEPHEN GATELEY also feat
ART GARFUNKEL and the ROYAL PHILHARMONIC ORCHESTRA
POLYDOR (Univ): 549 225-2 (CD)
WAY OF THE DRAGON (1973) Music score: JOSEPH KOO -S/T-
YX (CARGO): YX 7011 (LP)

WAY OF THE GUN (2000) Music score: JOE KREAMER -S/T-
  MILAN (BMG): 74321 78828-2 (CD)
WAY WE WERE The (1973) Mus: MARVIN HAMLISCH Lyr: ALAN
  /MARILYN BERGMAN -S/T- feat BARBRA STREISAND on
  Sony: 474911-2 (CD) 474911-4 (MC) see COLL.61,
WEAKEST LINK The (BBC2 14/08/2000) series music by
  PAUL FARRER (INTER ANGEL MUSIC)
  "Weakest Link" ECHOBASS feat RATPAC *BBC WORLDWIDE*
  BBC (Pinn): CDANNE 001 (CDs) 12ANNE 001 (12"s)
WEDDING BELL BLUES (1996) Music by Var.Artists -S/T-
  VARESE (Pinn): VSD 5853 (CD)
WEDDING MARCH (1928 silent) Contemporary score by
  CARL DAVIS *see Collections* 'The SILENTS'
WEDDING PLANNER (2001) Music score by MERVYN WARREN
  -S/T- *HOLLYWOOD-EDEL (Vital): 012 603-2HWR (CD)*
WEDDING SINGER The (1998) -S/T- with VARIOUS ARTISTS
  Volume 1 - *WBROS (TEN): 9362 46840-2 (CD) -4 (MC)*
  Volume 2 - *WBROS (TEN): 9362 46984-2 (CD) -4 (MC)*
WEDLOCK - *see COLL.51* DEADLOCK
WEEKEND IN HAVANA (1941) ALICE FAYE-CARMEN MIRANDA
  plus 'HOLIDAY IN MEXICO' selections on
  GREAT MOVIE THEMES (BMG): CD 60036 (CD)
WEEKEND WORLD (LWT 1987) theme "Nantucket Sleighride"
  (Felix Pappalardi-Les West) by MOUNTAIN 'Best Of'
  BEAT GOES ON (Pinn): BGO(CD)(LP) 33 (CD/LP)
WEISER (2000) Music score by ZBIGNIEW PREISNER -S/T-
  SILVA CLASSICS (Koch): 522 962-2 (CD)
WELCOME BACK KOTTER (USA TV) *see COLL.244,*
WEST The (BBC2 21/12/1998) Music: JAY UNGAR & others
  -S/T- *SONY CLASSICS: SK 62727 (CD)*
WEST SIDE STORY - songs by Leonard Bernstein and
  Stephen Sondheim
  1.FILM MUSICAL 1961 NATALIE WOOD *sung: Marnie Nixon*
    RICHARD BEYMER *by Jim Bryant* RITA MORENO *by Betty
    Wand* CHITA RIVERA-GEORGE CHAKIRIS-RUSS TAMBLYN
    COLUMBIA (Ten): 467606-2 (CD) -4(MC) and
  2.STUDIO RECORDING 1997 *feat* PAUL MANUEL-CAROLINE O'
    CONNOR-TINUKE OLAFIMIHAN *with* NATIONAL SYMPH ORCH.
    conducted by JOHN OWEN EDWARDS
    TER-Music Theatre Hour (Koch): CDTEH 6002 (CD)
  3.STUDIO RECORD 1984 TV-BBC1 10/5/1985 *with:* KIRI TE
    KANAWA-JOSE CARRERAS-TATIANA TROYANOS-KURT OLLMAN-
    MARILYN HORN and LEONARD BERNSTEIN *DG-POLYGRAM:*
    415253-2(2CD) -4(MC) Highl: 415963-2 (CD) -4 (MC)
  4.STUDIO RECORD 1993 MICHAEL BALL-BARBARA BONNEY-
    LA VERNE WILLIAMS-CHRISTOPHER HOWERD-MARY CAREWE-
    JENNY O'GRADY-LEE GIBSON + RPO: BARRY WORDSWORTH
    CARLTON-IMG (Carlton): IMGCD(IMGMC)1801 (CD/MC)
  5.LEICESTER HAYMARKET THEATRE PROD 1993 *with* Nat.
    Symph.Orch (John Owen Edwards) PAUL MANUEL-TINUKE
    OLAFIMIHAN-CAROLINE O'CONNOR-NICK FERANTI and Comp
    <u>Highlights</u>: *CURTAIN CALL-MCI (DISC): CURTCD 001 CD*
    <u>Complete</u>: *TER: CDTER2 1197 (2CD) ZCTER2 1197(2MC)*

6.ORIG BROADWAY CAST 1957 CAROL LAWRENCE-LARRY KERT
   CHITA RIVERA *COLUMBIA (Ten): SK 60724 (CD)*
7.ORIG NEW YORK CAST 1957 *with:* CAROL LAWRENCE-LARRY
   KERT-CHITA RIVERA etc.*COLUMBIA (Ten): SMK 60724 CD*
WEST WING (USA/C4 19/01/2001) music: W.G.SNUFFY WALDEN
   COLL 'MUSIC BY...' *BMG IMPORTS: 01934 11424-2 (CD)*
WESTERN FRONT (BBC2 31/07/1999) series music by NIGEL
   BEAHAM-POWELL and BELLA RUSSELL *unavailable*
WHAT A CRAZY WORLD (1963) Songs by ALAN KLEIN *featur:*
   MARTY WILDE-JOE BROWN-SUSAN MAUGHAN-ALAN KLEIN etc.
   -S/T- *CASTLE MUSIC (Pinn): CMRCD 396 (CD)*
WHAT A FEELING! (ORIG LONDON CAST 1997) featuring LUKE
   GOSS-SINITTA-SONIA *MCI (THE-Disc): MCCD 287 (CD)*
WHAT DID YOU DO IN THE WAR DADDY (1966) Music score by
   HENRY MANCINI *RCA IMPORT: 74321 66501-2 (CD)*
WHAT DREAMS MAY COME (1998) Music score: MICHAEL KAMEN
   -S/T- *DECCA (UNIV): 460 858-2 (CD)*
WHAT LIES BENEATH (2000) Music score by ALAN SILVESTRI
   -S/T- *VARESE (Pinn): VSD 6172 (CD)*
WHAT THE PAPERS SAY (BBC2 23/3/90 previous C4-Granada)
   "English Dance No.5" ('Eight English Dances')
   (Malcolm ARNOLD) *CHANDOS: CHAN 8867 (CD)*
WHAT WOMEN WANT (2000) Music score by ALAN SILVESTRI
   -S/T- *V.Arts COLUMBIA (TEN): 501 715-2 (CD) -4(MC)*
WHAT'S LOVE GOT TO DO WITH IT - *see* TINA
WHAT'S MY LINE (BBC 1951) *see COLL.119,*
WHAT'S NEW PUSSYCAT (1965) Music:BURT BACHARACH t.song
   by TOM JONES -S/T- *RYKODISC (Vit): RCD 10740 (CD)*
WHAT'S THE WORST THAT COULD HAPPEN (2001) Music: TYLER
   BATES -S/T- (V.ARTS) *POLYDOR (UNIV): 493 072-2 (CD)*
WHAT'S UP, TIGER LILY (1966) Music: JOHN SEBASTIAN The
   LOVIN' SPOONFUL -S/T- with 'YOU'RE A BIG BOY NOW'
   RCA CAMDEN (BMG): 74321 69952-2 (CD)
   RAZOR & TIE (Koch): RE 2167-2 (CD) previously
WHATEVER HAPPENED TO HAROLD SMITH (1999) Music score
   by HARRY GREGSON WILLIAMS -S/T- *VARIOUS ARTISTS on
   EAST WEST (TEN): 8573 82004-2 (CD) -4 (MC)*
WHATEVER HAPPENED TO THE LIKELY LADS (BBC2 9/1/1973)
   theme m: "Whatever Happened To You" (Mike Hugg-Ian
   La Frenais) by HIGHLY LIKELY *see COLL.3,*
WHEN A MAN LOVES A WOMAN (94) Music: ZBIGNIEW PRIESNER
   Songs PERCY SLEDGE-LOS LOBOS-RICKIE LEE JONES etc
   -S/T- *EDEL-HOLLYWOOD (Vital) 011 606-2HWR (CD)*
WHEN ANGELS FALL (1959) Music score: KRZYSZTOF KOMEDA
   -S/T- *POWER BROS (Harmonia Mundi): PB 00175 (CD)*
WHEN DINOSAURS RULED T.EARTH *see* ONE MILLION YEARS BC
WHEN GOOD GHOULS GO BAD (2001) Music sco: CHRISTOPHER
   GORDON -S/T- *VARESE (Pinn): VSD 6281 (CD)*
WHEN HARRY MET SALLY (89) Music adapted & arranged by
   Marc Shaiman and performed by Harry Connick Jnr.
   -S/T- *COLUMBIA 465 753-2 (CD) see COLL.182,*
WHEN THE BOAT COMES IN (BBC1 4/1/76)
   theme mus "Dance Ti Thi Daddy" (trad.arranged by
   David Fanshawe) sung by ALEX GLASGOW *see COLL.4,*

WHEN THE WIND BLOWS (Cartoon 1987) Music score: ROGER
   WATERS Title song sung by DAVID BOWIE / songs by
   Genesis-Hugh Cornwell-Squeeze-Paul Hardcastle
   -S/T- *VIRGIN (EMI): CDVIP 132 (CD) TCVIP 132 (MC)*

WHEN WE WERE KINGS -S/T- *MERCURY (Uni):534 462-2 (CD)*

WHERE EAGLES DARE (1968) Music score: RON GOODWIN
   for theme only *see COLL.265,*

WHERE THE HEART IS (ITV 6/4/97) theme "Home Is Where
   The Heart Is" sung by PADDY McALOON *see COLL.172,*

WHERE'S JACK (1969) Music score by ROY BUDD *featuring*
   MARY HOPKIN *(t.song) also inc.* 'KIDNAPPED' (1971)
   TICKERTAPE USA Impt.(S.Screen): TT 3008 (CD)

WHICKERS WORLD (BBC 60s) theme "West End" by LAURIE
   JOHNSON *see COLL.5,24,74,261,*

WHILE I LIVE (1947) Music score: CHARLES WILLIAMS inc
   'The Dream Of Olwen' *see COLL.48,235,*

WHILE YOU WERE SLEEPING (1995) Music: RANDY EDELMAN
   -S/T- *VARESE (Pinn): VSD 5627 (CD)*

WHISKY GALORE! (1949) *see COLL.161,*

WHISPERERS The (1966) Music score: JOHN BARRY -S/T- on
   RYKODISC (Vital): RCD 10720 (CD)

WHISTLE DOWN THE WIND (SHOW 1998)(ANDREW LLOYD WEBBER-
   JIM STEINMAN) title song by TINA ARENA / ORIG CAST
   Complete: *R.USEFUL Univ: 547 261-2 (2CD) -4 (2MC)*
   Highlights: *R.USEFUL Univ: 559 441-2 (CD) -4 (MC)*

WHISTLE DOWN THE WIND (1961) Music score by MALCOLM
   ARNOLD / LONDON Symphony Orchestra (Richard HICOX)
   on coll 'Film Music' *CHANDOS: CHAN 9100 (CD)*

WHITBREAD ROUND T.WORLD YACHT RACE *see* SAIL THE WORLD

WHITE CHRISTMAS (1954) Songs by IRVING BERLIN *feat:*
   BING CROSBY-DANNY KAYE -S/T- *MCA: MCLD 19191 (CD)*

WHITE MISCHIEF (1988) Music GEORGE FENTON title song
   by Tim Finn/ "Alphabet Song" sung by Sarah Miles
   -S/T- *JAY-TER (SSD): CDJAY 1347 (CD)*

WHITE ROCK (1976) Mus scored & perf. by RICK WAKEMAN
   A.& M.(Univ): RWCD 20 (CD Box Set)

WHITE ROCK 2 (1999) Music by RICK WAKEMAN
   MUSIC FUSION (Pinn): MFCD 004 (CD)

WHITE SANDS (1992) Music score: PATRICK O'HEARN -S/T-
   MORGAN CREEK (Univ): 002252-2 MCM (CD)

WHO IS SYLVIA *see COLL.24,*

WHO PAYS THE FERRYMAN (UKGold 24/4/93 orig BBC1 1977)
   music: YANNIS MARKOPOULOS *see COLL.200,*

WHO PLAYS WINS (ORIG LONDON CAST 1985) comp/performed
   by PETER SKELLERN-RICHARD STILGOE *re-issued on*
   FIRST NIGHT (Pinn): OCRCD 6037 (CD)

WHO WANTS TO BE A MILLIONAIRE (ITV 04/09/1998-2002)
   music composed/perf.by MATTHEW and KEITH STRACHAN
   'THE COMPLETE MUSIC AND QUESTIONS CARDS' on
   CELADOR (Univ): MILLION 1 (CD)

WHO'S AFRAID OF VIRGINIA WOOLF (1966) Music score by
   ALEX NORTH -S/T- *reiss* WB (TEN): 9362 47884-2 (CD)
   new recording by NATIONAL PHILHARMONIC ORCHESTRA
   (Jerry Goldsmith) on *VARESE (Pinn): VSD 5800 (CD)*

WHO'S THAT GIRL (1987) Music: STEPHEN BRAY -S/T- incl
MADONNA-SCRITTI POLITTI-CLUB NOUVEAU-COATI MUNDI
-S/T- *SIRE (TEN): WX 102C (MC) 7599 25611-2 (CD)*
WHO'S THE BOSS (USA TV) *see COLL.247,*
WHOLE 9 YARDS (2000) Music score: RANDY EDELMAN -S/T-
VARESE (Pinn): VSD 6114 (CD)
WHOSE LINE IS IT ANYWAY (C4/Hat Trick 23/9/88-1999)
theme music: PHILIP POPE *unavailable*
WICKER MAN The (1973) Music by PAUL GIOVANNI & MAGNET
-S/T- *TRUNK (SRD): BARKED 4CD (CD) BARKED 4 (LP)*
WIGGLES The (ITV 02/01/1999) Music & songs The WIGGLES
-S/T- 'GET READY TO WIGGLE' on
EDEL-DISNEY (Vital) 010246-2DNY (CD)
WILD AFRICA (BBC2 7/11/2001) Music CHRISTOPHER GUNNING
-S/T- *BBC WORLDWIDE (Pinn): WMSF 6049-2 (CD)*
WILD AMERICA (1997) Music score: JOEL McNEELY -S/T-
PROMETHEUS (Silva Screen): PCD 147 (CD)
WILD AT HEART (1990) Music score: ANGELO BADALAMENTI
-S/T- *SPECTRUM (Univ): 551 318-2 (CD)*
WILD BUNCH The (1969) Music sco: JERRY FIELDING
-S/T- reissue *WB (TEN): 9362 48086-2 (CD)*
also on *RETROGRADE (Film Score Monthly) Impt.(CD)*
WILD DUCK The (1983) Music score by SIMON WALKER -S/T-
also includes 'FROG DREAMING' (music by BRIAN MAY)
SOUTHERN CROSS (HOT): SCCD 1019 (CD)
WILD GEESE The (1978) Music score by ROY BUDD -S/T- on
CINEPHILE (Pinn): CINCD 014 (CD) see COLL.108,
WILD IN THE COUNTRY *see* ELVIS PRESLEY FILM INDEX p.348
WILD ONE (1953) Music score: LEITH STEVENS with SHORTY
ROGERS -S/T- *BEAR FAMILY (Roll): BCD 16393 (CD)*
WILD PARTY (ORIGINAL USA CAST) Songs by ANDREW LIPPA
BMG IMPORTS: 09026 63695-2 (CD)
WILD ROVERS (1971) Music score by JERRY GOLDSMITH -S/T-
including 'THE LAST RUN' (1971 Jerry Goldsmith) on
CHAPTER III (USA IMPORT): CHA 0135 (CD)
WILD ROVERS (1971) Music score by JERRY GOLDSMITH -S/T-
inc 'THE FIRST GREAT TRAIN ROBBERY' (78 GOLDSMITH)
MEMOIR-Castle (Pinn): CDMOIR 601 (CD)
WILD THINGS (1997) Music sco: GEORGE S.CLINTON. songs
by MORPHINE -S/T- *VARESE (Pinn): VSD 5924 (CD)*
WILD WEST The (USA/C4 14/5/95) original music: BRIAN
KEANE -S/T- *SHANACHIE (Koch): SHCD 6013 (2CD)*
WILD WILD WEST (1998) Music sco: ELMER BERNSTEIN -S/T-
score: *VARESE (Pinn): VSD 6042 (CD) see COLL.40,*
songs: *INTERSCOPE (Univ): IND 90344 (CD) INC 90344*
WILD WILD WEST (USA TV) *see COLL.84,279,*

WILDE (1997) Music score: DEBBIE WISEMAN -S/T- on
MCI (THE-DISC-Pinn): MPRCD 001 (CD)
WILLO THE WISP (BBC TV) *see COLL.100,132,*
WILLOW (1988) Music score: JAMES HORNER -S/T-
VIRGIN (EMI): CDV 2538 (CD) see COLL.148,240,
WILSONS The (C4 16/01/2000) series theme music by
DEBBIE WISEMAN *unavailable*

WIMBLEDON (BBC1/2 1972-2002)
opening theme music "Light & Tuneful" by KEITH
MANSFIELD *see COLL.5,101,122,*
Closing theme "Sporting Occasion" by ARNOLD STECK
see COLL.122,
WIND (1928) Contemporary score CARL DAVIS *see COLL.85,*
WIND AND THE LION The (1975) Music sc: JERRY GOLDSMITH
-S/T- *INTRADA (Silva Screen): MAF 7005D (CD)*
WINDS OF WAR The (ITV 9/1983 & 5/1985) Mus: BOB COBERT
-S/T- Nurnberg S.O. *TER Koch: ZCTER 1070 (MC) delet*
also WAR AND REMEMBRANCE
WINDTALKERS (2001) Music score by JAMES HORNER -S/T-
BMG IMPORTS: 09026 63867-2 (CD)
WING COMMANDER (1998) Mus.sc: DAVID ARNOLD-KEVIN KINER
-S/T- *SONIC IMAGES (Grey-Cargo):7828 278905-2 (CD)*
also on SID 8905 (CD)
WINGS (1927 silent) Contemporary score by CARL DAVIS
see COLL.85, 'The SILENTS'
WINGS OF THE DOVE (1998) Music score: EDWARD SHEARMUR
-S/T- *CONIFER (BMG): 74321 55881-2 (CD)*
WINNER The (1997) Music score: DANIEL LICHT -S/T- on
RYKODISC (Vital-ADA): RCD 10392 (CD)
WINTER GUEST The (1997) Music sco: MICHAEL KAMEN -S/T-
VARESE (Pinn): VSD 5895 (CD)
WINTER OLYMPIC GAMES 1992 (BBC1 1992) theme "Pop Looks
Bach" (Sam FONTEYN) also "Chorus Of Hebrew Slaves"
from 'Nabucco' (VERDI) *see COLL.197,*
WISH ME LUCK (LWT 8/1/89) theme JIM PARKER *see COLL.4,*
WISH YOU WERE HERE (Thames/Cent) theme 'Carnival" by
GORDON GILTRAP *MUNCHKIN GRCD 1 deleted* link music
"The Long Road" by MARK KNOPFLER -S/T- 'CAL'
VERTIGO Poly: 822 769-2 (CD) VERHC 17 (MC)
WISHMASTER 2: EVIL NEVER DIES (1999) Music score DAVID
C.WILLIAMS -S/T- *IMPORT BEYOND USA: 578 219-2 (CD)*
WITCHCRAFT (BBC 1992) Music score: JOHN SCOTT -S/T- on
JOHN SCOTT Rec. (Silva Screen): JSCD 121 (CD)
WITCHES OF EASTWICK The (1987) Music sc: JOHN WILLIAMS
classical music on NAXOS: 8551153 (CD)
WITCHES OF EASTWICK The (2000 MUSICAL)
ORIGINAL LONDON CAST RECORDING on
FIRST NIGHT (Pinn): CASTCD 79 (CD) CASTC 79 (MC)
WITHNAIL AND I (1986) Music score: DAVID DUNDAS-RICK
WENTWORTH -S/T- VARIOUS ARTISTS *reissue*
DRG USA (Pinn): DRGCD 12590 (CD) see COLL.84,97,
WITNESS (1985) Music score: MAURICE JARRE -S/T-
VARESE (Pinn): VCD 47227 (CD) +
TER (Koch): CDTER 1098 (CD) see COLL.153,154,252,
WIZARD OF OZ The- songs: Harold Arlen & E.Yip Harburg
1.FILM MUSICAL 1939 *with:* JUDY GARLAND-RAY BOLGER-
JACK HALEY-BERT LAHR-FRANK MORGAN -S/T- *reissue*
EMI PREMIER (EMI): CDODEON 7 (CD)
2.ROYAL SHAKESPEARE COMPANY CAST 1988 (Barbican)
<u>Highlights</u>: *SHOWTIME (MCI-THE): SHOW(CD)(MC) 003*
<u>Complete</u>: *TER (Koch): CDTER 1165 (CD)*

WOLF MAN The (1940) Music: HANS SALTER-FRANK SKINNER
new recording MOSCOW SYMPHONY ORCHEST (STROMBERG)
MARCO POLO (Select): 8.223748 (CD) also includes
INVISIBLE MAN RETURNS-SON OF FRANKENSTEIN

WOLFPACK (DIE HALBSTARKEN 1956) Music: MARTIN BOTTCHER
-S/T- *BEAR FAMILY (Rollecoaster): BCD 16403 (CD)*

WOLVES OF WILLOUGHBY CHASE (1989) Music: COLIN TOWNS
-S/T- *TER (Koch): CDTER 1162 (CD)*

WOMAN IN RED The (1984) Songs: STEVIE WONDER featur:
STEVIE WONDER-DIONNE WARWICK -S/T-
MOTOWN (Univ): 530 030-2 (CD)

WOMAN IN WHITE The (BBC1 28/12/1997) Music score by
DAVID FERGUSON *see COLL.104,*

WOMAN OF THE YEAR songs: John Kander and Fred Ebb
ORIG BROADWAY CAST 1981 with LAUREN BACALL
RAZOR & TIE (Koch): RE 21462 (CD)

WOMAN ON TOP (2000) Music score by LUIS BACALOV -S/T-
SONY CLASSICS (TEN): SK 89279 (CD)

WOMBLES The (BBC1 1973) theme and songs by MIKE BATT
CBS SONY: 466118-2 (CD) -4(MC) also see COLL.285,
also available 'THE WOMBLES COLLECTION' on
DRAMATICO (Vit): DRAMCD 0001 (CD) DRAMCA 0001 (MC)

WOMBLES The (ITV 4/3/1998) "Remember You're A Womble"
(Mike BATT) WOMBLES *SONY: 665 620-2 (CDs) -4 (MC)*

WOMEN TALKING DIRTY (2000) Music score by ELTON JOHN
-S/T- VAR.ARTISTS *MERCURY (UNIV): 585 744-2 (CD)*

WONDER BOYS The (2000) Music score: CHRISTOPHER YOUNG
-S/T- (score) *VARESE (Pinn): VSD 6126 (CD)*
-S/T- (songs) *COLUMBIA (TEN): 497 738-2 (CD)*

WONDER WOMAN (USA TV) *see COLL.244,*

WONDERFUL TOWN - songs: Leonard Bernstein-Betty Comden
and Adolph Green

1. *TER* STUDIO RECORD.1998 KAREN MASON-REBECCA LUKER-
   RON RAINES-GREG EDELMAN-DON STEPHENSON & Company
   NAT.SYMPHONY ORCH.*conductor:* JOHN OWEN EDWARDS
   TER (Koch): CDTER2 1223 (2CD, 11.1998)
2. ORIG LONDON CAST 1986 MAUREEN LIPMAN-JOHN CASSADY-
   NICHOLAS COLICOS-DANIEL COLL-ROY DURBIN-RAY LONNEN
   FIRST NIGHT (Pinn) OCRCD 6011 (CD)
3. ORIG BROADWAY CAST 1953 *w:* ROSALIND RUSSELL-SYDNEY
   CHAPLIN *SONY BROADWAY: SK 48021 (CD)*
   REMASTERED VERSION on *UNIV-IMS:AA.440014602-2 (CD)*
4. STUDIO RECORDING, conducted by SIMON RATTLE
   EMI CLASSICS: CDC 556 753-2 (CD)

WONDERLAND (1999) Music score by MICHAEL NYMAN -S/T-
VENTURE-VIRGIN (EMI): CDVE 942 (CD)

WONDERWALL (1968) Music score: GEORGE HARRISON *Re-iss:*
EMI-APPLE: CDSAPCOR 1 (CD) (TC)SAPCOR 1 (MC/LP)

WOO (1998) VARIOUS ARTISTS -S/T-
EPIC (Ten): 491 121-2 (CD) -4 (MC)

WOOD The (1998) VARIOUS ARTISTS -S/T-
JIVE (Pinn): 052 371-2 (CD) 523 711 (2LP)

WOODLANDERS The (1996) Mus score: GEORGE FENTON -S/T-
DEBONAIR (Pinn): CDDEB 1007 (CD)
WOODSTOCK 1969 Woodstock Music Festival *with* JOAN BAEZ
JOE COCKER-RICHIE HAVENS-COUNTRY JOE & FISH-CROSBY
NASH & NEIL YOUNG-ARLO GUTHRIE-JIMI HENDRIX-
SANTANA-ShaNaNa-JOHN SEBASTIAN-SLY & FAMILY STONE-
TEN YEARS AFTER-WHO -S/T- 'BEST OF WOODSTOCK'
WEA: 7567 82618-2 (CD) -4 (MC) -S/T- reissue
WEA: (1) 7567 80593-2 (2CD) (2) 7567 80594-2 (2CD)
WOODSTOCK II (1970) Woodstock festival 69 feat V.Arts
-S/T- re-issue: *ATLANTIC (TEN): 7567 81991-2 (CD)*
WOODY WOODPECKER (USA) ORIGINAL CARTOON CAST RECORDING
DRIVE ARCHIVE (Silver Sounds): 7806 747112-2 (CD)
song also by DANNY KAYE *(MCA) / see COLL.242,*
WOOF! (Carlton 18/2/89) theme: PAUL LEWIS *see COLL.4,*
WORKING GIRL (1988) Music score: ROB MOUNCEY songs by
CARLY SIMON -S/T- *feat:* CARLY SIMON-SONNY ROLLINS
POINTER SISTERS *reiss: ARISTA (BMG): 259 767 (CD)*
WORLD AT WAR The (BBC2 5/9/94 orig ITV 31/10/73) theme
music by CARL DAVIS *see COLL.131,200,*
WORLD CUP 1998 (France, 10 June 1998 - 12 July 1998)

1. BBC TV theme (arrangement of "Pavane" (FAURE) by
   ELIZABETH PARKER with WIMBLEDON CHORAL SOCIETY
   BBC-TELSTAR (TEN): CDSTAS(CASTAS) 2979 (CDs/MC)
2. ITV TV theme "Rendezvous" by JEAN MICHEL JARRE
   with APOLLO 440 *EPIC (Ten): EPC 666110-2 (CDs)*
3. England World Cup Song "(How Does It Feel) To Be
   On Top Of The World" (Ian McCulloch-Johnny Marr)
   ENGLAND UNITED *LONDON (Univ): LON(CD)(CS) 414*
4. Scotland "Don't Come Home Too Soon" by DEL AMITRI
   A.& M.(Univ): 582 705-2 (CDs) -4 (M C)
   FOR ALL OTHER 1998 ITEMS *see TELE-TUNES 1998*
WORLD CUP RUGBY 1999 /1995 - see RUGBY WORLD CUP
WORLD CUP RUGBY 1991 - *see COLL.101,*
WORLD DARTS (BBC) "Cranes" DOUGLAS WOOD *see COLL.122,*
WORLD FIGURE SKATING CHAMPIONSHIPS (BBC) theme music
"Mornings At Seven" (J.Last) JAMES LAST ORCH on
'By Request' *POLYDOR (Univ): 831 786-2 (CD)*
WORLD IS NOT ENOUGH The (1999 JAMES BOND) Music score
by DAVID ARNOLD. title song (D.Arnold-Don Black)
sung by GARBAGE -S/T- *UNIVERSAL: 112 161-2 (CD)*
WORLD OF PETER RABBIT AND FRIENDS (BBC1 9/4/93) music
COLIN TOWNS theme "Perfect Day" sung by MIRIAM
STOCKLEY on *Carlton: PWKS 4200 (CD) deleted*
WORLD OF SPORT (ITV) *see COLL.4,101,122,243,*
WORLD SNOOKER (BBC Embassy World Championship) theme
"Drag Racer" DOUGLAS WOOD GROUP *see COLL.101,122,*
WORLD OF TIM FRAZER The (BBC 1960) theme music
"Willow Waltz" by CYRIL WATTERS *see COLL.5,24,131,*
WORLD WRESTLING - see WWF
WRAPPERS (BBC2 17/11/1998) theme music "Sentimental
Journey" (Les Brown-Ben Homer-Bud Green) *TV vers.:*
ESQUIVEL on 'This is Easy' *VIRGIN: VTDCD 80 (2CD)*

WRESTLING - see WWF
WRESTLING WITH SHADOWS (-)
  NETTWERK (Pinn/Greyhound/S.Sounds): 34010-2 (CD)
WRONG BOX The (1966) Music: JOHN BARRY *see COLL.26,*
WRONG TROUSERS,The (Wallace & Gromit)(1993) M: JULIAN
  NOTT v/o PETER SALLIS *BBC Video: BBCV 5201 (VHS)*
WUTHERING HEIGHTS (ITVN 05/4/1998) Music score by
  WARREN BENNETT -S/T- *WEEKEND (BMG): CDWEEK 108 CD*
WUTHERING HEIGHTS (STUDIO REC.1991) Songs: BERNARD J.
  TAYLOR *with* DAVE WILLETTS-LESLEY GARRETT & Company
  SILVA SCREEN (Koch): SONG(CD)(C) 904 (CD/MC)
WUTHERING HEIGHTS (FILM 1991) Music: RYUICHI SAKAMOTO
  VIRGIN Classics (EMI): VC 759276-2 (CD)
WWF (WORLD WRESTLING FEDERATION) (SKY SPORTS VARIOUS)
  VARIOUS ARTIST COMPILATIONS / THE WRESTLING ALBUM
  WWF: THE MUSIC VOLUME 1   - *KOCH: 37994-2 (CD)*
  WWF: THE MUSIC VOLUME 2   - *KOCH: 38709-2 (CD)*
  WWF: THE MUSIC VOLUME 3   - *KOCH: 38803-2 (CD)*
  WWF: THE MUSIC VOLUME 4   - *KOCH: 38808-2 (CD)*
  WWF: THE MUSIC VOLUME 5   - *KOCH: KOCCD 8830 (CD)*
  WWF: TOUGH ENOUGH *DREAMWORKS UNIV: 450 336-2 (CD)*
WYATT EARP (Life and Legend of) (USA TV/ITV 1955-61)
  see COLL.245,279,
WYATT EARP (1993) Music score: JAMES NEWTON HOWARD
  -S/T- *WB (TEN): 9362 445660-2 (CD) -4 (MC)*
WYCLIFFE (ITV 7/8/93) music NIGEL HESS *see COLL.4,137,*
WYRD SISTERS (C4 18/5/97) m: KEITH HOPWOOD-PHIL BUSH
  see under 'SOUL MUSIC' *and* 'DISCWORLD'
X-FILES (BBC2 96) theme: MARK SNOW -S/T-"Songs In The
  Key Of X" with MARK SNOW-SHERYL CROW-FOO FIGHTERS-
  WEA: 9362 46079-2 (CD)
  see COLL.38,82,83,139,188,219,229,266,
X-FILES: FIGHT THE FUTURE (FILM 1998) Music: MARK SNOW
  music score: *WARNER BROS: 7559 62217-2 (CD) -4(MC)*
  songs by VA: *WARNER BROS: 7599 62266-2 (CD) -4(MC)*
X-MEN (2000) Music score by MICHAEL KAMEN -S/T- on
  DECCA (UNIV): 467 270-2 (CD) -4 (MC)
XANADU (1980) Music score: BARRY DE VORZON -S/T- *feat:*
  OLIVIA NEWTON JOHN-ELECTRIC LIGHT ORCHESTRA-CLIFF
  RICHARD -S/T- *re-issue EPIC (Ten): 486 620-2 (CD)*
XENA: WARRIOR PRINCESS (SKY2 8/9/96) mus.theme & score
  JOSEPH LoDUCA song "Burial" sung by LUCY LAWLESS
  -S/T- VOLUME 1 - *VARESE (Pinn): VSD 5750 (CD)*
  -S/T- VOLUME 2 - *VARESE (Pinn): VSD 5883 (CD)*
  -S/T- VOLUME 3*- *VARESE (Pinn): VSD 5918 (CD)*
  -S/T- VOLUME 4 - *VARESE (Pinn): VSD 6031 (CD)*
  -S/T- VOLUME 5 - *VARESE (Pinn): VSD 6145 (CD)*
  -S/T- VOLUME 6 - *VARESE (Pinn): VSD 6255-2 (CD)*
  see COLL.38,84,
  ***XENA: WARRIOR PRINCESS** (THE BITTER SUITE, all
  musical episode) feat music by JOSEPH LoDUCA with
  vocals by LUCY 'XENA' LAWLESS, MICHELLE NICASTRO,
  KEVIN SMITH and the cast of XENA: WARRIOR PRINCESS
  VARESE (Pinn): VSD 5918 (CD)

YAKSA (1985) *Music by* Nancy Wilson-Toots Thielmans-
   Masahiko Satoh -S/T- *DENON: C38-7556 (CD)*
YARDS The (1999) Music score: HOWARD SHORE and EDWARD
   SHEARMUR -S/T- *SONY CLASSICS (TEN): SK 89442 (CD)*
YEAR OF LIVING DANGEROUSLY (1981) *see COLL.153,*
YELLOW SUBMARINE (1967) Music score: GEORGE MARTIN
   songs by JOHN LENNON and PAUL McCARTNEY
   digitally remastered/remixed (1999) 'songtrack' on
   APPLE-PARL.(EMI): 521 481-2 (CD) -4 (MC) -1 (LP)
   orig -S/T- (George Martin score and 6 songs) on
   APPLE EMI:CDP 746 445-2(CD) & (TC)PCS7070 (MC/LP)
YENTL (1983) Music: MICHEL LEGRAND Songs (M.LEGRAND-
   Alan & Marilyn BERGMAN) *sung by* BARBRA STREISAND
   -S/T- *SONY EUROPE (Discovery): CD 86302 (CD)*
YEOMAN OF THE GUARD (operetta) Gilbert & Sullivan
   1.PRO-ARTE ORCHEST (Malcolm Sargent) GLYNDEBOURNE
     FESTIVAL CHOIR Soloists: ALEX YOUNG-DENIS DOWLING
     RICHARD LEWIS-JOHN CAMERON *EMI:CMS 764415-2 (2CD)*
   2.D'OYLY CARTE OPERA COMPANY *incl* 'TRIAL BY JURY'
     LONDON (Univ): 417 358-2 (2CD)
   3.D'OYLY CARTE OPERA COMPANY *feat:* DAVID FIELDSEND-
     FENTON GRAY-DONALD MAXWELL / MD: JOHN OWEN EDWARDS
     TER (Koch): CDTER2 1195 (2CD)
   4.D'OYLY CARTE OPERA COMPANY CHORUS AND ORCHESTRA
     inc recording of 'THE MIKADO' (1940s)
     PEARL (Harmonia Mundi): GEMS 0134 (3CDs)
YOLANDA AND THE THIEF (1945) *feat* FRED ASTAIRE
   plus 'THE FLEET'S IN' -S/T- selections on
   GREAT MOVIE THEMES (BMG): CD 60033 (CD)
YO-YO MA: INSPIRED BY BACH (BBC2 7/2/1998) 'Suites For
   Cello Solo' (J.S.Bach) YO-YO MA 'The Cello Suites
   Inspired by BACH' *SONY CLASSICS: S2K 63203 (2CD)*
YOGI BEAR (USA TV) *see COLL.242,259,*
YOU CAN'T HAVE EVERYTHING 1937 ALICE FAY-DON AMECHE
   -S/T- select.including songs from 'MELODY FOR TWO'
   'GO INTO YOUR DANCE'/'YOU'LL NEVER GET RICH' on
   GREAT MOVIE THEMES (Target-BMG): CD 60014 (CD)
**YOU GOTTA WALK IT LIKE YOU TALK IT OR YOU'LL LOSE THAT
   BEAT** (1971) Mus:Walter BECKER-Donald FAGEN (Steely
   Dan) -S/T- *SEE FOR MILES (Pinn): SEECD 357 (CD)*
YOU ONLY LIVE TWICE (1967) Music score: JOHN BARRY
   t.song (John BARRY-L.BRICUSSE) by NANCY SINATRA
   -S/T- *EMI: CZ 559 (CD)* see JAMES BOND FILM INDEX
   p.346 *see COLL.26,36,45,46,47,75,171,204,*
YOU'LL NEVER GET RICH (1941) Film Musical: COLE PORTER
   feat: FRED ASTAIRE-RITA HAYWORTH -S/T- including
   songs from 'MELODY FOR TWO'/'YOU CAN'T HAVE
   EVERYTHING'/'GO INTO YOUR DANCE'
   GREAT MOVIE THEMES (Target-BMG): CD 60014 (CD)
YOUNG AMERICANS The (1993) Music: DAVID ARNOLD songs:
   -S/T- *ISLAND MAST (Univ): IMCD 220 (CD) ICT 8019*
YOUNG AND THE RESTLESS The (US soap 73)'Nadia's theme'
   (H.MANCINI) JAMES GALWAY *RCA (BMG): 09026 61178-2
   (CD) -4 (MC)*

YOUNG DOCTORS The (Australian TV/ITV 80's) theme mus
(King-Ollman) *deleted*
YOUNG GIRLS OF ROCHEFORT The (1968) Music sco: MICHEL
LEGRAND -S/T- *POLYGRAM FRANCE (Discov): 558 408-2
(CD) also on 834 140-2 (CD)*
YOUNG GUARD (1948) Music: D.SHOSTAKOVICH *see* ZOYA
YOUNG GUNS (BBC2 01/01/1999) title song by WHAM! on
'Fantastic' *EPIC (Ten): 450 090-2 (CD)*
YOUNG GUNS GO FOR IT (BBC2 06/09/2000) theme music by
WHAM! / VARIOUS ARTISTS (1980's) COMPILATION ALBUM
VIRGIN (EMI): VTDCD 346 (2CD) VTDMC 346 (2MC)
YOUNG HERCULES (USA TV) Music score: JOSEPH LoDUCA
-S/T- *VARESE (Pinn): VSD 5983 (CD)*
see also HERCULES
YOUNG INDIANA JONES CHRONICLES (BBC1 20/11/94) mus:
LAURENCE ROSENTHAL -S/T- *VARESE (Pinn): VSD 5381
Vol.1 VSD 5391 (2) VSD 5401 (3) VSD 5421 (4) CDs*
YOUNG LIONS The (1958) Music sc: HUGO FRIEDHOFER -S/T-
+THIS EARTH IS MINE *VARESE (Pinn): VSD 25403 (2CD)*
YOUNG MAN OLDER WOMAN (O.CAST ALBUM) *feat* REYNALDO REY
ICHIBAN (Koch): ICHO 1159-2 (CD) -4 (MC)
YOUNG MAN WITH A HORN (1949) Music of BIX BEIDERBECKE
SOUNDTRACK FACTORY (Discov): SFCD 33556 (CD)
YOUNG ONES The (1962) CLIFF RICHARD & SHADOWS -S/T-
MFP (EMI): CDMFP 6020 (CD) see COLL.210,247,
YOUNG PERSON'S GUIDE TO BECOMING A ROCK STAR The
(C4 10/11/1998) Music score: GUY PRATT -S/T- with
V/A *VIRGIN (EMI): VTDCD 231 (2CD) VTDMC 231 (MC)*
YOUNG RIDERS The (USA 90/ITV 5/91) theme: JOHN DEBNEY
see COLL.14,
YOUR OWN THING (USA MUSICAL 1999) Songs by HAL HESTER
and DANNY APOLINAR - ORIGINAL USA CAST RECORDING
RCA VICTOR (BMG): 09026 63582-2 (CD)
YOU'RE A BIG BOY NOW (1967) Music: JOHN SEBASTIAN The
LOVIN' SPOONFUL -S/T- with 'WHAT'S UP, TIGER LILY'
RCA CAMDEN (BMG): 74321 69952-2 (CD)
RAZOR & TIE (Koch): RE 2167-2 (CD)
YOU'VE GOT MAIL (1998) Music score: GEORGE FENTON
-S/T- (score) *VARESE (Pinn): VSD 6015 (CD)*
-S/T- (songs) *ATLANTIC (TEN): 7567 83153-2 (CD)*
Z (1969) Mus: MIKIS THEODORAKIS Suite on
DRG (Pinn): 32901-4 (2MC)
Z CARS (BBC1 began 2/1/62) theme "Johnny Todd" (Trad.)
see COLL.2,74,
ZABRISKIE POINT (1969) Music: PINK FLOYD-KALEIDOSCOPE
GRATEFUL DEAD-PATTI PAGE-YOUNGBLOODS-JERRY GARCIA-
-S/T- *reissue EMI S/TRACKS: 823 364-2 (2CD)*
ZED AND TWO NOUGHTS, A (1985) Music sco: MICHAEL NYMAN
-S/T- *VIRGIN (EMI): CDVE 54 (CD) TCVE 54 (MC)*
ZEUS AND ROXANNE (1997) Music: BRUCE ROWLAND -S/T- *IMP.*
including 'PHAR LAP' *PERCEPTO USA:PERCEPTO 004 (CD)*
ZEPPELIN (1971) Music score: ROY BUDD -S/T- Coll.also
feat 'SOLDIER BLUE' (1970) & 'CATLOW' (1971) on
CINEPHILE (Pinn): CINCD 022 (CD)

ZIEGFELD FOLLIES (1944) *feat:* FRED ASTAIRE-GENE KELLY-
LUCILLE BALL *SOUNDTRACK FACT (Discov): SFCD 33522
(CD) -S/T-* also reiss.on *EMI PREM: CDODEON 3 (CD)*
ZIEGFELD GIRL (1941) *feat* JUDY GARLAND-TONY MARTIN
plus 'EVERY SUNDAY' -S/T- selections on
GREAT MOVIE THEMES (BMG): CD 60026 (CD)
ZIGGY STARDUST (THE MOTION PICTURE) (1982) *featuring*
DAVID BOWIE -S/T- *EMI: CDP 780 411-2 (CD)*
ZOMBIE PROM (1997) ORIGINAL BROADWAY CAST RECORDING
FIRST NIGHT (Pinn): CASTCD 66 (CD)
ZOMBIES DAWN OF THE DEAD (1979) Music by GOBLIN -S/T-
DAGORED (Koch): RED 117LP (LP)
ZOO (BBC1 07/07/1999-2000) theme mus by DEBBIE WISEMAN
performed by BBC CONCERT ORCHESTRA *unavailable*
ZOOLANDER (2001) Music score by DAVID ARNOLD with add.
music by RANDY KERBER -S/T- with VARIOUS ARTISTS
HOLLYWOOD-WEA (TEN): 0927 42408-2 (CD) -4 (MC)
ZORBA THE GREEK (1964) Music composed and performed by
MIKIS THEODORAKIS *INTUITION (Pinn): INT 31032 (CD)*
ZOYA (1944) Music score: DIMITRI SHOSTAKOVICH + 'THE
YOUNG GUARD' *RUSSIAN DISC (Koch): RDCD 10002 (CD)*
ZULU! (1963) Music score by JOHN BARRY -S/T- + 'FOUR
IN THE MORNING' *RPM (Pinn): RPM 195 (CD)*
CITY OF PRAGUE PHILH.& CROUCH END FESTIVAL CHORUS
(NIC RAINE) + other tracks on *SILVA SCREEN (Koch):
FILMXCD 305 (2CD)* also *FILMCD 022 (CD)*
see *COLL.26,30,31,34,35,37,146,*

TELE-TUNES REFERENCE BOOK IS PUBLISHED TWICE A YEAR IN
JANUARY AND JUNE. THE SECOND EDITION IS ONLY AVAILABLE
BY SUBSCRIPTION AND IN ADDITION TO THIS, MIKE PRESTON
MUSIC ALSO OPERATE A TELEPHONE DATABASE INFORMATION
SERVICE WHICH CAN BE CONTACTED MONDAY TO FRIDAY FROM
09.30am - 16.30pm. OR AFTER HOURS VIA EMAIL OR FAX.
SUBSCRIBERS TO THE FULL TELE-TUNES SERVICE HAVE ACCESS
TO DATABASE INFORMATION.
THIS SERVICE PROVIDES EXTREMELY FAST ANSWERS TO THE
VERY LATEST QUERIES ON TV AND FILM MUSIC.

PLEASE NOTE THE TELEPHONE DATABASE INFO.LINE IS FOR
SUBSCRIBERS TO THE FULL SERVICE ONLY. DETAILS FROM:
SUBSCRIPTION DEPT. MIKE PRESTON MUSIC THE GLENGARRY
3 THORNTON GROVE MORECAMBE BAY LANCASHIRE LA4 5PU

E-MAIL: mikepreston@beeb.net
TELEPHONE & FAX: 0 1 5 2 4 - 4 2 1 1 7 2

NOTE: BACK ISSUES (1979-2000) OF TELE-TUNES REFERENCE
BOOKS AND SUPPLEMENTS ARE NO LONGER AVAILABLE

E.& O.E.

1.20TH CENTURY FOX: MUSIC FROM THE GOLDEN AGE V.Arts.
Orig Soundtrack Recordings by Orig Composers
VARESE (Pinn): VSD 5937 (CD)   *1998*
Alfred Newman: 20TH CENTURY FOX FANFARE/SEVEN YEAR
ITCH/RAZOR'S EDGE/CAPTAIN FROM CASTILE/LEAVE HER TO
HEAVEN/ALL ABOUT EVE/THE SONG OF BERNADETTE/BEST OF
EVERYTHING/THE PRESIDENT'S LADY/A MAN CALLED PETER
Franz Waxman: PRINCE VALIANT
Bernard Herrmann: ANNA AND THE KING/BENEATH THE 12
MILE REEF/THE GHOST AND MRS.MUIR/PRINCE OF PLAYERS/
THE MAN IN THE GREY FLANNEL SUIT-THE GARDEN OF EVIL
JOURNEY TO THE CENTRE OF THE EARTH Alex North VIVA
ZAPATA/DADDY LONG LEGS Victor Young THE TALL MEN
Sammy Fain: LOVE IS A MANY SPLENDORED THING Hugo
Friedhofer: THE RAINS OF RANCHIPUR/VIOLENT SATURDAY
Cyril Mockridge: WILL SUCCESS SPOIL ROCK HUNTER
Jerry Goldsmith: THE STRIPPER/RIO CONCHOS/PATTON

2.A-Z OF BRITISH TV THEMES FROM THE 60's and 70's
PLAY IT AGAIN: PLAY 004 (CD) 1993 *-DELETED 2000-*
AVENGERS-CAPTAIN SCARLET & MYSTERONS-CATWEAZLE-THE
CHAMPIONS-CROSSROADS-DAD'S ARMY-DANGER MAN-DEPT.S
DOCTOR IN THE HOUSE-DR.WHO-EMMERDALE FARM-FIREBALL
XL5-FORSYTE SAGA-HADLEIGH-HANCOCK-MAIGRET-MAN ALIVE
MAN IN A SUITCASE-NO HIDING PLACE-PLEASE SIR-POWER
GAME-RETURN OF THE SAINT-THE SAINT-SPORTSNIGHT-STEP
TOE AND SON-STINGRAY-THANK YOUR LUCKY STARS-THUNDER
BIRDS-TOP SECRET-Z CARS *incl: 21 original versions*

3.A-Z OF BRITISH TV THEMES VOLUME 2 - Various Artists
PLAY IT AGAIN (S.Screen-Koch): PLAY 006 (CD)   *1994*
ADVENTURES OF BLACK BEAUTY-ALL CREATURES GREAT AND
SMALL-ANGELS-ANIMAL MAGIC-AUF WIEDERSEHEN PET-BBC
CRICKET-BERGERAC-BREAD-BUDGIE-DANGER MAN-DOCTOR WHO
THE FENN STREETGANG-FOUR FEATHER FALLS-FREEWHEELERS
GRANDSTAND-HERE'S HARRY-HUMAN JUNGLE-JUKE BOX JURY-
LIVER BIRDS-MAN ABOUT THE HOUSE-THE NEW AVENGERS-
OWEN MD-THE PERSUADERS-RUGBY SPECIAL-SUPERCAR-TALES
OF THE UNEXPECTED-UPSTAIRS DOWNSTAIRS-VAN DER VALK-
VISION ON-WHATEVER HAPPENED TO THE LIKELY LADS

4.A-Z OF BRITISH TV THEMES VOLUME 3 - Various Artists
PLAY IT AGAIN (S.Screen-Koch): PLAY 010 (CD)   *1996*
THE BEIDERBECKE CONNECTION *(CRYIN' ALL DAY)* Frank
Ricotti All Stars BLAKE'S 7 Dudley Simpson BLOTT ON
THE LANDSCAPE Dave MacKay DANGERFIELD Nigel Hess
DEMPSEY AND MAKEPEACE South Bank Or DOCTOR FINLAY'S
CASEBOOK *(MARCH FROM A LITTLE SUITE)* Trevor Duncan
EMERGENCY WARD 10 *(SILKS AND SATINS)* Peter Yorke
HETTY WAINTHROPP INVESTIGATES Nigel Hess INTERNATIO
NAL DETECTIVE Edwin Astley   JUST WILLIAM Nigel Hess
LOVEJOY Denis King   MIDWEEK /NATIONWIDE *(Good Word)*
John Scott   THE NEWCOMERS *(FANCY DANCE)* John Barry
THE ONE GAME *(SAYLON DOLAN)* Nigel Hess / Chameleon
POIROT Christopher Gunning THE PROFESSIONALS South
Bank Orch   RUTH RENDELL MYSTERIES Brian Bennett
SEXTON BLAKE Vic Flick Snd SHOESTRING George Fenton

SKI SUNDAY (POP LOOKS BACH) Sam Fonteyn THE SWEENEY
Harry South TERRY & JUNE *(BELL HOP)*John Shakespeare
THIS IS YOUR LIFE *(GALA PERFORMANCE)* Laurie Johnson
TRIALS OF LIFE George Fenton WHEN THE BOAT COMES IN
(DANCE TI THI DADDY) Alex Glasgow WISH ME LUCK Jim
Parker WOOF! Paul Lewis Woof Band WORLD OF SPORT
(W.OF SPORT MARCH) Don Jackson WYCLIFFE Nigel Hess

5.A-Z OF BRITISH TV THEMES VOLUME 4 - Various Artists
PLAY IT AGAIN (S.Screen-Koch): PLAY 009 (CD)   1998
1.ADVENTURES OF NICHOLAS NICKELBY Stephen Oliver 2.
ASK THE FAMILY *SUNRIDE* John Leach 3.AUF WIEDERSEHEN
PET *BACK WITH THE BOYS* Joe Fagin 4.BBC WIMBLEDON
LIGHT & TUNEFUL Keith Mansfield 5.BIG DEAL Bobby G.
6.BIG MATCH *LA SOIREE* David Ordini 7.BIRD OF PREY
Dave Greenslade8.CAMPION Nigel Hess 9.CRIMEWATCH UK
EMERGENCY John Cameron 10.DID YOU SEE Francis Monkm
an 11.FOLLYFOOT *THE LIGHTNING TREE* The Settlers 12.
GRANDSTAND (1950's-60's) *NEWSCOOP* Len Stevens 13.
HOLIDAY *HEARTSONG* Gordon Giltrap 14.JAMAICA INN
Francis Shaw 15.KINSEY Dave Greenslade 16.MAIGRET
(1990s) Nigel Hess 17.MASTERMIND *APPROACHING MENACE*
Neil Richardson 18.ON THE BUSES Tony Russell 19.
PEOPLE IN LONDON *SPANISH ARMADA* Les Reed 20.
PORTERHOUSE BLUE Flying Picketts 21.QUATERMASS II
MARS (G.HOLST) 22.RANDALL AND HOPKIRK DECEASED
Edwin Astley 23.RESORT TO MURDER Bill Connor 24.
SHADOW OF THE NOOSE Isabel Buchanan 25.SPORTSVIEW
SATURDAY SPORTS Wilfred Burns 26.TINKER TAILOR
SOLDIER SPY *(Main title)* Geoffrey Burgon 27.TINKER
TAILOR SOLDIER SPY *(NINC DIMITIS)* Lesley Garrett 28
TRAVELLING MAN *(MAX'S THEME)* Duncan Browne 29.
WHICKER'S WORLD *(THE TRENDSETTERS)* Laurie Johnson
30.WORLD OF TIM FRAZER *(WILLOW WALTZ)* Cyril Watters

6.A-Z OF BRITISH TV THEMES - THE RON GRAINER YEARS
PLAY IT AGAIN (S.Screen-Koch): PLAY 008 (CD)   1994
A TOUCH OF VELVET A STING OF BRASS *(M.Wirtz)(Disco)*
ALONG THE BOULEVARDS *(from 'MAIGRET')*-ANDORRA *(from
'Andorra' and 'Danger Island')*-ASSASSINATION TROT
'Andorra' and 'Danger Island')-ASSASSINATION TROT
(Assassination Bureau)-BORN AND BRED-BOY MEETS GIRL
-HAPPY JOE *('Comedy Playhouse')*-DETECTIVE-DR.WHO
(orig) - DR.WHO *(disco)*- BUTTERED CRUMPET *('Fanny
Craddock')*-JAZZ AGE-JOHNNY'S TUNE *('Sunday Break' &
'Some People')* -LOVE THEME FROM 'ONLY WHEN I LARF'-
MAIGRET-MALICE AFORETHOUGHT-MAN IN A SUITCASE-ILLIC
IT CARGO *('Man In The News')*-OLIVER TWIST *performed
by The Eagles* - PAUL TEMPLE-THE PRISONER *(original)*
THE PRISONER *(orch)*- REBECCA-SOUTH RIDING-TALES OF
THE UNEXPECTED *(orig)*-TALES OF T.UNEXPECTED *(disco)*
OLD NED *('Steptoe & Son')*-TRAIN NOW STANDING *(Green
Pastures)*-TROUBLE WITH YOU LILIAN *('Counting The Co
ster')*-WHEN LOVES GROWS COLD *(Edward & Mrs.Simpson)*

----.**A-Z OF FANTASY TV THEMES** - *see* **BATTLESTAR GALACTICA**

7.**ADDINSELL Richard** - **BRITISH LIGHT MUSIC** BBC Concert
Orch (Kenneth Alwyn) +Philip Martin & Roderick Elms
MARCO POLO (Select): 8.223732 (CD) *1995*
GOODBYE MR.CHIPS (1939) THE PRINCE AND THE SHOWGIRL
(1957) TOM BROWN'S SCHOOLDAYS (1951) A TALE OF TWO
CITIES (58) FIRE OVER ENGLAND (1937) + other music

8.**ADDINSELL Richard** - **FILM MUSIC**
Royal Ballet Sinfonia conducted by Kenneth Alwyn
ASV-WHITE LINE (Select): CDWHL 2115 *1999*
BLITHE SPIRIT-ENCORE-FIRE OVER ENGLAND-GASLIGHT
PRELUDE-PARISIENNE-PASSIONATE FRIENDS-SCROOGE-SOUTH
RIDING-SOUTHERN RHAPSODY-WALTZ OF THE TORREADORS-
WRNS MARCH

9.**ADDINSELL Richard** - **WARSAW CONCERTO**
Royal Ballet Sinfonia (Kenneth Alwyn) *
ASV-WHITE LINE (Select) CD(ZC)WHL 2108 (CD/MC) 1997
INVOCATION for Piano and Orchestra (1955)-MARCH OF
THE UNITED NATIONS (1942)-WARSAW CONCERTO (1941)
BLITHE SPIRIT (1945)-THE DAY WILL DAWN (1942)-THE
GREENGAGE SUMMER (1961)-HIGHLY DANGEROUS (1950)-
THE LION HAS WINGS (1939)-OUT OF THE CLOUDS (1954)
PASSIONATE FRIENDS (1948)-THE SEA DEVILS (1953)-
UNDER CAPRICORN (1949) * Concert recorded 1996

10.**ADIEMUS IV** - **THE ETERNAL KNOT**
VIRGIN VENTURE (EMI): CDVE 952 (CD) *2000*
ETERNAL KNOT-PALACE OF T.CRYSTAL BRIDGE-CU CHALLAIN
WOOING OF ETAIN-KING OF T.SACRED GROVE-ST.DECLAN'S
DRONE-SALM O DEWI SANT-CONNIA'S WELL-DAGDA-CHILDREN
OF DANNU-CERIDWEN'S CURSE-HERMIT OF THE SEA ROCK-
ISLE OF THE MYSTIC LAKE-MATH WAS A WIZARD
ADIEMUS III - **THE JOURNEY: BEST OF ADIEMUS**
VIRGIN (EMI): (CD)(TC)(MD)VE 946 (CD/MC/MD) *1999*
DELTA AIRLINES AD MUSIC / CHELTENHAM & GLOUCESTER
BUILDING SOC.AD MUSIC (Cantus Song Of Tears) / etc.
ADIEMUS II - **CANTATA MUNDI**
VIRGIN (EMI): CDVE 932 *1997*
SONG OF TEARS *(CHELTENHAM & GLOUCESTER AD)* + others
see COLL 'NEW PURE MOODS' VIRGIN: VTDCD 158 (2CD)
ADIEMUS I - **SONGS OF SANCTUARY** with London Philhar.
Orch (Karl Jenkins) with Miriam Stockley
VIRGIN (EMI): CDVE 925 *1995*
ADIEMUS *(DELTA AIRLINES AD / TESTAMENT:THE BIBLE IN
ANIMATION BBC2)* + 8 all composed by KARL JENKINS

11.**ALL TIME GREATEST MOVIE SONGS** - Various Artists
SONYMUSIC TV: MOODCD 61 (2CD) MOODC 61 (MC) *1998*
1.LOVE IS ALL AROUND Wet Wet Wet 2.BECAUSE YOU LOVE
ME Celine Dion 3.HOW DEEP IS YOUR LOVE Bee Gees 4.
OCEAN DRIVE Lighthouse Family 5.TAKE MY BREATH AWAY
Berlin 6.STARS Simply Red 7.MY GIRL Temptations 9.
LADY IN RED Chris DeBurgh 10.UP WHERE WE BELONG Joe
Cocker-Jennifer Warnes 11.A WHOLE NEW WORLD Regina
Belle-Peabo Bryson 12.DREAM A LITTLE DREAM OF ME
Mama Cass 13.ARTHUR'S THEME Christopher Cross 14.
CRYING GAME Boy George 15.SON OF A PREACHER MAN

Dusty Springfield 16.SOMEDAY Eternal 17.TURN BACK
TIME Aqua 18.WAITING FOR A STAR TO FALL Boy Meets
Girl 19.SAN FRANCISCO Scott MacKenzie 20.CALFORNIA
DREAMIN'Mamas & Papas 21.UNCHAINED MELODY Righteous
Brothers 22.MISSION IMPOSSIBLE Adam Clayton-Larry
Mullen 23.MEN IN BLACK Will Smith 24.DEEPER UNDERGR
OUND Jamiroquai 25.HOLD ME THRILL ME KISS ME KILL
U2 26.BLAZE OF GLORY Bon Jovi 27.HOT STUFF Donna
Summer 28.GOT TO BE REAL Cheryl Lynn 29.GANGSTA'S
PARADISE Coolio 30.SOMEDAY Lisa Stansfield 31.LET'S
STAY TOGETHER Al Green 32.LOVETRAIN O'Jays 33.THE
SHOOP SHOOP SONG Cher 34.A GIRL LIKE YOU Edwyn
Collins 35.SHY GUY Diana King 36.LOVEFOOL Cardigans
37.SHOW ME HEAVEN Maria McKee 38.PICTURE OF YOU
Boyzone 39.WHAT A FOOL BELIEVES Doobie Br.40.BROWN
EYED GIRL V.Morrison 41.18 WITH A BULLET Pete Wing
field 42.OH PRETTY WOMAN R.Orbison 43.WATERLOO Abba

12.ALL TIME GREATEST MOVIE SONGS VOLUME 2 - V.Artists
SONYMUSIC TV: MOODCD 67 (2CD) MOODC 67 (MC)   1999
1.MY HEART WILL GO ON Celine Dion 2.WHEN YOU SAY
NOTHING AT ALL R.Keating 3.STREETS OF PHILADELPHIA
B.Springsteen 4.AS I LAY ME DOWN Sophie B.Hawkins 5
I SAY A LITTLE PRAYER Diana King 6.WHOLE NEW WORLD
P.Bryson-Regina Belle 7.I'M KISSING YOU Des'Ree 8.
ABY CAN I HOLD YOU Boyzone 9.TOO MUCH Spice Girls
10.FROM THE HEART Another Level 11.I WANT TO SPEND
MY LIFETIME LOVING YOU Tina Arena-Marc Anthony 12.
HEART OF A HERO Luther Vandross 13.FOR THE FIRST
TIME Kenny Loggins 14.YOU WERE THERE Babyface 15.I
FINALLY FOUND SOMEONE B.Streisand-Bryan Adams 16.A
KISS FROM A ROSE Seal 17.WILL YOU BE THERE Michael
Jackson CD2: 1.MEN IN BLACK Will Smith 2.I DON'T
WANT TO MISS A THING Aerosmith 3.SWEETEST THING
Lauryn Hill 4.KISS ME Sixpence None The Richer 5.
MANEATER Hall & Oates 6.HEAVEN'S WHAT I FEEL Gloria
Estefan 7.ARMAGEDDON Trevor Rabin 8.PLAY DEAD Bjork
D.Arnold 9.GO THE DISTANCE M.Bolton 10.KNOCKIN' ON
HEAVEN'S DOOR Bob Dylan 11.BLAZE OF GLORY Bon Jovi
12.MODERN WOMAN Billy Joel 13.ALL AROUND THE WORLD
Lisa Stansfield 14.SPOOKY D.Springfield 15.AIN'T
NO SUNSHINE B.Withers 16.IT HAD TO BE YOU H.Connick
17.WAY YOU LOOK TONIGHT Tony Bennett 18.DANCING
QUEEN Abba 19.BUILD ME UP BUTTERCUP Foundations

13.ALL TIME GREATEST MOVIE SONGS 2001 Various Artists
SONYMUSIC TV: STVCD 113 (2CD) STVMC 113 (2MC) 2001
1.INDEPENDENT WOMAN Destiny's Child 2.WILD WILD
WEST Will Smith 3.PURE SHORES All Saints 4.PRAISE
YOU Fatboy Slim 5.SHAFT Isaac Hayes 6.DON'T CALL ME
BABY Madison Avenue 7.SEPTEMBER Earth Wind and Fire
8.STEAL MY SUNSHINE Len 9.WHEN DOVES CRY Prince 10.
PORCELAIN Moby 11.YOUR LOVE GETS SWEETER Finlay
Quay 12.YES SIR I CAN BOOGIE Nina Miranda 13.I'M SO
EXCITED Pointer Sisters 14.DON'T GET ME WRONG The
Pretenders 15.LET'S GROOVE Earth Wind and Fire 16.

IT'S RAINING MENWeather Girls 17.ONCE IN A LIFETIME
Michael Bolton 18.FLYING WITHOUT WINGS Westlife 19.
CAN'T FIGHT THE MOONLIGHT LeAnn Rimes 20.SO YOUNG
Corrs 21.LOVE BEFORE TIME Coco Lee 22.SLAVE TO LOVE
Bryan Ferry 23.IN ALL THE RIGHT PLACES L.Stansfield
24.PUPPY SONG Harry Nilsson 25.SOMETHING IN THE AIR
Thunderclap Newman 26.MAYBE BABY Paul McCartney 27.
STAND BY ME Ben E.King 28.IS SHE REALLY GOING OUT
WITH HIM Joe Jackson 29.GOLDEN BROWN Stranglers 30.
PICK UP THE PIECES AWB 31.VIRGINIA PLAIN Roxy Music
32.KING OF WISHFUL THINKING Go West 33.TRUE Spandau
Ballet 34.RED RED WINE UB 40 35.CAN'T TAKE MY EYES
OFF YOU Andy Williams 36.GOOD LIFE Tony Bennett

14.**AMERICAN TELEVISION'S GREATEST HITS** - Daniel Caine
SILVA SCREEN (Koch): TVPMCD 804 (2CD) 1994 A.TEAM-
AIRWOLF-BARNABY JONES-BATTLESTAR GALACTICA-BAYWATCH
BEVERLY HILLS 90210-BUCK ROGERS IN T.25TH CENTURY-
CAGNEY & LACEY-CHEERS-COSBY SHOW-DOOGIE HOWSER MD-
EERIE INDIANA-EQUALIZER-EVENING SHADE-FALCON CREST-
FREDDY'S NIGHTMARES-HARDCASTLE & McCORMICK-HILL ST.
BLUE-HIGHWAY TO HEAVEN-INCREDIBLE HULK-KNIGHT RIDER
HUNTER-L.A.LAW-LITTLE HOUSE ON T.PRAIRIE-LOU GRANT-
MacGYVER-MAGNUM-MAN FROM UNCLE-MELROSE PLACE-MORK &
MINDY-MIDNIGHT CALLER-MUNSTERS-MURDER SHE WR.-NIGHT
COURT-NORTH & SOUTH-NORTHERN EXPOSURE-POLICE STORY-
PURSUIT-QUANTUM LEAP-ROCKFORD FILES-REMINGTON STEEL
ROSEANNE-SLEDGEHAMMER-STAR TREK: NEXT GEN.-SPENSER
FOR HIRE-ST.ELSEWHERE-TAXI-TWIN PEAKS-STREETHAWK
21 JUMP STREET-V: THE SERIES-WALTONS-YOUNG RIDERS

15.**ANDERSON Gerry** - **EVOCATION (Various Artists)**
EMI SONGBOOK: 7243 496612-2 (CD)   *1999*
1.THE EVE OF WAR *JEFF WAYNE* 2.ADAGIO *(ALBINONI)* 3.
COSSACK PATROL *RED ARMY CHOIR* 4.RHAPSODY IN BLUE
(GERSHWIN) 5.PRELUDE BEN HUR *(ROSZA)* 6.THUNDERBIRDS
BAND OF ROYAL MARINES 7.CALLING ELVIS *DIRE STRAITS*
8.FOUR FEATHER FALLS *MICHAEL HOLLIDAY* 9.SINGIN' IN
THE RAIN *GENE KELLY* 10.PUPPET ON A STRING *SANDIE
SHAW*11.SHOOTING STAR *SHADOWS* 12.TAKE 5 *DAVE BRUBECK*
13.GALLEY BEN HUR *(ROSZA)*14.RITUAL FIRE DANCE *LARRY
ADLER* 15.WHO DONE IT *HARRY NILSSON* 16.FINGAL'S CAVE
(MENDELSSOHN) 17.LAVENDER CASTLE *CRISPIN MERRELL*

16.**ANDERSON Leroy** - **The Typewriter & Other Favorites** *
RCA VICTOR Red Seal (BMG): 09026 68048-2 (CD) 1995
BELLE OF THE BALL-PHANTOM REGIMENT-THE FIRST DAY OF
SPRING-SLEIGH RIDE-PLINK PLANK PLUNK!-BLUE TANGO-
FORGOTTEN DREAMS-BUGLER'S HOLIDAY-THE PENNY WHISTLE
SONG-CLARINET CANDY-HORSE AND BUGGY-A TRUMPETER'S
LULLABY-FIDDLE FADDLE-JAZZ PIZZICATO-JAZZ LEGATO-
SYNCOPATED CLOCK-SANDPAPER BALLET-THE TYPEWRITER-
THE WALTZING CAT-PROMENADE-SARABAND-SERENATA-
BALLADETTE-ARIETTA-HOME STRETCH
    * Saint Louis Symphony Orchestra (Leonard Slatkin)

17.**APOCALYPSE - CINEMA CHORAL CLASSICS**
SILVA SCREEN (Koch): SILKD 6025   *2001*

1.GLORY 2.SAVING PRIV.RYAN 3.LONGEST DAY 4.HANNIBAL
5.HENRY V 6.NINTH GATE 7.BRAM STOKER'S DRACULA 8/9.
LION IN WINTER 10.AMISTAD 11.DUNE 12.ZULU 13.APOCAL
YPSE NOW 14.LAST VALLEY 15.YOUNG SHERLOCK HOLMES 16
STARMAN 17.STAR WARS THE PHANTOM MENACE 18.SUNSHINE

18.ARNOLD Malcolm - Film Music Of (London Symph.Orch*)
CHANDOS (Chandos): CHAN 9100 (CD)
THE BRIDGE ON THE RIVER KWAI (Suite For Large Orch
feat 'Colonel Bogey' (Kenneth Alford)-WHISTLE DOWN
THE WIND (Small Suite For Small Orchest)-THE SOUND
BARRIER (A Rhapsody For Orchestra Op.38)-HOBSON'S
CHOICE (Orchestral Suite)-THE INN OF THE SIXTH HAPP
INESS (Orchestral Suite) *Conductor: *RICHARD HICKOX*

19.ARNOLD Malcolm - Film Music Vol.2 (BBC Philharmonic
Orch & Phillip Dyson) Rumon Gamba-M.Arnold (cond.)
CHANDOS (Chandos): CHAN 9851 (CD)
1.TRAPEZE (Suite) 2.ROOTS OF HEAVEN (Overture) 3.
MACHINES (Symphonic Study for Brass Percussion and
Strings OP.30 theme and five variations) 4.NO LOVE
FOR JOHNNIE 5.DAVID COPPERFIELD (Suite) 6.YOU KNOW
WHAT SAILORS ARE (Scherzetto for Clarinet & Orch.)
7.STOLEN FACE Ballade for Piano & Orch 8.BELLES OF
ST.TRINIANS (Comedy Suite/Exploits for Orchestra)
9.HOLLY AND THE IVY (Fantasy on Christmas Carols)
10.CAPTAIN'S PARADISE (Postcard from the Med)

20.AS SEEN ON TV - *GEORGE FENTON + Various Artists
DEBONAIR (Pinn): CDDEB 1010 (CD)   *1999*
1.BEYOND THE CLOUDS* 2.SALVA ME:SHADOW OF THE NOOSE
Isobel Buchanon 3.FRIENDS IN HIBERNATION:FIRST SNOW
OF WINTER) Music Sculptors 4.TRAVELLING MAN Duncan
Browne 5.HANNAY Denis King 6.THAT'S LIVIN' ALRIGHT
Joe Fagin 7.UNION GAME Andy Price 8.BARNEY MILLER
Elliott & Ferguson 9.HOME (BREAD) Cast 10.BERGERAC*
11.LOVEJOY Denis King 12.MARCH OF THE LOBSTERS (THE
TRIALS OF LIFE* 13.SHANGHAI VICE* 14.DR.WILLOUGHBY
David Mackay 15.HENRY VIII Adrian Thomas 16.STREETS
APART Neil Lockwood 17.THIEF IN THE NIGHT:RESORT TO
MURDER) Bill Connor 18.MONOCLED MUTINEER* 19.MOON &
SON Denis King 20.BLOTT ON THE LANDSCAPE Viv Fisher

21.ASTAIRE Fred - Songs From The Movies (Orig Tracks)
PAST PERFECT (THE): PPCD 78115   *1994*
Top Hat (35): NO STRINGS-ISN'T THIS A LOVELY DAY-
TOP HAT WHITE TIE & TAILS-CHEEK TO CHEEK-PICCOLINO
Follow The Fleet (36): WE SAW THE SEA-LET YOURSELF
GO-I'D RATHER LEAD A BAND-I'M PUTTING ALL MY EGGS
IN ONE BASKET-LET'S FACE THE MUSIC AND DANCE
Swing Time (36): PICK YOURSELF UP-THE WAY YOU LOOK
TONIGHT-A FINE ROMANCE-BOJANGLES OF HARLEM-NEVER
GONNA DANCE / Shall We Dance (37): BEGINNER'S LUCK
SLAP THAT BASS-THEY ALL LAUGHED-LET'S CALL THE
WHOLE THING OFF-THEY CAN'T TAKE THAT AWAY FROM ME
SHALL WE DANCE / A Damsel In Distress (37): I CAN'T
BE BOTHERED NOW-THINGS ARE LOOKING UP-A FOGGY DAY-
NICE WORK IF YOU CAN GET IT

*22.***AURIC Georges** - Film Music of Georges Auric
The BBC Philharmonic conducted by Rumon Gamba
CHANDOS (Chandos): CHAN 9774 (CD)   *1999*
1.CAESAR & CLEOPATRA (1945) 2.TITFIELD THUNDERBOLT
(1952) 3.DEAD OF NIGHT (1945) 4.PASSPORT TO PIMLICO
(1949) 5.THE INNOCENTS (1961) 6.LAVENDER HILL MOB
(1951) 7.MOULIN ROUGE(1952) 8.FATHER BROWN (54) 9.
IT ALWAYS RAINS ON SUNDAY (47) 10.HUE AND CRY (46)

*23.***AURIC Georges** - Classic Film Music Volume 4
Slovak Radio Symphony Orchestra cond: Adriano
MARCO POLO (Select): 8225136 (CD)   *2000*
FOUR CLASSIC FILMS FROM THE FRENCH POST-WAR PERIOD
1.LA SYMPHONIE PASTORALE (1946) 2.MACAO L'ENFER DU
JEU (1942) 3.DU RIFIFI CHEZ LES HOMMES (1955) 4.LE
SALAIRE DE LA PEUR (1953)

*24.***AVENGERS AND OTHER TOP 60s TV THEMES** V.Artists *1998*
SEQUEL-CASTLE (Pinn):NEMCD 976 (2CD) NELP 976 (3LP)
1.AVENGERS 2.MAN IN A SUITCASE 3.THUNDERBIRDS 4.DR.
WHO 5.STEPTOE & SON 6.DAD'S ARMY 7.CAPTAIN SCARLET
8.Z-CARS 9.SAINT 10.DEPARTMENT S 11.JOE 90 12.
CROSSROADS 13.THANK YOUR LUCKY STARS 14.TAKE THREE
GIRLS 15.STINGRAY 16.DANGER MAN 17.THE CHAMPIONS 18
HANCOCK 19.FORSYTE SAGA 20.WORLD CUP THEME 'ON THE
BALL' 21.POWER GAME 22.DOCTOR FINLAY'S CASEBOOK 23.
FIREBALL XL5 24.MAIGRET 25.OUT OF THIS WORLD 26.NO
HIDING PLACE 27.FUGITIVE 28.WHODUNIT 29.W.SOMERSET
MAUGHAM 30.COMEDY PLAYHOUSE **CD2:** 1.SCARLETT HILL
2.RICHARD BOONE SHOW 3.TIM FRAZER THEME 4.MR.ROSE
INVESTIGATES 5.THE DOCTORS 6.SAM BENEDICT 7.BEN
CASEY 8.SIR FRANCIS DRAKE9.PERRY MASON 10.OUR HOUSE
11.WHO IS SYLVIA 12.RIVIERA POLICE 13.GHOST SQUAD
14.ECHO FOUR-TWO 15.LOVE STORY 'OUR LOVE STORY' 16.
NAKED CITY 17.TOP SECRET 18.CRANE 19.(-) 20.SENTIME
NTAL AGENT 21.SPIES 22.THE DEPUTY 23.MAN ALIVE 24.
LOVE STORY 'MEMORIES OF SUMMER' 25.THANK YOUR LUCKY
STARS 'LUNA WALK' 26.WHICKER'S WORLD 27.THREE LIVE
WIRES 28.QUICK BEFORE THEY CATCH US 29.RONNIE CORBE
TT'S THEME 'THAT'S ME OVER HERE' 30.PEYTON PLACE

*25.***BALL Michael** - Centre Stage
UNIVERSAL MUSIC TV: 016 071-2 (CD)   *2001*
1.EVERY STORY *AIDA* 2.CAN YOU FEEL THE LOVE TONIGHT
LION KING 3.BOY FROM NOWHERE *MATADOR* 4.NOTHING'S
GONNA HARM YOU *SWEENEY TODD* 5.LIFT THE WINGS
RIVERDANCE 6.BRING HIM HOME *LES MIS.* 7.PHANTOM OF
THE OPERA with Lesley Garrett 8.MUSIC OF THE NIGHT
PHANTOM OF THE OPERA 9.SEASONS OF LOVE *RENT* 10.
WINNER TAKES IT ALL *MAMMA MIA* 11.SEND IN THE CLOWNS
A LITTLE NIGHT MUSIC 12.TELL ME ON A SUNDAY *SONG &
DANCE* 13.IMMORTALITY *SATURDAY NIGHT FEVER* 14.TELL
ME IT'S NOT TRUE *BLOOD BROTHERS*

*26.***BARRY** John - 40 YEARS OF FILM MUSIC: The Collection
New Recording by CITY OF PRAGUE PHILHARMONIC & The
Crouch End Festival Chorus (conducted by NIC RAINE)
SILVA SCREEN (Koch): FILMXCD 349 (4CD)   *2001*

ZULU-FROM RUSSIA WITH LOVE-007-GOLDFINGER-IPCRESS
FILE-THE KNACK-MISTER MOSES-THUNDERBALL-WRONG BOX-
BORN FREE-QUILLER MEMORANDUM-YOU ONLY LIVE TWICE-
GIRL WITH THE SUN IN HER HAIR-DEADFALL-THE LION IN
WINTER-ON HER MAJESTY'S SECRET SERVICE-MIDNIGHT
COWBOY-THE APPOINMENT-LAST VALLEY-WALKABOUT-MONTE
WALSH-DIAMONDS ARE FOREVER-PERSUADERS-MARY QUEEN
OF SCOTS-MAN WITH THE GOLDEN GUN-THE DOVE-TAMARIND
SEED-KING KONG-ELEANOR AND FRANKLIN-ROBIN & MARIAN
THE DEEP-HANOVER STREET-BLACK HOLE-MOONRAKER-
SOMEWHERE IN TIME-RAISE THE TITANIC-BODY HEAT-
FRANCES-OCTOPUSSY-COTTON CLUB-HIGH ROAD TO CHINA-
VIEW TO A KILL-OUT OF AFRICA-THE LIVING DAYLIGHTS-
DANCES WITH WOLVES-CHAPLIN-MOVIOLA-INDECENT
PROPOSAL-THE SPECIALIST-SCARLET LETTER-CRY THE
BELOVED COUNTRY-MERCURY RISING-JAMES BOND THEME

27. BARRY John - **BEAT FOR BEATNIKS and BEAT GIRLS**
CONNOISSEUR COLL (Pinn): VSOPCD 281 (CD)   *1999*
1.BEAT FOR BEATNIKS 2.JAMES BOND THEME 3.WALK DON'T
RUN 4.MAGNIFICENT SEVEN 5.HUMAN JUNGLE 6.HIT & MISS
JUKE BOX JURY 7.ZAPATA 8.BIG FELLA 8.SEVEN FACES 9.
RUM DEE DUM DEE DAH 10.RODEO 11.CUTTY SARK 12.SWEET
TALK 13.SATURDAY TALK 14.BLACK STOCKINGS 15.DONNA'S
THEME 16.PANCHO 17.BEAT GIRL 18.MARCH OF MANDARINS
19.HIDEAWAY 20.LIKE WALTZ 21.LOLLY THEME 22.I'M
MOVIN' ON 23.CHALLENGE 24.ROCKIN' STEADY 25.BIG
GUITAR 26.ONWARD CHRISTIAN SPACEMAN 27.MOODY RIVER
28.MIDNIGHT COWBOY 29.FLORIDA FANTASY

28. BARRY John - **BEST OF JOHN BARRY (Film & TV Themes)**
POLYDOR: 849 095-2 (CD) 849 095-4 (MC)   *1991*
GOLDFINGER-SAIL THE SUMMER WINDS *(The Dove)*-LOVE AM
ONG THE RUINS-LOLITA-A DOLL'S HOUSE-FOLLOW FOLLOW
(Follow Me)-DIAMONDS ARE FOREVER-BOOM-MIDNIGHT COWB
OY-THIS WAY MARY *(Mary Queen Of Scots)*-THE GLASS ME
NAGERIE-THUNDERBALL-007-PLAY IT AGAIN *(The Tamarind
Seed)*-ORSON WELLES GREAT MYSTERIES-WE HAVE ALL THE
TIME IN THE WORLD *(On Her Majesty's Secret Service)*
THE WHISPERERS-CURIOUSER AND CURIOUSER *(Alice's Adv
entures In Wonderland)*-BILLY-THE GOOD TIMES ARE COM
ING *(Monte Walsh)*-WALKABOUT-THE ADVENTURER

29. BARRY John - **BEST OF THE EMI YEARS**   1999
EMI:523 073-2 (CD) SIMPLY VINYL Vit: SVLP 330 (2LP)
1.HIT AND MISS *(JUKE BOX JURY THEME)* 2.BEAT GIRL 3.
BEAT FOR BEATNIKS 4.THE CHALLENGE 5.THE AGRESSOR 6.
SPINNEREE **Michael Angelo Orch** 7.SATIN SMOOTH 8.THE
JAMES BOND THEME 9.HUMAN JUNGLE *alternative version*
10.ROMAN SPRING OF MRS.STONE **Michael Angelo Orch** 11
TEARS **Michael Angelo Orch** 12.THE PARTY'S OVER 13.
CUTTY SARK *(DATELINE THEME)* 14.MARCH OF T.MANDARINS
15.ONWARD CHRISTIAN SPACEMEN 16.HUMAN JUNGLE *THEME*
17.GOLDFINGER **Shirley Bassey** 18.OUBLIE CA 19.SEVEN
FACES 20.SEANCE ON A WET AFTERNOON 21.MR.KISS KISS
BANG BANG **Shirley Bassey** 22.BORN FREE **Matt Monro** 23
MIDNIGHT COWBOY 24.DIAMONDS ARE FOREVER **Shir.Bassey**

30.BARRY John - CLASSIC JOHN BARRY - City Of Prague
Symphony Orch (Nicholas Raine) Suites and Themes
SILVA SCREEN (Koch): FILMCD 141 (CD) *1993*
ZULU-OUT OF AFRICA-BODY HEAT-MIDNIGHT COWBOY-THE
LAST VALLEY-BORN FREE-CHAPLIN-ELEANOR AND FRANKLIN-
DANCES WITH WOLVES-INDECENT PROPOSAL-THE PERSUADERS
ROBIN AND MARIAN-SOMEWHERE IN TIME-THE LION IN
WINTER-HANOVER STREET-RAISE THE TITANIC

31.BARRY John - JOHN BARRY COLLECTION
E2-MCI (DISC-THE): ETDCD 011 (CD) *1999*
ZULU-007-FROM RUSSIA WITH LOVE-LONELINESS OF AUTUMN
LONDON THEME-ELIZABETH'S THEME-FOUR IN THE MORNING-
KINKY-FANCY DANCE-MONKEY FEATHERS-TROUBADOUR-HIGH
GRASS-NGENZINI-BIG SHIELD-TETHATA LEYANTO

32.BARRY John - MOVIOLA *EPIC: 472490-2 (CD)* *1992*
OUT OF AFRICA-MIDNIGHT COWBOY-BODY HEAT-SOMEWHERE
IN TIME-MARY QUEEN OF SCOTS-BORN FREE-DANCES WITH
WOLVES-CHAPLIN-COTTON CLUB-WALKABOUT-FRANCES-ON HER
MAJESTY'S S.SERVICE (WE HAVE ALL THE TIME)-MOVIOLA

33.BARRY JOHN - READY WHEN YOU ARE J.B.
PEG Reiss: PEG 043 (CD 1999) orig: CBS 63952 (1970)
MIDNIGHT COWBOY THEME-WE HAVE ALL THE TIME IN THE
WORLD-ROMANCE FOR GUITAR & ORCH *(DEADFALL)*-WHO WILL
BUY MY YESTERDAYS-FUN CITY*(MIDNIGHT COWBOY)*-LION IN
WINTER-ON HER MAJESTY'S S.SERVICE-THE APPOINTMENT-
TRY-MORE THINGS CHANGE-AFTERNOON-BORN FREE theme

34.BARRY John - SIXTIES SCREEN THEMES
CASTLE PIE (Pinn): PIESD 195 (CD) *2000*
007 2.FROM RUSSIA WITH LOVE 3.LONELINESS OF AUTUMN
4.FOUR IN THE MORNING 5.RIVER WALK 6.ELIZABETH IN
LONDON 7.LONDON THEME 8.LOVERS 9.ALIKI 10/11.ZULU
EXTRACTS 12.ZULU STOMP 13.TETHA LEYANTO 14.MONKEY
FEATHERS 15.FANCY DANCE 16.CHRISTINE

35.BARRY John - THE NAME IS BARRY...JOHN BARRY
EMBER (TKO-Magnum-Pinn): EMBCD 001 (CD) *1999*
ZULU-FROM RUSSIA WITH LOVE-007-KINKY-LONELINESS OF
AUTUMN-FANCY DANCE-TROUBADOR-FOUR IN THE MORNING-
ELIZABETH-LONDON THEME-MONKEY FEATHERS-BIG SHIELD-
JUDI COMES BACK-RIVER WALK-NORMAN LEAVES-MOMENT OF
DECISION-ALIKI-NGENZENI-THETHA LAVANTO-FIRST RECON.
LOVERS TENSION-LOVERS CLASP-FIRE OF LONDON-RIVER R.

36.BARRY John - THEMEOLOGY: THE BEST OF JOHN BARRY
SIMPLY VINYL (Vital): SVLP 29 (2LP) *1999*
COLUMBIA (Ten): 488 582-2 (CD) -4 (MC) *1997*
1.PERSUADERS THEME 2.MIDNIGHT COWBOY 3.IPCRESS FILE
4.THE KNACK 5.WEDNESDAY'S CHILD 6.SPACE MARCH (CAPS
ULE IN SPACE) 7.THE GIRL WITH THE SUN IN HER HAIR
(SUNSILK 70's AD) 8.VENDETTA 9.DANNY SCIPIO THEME
10.JAMES BOND THEME 11.GOLDFINGER 12.DIAMONDS ARE
FOREVER 13.FROM RUSSIA WITH LOVE 14.YOU ONLY LIVE
TWICE 15.THUNDERBALL 16.ON HER MAJESTY'S SECRET SER
VICE 17.007 18.WALK DON'T RUN 19.BEAT FOR BEATNIKS
20.HIT AND MISS 21.BORN FREE 22.I HAD A FARM IN
AFRICA 23.JOHN DUNBAR THEME (DANCES WITH WOLVES)

*37.*BARRY John - ZULU -S/T- plus other filmworks
New Recording by CITY OF PRAGUE PHILHARMONIC & The
Crouch End Festival Chorus (conducted by NIC RAINE)
SILVA SCREEN (Koch): FILMXCD 305 (2CD)   *1999*
COMPLETE 'ZULU' MUSIC + selections from: THE COTTON
CLUB-DANCES WITH WOLVES-KING KONG-THE DEEP-KING RAT
THE SPECIALIST-MERCURY RISING-FRANCES-THE TAMARIND
SEED-'SUNSILK AD'GIRL WITH THE SUN IN HER HAIR HAIR
LAST VALLEY-LOVE AMONG THE RUINS-'FLORIDA FANTASY'
(from MIDNIGHT COWBOY)-MY SISTERS KEEPER-HAMMETT-
MISTER MOSES

*38.*BATTLESTAR GALACTICA - The A-Z Of Fantasy TV Themes
The Ultimate Collection of Classic & Cult Fantasy
SILVA SCREEN: TVPMCD 806 (2CDs)   *1999*
ADDAMS FAMILY-AIRWOLF-AVENGERS-BATMAN-BLAKE'S 7-
BUCK ROGERS-CAPTAIN SCARLET-DOCTOR WHO-FIREBALL XL5
HERCULES-JOE 90-KNIGHT RIDER-LAND OF THE GIANTS-
LOST IN SPACE-THE OUTER LIMITS-THE PRISONER-QUANTUM
LEAP-RED DWARF-SEAQUEST DSV-SPACE 1999-STAR TREK-
STINGRAY-THE SURVIVORS-THUNDERBIRDS-THE TIME TUNNEL
TWLIGHT ZONE-TWIN PEAKS-V-VOYAGE TO THE BOTTOM OF
THE SEA-XENA WARRIOR PRINCESS-X.FILES *and others*

*39.*BENNETT Richard Rodney - The Film Music of
CHANDOS MOVIES: CHAN 9867   *2000*
BBC Philharmonic Orchestra conducted by Rumon Gamba
MURDER ON THE ORIENT EXPRESS-FAR FROM THE MADDING
CROWD-FOUR WEDDINGS AND A FUNERAL and others

*40.*BERNSTEIN Elmer - Great Composers
VARESE (Pinn): VSD 6077 (CD)   *2000*
Royal Scottish National Orchestra (Joel McNeely)
Utah Symphony Orchestra (Elmer Bernstein) and
Seattle Symphony Orchestra (C|iff Eidelman)
MAGNIFICENT 7-GREAT ESCAPE-THE SHOOTIST-COMANCHEROS
TRUE GRIT-WILD WILD WEST-TO KILL A MOCKINGBIRD-A
RAGE IN HARLEM-MY LEFT FOOT-BLACK CAULDRON-FRANKIE
STARLIGHT-THE AGE OF INNOCENCE-LOST IN YONKERS-THE
GRIFTERS-BUDDY-TEN COMMANDMENTS

*41.*BERGMAN SUITES: Classic Film Music of ERIK NORDGREN
Slovak Radio Symphony Orch.conducted by Adriano
MARCO POLO (Select): 8.22368-2 (CD)   *1998*
Suites from scores for INGMAR BERGMAN films: SMILES
OF A SUMMER NIGHT (1955) WAITING WOMEN (1952) THE
FACE (1958) WILD STRAWBERRIES (1957) GARDEN OF EDEN

*42.*BEST OF BRITISH TV MUSIC Original Music From Hit TV
Series / Var.Original Artists *(orig issued 1993)*
SOUNDTRACKS EMI GOLD: 520 688-2 (CD)   *revised 1999*
1.CASUALTY 2.THE BILL *(OVERKILL)* 3.PEAK PRACTICE
4.CADFAEL *(FLAMED MY HEART)* 5.DALLAS 6.DYNASTY 7.
EASTENDERS 8.RUTH RENDELL MYSTERIES *(KISSING THE
GUNNER'S DAUGHTER)* 9.BREAD *(HOME)* 10.JULIET BRAVO
11.MISS MARPLE 12.BERGERAC 13.DARLING BUDS OF MAY
14.DOCTOR WHO 15.DUCHESS OF DUKE STREET 16.THE
PALLISERS 17.TO SERVE THEM ALL MY DAYS 18.POLDARK
19.SHOESTRING 20.THE BROTHERS 21.THE ONEDIN LINE

---.<u>BEST TV ADS...EVER</u> - see pages 48 and 336

43.<u>BLUE TV</u> - Blue Note Takes A Commercial Break V.Arts
BLUE NOTE (EMI): 531 151-2 (CD) -4 (MC)   2000
1.UNFORGETTABLE Peggy Lee 2.DON'T WORRY BE HAPPY
Bobby McFerrin 3.LET THERE BE LOVE June Christie 4.
THINKIN' 'BOUT YOUR BODY Bobby McFerrin 5.THEY ALL
LAUGHED Chet Baker 6.BULLITT Wilton Felder 7.FLY ME
TO THE MOON Julie London 8.SUMMERTIME Joe Williams
9.WILD IS THE WIND Nina Simone 9.SITTIN'ON THE DOCK
OF THE BAY Peggy Lee 10.I CAN SEE CLEARLY NOW Holly
Cole 11.ON THE STREET WHERE YOU LIVE Holly Cole 12.
LET'S FACE THE MUSIC...Jackie McLean 13.LAZY BONES
Jeri Southern 14.COMING HOME BABY Buddy Rich 15.
FEELING GOOD Stanley Turrentine 16.US3 Cantaloop

44.<u>BOND James: BACK IN ACTION!</u> - **Various Artists**
SILVA SCREEN (Koch): FILMCD 317 (CD)   1999
New Digital Recordings of Suites from the first 7
James Bond films inc.previously unreleased material
CITY OF PRAGUE PHILHARMONIC ORCHESTRA (NIC RAINE)
DR.NO-FROM RUSSIA WITH LOVE-GOLDFINGER-THUNDERBALL-
YOU ONLY LIVE TWICE-ON HER MAJESTY'S SECRET SERVICE
DIAMONDS ARE FOREVER

45.<u>BOND James: BACK IN ACTION!</u> VOL.2- **Various Artists**
SILVA SCREEN (Koch): FILMCD 340 (CD)   2001
New Digital Recordings of Suites from Bond films
inc.previously unreleased material
CITY OF PRAGUE PHILHARMONIC ORCHESTRA (NIC RAINE)
Suites include MOONRAKER-A VIEW TO A KILL-OCTOPUSSY

46.<u>BOND James: BEST OF JAMES BOND</u> - **30th Anniversary**
EMI: 523 294-2 (CD) -4 (MC)   1999
1.JAMES BOND THEME Monty Norman Orch 2.GOLDFINGER
Shirley Bassey 3.NOBODY DOES IT BETTER Carly Simon
4.A VIEW TO A KILL Duran Duran 5.FOR YOUR EYES ONLY
Sheena Easton 6.WE HAVE ALL THE TIME IN THE WORLD
Louis Armstrong 7.LIVE AND LET DIE Paul McCartney &
Wings 8.ALL TIME HIGH Rita Coolidge 9.THE LIVING
DAYLIGHTS A-Ha 10.LICENCE TO KILL Gladys Knight 11.
FROM RUSSIA WITH LOVE Matt Monro 12.THUNDERBALL Tom
Jones 13.YOU ONLY LIVE TWICE Nancy Sinatra 14.
MOONRAKER Shirley Bassey 15.ON HER MAJESTY'S SECRET
SERVICE John Barry Orch 16.MAN WITH THE GOLDEN GUN
Lulu 17.DIAMONDS ARE FOREVER S.Bassey 18.GOLDENEYE
Tina Turner 19.TOMORROW NEVER DIES Sheryl Crow

47.<u>BOND James: THE ESSENTIAL</u> City Of Prague Symph.Orch
cond: Nicholas Raine   *(1993, revised reissue 1998)*
S.Screen (Koch): FILMCD 007 (CD) DR.NO-FROM RUSSIA
WITH LOVE-007-GOLDFINGER-THUNDERBALL-YOU ONLY LIVE
TWICE-ON HER MAJESTY'S SECRET SERVICE-DIAMONDS ARE
FOREVER-MAN WITH T.GOLDEN GUN-SPY WHO LOVED ME-MOON
RAKER-FOR YOUR EYES ONLY-OCTOPUSSY-LIVING DAYLIGHTS
A VIEW TO A KILL-LICENCE TO KILL-GOLDENEYE

--- **BRIDESHEAD REVISITED** - *see* **BURGON Geoffrey**

48.BRITISH FILM MUSIC VOLUME 1 - Original Orchestras
PEARL (Harmonia Mundi): GEMMCD 0100 (CD)   2000
1.THE RED SHOES *(comp:BRIAN EASDALE)* 2.SCOTT OF THE
ANTARCTIC *(VAUGHAN WILLIAMS)* 3.OLIVER TWIST *(ARNOLD
BAX)* 4.THE OVERLANDERS *(JOHN IRELAND)* 5.MEN OF TWO
WORLDS *(ATHUR BLISS)* 6.NICHOLAS NICKLEBY *(LORD
BERNERS)* 7.WHILE I LIVE (feat 'The Dream Of Olwen)
CHARLES WILLIAMS
49.BRITISH FILM MUSIC VOLUME 2 - Original Orchestras
PEARL (Harmonia Mundi): GEMMCD 0101 (CD)   2000
1.THINGS TO COME *(ARTHUR BLISS)* 2.COASTAL COMMAND
(VAUGHAN WILLIAMS) 3.49TH PARALLEL *VAUGHAN WILLIAMS*
4.MALTA G.C. *(ARNOLD BAX)* 5.DANGEROUS MOONLIGHT
(R.ADDINSELL) 6.THEIRS IS THE GLORY *(GUY WARRACK)*
7.WESTERN APPROACHES *(CLIFFORD PARKER)* 8.LOVE STORY
(HUBERT BATH) 9.STORY OF A FLEMISH FARM *V.WILLIAMS*
50.BRITISH FILM MUSIC VOLUME 3 - Original Orchestras
PEARL (Harmonia Mundi): GEMMCD 0141 (CD)   2001
1.THE FIRST OF THE FEW / 2.HENRY V *(WILLIAM WALTON)*
3.THE LOVES OF JOANNA GODDEN *(VAUGHAN WILLIAMS)* 4.
ODETTE *(ANTHONY COLLINS)* 5.SPELLBOUND *MIKLOS ROZSA*
6.DESERT VICTORY / 7.THE RAKE'S PROGRESS *(WILLIAM
ALWYN)* 8.ESTHER WATERS *(GORDON JACOB)* 9.A MATTER OF
LIFE AND·DEATH / 10.THIS MAN IS MINE *(ALLAN GRAY)*
11.SLEEPING CAR TO TRIESTE /12.SO LONG AT THE FAIR
(BENJAMIN FRANKEL)
--- **BRITISH LIGHT MUSIC**   - *see* **ADDINSELL Richard**
--- **BRITISH LIGHT MUSIC**   - *see* **ELIZABETHAN SERENADE**
--- **BRITISH LIGHT MUSIC**   - *see* **ESSENTIAL BRITISH LIGHT**
--- **BRITISH LIGHT MUSIC**   - *see* **GOODWIN Ron**

51.BRITISH LIGHT MUSIC CLASSICS - NEW LONDON ORCHEST *
HYPERION Records (Select): CDA 66868 (CD)   1996
1.CALLING ALL WORKERS *(Eric Coates/BBC:MUSIC WHILE
YOU WORK)* 2.HAUNTED BALLROOM *(Geoffrey Toye/BALLET)*
3.VANITY FAIR *(Anthony Collins)* 4.JUMPING BEAN *(Rob
ert Farnon)* 5.DESTINY *(Sydney Baynes/WALTZ)* 6.THE
BOULEVARDIER *(Frederic Curzon)* 7.PAS DE QUATRE *(W.
Meyer Lutz/FAUST UP TO DATE)* 8.THE WATERMILL*(Ronald
Binge/BBC:THE SECRET GARDEN)* 9.THE DEVIL'S GALLOP
(Charles Williams/BBC:DICK BARTON) 10.DUSK *(Armstro
ng Gibbs/FANCY DRESS)* 11.PUFFIN'BILLY*(Edward White/
BBC:CHILDREN'S FAVOURIT.)*12.BELLS ACROSS THE MEADOW
(Albert Ketelby) 13.THE OLD CLOCKMAKER *(Charles Wil
liams/BBC:JENNING'S AT SCHOOL)* 14.DREAMING *(Archiba
ld Joyce/WALTZ)* 15.ELIZABETHAN SERENADE *(Ronald Bin
ge/BBC)* 16.CORONATION SCOTT *(Vivian Ellis/BBC: PAUL
TEMPLE)* 17.NIGHTS OF GLADNESS *(Charles Ancliffe/WAL
TZ)* * NEW LONDON ORCHESTRA conducted by RONALD CORP*
52.BRITISH LIGHT MUSIC CLASSICS 2 - NEW LONDON ORCHES*
*HYPERION (Select): CDA 66968 (CD) *Ronald Corp 1997*
1.KNIGHTSBRIDGE *(Eric Coates/BBC:IN TOWN TONIGHT)*
2.BAL MASQUE *(Percy Fletcher/WALTZ)* 3.GRASSHOPPER'S
DANCE *(Ernest Bucalossi/MILK TV AD)* 4.BARWICK GREEN

(Arthur Wood/ARCHERS THEME) 5.ROUGE ET NOIR *(Fred Hartley)* 6.PEANUT POLKA *(Robert Farnon)* 7.CARRIAGE AND PAIR *(Benjamin Frankel/SO LONG AT THE FAIR)* 8. HORSE GUARDS WHITEHALL *(Haydn Wood/BBC:DOWN YOUR WAY)* 9.MARCH FROM A LITTLE SUITE *(Trevor Duncan/BBC DR.FINLAY'S CASEBOOK)* 10.SAILING BY *(Ronald Binge/ BBC: RADIO 4 CLOSING MUSIC)* 11.PORTUGESE PARTY *(Gil bert Vinter)* 12.BEACHCOMBER *(Clive Richardson)* 13. IN THE SHADOWS *(Herman Finck)* 14.TABARINAGE *(Robert Docker)* 15.SANCTUARY OF THE HEART *(Albert Ketelbey)* 16.WESTMINSTER WALTZ *(Robert Farnon/BBC:IN TOWN TON IGHT PROGAMME LINK MUS)* 17.CARISSIMA *(Edward Elgar)* 18.GIRLS IN GREY *(Charles Willliams/BBC: TELEVISION NEWSREEL)* 19.RUNAWAY ROCKING HORSE *(Edward White)* 20.MARCH OF THE BOWMEN *(Fr.Curzon/ROBIN HOOD SUITE)*

53.BRITISH LIGHT MUSIC CLASSICS 3 – NEW LONDON ORCHES*
HYPERION (Select): CDA 67148 (CD) *Ronald Corp 2000
1.MONTMARTRE 'Paris' suite *(Haydn Wood)* 2.MELODY ON THE MOVE *(Clive Richardson/BBC RADIO)* 3.IN PARTY MOOD *(Jack Strachey/HOUSEWIVES CHOICE)* 4.GIRL FROM CORSICA *(Trevor Duncan)* 5.SOLDIERS IN THE PARK *(Lionel Moncton)* 6.VALSE SEPTEMBRE *(Felix Godin)* 7. MISS MELANIE *(Ronald Binge)* 8.PINK LADY WALTZ *(Ivan Caryll)* 9.PORTRAIT OF A FLIRT *(Robert Farnon/IN TOWN TONIGHT and many others)* 10.SICILIANO *(Harry Dexter)* 11.IN A PERSIAN MARKET *(Albert Ketelbey)* 12.THEATRELAND *(Jack Strachey)* 13.SONG d'AUTOMNE *(Archibald Joyce)* 14.ALPINE PASTURES *(Vivian Ellis)* 15.LITTLE SERENADE *(Ernest Tomlinson)* 16.WOODLAND REVEL *(George Melachrino)* 17.LADY OF SPAIN *(Tolchard Evans)* 18.SMILES THEN KISSES *(Charles Ancliffe)* 19. ON A SPRING NOTE *(Sidney Torch/PATHE GAZETTE)* 20. MUSIC EVERYWHERE *(Eric Coates/REDIFFUSION MARCH)*

--- **BRITISH TV MUSIC – see BEST OF BRITISH TV MUSIC**

54.BUDD Roy – Buddism (The Best of Roy Budd)
CINEPHILE (Pinn): CMOCD 016 (CD)   2000
GET CARTER / DIAMONDS / THE MARSEILLE CONTRACT / THE STONE KILLER / THE INTERNICENE PROJECT / FEAR IS THE KEY / THE BLACK WINDMILL / FOXBAT

55.BURGON Geoffrey – BRIDESHEAD REVISITED: TV Scores
SILVA SCREEN (Koch): FILMCD 723 (CD,1992) reis 2000
THE CHRONICLES OF NARNIA-BLEAK HOUSE-TESTAMENT OF YOUTH-BRIDESHEAD REVISITED (Suite)-NUNC DIMITTIS fr om TINKER TAILOR SOLDIER SPY sung by *LESLEY GARRETT Philharmonia Orchestra conducted by Geoffrey Burgon*

56.CAINE Michael (MUSIC FROM THE FILMS OF) V.Artists
SILVA SCREEN (Koch) FILMCD 338 (CD)   2001
MADNESS (Michael Caine)-GET CARTER-THE ITALIAN JOB-ALFIE-ZULU-CIDER HOUSE RULES-LAST VALLEY-THE EAGLE HAS LANDED-IPCRESS FILE-EDUCATING RITA-MONA LISA (Nat King Cole)-SLEUTH-DRESSED TO KILL-THE BATTLE OF BRITAIN-HANNAH AND HER SISTERS-THE SWARM-MAN WHO WOULD BE KING-ON DAYS LIKE THESE (Matt Monro)-ALFIE (Helen Hobson)

57. **CARPENTER John** - The Best Of Volume 1
VARESE (Pinn): VSD 5266 (CD)
music composed by John Carpenter and Alan Howarth
tracks include: DARK STAR / ESCAPE FROM NEW YORK /
THE FOG / PRINCE OF DARKNESS / HALLOWEEN etc.
music composed by John Carpenter and Alan Howarth

58. **CARPENTER John** - The Best Of Volume 2
VARESE (Pinn): VSD 5336 (CD)
tracks include: ESCAPE FROM NEW YORK / PRINCE OF
DARKNESS / HALLOWEEN 4 and 5 / CHRISTINE etc

59. **CARRY ON ALBUM** Bruce Montgomery & Eric Rogers Music
City Of Prague Philharmonic.cond: Gavin Sutherland
James Hughes (harmoncia) Vladimir Pilar (violin)
WHITE LINE-ASV (Select): CDWHL 2119 (CD)   1999
ANGLO-AMALGAMATED FANFARES + music from CARRY ON..
AT YOUR CONVENIENCE / BEHIND / CABBY / CAMPING /
CLEO / DOCTOR/DOCTOR AGAIN / JACK / CARRY ON SUITE
CARRY ON THEME / UP THE KHYBER / RAISING THE WIND

---. **CHILDREN'S FAVOURITE TV THEMES** - *see COLL.285*

60. **CINEMA CAFE: EUROPEAN FILM MUSIC ALBUM** - **Mark Ayres**
SILVA SCREEN (Koch/S.Scr): FILMXCD 302 (2CD)   1998
37 Tracks including: JEAN DE FLORETTE-A MAN AND A
WOMAN-BILITIS-DIVA-BETTY BLUE-THE TIN DRUM-OPERA
SAUVAGE-SUBWAY-LA FEMME NIKITA-ATLANTIS-LE GRAND
BLUE (THE BIG BLUE)-THE DOUBLE LIFE OF VERONIQUE
EMMANUELLE-LAST TANGO IN PARIS-PLAYTIME-MON ONCLE-
IL POSTINO-CINEMA PARADISO-CYRANO DE BERGERAC-THE
HAIRDRESSER'S HUSBAND etc.

61. **CINEMA CENTURY 2000** - **Various Artists**
SILVA SCREEN (Koch): FILMXCD 318 (2CDs)   1999
56 Classic Themes: KING KONG-WUTHERING HEIGHTS-THE
SEA HAWK-LAURA-THE VIKINGS-BREAKFAST AT TIFFANY'S-
EL CID-THE LONGEST DAY-HATARI-THE SANDPIPER-RYAN'S
DAUGHTER-THE THOMAS CROWN AFFAIR-THE WAY WE WERE-
DEER HUNTER-PAPILLON-JEAN DE FLORETTE-BATMAN-THE
MASK OF ZORRO-ADVENTURES OF ROBIN HOOD-ALEXANDER
NEVSKY-THIEF OF BAGDAD-TREASURE OF THE SIERRA MADRE
WAR OF THE WORLDS-PRINCE VALIANT-THE CAINE MUTINY-
TO CATCH A THIEF-GUNS OF NAVARONE-DOCTOR NO-HOW THE
WEST WAS WON-DR.STRANGELOVE-ROMEO AND JULIET-2001 A
SPACE ODYSSEY-ONCE UPON A TIME IN THE WEST-SUMMER
OF 42-LAST TANGO IN PARIS-GODFATHER-STAR TREK-BODY
HEAT-EXCALIBUR-RIGHT STUFF-COTTON CLUB-GHOST-LETHAL
WEAPON-BASIC INSTINCT-PRINCE OF TIDES-LAST OF THE
MOHICANS-BODYGUARD-IL POSTINO-BRAVEHEART-APOLLO 13-
INDEPENDENCE DAY-ENGLISH PATIENT-TITANIC-SAVING
PRIVATE RYAN-MARK OF ZORRO

62. **CINEMA CHORAL CLASSICS** - **City Of Prague Philh.Orch***
SILVA SCREEN (Koch): SILK(D)(C) 6015 (CD/MC)   1997
EXCALIBUR-SCARLET LETTER-JESUS OF NAZARETH-KING OF
KINGS-LION IN WINTER-MISSION-CONAN THE BARBARIAN-
ABYSS-FIRST KNIGHT-1492 CONQUEST OF PARADISE-HENRY
V-OMEN-VIKINGS * *Nic Raine conducting The*
Crouch End Festival Chorus *(David Temple)*

63.CINEMA CHORAL CLASSICS 2 - **City Of Prague Phil.Orch**
(Paul Bateman) and Crouch End Festival Chorus
SILVA SCREEN (Koch-S.Scr): SILK(D)(C) 6017 (CD/MC)
THE MADNESS OF KING GEORGE-DOUBLE LIFE OF VERONIQUE
HOW THE WEST WAS WON-IF-EMPIRE OF THE SUN-ALEXANDER
NEVSKY-MUCH ADO ABOUT NOTHING-SENSE AND SENSIBILITY
EDWARD SCISSORHANDS-PARADISE ROAD-ALAMO-THE ROBE-
THE GREATEST STORY EVER TOLD-TRADITION OF THE GAMES
64.CINEMA CLASSICS (EMI) 2 Collection - Var.Artists
EMI Classics: CMS 566647-2 (2CD) 1997
CD1: 1.SHINE: *1st m/m PIANO CON.NO.3 Rachmaninov* 3.
ENGLISH PATIENT: *I'LL ALWAYS GO BACK TO THAT CHURCH
Yared* 3.BABE: *PIZZICATO from SYLVIA Delibes* 4.ROMEO
& JULIET: *OST VOL.2* 5.HEAVENLY CREATURES: *E LUCEVAN
LE STELLE Puccini* 6.COURAGE UNDER FIRE *Horner* 7.
SEVEN: *AIR ON THE G STRING FROM SUITE 3 Bach* 8.LAST
ACTION HERO: *LE NOZZE DI FIGARO OVERTURE Mozart* 9.
HOWARDS END: *MOCK MORRIS Grainger* 10.THE FRENCH
LIEUTENANT'S WOMAN: *PIANO SONATA IN D.K576 Mozart*
11.SHAWSHANK REDEMPTION: *SULL'ARIA: FIGARO Mozart*
12.PRINCE OF TIDES: *SYMPHONY NO.104 'LONDON' Haydn*
13.PORTRAIT OF A LADY: *IMPROMPTU A.FLAT NO.4 D899
Schubert* 14.DANGEROUS LIAISONS:*CUCKOO & NIGHTINGALE
ORGAN CONCERTO Handel* 15.MRS.DOUBTFIRE: *LARGO AL FA
FACTOTUM:BARBER OF SEVILLE Rossini* 16.FOUR WEDDINGS
AND A FUNERAL: *THE WEDDING MARCH Mendelssohn* 17.
SLEEPING WITH THE ENEMY: *WITCHES'SABBATH Berlioz.*
CD2 MANHATTAN: *RHAPSODY IN BLUE Gershwin* 2.FANTASIA
SORCERER'S APPRENTICE Dukas 3.BRIDGES OF MADISON
COUNTY: *MON COEUR S'OUVRE A TA VOIX: Saint Saens* 4.
EVENING STAR: *-S/T- Ross* 5.UN COUER EN HIVER: *PIANO
TRIO Ravel* 6.HANNAH AND HER SISTERS: *HARPSICHORD
CONC.NO.5 Bach* 7.THE SAINT: *LOVE THEME Revell* 8.THE
FIFTH ELEMENT: *LUCIA DI LAMMERMOOR Donizetti* 9.JFK:
HORN CON.NO.2 Mozart 10.SOMEWHERE IN TIME: *18th VAR
IATION ON THEME OF PAGANINI Rachmaninov* 11.LOOKING
FOR RICHARD: *-S/T- Shore* 12.HENRY V *-S/T- Doyle* 13.
KILLING FIELDS: *NESSUN DORMA Puccini* 14.MY DINNER
WITH ANDRE: *GYMNOPEDIE NO.1 Satie* 15.SILENCE OF THE
LAMBS: *GOLDBERG VAR.ARIA Bach* 16.AMADEUS: *EINE KLEI
KLEINE NACHT MUSIK Mozart* 17.JEAN DE FLORETTE/MANON
DES SOURCES: *LA FORZA DEL DESTINO OVERTURE Verdi*
65.CINEMA CLASSICS (NAXOS) 1999 - Various Artists
NAXOS (Select): 8.551183 (CD) 1999
1.BABE: PIG IN IN THE CITY *ORGAN SYMPH.NO.3 (SAINT-
SAENS)* 2.THE BIG LEBOWSKI *GLUCK DAS MIR VERBLEIB
from DIE TOTE STADT (KORNGOLD)* 3.BULWORTH *STARS &
STRIPES FOREVER (SOUZA)* 4.ELIZABETH *NIMROD (ELGAR)*
5.HILARY AND JACKIE *ADAGIO MODERATO from CELLO
CONCERTO (ELGAR)* 6.LIFE IS BEAUTIFUL *BARCAROLLE fr.
TALES OF HOFFMAN (OFFENBACH)* 7.PROPOSITION *ANDANTE
from STRING QUARTET D804 (SCHUBERT)* 8.ROUNDERS
ALLEGRO from BRANDENBURG CONCERTO 1 (BACH)* 9.STAR
TREK: INSURRECTION *FINALE from STRING QUARTET OP.64*

No.5 (HAYDN) 10.THIN RED LINE *IN PARADISUM from The*
REQUIEM (FAURE) 11.TRUMAN SHOW *ROMANZA LARGHETTO fr*
PIANO CONCERTO NO.1 (CHOPIN)
66.**CINEMA CLASSICS (NAXOS) 1998** - Various Artists
NAXOS (Select): 8.551182 (CD) *1998*
1.BRASSED OFF *WILLIAM TELL OVERTURE (ROSSINI)* 2.THE
DEVIL'S OWN *FRUHLINGSSTIMMEN (JOHANN STRAUSS II)* 3.
FACE OFF *PAMIN'A ARIA from The MAGIC FLUTE (MOZART)*
4.FIFTH ELEMENT *MAD SCENE from LUCIA DI LAMMERMOOR*
(DONIZETTI) 5.G.I.JANE *O MIO BABBINO CARO (PUCCINI)*
6.JURASSIC PARK 2 *ADAGIO CANTABILE from PATHETIQUE*
SONATA (BEETHOVEN) 7.L.A.CONFIDENTIAL *HEBRIDES OVER*
TURE (MENDELSSOHN) 8.ONE NIGHT STAND *AIR (J.S.BACH)*
9.PARADISE ROAD *MARCH fr.PIANO SONATA NO.2 (CHOPIN)*
10.THE PEACEMAKER *NOCTURNE IN F.MINOR (CHOPIN)* 11.
TITANIC *THE BLUE DANUBE (J.STRAUSS II)*
67.**CINEMA CLASSICS (NAXOS) 1997** - Various Artists
NAXOS (Select): 8.551181 (CD) *1997*
1.THE PEOPLE VS.LARRY FLYNT *POLONAISE FROM RUSALKA*
(DVORAK) 2.THE PEOPLE VS.LARRY FLYNT *MAZURKA NO.47*
IN A.MINOR OP.68 NO.2 (CHOPIN) 3.BREAKING THE WAVES
SONATA IN E.FLAT MAJOR BWV 1031.SICILIANA (BACH) 4.
THE ENGLISH PATIENT *ARIA FROM 'GOLDBERG VARIATIONS'*
BWV 988 (BACH) 5.TIN CUP *WINTER FROM FOUR SEASONS*
SUITE Allegro Non Molto(VIVALDI) 6.ROMEO AND JULIET
SYMPHONY NO.25 IN G.MINOR K.183 Allegro Con Brio
(MOZART) 7.THE PORTRAIT OF A LADY *STRING QUARTET NO*
14 IN D.MINOR D.810 Death and The Maiden (SCHUBERT)
8.PRIMAL FEAR *REQUIEM: LACRYMOSA (MOZART)* 9.SHINE
POLONAISE 6 A.FLAT MAJ.OP53 (CHOPIN) 10.SHINE *PIANO*
CONC.3 IN D.MIN.OP30 Allegro Ma Non..(RACHMANINOV)
68.**CINEMA SERENADE** - Pittsburgh Symphony Orchestra *
SONY CLASSICS: SK 63005 (CD) *1998*
Excerpts: THE COLOR PURPLE *(composer: QUINCY JONES)*
TRUE LIES *(Por Una Cabeza) (CARLOS GARDEL)* / YENTL
(MICHEL LEGRAND) / IL POSTINO *(LUIS BACALOV)* / THE
AGE OF INNOCENCE *(ELMER BERNSTEIN)* / FAR AND AWAY
(JOHN WILLIAMS) /UMBRELLAS OF CHERBOURG *(M.LEGRAND)*
FOUR HORSEMEN OF THE APOCALYPSE *(ANDRE PREVIN)* /
SABRINA *(JOHN WILLIAMS)* /OUT OF AFRICA *(JOHN BARRY)*
BLACK ORPHEUS *(LUIS BONFA)* / SCHINDLER'S LIST *(JOHN*
WILLIAMS) / CINEMA PARADISO *(ENNIO MORRICONE)*
* conducted by John T.Williams with I.Perlman (vln)
69.**CINEMA SERENADE 2: The Golden Age** - Various Artists
SONY CLASSICS: SK 60773 (CD) SM 60773 (MC) *1999*
1.LAURA *(DAVID RASKIN)* 2.NOW VOYAGER *(MAX STEINER)*
3.MODERN TIMES *(CHARLES CHAPLIN)* 4.LOST WEEKEND
(MIKLOS ROZSA) 5.THE QUIET MAN *(VICTOR YOUNG)* 6.THE
ADVENTURES OF ROBIN HOOD *(ERICH WOLFGANG KORNGOLD)*
7.AS TIME GOES BY (from CASABLANCA)*(HERMAN HUPFELD)*
8.HENRY V *(WILLIAM WALTON)* 9.THE UNINVITED *V.YOUNG*
10.GONE WITH THE WIND *(MAX STEINER)* 11.WUTHERING
HEIGHTS *(ALFRED NEWMAN)* 12.MY FOOLISH HEART *(VICTOR*
YOUNG) Isaac Perlman *(vln)* Boston Pops Orchestra

70.CLASSIC CHILLOUT ALBUM - Various Original Artists
SONYTV (TEN): STVCD 115 (2CD)   *2001*
1.SLIP INTO SOMETHING MORE COMFORTABLE Kinobe *KRONE NBOURG* 2.AT THE RIVER Groove Aramda 3.MISSING Every thing But The Girl 4.DAYDREAM IN BLUE I Monster 5. ADAGIO FOR STRINGS (Barber) William Orbit 6.SWEET HARMONY Beloved 7.ADAGIO Robin Young-Smith 8. DRIFTING AWAY Faithless 9.X-FILES Music Sculptors 10.CHILDREN Robert Miles 11.NIMROD Chris Davis 12. NOVIA Moby 13.SILVER Joolz Gianni 14.WORLD LOOKING IN Morcheeba *FORD MONDEO* 15.SALTWATER Chicane with Maire Brennan 16.AMERICAN DREAM Jakatta
CD 2.1.SWEET LULLABY Deep Forest 2.MOMENTS IN LOVE Art Of Noise 3.CHI MAI Ennio Morricone 4.THEME FROM Harry's Game Clannad 5.TO A WILD ROSE Chris Davis 6.MOLLY from WONDERLAND Michael Nyman 7.SADENESS 1 Enigma 8.MERRY XMAS MR.LAWRENCE Ryiuchi Sakamoto 9. THE MISSION Ennio Morricone 10.PORCELAIN Moby 11. NO ORDINARY MORNING Chicane 12.OXYGENE Pt.2 Jean M. Jarre 13.SILENCE Delirium 14.PAVANE Op.50 Joolz Gianni 15.ROSE James Horner 16.FLOWER DUET (LAKME) (Delibes) Robin Young-Smith 17.CANTUS:SONG OF TEARS Adiemus *(CHELTENHAM & GLOUCESTER)*

71.CLASSIC FM: RELAX.. - Var.Artists & Orchestras *1999*
BMG-CONIFER (BMG): CFMCD 30 (3CDs) CFMMC 30 (2MC)
CD1: PIANO CONC.NO.2 IN C.MIN (2nd m/m) *RACHMANINOV* 2.THE LARK ASCENDING *VAUGHAN WILLIAMS* 3.CANON IN D. *PACHELBEL* 4.CONCIERTO DE ARANJUEZ (2nd m/m) *RODRIGO* 5.NULLA IN MUNDO PAX SINCERA *VIVALDI* 6.SYMPH.NO 5 IN C.SHARP MIN. (4th m/m) *MAHLER* 7.THE WALK TO THE PARADISE GARDEN *DELIUS* CD2: MEDITATION from THAIS *MASSENET* 2.VIOLIN CON.NO.1 IN G.MIN.(2nd m/m) *BRUCH* 3.RHAPSODY ON A THEME OF PAGANINI (18th Variation) *RACHMANINOV* 4.AIR ON THE G.STRING *BACH* 5.RECUERDOS DE LA ALHAMBRA *TARREGA* 6.SYMPH.6 IN B.MIN (2nd m/m) *TCHAIKOVSKY* 7.SPARTACUS (Adagio) *KHACHATURIAN* 8. CAVALLERIA RUSTICANA *(MASCAGNI)* 9.CELLO SUITE NO.1 IN G (1st m/m) *J.S.BACH* 10.FANTASIA ON A THEME OF THOMAS TALLIS *V.WILLIAMS* 11.THE GADFLY *SHOSTAKOVICH* CD3: ADAGIO FOR STRINGS *S.BARBER* 2.PAVAVE *FAURE* 3. PIANO CONC.IN A.MINOR (2nd m/m) *GRIEG* 4.ADAGIO IN G MINOR *ALBINONI* 5.ON HEARING THE FIRST CUCKOO IN SPRING *DELIUS* 6.GYMNOPEDI NO.1 *SATIE* 7.PRELUDE A L'APRES-MIDI D'UN FAUNE *DEBUSSY* 8.CHANSON DE MATIN *ELGAR* 9.MISERERE MEI, DEUS *ALLEGRI*

72.CLASSIC FM: RELAX..MORE - V.Arts & Orchestras *2000*
BMG-CONIFER (BMG): CFMCD 32 (3CDs) CFMMC 32 (2MC)
CD1: 1.SYMPHONY NO.2 (Adagio) *RACHMANINOV* 2.PIANO SONATA NO.14 (Moonlight) *BEETHOVEN* 3.CANTIQUE DE JEAN RACINE *FAURE* 4.SERENADE FOR STRINGS *ELGAR* 5. FANTASIA PARA UN GENTILHOMBRE (Villano y Recerare) *RODRIGO* 6.PIANO CONCERTO NO.2 Andante *SHOSTAKOVICH* 7.PEER GYNT SUITE 1 (Morning) *GRIEG* 8.MADAM BUTTER FLY (Humming Chorus) *PUCCINI* 9.KOL NIDRI (Adagio on

Hebrew Melodies) *BRUCH* **CD2:** 1.CLARINET CONCERTO IN
A.(Adagio) *MOZART* 2.L'ARLESIENNE SUITE 2 (Minuet)
BIZET 3.PIANO CONCERT.NO.1 Romanze Larghetto *CHOPIN*
4.MORS ET VITA *GOUNOD* 5.WINTER FOUR SEASONS (Largo)
VIVALDI 6.NIMROD (Enigma Var) *ELGAR* 7.MIDSUMMER
NIGHT'S DREAM Nocturne *MENDELSSOHN* 8.PAVANE *FAURE* 9
CAVATINA *MYERS* 10.SPEM IN ALIUM *TALLIS* 11.KOANGA
(La Calinda) *DELIUS* **CD3:** 1.SCHINDLER'S LIST THEME
WILLIAMS 2.AGNUS DEI *BARBER* 3.SYMPH.NO.6 PASTORALE
(Andante Molto Molti) *BEETHOVEN* 7.CARNIVAL OF THE
ANIMALS (Swan) *SAINT SAENS* 8.VOCALISE *RACHMANINOV*
9.PRELUDE NO.15 (Raindrop) *CHOPIN* 10.SPIEGEL IM
SPIEGEL *PART* 11.DIVES AND LAZZARUS (Five Variants)
VAUGHAN WILLIAMS / *SEE ALSO COLLECTION 63*

73.CLASSIC LOVE AT THE MOVIES - Various Artists
DECCA (Univ): 466 563-2 (2CDs)   *1999*
1.MY HEART WILL GO ON *TITANIC* 2.I WILL ALWAYS LOVE
YOU *THE BODYGUARD* 3.LOVE THEME FROM *ROMEO & JULIET*
4.WE HAVE ALL THE TIME IN T.WORLD *ON HER MAJESTY'S
SECRET SERVICE* 5.UP WHERE WE BELONG *AN OFFICER AND
A GENTLEMAN* 6.JOHN BUNBAR THEME *DANCES WITH WOLVES*
7.FOR THE LOVE OF A PRINCESS *BRAVEHEART* 8.AS TIME
GOES BY *CASABLANCA* 9.MAIN THEME *OUT OF AFRICA* 10.
TAKE MY BREATH AWAY *TOP GUN* 11.CAN YOU FEEL THE
LOVE TONIGHT *LION KING* 12.UNCHAINED MELODY *GHOST*
13.LOVE IS ALL AROUND *4 WEDDINGS & A FUNERAL* 14.
EVERYTHING I DO I DO IT FOR YOU *ROBIN HOOD PRINCE
OF THIEVES* 15.PIANO CONCERTO NO.2 (RACHMANINOV)
BRIEF ENCOUNTER 16.MAIN THEME *CINEMA PARADISO* 17.
FINALE CAVALLERIA RUSTICANA (MASCAGNI) *GODFATHER 3*
18.GABRIEL'S OBOE *THE MISSION* 19.TRY A LITTLE TEND
ERNESS *COMMITMENTS* 20.EVERGREEN *A STAR IS BORN* 21.
MOON RIVER *BREAKFAST AT TIFFANYS* 22.WHERE DO I
BEGIN *LOVE STORY* 23.MAIN THEME *WHEN A MAN LOVES A
WOMAN* 24.LEIA'S THEME *STAR WARS* 25.CLARINET
CONCERTO IN A.K622 (MOZART) *OUT OF AFRICA* 26.CANON
IN D.(PACHELBEL) *ORDINARY PEOPLE* 27.CELLO SONATA
NO.3.IN D.MINOR (BACH) *TRULY MADLY DEEPLY* 28.
RHAPSODY IN BLUE (GERSHWIN) *MANHATTAN* 29.BOLERO *TEN*
30.THEME *THE PIANO* 31.SOMEWHERE IN MY HEART *DOCTOR
ZHIVAGO* 32.HOW DEEP IS YOUR LOVE *SATURDAY N.FEVER*

74.CLASSIC SIXTIES TV THEMES - Various Artists
CASTLE SELECT (Pinn): SELM(CD)(C) 561 (CD/MC) *2000*
1.MAN IN A SUITCASE Ron Grainer 2.WHO DO YOU THINK
YOU'RE KIDDING MT.HITLER (DAD'S ARMY) Bud Flanagan
3.THUNDERBIRDS Barry Gray 4.AVENGERS Laurie Johnson
5.THE SAINT Cyril Stapleton 6.JOE 90 Barry Gray 7.
DOCTOR WHO Eric Winstone 8.CROSSROADS Tony Hatch 9.
STINGRAY Gary Miller 10.STEPTOE & SON Ron Grainer
11.CHAMPIONS Tony Hatch 12.CAPTAIN SCARLET Barry
Gray 13.DEPARTMENT S Cyril Stapleton 14.MAN ALIVE
Tony Hatch 15.FIREBALL XL5 Fleerekkers 16.HANCOCK
Derek Scott 17.DANGER MAN Bob Leaper 18.POWER GAME
19.WHICKER'S WORLD Laurie Johnson 20.PEYTON PLACE

Jack Dorsey 21.Z CARS John Keating 22.LIGHT FLIGHT
(TAKE THREE GIRLS) Pentangle 23.FORSTYE SAGA Cyril
Stapleton 24.DOCTOR FINLAY'S CASEBOOK Les Reed 25.
ON THE BALL (WORLD CUP TV) John Schroeder

75.COCKTAIL THEME COLLECTION - Various Artists
HMV EASY (EMI): 527 431-2 (CD)   *2000*
1.JAMES BOND THEME Leroy Holmes 2.MAGNIFICENT SEVEN
Tito Rodriguez 3.GOLDFINGER Count Basie Or.4.BATMAN
David McCallum 5.MISSION IMPOSSIBLE Billy May 6.THE
DICK VAN DYKE THEME/ALVIN SHOW THEME Nelson Riddle
Orch 7.MAN FROM UNCLE THEME/THE SPIES Al Caiola 8.
THE FUGITIVE Si Zentner 9.APARTMENT Tito Rodriguez
10.YOU ONLY LIVE TWICE Sir Julian/THUNDERBALL
Elliot Fisher 11.GOOD THE BAD AND THE UGLY Leroy
Holmes 12.THIRD MAN THEME Don Baker 13.FROM RUSSIA
WITH LOVE Count Basie 14.UNTOUCHABLES Nelson Riddle
15.MAN WITH THE GOLDEN ARM Billy May 16.DRAGNET/
ROOM 43 Ray Anthony 17.ONE STEP BEYOND (FEAR)/ THE
TWILIGHT ZONE Ventures 18.OUR MAN FLINT Elliot
Fisher 19.PLAYBOY'S THEME Cy Coleman 20.ROUTE 66
Nelson Riddle 21.SHAFT Hollyridge Strings-

---.COMMERCIAL BREAK: Old Tunes New Ads *see p.49 & 336*
---.COMMERCIAL BREAKS *see page 49 & 336 & 337*

76.COPLAND Aaron - Celluloid Copland (World Premiere)
EOS Orchestra & Collegiate Chorale (Robert Bass)
TELARC (BMG): CD 80583 (CD)   *2001*
THE CITY (Suite) / FROM SORCERY TO SCIENCE / THE
CUMMINGTON STORY (Suite) / NORTH STAR (Suite)

77.COPS ON THE BOX - 26 Great Cop Themes / V.Artists
CASTLE COMM (Pinn): MACCD 367 (CD)   *1998*
1.Medley:HAWAII FIVE-O/CAGNEY AND LACEY/HILL STREET
BLUES/Z.CARS/DRAGNET/MIAMI VICE 2.INSPECTOR MORSE
3.MISSION IMPOSSIBLE 4.THE AVENGERS 5.MISS MARPLE
6.KOJAK 7.THE SWEENEY 8.THE A.TEAM 9.ROCKFORD FILES
10.CHARLIE'S ANGELS 11.MAGNUM P.I. 12.PERRY MASON
13.MAN FROM UNCLE 14.Medley: THE BILL/JULIET BRAVO/
BERGERAC/NO HIDING PLACE/POLICE WOMAN/STREETS OF
SAN FRANCISCO/MAIGRET/HEARTBEAT

78.COWARD Noel - 20TH CENTURY BLUES: Words & Music of
Noel Coward (BBC2 11/4/1998) *contemporary artists*
EMI: 494 631-2 (CD) 494 631-2 (MC) featuring:-
SHOLA AMA with CRAIG ARMSTRONG/DAMON ALBARN with
MICHAEL NYMAN/THE DIVINE COMEDY/MARIANNE FAITHFULL
BRYAN FERRY/ELTON JOHN/PAUL McCARTNEY/PET SHOP BOYS
VIC REEVES/SPACE/STING/SUEDE featuring RAISSA-TEXAS
ROBBIE WILLIAMS

79.COWARD Noel - MARVELLOUS PARTY Songs of Noel Coward
& Friends. PICCADILLY DANCE ORCH (Michael Law) *with*
Janice Day-Julia Shore-Alison Williams-Michael Law
TER (Koch): CDVIR 8333 (CD)   *1999*
1.DANCE LITTLE LADY 2.ROOM WITH A VIEW 3.I WENT TO
A MARVELLOUS PARTY 4.CHANGE PARTNERS 5.BEGIN THE
BEGUINE 6.NINA 7.NEVER GONNA DANCE 8.MAD ABOUT THE
BOY 9.I'VE GOT YOU UNDER MY SKIN 10.LONDON PRIDE 11

HALF-CASTE WOMAN 12.LADY IS A TRAMP 13.POOR LITTLE
RICH GIRL 14.DEAREST LOVE 15.MAD DOGS & ENGLISHMEN
16.THE PARTY'S OVER NOW

80.**COWARD Noel - THE GREAT SHOWS** *EMI: 521 808-2 (2CDs)*
CD1: I'LL SEE YOU AGAIN-IF LOVE WERE ALL-ZIGEUNER-
DEAR LITTLE CAFE-LOVER OF MY DREAMS-20TH CENTURY
BLUES-TOAST TO ENGLAND-I'LL FOLLOW MY SECRET HEART-
REGENCY RAKES-CHARMING CHARMING-ENGILSH LESSON-DEAR
DEAR LITTLE SOLDIERS-THERE'S ALWAYS SOMETHING FISHY
ABOUT THE FRENCH-MELANIE'S ARIA-NEVERMORE
CD2:-COUNTESS MITZI-DEAREST LOVE-GYPSEY MELODY-
STATELY HOMES OF ENGLAND-WHERE ARE THE SONGS WE
SUNG-OPERETTE-NOTHING CAN LAST FOREVER-I'D NEVER
KNOW-SOMETHING ABOUT A SOLDIER-MY KIND OF MAN-THIS
COULD BE TRUE-JOSEPHINE-SAIL AWAY-WHY DOES LOVE GET
IN THE WAY-IN A BOAT ON THE LAKE WITH MY DARLING-
CHASE ME CHARLIE-EVENING IN SUMMER-I LIKE AMERICA-
THREE JUVENILE DELINQUENTS-JOSEPHINE

81.**COWARD Noel - THE SONGS OF NOEL COWARD**
FLAPPER-PAVILION (Pinn): PASTCD 7080   *1996*
1.MRS.WORTHINGTON 2.PARISIAN PIERROT 3.THERE'S LIFE
IN THE OLD GIRL YET 4.POOR LITTLE RICH GIRL 5.I'LL
SEE YOU AGAIN 6.IF LOVE WERE ALL 7.ZIEGUENER 8.A
ROOM WITH A VIEW 9.DANCE LITTLE LADY 10.I'LL FOLLOW
MY SECRET HEART 11.REGENCY RAKES 12.THERE'S ALWAYS
SOMETHING FISHY ABOUT THE FRENCH13.HAS ANYBODY SEEN
OUR SHIP 14.YOU WERE THERE 15.SOMEDAY I'LL FIND YOU
16.DEAREST LOVE 17.THE STATELY HOMES OF ENGLAND 18.
LONDON PRIDE19.ANY LITTLE FISH 20.MAD ABOUT THE BOY
21.MAD DOGS AND ENGLISHMEN 22.THE PARTY'S OVER NOW

82.**CREATURE FEATURES** (*prev* 'MONSTER MOVIE THEMES')
DRESSED TO KILL (BMG): DRESS 166 (CD)   *2000*
1.COME WITH ME *from GODZILLA* 2.PRESIDENT'S SPEECH
INDEPENDENCE DAY 3.MEN IN BLACK 4.X-FILES THEME 5.
ROSEMARY'S BABY 6.BURN *THE CROW* 7.LOVE SONG FOR A
VAMPIRE *DRACULA* 8.TO THINK OF A STORY *FRANKENSTEIN*
9.ADDAM'S GROOVE *THE ADDAMS FAMILY* 10.JURASSIC PARK
11.CANDYMAN 12.PAZUZO *EXCORCIST 2 THE HERETIC* 13.
EDWARD SCISSORHANDS 14.DEEPER UNDERGROUND *GODZILLA*
15.THE LOST WORLD 16.WALK THE DINOSAUR *SUPER MARIO
BROTHERS* 17.IF WE HOLD ON TOGETHER *THE LAND BEFORE
TIME* 18.WE JUST WANNA PARTY WITH YOU *MEN IN BLACK*

83.**CULT FILES The** Royal Phil.Concert O.(Mike Townsend)
SILVA SCREEN (Koch): FILMX(CD)(C)184 (2CD/2MC) 1996
X.FILES-PRISONER-SAINT-DANGERMAN-RANDALL & HOPKIRK
DECEASED-AVENGERS-JASON KING- PERSUADERS-BLAKE'S 7-
RED DWARF-DOCTOR WHO-ADVENTURES OF ROBINSON CRUSOE-
ALFRED HITCHCOCK PRESENTS-HAWAII 50-PERRY MASON-MAN
CALLED IRONSIDE-KOJAK-MISSION IMPOSSIBLE-STAR TREK-
SEAQUEST DSV-BABYLON 5 **CD2:** 2001-EXCALIBUR-ALIEN-
MAD MAX:BEYOND THUNDERDOME-BODY HEAT-OMEN-HALLOWEEN
ASSAULT ON PREC.13-BATMAN-BLADERUNNER-SUPERMAN-THE
SHADOW-ROCKETEER-HEAVEN'S GATE-LEGEND-SOMEWHERE IN
TIME-TAXI DRIVER-PINK PANTHER-THE BLUES BROTHERS

84.CULT FILES: RE-OPENED Royal Phil.Concert Orch (Mike Townsend) + City Of Prague Philharmonic (Nic Raine) *Silv.Screen (Koch): FILMX(CD)(C)191 (2CD/2MC) 1997* CD1: XENA THE WARRIOR PRINCESS-BATTLESTAR GALACTICA HITCHHIKERS GUIDE TO THE GALAXY-SPACE: ABOVE AND BEYOND-TWILIGHT ZONE-THE OUTER LIMITS-THUNDERBIRDS-FIREBALL XL5:ZERO G-FIREBALL XL5:FIREBALL-STINGRAY vocal-STINGRAY:MARCH OF THE OYSTERS-CAPTAIN SCARLET JOE 90-UFO-SPACE 1999:1st series-SPACE 1999:2nd ser BATMAN-THE TIME TUNNEL-LOST IN SPACE-VOYAGE TO THE BOTTOM OF THE SEA-LAND OF THE GIANTS-HERCULES-STINGRAY:Orch.version CD2: POLICE SQUAD-BURKE'S LAW FUGITIVE-KOJAK-MIAMI VICE-STREETS OF SAN FRANCISCO-BEAUTY & THE BEAST TV-SUPERMAN-EDWARD SCISSORHANDS-BEETLEJUICE-YOUNG FRANKENSTEIN-MIDNIGHT EXPRESS-SUSPIRIA-MERRY CHRISTMAS MR.LAWRENCE-WITHNAIL AND I CLOCKWORK ORANGE-WILD WILD WEST-ADDAMS FAMILY-MASH-MONTY PYTHON'S FLYING CIRCUS *NOTE: ITEMS 76/77 LISTED* 'CULT FILES BIG BOX' *on FILMXCD 343 (4CDs) 2000*

85.DAVIS Carl - THE SILENTS (Contemporary Scores) *SILVA CLASSICS (Koch): FILMXCD 326 (2CD)   2000* Carl Davis with the London Philharmonic Orchestra 1.NAPOLEON 2.THE BIG PARADE 3.FOUR HORSEMEN OF THE APOCALYPSE 4.CITY LIGHTS 5.WINGS 6.THE IRON MASK 7. PHANTOM OF THE OPERA 8.GREED 9.THE THIEF OF BAGDAD 10.OLD HEIDELBERG 11.WIND 12.WEDDING MARCH 13.THE FLESH AND THE DEVIL 14.THE CROWD 15.BROKEN BLOSSOMS 16.SHOW PEOPLE 17.BEN HUR

86.DAY Doris - THE MAGIC OF THE MOVIES *SONY (Ten): SONYTV79(CD)(MC)(MD) (2CD/MC/MD) 1999* 1.IT'S MAGIC 2.MOVE OVER DARLING 3.SECRET LOVE 4. TUNNEL OF LOVE 5.LET'S FACE THE MUSIC AND DANCE 6. THREE COINS IN THE FOUNTAIN 7.NIGHT AND DAY 8.ON THE STREET WHERE YOU LIVE 9.I'VE GROWN ACCUSTOMED TO HIS FACE 10.THEY SAY IT'S WONDERFUL 11.LOVER COME BACK 12.SINGIN' IN THE RAIN 13.A WONDERFUL GUY 14.SOMETHING WONDERFUL 15.AS LONG AS HEE NEEDS ME 16.PILLOW TALK 17.I'LL NEVER STOP LOVING YOU 18.THE BLACK HILLS OF DAKOTA 19.TEACHER'S PET 20.DEADWOOD STAGE CD2 QUE QUE SERA SERA 2.HOLD ME IN YOUR ARMS 3.CHEEK TO CHEEK 4.OVER THE RAINBOW 5.I SPEAK TO THE STARS 6.PRETTY BABY 7.VERY THOUGHT OF YOU 8. I WANT TO BE HAPPY 9.MAKIN' WHOOPEE 10.I KNOW A PLACE 11.NO TWO PEOPLE 12.LOVE YOU DEARLY 13.APRIL IN PARIS 14.WHITE CHRISTMAS 15.THIS CAN'T BE LOVE 16.SWINGING ON A STAR 17.HIGH HOPES 18.TILL WE MEET AGAIN 19.WHEN I FALL IN LOVE 20.THE PARTY'S OVER

87.DELERUE Georges - Great Composers *VARESE USA (Pinn): VSD 6223-2 (2CD)   2001* *Suites & Themes from:* PLATOON-RICH AND FAMOUS-HER ALIBI-BEACHES-EXPOSED-BILOXI BLUES-CRIMES OF THE HEART-STEEL MAGNOLIAS-INTERLUDE-THE ESCAPE ARTIST-SALVADOR and 'HOMMAGE TO FRANCOIS TRUFFAUT' select.

SOMETHING WICKED THIS WAY COMES-THE HOUSE ON CAROLL
STREET-A LITTLE SEX-MAID TO ORDER-MAN WOMAN AND
CHILD-MEMORIES OF ME-AGNES OF GOD-TRUE CONFESSIONS
tracks taken from the following three albums
DELERUE Georges - **The London Sessions (1/2/3)**
VARESE USA (Pinn): VSD 5241 (CD) 1990
VARESE USA (Pinn): VSD 5245 (CD) 1990
VARESE USA (Pinn): VSD 5256 (CD) 1992

88.**DR.STRANGELOVE MUSIC FROM STANLEY KUBRICK FILMS**
SILVA SCREEN (Koch): FILMCDC 303 (CD) 1999
City Of Prague Philharmonic Orchest (Paul Bateman)
Electronic music produced by Mark Ayres
including LOLITA-2001 A SPACE ODYSSEY-BARRY LYNDON-
A CLOCKWORK ORANGE-DOCTOR STRANGELOVE-FULL METAL
JACKET-DAY OF THE FIGHT-THE KILLING-FEAR AND DESIRE
PATHS OF GLORY-KILLER'S KISS-THE SHINING-SPARTACUS
includes orig songs by Al Bowlly-Vera Lynn-Trashmen

89.**DURBIN Deanna** - **Can't Help Singing**
LIVING ERA-ASV (Select): CDAJA 5149 (CD) 1995
ANNIE LAURIE-AVE MARIA (Bach-Gounod)-IL BACHIO (The
Kiss)-BECAUSE-BENEATH THE LIGHTS OF HOME-CAN'T HELP
SINGING (with Robert Paige)-ESTRELLITA (Ponce)-GOD
BLESS AMERICA-HOME SWEET HOME-IT'S RAINING SUNBEAMS
IT'S FOOLISH BUT IT'S FUN-KISS ME AGAIN-LAST ROSE
OF SUMMER-LOCH LOMOND-LOVE IS ALL-LOVE'S OLD SWEET
SONG-MAIDS OF CADIZ-MUSETTA'S WALTZ SONG(La Boheme)
MY HERO MY OWN-ONE FINE DAY (from Madame Butterfly)
PERHAPS-POOR BUTTERFLY-SPRING IN MY HEART-WALTZING
IN THE CLOUDS-WHEN APRIL SINGS

90.**DURBIN Deanna** - **Sensational Songbird**
PRESIDENT (BMG): PLCD 567 (CD) 1998
1.THE TURNTABLE SONG 2.MORE AND MORE 3.SPRING WILL
BE A LITTLE LATE THIS YEAR 4.UN BEL DI VEDREMO (ONE
FINE DAY 5.ALWAYS 6.BENEATH THE LIGHTS OF HOME 7.
ANY MOMENT NOW 8.CALIFORN-I-AY 9.CAN'T HELP SINGING
10.LOVE IS ALL 11.AVE MARIA 12.OLD FOLKS AT HOME 13
SOMEONE TO CARE FOR ME 14.IL BACIO (THE KISS) 15.
ALLELUJAH 16.IT'S FOOLISH BUT IT'S FUN 17.WHEN THE
ROSES BLOOM AGAIN 18.LOVE'S OLD SWEET SONG 19.
AMAPOLA 20.LES FILLES DE CADIZ (MAIDS OF CADIZ) 21.
AVE MARIA 22.SAY A PRAYER FOR THE BOYS OVER THERE

91.**DURBIN Deanna** - **The Fan Club**
FLAPPER-PAVILION (Pinn): PASTCD 9781 (CD) 1992
AMAPOLA-BECAUSE-WHEN APRIL SINGS-WALTZING IN THE CL
OUDS-MY OWN-BRINDISI-BENEATH THE LIGHTS OF HOME-SPR
ING IN MY HEART-IT'S RAINING SUNBEAMS-MUSETTA'S WAL
TZ SONG-LOVE IS ALL-PERHAPS-ONE FINE DAY-HOME SWEET
HOME-LAST ROSE OF SUMMER-IL BACIO-AVE MARIA-LOCH LO
MONS-ALLELULIA-AVE MARIA   *DEANNA DURBIN Film Songs*

92.**ELIZABETHAN SERENADE** - **Best Of BRITISH Light Music**
NAXOS (Select): 8.553515 (CD) 1996
1.BY THE SLEEPY LAGOON *(E.COATES)* 2.MARCH OF THE BO
WMAN 'Robin Hood Suite' *(F.CURZON)* 3.BELLS ACROSS
THE MEADOWS *(A.KETELBEY)* 4.CORONATION SCOT *V.ELLIS)*

COLLECTIONS

5.SKETCH OF A DANDY *(H.WOOD)* 6.WESTMINSTER WALTZ
(R.FARNON) 7.MARCH FROM A LITTLE SUITE *(T.DUNCAN)*
8.SAILING BY *(R.BINGE)* 9.JAMAICAN RHUMBA *A.BENJAMIN*
10.KNIGHTSBRIDGE MARCH from 'London Suite' *E.COATES*
11.IN A MONASTERY GARDEN *(A.KETELBEY)* 12.LITTLE SER
ENADE *(E.TOMLINSON)* 13.ROSES OF PICARDY *(H.WOOD)* 14
PUFFIN' BILLY *(E.WHITE)* 15.ELIZABETHAN SERENADE *(R.
BINGE)* 16.TOM JONES WALTZ *(E.GERMAN)* 17.VANITY FAIR
(A.COLLINS) 18.MARIGOLD *(B.MAYERL)* 19.IN A PERSIAN
MARKET *(A.KETELBEY)* 20.DAM BUSTERS MARCH *(E.COATES)*
93.<u>ENYA</u> *VARIOUS MUSIC USED IN FILM AND TV taken from*
'A Day Without Rain'   WEA: 8573 85878-2 *(CD)* 2000
'Paint The Sky With Stars'   3984 20895-2 *(CD)* 1997
'Memory Of Trees' WEA: 06301287-2 *(CD)* -4(MC) 1995
'Shepherd Moons' WEA: 9031 75572-2(CD) -4(MC) 1991
'Watermark'   WEA: 243 875-2 *(CD)* -4(MC) 1988
'The Celts' WEA: 4509 91167-2(CD) WX 498C(MC) 1987
94.<u>ESSENTIAL BRITISH LIGHT MUSIC COLLECT</u>. - Classic FM
BBC Concert Orchestra conducted by Vernon Handley
BMG-CLASSIC FM (BMG): 75605 57003-2 *(CD)*   1997
1.633 SQUADRON *(RON GOODWIN)* 2.CORONATION SCOTT
(V.ELLIS) 3.WESTMINSTER WALTZ *(R.FARNON)* 4/5.LONDON
SUITE: KNIGHTSBRIDGE MARCH/COVENT GARDEN *(E.COATES)*
6.NIGHTS OF GLADNESS *(C.ANCLIFFE)* 7.MEXICAN HAT
DANCE *(P.HOPE)* 8.SAILING BY *(R.BINGE)* 9.HORSEGUARDS
WHITEHALL *(H.WOOD)* 10.ELIZABETHAN SERENADE *(BINGE)*
11.MARCH FROM A LITTLE SUITE *(T.DUNCAN)* 12.JAMAICAN
RUMBA *(A.BENJAMIN)* 13.CONCERT JIG *(E.TOMLINSON)* 14.
BY THE SLEEPY LAGOON *(E.COATES)* 15.PUFFIN' BILLY*(E.
WHITE)* 16.VANITY FAIR *(A.COLLINS)* 17.JUMPING BEAN
(R.FARNON) 18.GRASSHOPPER'S DANCE *(E.BUCALOSSI)* 19.
BARWICK GREEN*(H.WOOD)* 20.DAM BUSTERS MARCH *(COATES)*
--- <u>ESSENTIAL JAMES BOND</u> The - *see under* BOND James
95.<u>ESSENTIAL SOUNDTRACKS</u> - THE NEW MOVIE COLLECTION
TELSTAR: TTVCD 3121 (2CD) TTVMC 3121 (2MC)   2000
1.PURE SHORES All Saints *THE BEACH* 2.MISSION IMPOSS
Adam Clayton-Larry Mullen 3.USE ME Bill Withers
AMERICAN BEAUTY 4.THEME FROM SHAFT Isaac Hayes 5.
MOVING Supergrass *EAST IS EAST* 6.YOU AND ME SONG
Wannadies *ROMEO & JULIET* 7.GANGSTER TRIPPIN' Fatboy
Slim *GO* 8.IT AIN'T GONNA BE ME CJ Bolland *HUMAN
TRAFFIC* 9.PORCELAIN Moby *THE BEACH* 10.HISTORY
REPEATING Propellerheads & Shirley Bassey *THERE'S
SOMETHING ABOUT MARY* 11.WICKED WAYS Garbage *THIS
YEARS'S LOVE* 12.LOVE SONG FOR A VAMPIRE Annie
Lennox *BRAM STOKER'S DRACULA* 13.NATURE BOY Miles
Davis *THE TALENTED MR.RIPLEY* 14.FEELING GOOD Nina
Simone *ASSASSIN* 15.FREDDIE'S DEAD Curtis Mayfield
SUPERFLY 16.GIRL YOU'LL BE A WOMAN SOON Urge
Overkill *PULP FICTION* 17.MUSTANG SALLY Commitments
COMMITMENTS 18.MANNISH BOY Muddy Waters *GOODFELLAS*
19.EL CUARTO DE TULA Buena Vista Social Club feat
Ry Cooder *BUENA VISTA SOCIAL CLUB* 20.DON'T LEAVE
Faithless *A LIFE LESS ORDINARY*

Disc 2: 1.BOOM BOOM BA Metisse *NEXT BEST THING* 2.
PRECIOUS MAYBE Beth Orton *THE ACID HOUSE* 3.STREET
LIFE Randy Crawford *JACKIE BROWN* 4.WONDERFUL WORLD
BEAUTIFUL PEOPLE Jimmy Cliff *EAST IS EAST* 5.BOSS
James Brown *LOCK STOCK & 2 SMOKING BARRELS* 6.YOU
NEVER CAN TELL Chuck Berry *PULP FICTION* 7.LOOK FOR
THE SILVER LINING Chet Baker *L.A.CONFIDENTIAL* 8.
GOT TO GIVE IT UP Pt.1 Marvin Gaye *SUMMER OF SAM* 9.
HAPPY HEART Andy Williams *SHALLOW GRAVE* 10.YOU'RE
NOBODY TILL SOMEBODY LOVES YOU Dean Martin *SWINGERS*
11.JUST DROPPED IN (TO SEE WHAT CONDITION MY CONDIT
ION WAS IN) Kenny Rogers *BIG LEBOWSKY* 12.EVERY DAY
SHOULD BE A HOLIDAY Dandy Warhols *THERE'S SOMETHING
ABOUT MARY* 13.SPEAKING OF HAPPINESS Gloria Lynn 7
14.WALK THIS LAND Ez Rollers *LOCK STOCK & 2 S.B.*15
CLUBBED TO DEATH Rob D *MATRIX* 16.KINGDOM'S COMING
Bauhaus *BLAIR WITCH PROJECT* 17.WHERE IS MY MIND
Pixies *FIGHT CLUB* 18.RELEASE THE DUBS Leftfield
SHALLOW GRAVE 19.CHOOSE LIFE P.F.Project feat Ewan
McGregor *TRAINSPOTTING* 20.MINDFIELDS Prodigy *MATRIX*

*96.*ESSENTIAL SOUNDTRACKS - FILM FOUR / Var.Orig.Arts.
TELSTAR: TTVCD 3038 (2CD) TTVMC 3038 (2MC) 1999
1.LUST FOR LIFE Iggy Pop *TRAINSPOTTING* 2.MISIRLOU
Dick Dale & Deltones *PULP FICTION* 3.PAYBACK James
Brown *LOCK STOCK & 2 SMOKING BARRELS* 4.THERE SHE
GOES La's *FEVER PITCH* 5.JUST LOOKIN' Stereophonics
THIS YEAR'S LOVE 6.SHALLOW GRAVE Leftfield *S.GRAVE*
7.BIG SPENDER Shirley Bassey *LITTLE VOICE* 8.LET'S
STAY TOGETHER Al Green *PULP FICTION* 9.STUCK IN THE
MIDDLE WITH YOU Stealers Wheel *RESERVOIR DOGS* 10.
PLAY DEAD Bjork & David Arnold *YOUNG AMERICANS*
11.FOR WHAT YOU DREAM OF Bedrock feat KYO *TRAIN
SPOTTING* 12.SAINT Orbital *THE SAINT* 13.FOOL'S GOLD
Stone Roses *LOCK STOCK..*14.A LIFE LESS ORDINARY
Ash *A LIFE LESS ORDINARY* 15.HUNDRED MILE HIGH CITY
Ocean Colour Scene *LOCK STOCK..*16.HEROIN The Doors
THE DOORS 17.OYE COMO VA Santana *CARLITO'S WAY* 18.
JUNGLE BOOGIE Kool & The Gang *PULP FICTION* 19.
MACHINE GUN Commodores *BOOGIE NIGHTS* 20.ACROSS
110TH STREET Bobby Womack *JACKIE BROWN* CD2: 1.BORN
SLIPPY Underworld *TRAINSPOTTING* 2.LITTLE GREEN BAG
George Baker Selection *RESERVOIR DOGS* 3.SON OF A
PREACHER MAN Dusty Springfield *PULP FICTION* 4.
DON'T BLOW YOUR MIND THIS TIME Delfonics *JACKIE
BROWN* 5.TROUBLE MAN Marvin Gaye *SEVEN* 6.BULLITT
Lalo Schifrin *BULLITT* 7.BLUE VELVET Bobby Vinton
BLUE VELVET 8.AC-CENT-CHU-ATE THE POSITIVE Johnny
Mercer *L.A.CONFIDENTIAL* 9.KING OF THE ROAD Roger
Miller *SWINGERS* 10.SOUL ON FIRE LaVern Baker *ANGEL
HEART* 11.YOU'RE THE FIRST THE LAST MY EVERYTHING
Barry White *FOUR WEDDINGS AND A FUNERAL* 12.HOT
STUFF Donna Summer *FULL MONTY* 13.BEST OF MY LOVE
Emotions *BOOGIE NIGHTS* 14.GOT TO BE REAL Cheryl
Lynn *LAST DAYS OF DISCO* 15.I'LL TAKE YOU THERE

Staple Singers *CASINO* 16.MAKE ME SMILE Steve Harley
Cockney Rebel *VELVET GOLDMINE* 17.BORN TO BE WILD
Steppenwolf *EASY RIDER* 18.GREEN ONIONS Booker T.&
MG's *GET SHORTY* 19.LAURA'S THEME Angelo Badalemnti
TWIN PEAKS 20.PERFECT DAY Lou Reed *TRAINSPOTTING*

97.<u>ESSENTIAL SOUNDTRACKS</u> - THE CLASSIC COLLECTION
TELSTAR: TTVCD 3082 (2CD) TTVMC 3082 (2MC)   *1999*
CD1: 1.HEART ASKS PLEASURE FIRST/THE PROMISE *PIANO*
2.ZADOK THE PRIEST *THE MADNESS OF KING GEORGE* 3.
ELIZABETH OVERTURE *ELIZABETH* 4.DUETTINO SULL'ARIA
from MARRIAGE OF FIGARO *SHAWSHANK REDEPTION* 5.CHE
GELIDA MANINA from LA BOHEME *MIDSUMMER NIGHTS DREAM*
6.INTERMEZZO CAVALLERIA RUSTICANA *RAGING BULL* 7.
CHASING SHEEP IS BEST LEFT TO SHEPHERDS
DRAUGHTSMAN'S CONTRACT 8.CONCERTO IN A.MINOR for 4
HARPSICHORDS *DANGEROUS LIAISONS* 9.SILENCE OF THE
LAMBS MAIN TITLE 10.ON EARTH AS IT IS IN HEAVEN
THE MISSION 11.LAST OF THE MOHICANS MAIN TITLE
12.THE ENGLISH PATIENT 13.EN ARANJUEZ CON TU AMOR
BRASSED OFF CD2: 1.WALTZ TWO from THE JAZZ SUITE
EYES WIDE SHUT 2.MATTHAUS PASSION *CASINO* 3.DRAMATIC
DEPARTURE *DAMAGE* 4.AIR ON A G.STRING *SEVEN* 5.THEME
FROM TWIN PEAKS 'FIRE WALK WITH ME' 6.ONCE UPON A
TIME IN AMERICA 7.PRELUDE AND ROOFTOP *VERTIGO* 8.
WAR ZONE THEME 9.MONTY REMEMBERS *WITHNAIL AND I*
10.LOVE THEME FROM BLADERUNNER 11.NUOVO CINEMA
PARADISO *CINEMA PARADISO* 12.BILITIS 13.4TH M/M 9TH
SYMPHONY (ABRIDGED) *CLOCKWORK ORANGE*

98.<u>EUROPEAN LIGHT MUSIC CLASSICS</u> - New London Orch *
HYPERION: CDA 66998 (CD)   *1998*
1.PARADE OF THE TIN SOLDIERS *(L.JESSEL)* 2.GOLD AND
SILVER *(LEHAR)* 3.MARCH OF THE LITTLE LEAD SOLDIERS
(G.PIERNE) 4.TRITSCH TRATSCH POLKA *(J.STRAUSS II)*
5.GLOW WORM IDYLL *(P.LINKE)* 6.SWEDISH POLKA *(HUGO
ALFVEN)* 7.FUNERAL MARCH OF A MARIONETTE *(C.GOUNOD)*
8.THE SKATERS (LES PATINEURES) *(E.WALDTEUFEL)* 9.
SERENADE *(J.HEYKENS)* 10.EL RELICARIO *(J.PADILLA)*
11.TESORO MIO MY TREASURE*(E.BECUCCI)* 12.BALL SCENE
(J.HELLMESBERGER) 13.POLKA (SCHWANDA THE BAGPIPER)
(J.WEINBERGER) 14.MOONLIGHT ON THE ALSTER *O.FETRAS*
15.ENTRY OF THE BOYARS *(J.HALVORSEN)* * *Ronald Corp*

99.<u>EUROVISION SONG CONTEST 1956-1999</u> - Various Artists
UNIVERSAL IMPT: 541 347-2 (2CD)   *2000*
CD1: 1.TAKE ME TO YOUR HEAVEN Charlotte Nilsson 2.
DIVA Dana Internat. 3.LOVE SHINE A LIGHT Katrina &
Waves 4.THE VOICE Eimear Quinn 5.NOCTURNE Secret
Garden 6.ROCK'N'ROLL KIDS Paul Harrington-Charlie
McGettigan 7.IN YOUR EYES Niamh Kavanagh 8.WHY ME
Linda Martin 9.FANGAD AV EN STORMVIND Carola 10.
INSIEME 1992 Toto Cuagno 11.ROCK ME Riva 12.NE
PARTEZ PAS SANS MOI Celine Dion 13.HOLD ME NOW
Johnny Logan 14.J'Aime La Vie Sandra Kim 15.LET DET
SWINGE Bobbysocks 16.DIGGI LOO DIGGI LEY Herreys
17.A LITTGLE LOVE Nicole 18.MAKING YOUR MIND UP

Bucks Fizz 19.WHAT'S ANOTHER YEAR Johnny Logan 20.
HALLELUJAH Galti Atari-Milk & Honey 21.PARLEZ-VOUS
FRANCAIS Baccara 22.A-BA-NI-BI Izhar Cohen & Alpha
beta 23.L'OISEAU ET L'ENFANT Marie Myriam
CD2: 1.SAVE YOUR KISSES FOR ME Brotherhood Of Man
2.DING DINGE DONG Teach-In 3.WATERLOO Abba 4.TUTE
RECONNAITRAS Anne-Marie David 5.APRES TOIS Vicky
Leandros 6.UN BANC UN ARBRE UN RUE Severine 7.ALL
KINDS OF EVERYTHING Dana 8.UN JOUT UN ENFANT Frida
Boccara 9.DE TROUBADOUR Lenny Kuhr 10.BOOM BANG A
BANG Lulu 11.CONGRATULATIONS Cliff Richard 12.LA LA
LA Massiel 13.PUPPET ON A STRING Sandie Shaw 14.
MERCI CHERIE Udo Jurgens 15.POUPPEE DE CIRE POUPPEE
DE SON France Gall 16.NON HO L'ETA Gigliola
Cinquetti 17.DANSEWISE Greta & Jurgen Ingmann 18.UN
PREMIER AMOUR Isabelle Aubrel 19.NOUS LE AMOUREUX
Jean Claude Pascal 20.TOM PILLIBI Jacqueline Boyer
21.EEN BEETJE Teddy Scholten 22.NEL BLU DIPINTO DI
BLUE (VOLARE) Domenico Modugno 23.DORS MON AMOUR
Andre Claveau 24.REFRAIN Lys Assia
*100.*__FAMOUS THEMES (1)__**: Remember These ?** - Var.Artists
GRASMERE (BMG): GRCD 10 (CD) GRTC 10 (MC)   *1986*
PUFFIN' BILLY (Childrens Fav)-MUSIC EVERYWHERE (Red
iffusion)-CORONATION SCOT (Paul Temple)-ON A SPRING
NOTE (Pathe Gazette)-RHYTHM ON RAILS Morning Mus-BY
THE SLEEPY LAGOON(Desert Island Discs) HORSE GUARDS
WHITEHALL (Down Your Way)-DEVIL'S GALLOP (Dick Bart
on)-DESTRUCTION BY FIRE (Pathe News)-ALL SPORTS MAR
CH (Pathe News)-SPORTSMASTER (Peter Styvestant)-ALP
INE PASTURES (My Word)-CAVALCADE OF YOUTH (Barlowes
Of Beddington)-DRUM MAJORETTE (Match Of The Day)
ELIZABETHAN SERENADE (Music in Miniature)-MELDOY ON
THE MOVE/YOUNG BALLERINA (The Potter's Wheel)-GIRLS
IN GREY (BBC TV News)-WILLO THE WISP/PORTRAIT OF A
FLIRT/JUMPING BEAN (In Town Tonight)-HORSE FEATHERS
Meet The Huggetts)-JOURNEY INTO MELODY/SAPPHIRES &
SABLES/INVITATION WALTZ (Ring Around The Moon)
*101.*__FAVOURITE SPORT THEMES__ - **Various Artists**
HALLMARK (ABM): 31113-2 (CD)   *1999*
ABC WIDE WORLD OF SPORTS-MATCH OF THE DAY-HORSE OF
THE YEAR SHOW-GARY LINEKER'S GOLDEN BOYS (How Does
It Feel To Be On Top Of The World)-POT BLACK (Black
& White Rag)-RADIO 5 LIVE SPORTS REPORT (Out Of The
Blue)-GRANDSTAND-WORLD OF SPORT (Sporty Type)-BBC
SNOOKER (Drag Racer)-WIMBLEDON (Light and Tuneful)-
SPORTNIGHT-SPORTS ARENA MARCH-RUGBY SPECIAL (Holy
Mackerel)-RUGBY WORLD CUP (World in Union)-BBC
CRICKET (Soul Limbo)-BBC GRAND PRIX (The Chain)-
A QUESTION OF SPORT-EURO 96 THEME (Three Lions)
--- __FAVOURITE THEMES FROM BBC TV__ *see* WORLD OF SOUND
--- __FELLINI Federico__ - *see* ROTA Nino
*102.*__FERGUSON David__ - **The View From Now (TV Soundtracks)**
CHANDOS RECORDS: CHAN 9679 (CD)   *1998*
1.WILDERNESS AND WEST *(AMERICAN VISIONS)* 2.FLOWERS

ON THE ROAD *(SOME KIND OF LIFE)* 3.TO BE A SOMEBODY
(CRACKER) 4.ME OR THE SCULPTURE *(ICE HOUSE)* 5.LA
PESTE *(ALBERT CAMUS COMBAT CONTRE L'ABSURDE)* 6.LONG
RUN *(BRAVO 2 ZERO)* 7.GRAVEYARD SUITE *(THE WOMAN IN
WHITE)* 8.I DIDN'T ASK YOU TO FIGHT*(LIFE AFTER LIFE)*
9.LUMINISTYS AND RAILWAYS *(AMERICAN VISIONS)* 10.BIG
CRUNCH *(CRACKER)* 11.TWO WELCOMES *(HOSTILE WATERS)*
12.RABBIT'S FOOT *(BREAKOUT)* 13.GENTLE KIDNAP *(DARK
ADAPTED EYE)* 14.OBJECTS TROUVEES *(AMERICAN VISIONS)*
15.MAGGIE'S BABY *(BAD GIRL)* 16.NOT WAVING *(DISASTER
AT VALDEZ)* 17.MARILYN/EDEN'S DEBT*(DARK ADAPTED EYE)*

103.FIGGIS ON FIGGIS - MIKE FIGGIS
BMG IMPORTS: 74321 82560-2 (CD)   *2001*
STORMY MONDAY / INTERNAL AFFAIRS / LIEBESTRAUME /
LEAVING LAS VEGAS / ONE NIGHT STAND / THE LOSS OF
SEXUAL INNOCENCE / MISS JULIE / TIME CODE

104.FILM 2000 WITH JONATHAN ROSS - Various Artists
VIRGIN (EMI): VTDCD 328 (2CD) VTDMC 328 (2MC)   *2000*
1.I WISH I KNEW HOW IT WOULD FEEL TO BE FREE Billy
Taylor Trio 2.A TOUCH OF EVIL Henry Mancini 3.THE
IPCRESS FILE John Barry 4.GOLDFINGER Shirley Bassey
5.WHEEL OF FORTUNE Kay Starr 5.YOU ONLY LIVE TWICE
Nancy Sinatra 6.ON HER MAJESTY'S S.SERVICE John
Barry 7.AIN'T THAT A KICK IN THE HEAD Dean Martin
8.NATURE BOY Miles Davis 9.WINDMILLS OF YOUR MIND
Noel Harrison 10.EVERYBODY'S TALKIN' Nilsson 11.
RAINDROPS KEEP FALLING ON MY HEAD B.J.Thomas 12.
RAGS TO RICHES Tony Bennett 13.YOU NEVER CAN TELL
Chuck Berry 14.LAND OF A 1000 DANCESWilson Pickett
15.GREEN ONIONS Booker T.& MG's 16.I'LL TAKE YOU
THERE Staple Singers 17.TAXI DRIVER 18.TROUBLE MAN
Marvin Gaye 19.DIDN'T I BLOW YOUR MIND Delfonics
20.SHAFT Isaac Hayes 21.BULLITT Lalo Schifrin 22.
FISTFUL OF DOLLARS Ennio Morricone 23.PAYING OFF
SCORES EM 24.SUPERFLY Curtis Mayfield 25.ENTER THE
DRAGON LS 26.PAYBACK James Brown 27.USE ME Bill
Withers 28.GOT TO BE REAL Cheryl Lynn 29.MACHINE
GUN Commodores 30.GHOST TOWN Specials 31.MOVING
Supergrass 32.SHIPBUILDING Elvis Costello 33.
DUELLING BANJOS Eric Weissberg-Steve Mandell 34.
PUSHER Steppenwolf 35.THERE SHE GOES La's 36.SAFE
FROM HARM Massive Attack 37.CLUBBED TO DEATH Rob D
38.PORCELAIN Moby 39.PLAYGROUND LOVE Air 40.MERRY
CHRISTMAS MR.LAWRENCE

105.FILM NOIR 18 Classic Tracks from The Dark Side
MUSIC COLLECTION (Disc-THE): MCCD 416 (CD)   *2000*
1.CANTATA *MAN WHO KNEW TOO MUCH* 2.USUAL SUSPCTS
3.DEATH OF A VISIONARY *DEAD ZONE* 4.PRELUDE/MURDER
PSYCHO 5.SHOOT THE PIANO PLAYER *CHARLIE* 6.PRELUDE
NORTH BY NORTHWEST 7.INTERSECTION *HOME* 8.BRIDE OF
FRANKENSTEIN 9.PRELUDE *WRONG MAN* 10.SCENE D'AMOUR
VERTIGO 11.FEMME FATALE *BRIDE WORE BLACK* 12.BLUES
TAXI DRIVER 13.TRANSFORMATION / STORM / REVELATION
DRESSED TO KILL 14.ELEPHANT MAN 15.PEACEFUL LAND

CONSENTING ADULTS 16.MURDER SCENE *PRIMAL FEAR* 17.
NAKED LUNCH 18.AS TIME GOES BY *CASABLANCA*

106.FORMBY George - At The Flicks   *1996*
PRESIDENT: PLCD 554 1.I COULD MAKE A GOOD LIVING AT
THAT 2.BABY *(BOOTS BOOTS)* 3.IT'S IN THE AIR 4.THEY
CAN'T FOOL ME *(IT'S IN THE AIR)* 5.GOODNIGHT LITTLE
FELLOW 6.PARDON ME 7.I'M MAKING HEADWAY NOW 8.I COU
LDN'T LET THE STABLE DOWN *COME ON GEORGE* 9.I WISH I
WAS BACK ON THE FARM *SPARE A COPPER* 10.COUNT YOUR
BLESSINGS AND SMILE 11.OH DON'T THE WIND BLOW COLD
(LET GEORGE DO IT) 12.THE EMPEROR OF LANCASHIRE 13.
YOU'RE EVERYTHING TO ME 14.YOU CAN'TGO WRONG IN
THESE *(TURNED OUT NICE AGAIN)* 15.I PLAYED ON MY SPA
NISH GUITAR 16.I'D DO IT WITH A SMILE 17.BARMAID AT
THE ROSE AND CROWN *(SOUTH AMERICAN GEORGE)* 18.WHEN
THE LADS OF THE VILLAGE GET CRACKIN' 19.HOME GUARD
BLUES *(GET CRACKIN')* 20.BELL BOTTOM GEORGE 21.IT
SERVES YOU RIGHT *(BELL BOTTOM GEORGE)* 22.GOT TO GET
YOUR PHOTO IN THE PRESS 23.HILL BILLY WILLY 24.
UNCONDITIONAL SURRENDER *(SHE SNOOPS TO CONQUER)*

107.FORMBY George - When I'm Cleaning Windows
PRESIDENT (BMG): PLCD 538 (CD)   *1995*
SITTING ON THE ICE IN THE ICE RINK -WHY DON'T WOMEN
LIKE ME *(from BOOTS BOOTS)* / DO DE OH DOH-CHINESE
LAUNDRY BLUES-YOU CAN'T STOP ME FROM DREAMING /
PLEASURE CRUISE *(ZIP GOES A MILLION)* / KEEP FIT
(KEEP FIT) / RIDING IN THE TT RACES *(NO LIMIT)* /
HINDOO MAN-IT AIN'T NOBODY'S BIZ'NESS WHAT I DO/
GOODY GOODY/I LIKE BANANAS-THE LANCASHIRE TOREADOR
A FARMER'S BOY-YOU CAN'T KEEP A GROWING LAD DOWN
YOU'RE A LI-A-TY/ WITH MY LITTLE STICK OF BLACKPOOL
ROCK-TRAILING AROUND IN A TRAILER-DARE DEVIL DICK-
SOMEBODY'S WEDDING DAY-SITTING ON THE SANDS ALL NIG
HT-MADAME MOSCOVITCH/WITH MY LITTLE UKELELE IN MY
HAND *(OFF THE DOLE)* FANLIGHT FANNY*(TROUBLE BREWING)*
WHEN I'M CLEANING WINDOWS *(KEEP YOUR SEATS PLEASE)*
LEANING ON A LAMP POST *(FEATHER YOUR NEST)*

108.GALWAY James and PHIL COULTER - Legends
RCA Victor (BMG): 09026 68776-2 (2CD) -4 (2MC) 1997
RIVERDANCE-HARRY'S GAME-BELIEVE ME IF ALL THOSE END
EARING YOUNG CHARMS-THE GENTLE MAIDEN-WOMEN OF IREL
AND (Mna Na Ehireann)-THE BATTLE OF KINSDALE (THE
VALLEY OF TEARS)-THE THORNBIRDS-LANNIGAN'S BALL-
KERRY DANCES-DANNY BOY-MUSIC FOR A FOUND HARMONIUM-
LAMENT FOR THE WILD GEESE-MY LAGAN LOVE-NATASHA (An
Cailin Fionn)-ASHOKAN FAREWELL (CIVIL WAR')-HOEDOWN

109.GARLAND Judy - Collector's Gems From The MGM Films
EMI ODEON: CDODEON 22 (7243 854533-2) (CD)   *1997*
WALTZ WITH A SWING/AMERICANA-OPERA V.JAZZ-EVERYBODY
SING-YOURS AND MINE-YOUR BROADWAY AND MY BROADWAY-
GOT A PAIR OF NEW SHOES-SUN SHOWERS-DOWN ON MELODY
FARM-WHY BECAUSE-EVER SINCE THE WORLD BEGAN/SHALL I
SING A MELODY-IN BETWEEN-IT NEVER RAINS BUT WHAT IT
POURS-BEI MIR BIST DU SCHOEN-MEET THE BEAT OF

ART-ZING WENT THE STRINGS OF MY HEART-ON THE BUMPY
ROAD TO LOVE-TEN PINS IN THE SKY-I'M NOBODY'S BABY-
ALL I DO IS DREAM OF YOU-ALONE-IT'S A GREAT DAY FOR
THE IRISH-DANNY BOY-A PRETTY GIRL MILKING HER COW-
SINGIN' IN THE RAIN-EASY TO LOVE-WE MUST HAVE MUSIC
I'M ALWAYS CHASING RAINBOWS-MINNIE FROM TRINIDAD-
EVERY LITTLE MOMENT HAS A MEANING OF IT'S OWN-TOM
TOM THE PIPER'S SON-WHEN I LOOK AT YOU-PAGING MR.GR
EENBACK-WHERE THERE'S MUSIC-JOINT IS REALLY JUMPIN'
DOWN AT CARNEGIE HALL-D'YA LOVE ME-MACK THE BLACK-
LOVE OF MY LIFE-VOODOO-YOU CAN'T GET A MAN WITH A
GUN-THERE'S NO BUSINESS LIKE SHOW BUSINESS-THEY SAY
IT'S WONDERFUL-THE GIRL THAT I MARRY-I'VE GOT THE
SUN IN THE MORNING-LET'S GO WEST AGAIN-ANYTHING YOU
CAN DO-THERE'S NO BUSINESS LIKE SHOW BUSINESS

110.GILBERT & SULLIVAN (Best Of) - D'OYLY CARTE OPERA
SONY CLASSICS (TEN); SMK 89248 (CD) *2000*
1.HMS Pinafore: OVERTURE/WE SAIL THE OCEAN BLUE/
NEVER MIND THE WHY AND WHEREFORE 2.Yeoman Of The
Guard: WHEN MAIDEN LOVES SHE SITS AND SIGHS/HERE'S
A MAN OF JOLLITY 3.Iolanthe: TRIPPING HITHER
TRIPPING THITHER/LAW IS THE TRUE EMBODIMENT/WHEN I
WENT TO THE BAR/STREPHON'S A MEMBER OF PARLIAMENT/
WHEN BRITAIN REALLY RUL'D THE WAVES 4.Pirates Of
Penzance: OVERTURE/POOR WANDR'IN ONE/I AM THE VERY
MODEL/WHEN THE FOE MAN BEARS HIS STEEL/WITH CAT
LIKE TREAD 5.The Mikado: IF YOU WANT TO KNOW WHAT
WE ARE/FLOWERS THAT BLOOM IN THE SPRING/ON A TREE
BY A RIVER 6.Patience: SOLDIERS OF OUR QUEEN/IF YOU
WANT A RECEIPT/AM I ALONE 7.The Gondoliers: WE'RE
CALLED THE GONDOLIERI/FROM THE SUNNY SPANISH SHORE/
FOR EV'RY ONE WHO FEELS INCLINED/TAKE A PAIR OF....

111.GILTRAP Gordon - **Music For The Small Screen**
LA COOKA RATCHA (Apex/BMG): LCVP 110CD (reiss) 2000
HEARTSONG *(Holiday theme BBC1 1980-85)* THE LAST OF
ENGLAND *(BBC Screen 2 'Will You Love Me Tomorrow')*
SHADY TALES *(Mike Mansfield/Thames - unissued)*
THE LORD'S SEAT *('Working Titles' BBC1 1990)*
HOLIDAY ROMANCE *('Holiday' theme BBC1 1991-1993)*
UNBROKEN PROMISE *(BBC Scr.2 'Close Relations')*
BRUTUS *('World Bowls' theme BBC2 sports series)*
THE CARNIVAL *('Wish You Were Here' Theme,Thames TV)*
HOLD THE BACK PAGE *(BBC1 1985 drama ser)* SUNBURST-
REVELATION HIGHWAY-INDOMITABLE / IN UNISON-LUCKY
(theme & incid.mus.for YTV's 'Benny On The Common')

---.GLASS Philip - **Music From The Screens**
PHILIPS CLASSICS (Univ): 432 966-2 *2001*

--- **GODZILLA VS KING KONG** see Monster Movie Music Album

112.GOLD Ernest - **Film Music Vol.1** - **London Symph.Orch.**
ARTEMIS (HOT): ARTF 001 (CD) *2000*
IT'S A MAD MAD MAD MAD MAD WORLD-YOUNG PHILADELPHIA
JUDEMENT AT NUREMBOURG-LAST SUNSET-INHERIT THE WIND
PLEASURE POINT-CHILD IS WAITING-ON THE BEACH-SADDLE
PALS-EXODUS-TOO MUCH TOO SOON

113. **GOLDSMITH Jerry** - FILM MUSIC OF JERRY GOLDSMITH
London Symphony Orchestra (Jerry Goldsmith cond.)
TELARC (Pinn): CD 80433 SACD 80433 (CD) 2000
includes themes from STAR TREK: THE MOTION PICTURE-
Medley: SAND PEBBLES/CHINATOWN/AIR FORCE ONE/PATCH
OF BLUE/POLTERGEIST/PAPILLON/BASIC INSTINCT/THE
WIND AND THE LION *end of medley.* THE RUSSIA HOUSE
THEME-BOYS FROM BRAZIL-SLEEPING WITH THE ENEMY
Medley: MAN FROM UNCLE/DOCTOR KILDARE/ROOM 222/STAR
TREK VOYAGER/WALTONS/BARNABY JONES *end of medley*
RUDY THEME-TWILIGHT ZONE THE MOVIE-FOREVER YOUNG
LOVE THEME-GENERALS (MACARTHUR / PATTON)

114. **GOLDSMITH Jerry** - FRONTIERS Royal Scottish Nat.Orch
VARESE (Pinn): VSD 5871 (CD) 1997
STAR TREK: THE MOTION PICTURE-ALIEN-LOGAN'S RUN-
TOTAL RECALL-TWILIGHT ZONE: THE MOVIE-STAR TREK:
VOYAGER-STAR TREK: FIRST CONTACT-CAPRICORN ONE-
DAMNATION ALLEY-THE ILLUSTRATED MAN

115. **GOLDSMITH Jerry** The OMEN (Essential Jerry Goldsmith
Film Music Collection) City Of Prague Philharmonic
SILVA SCREEN (Koch): FILMXCD 199 (2CD) 1998
FIRST BLOOD-RAMBO 2-THE FIRST GREAT TRAIN ROBBERY-
SHADOW-SWARM-THE RUSSIA HOUSE-MEDICINE MAN-
BASIC INSTINCT-MASADA-CAPRICORN ONE-UNDER FIRE-
BABY:SECRET OF A LOST LEGEND-THE BLUE MAX-BOYS FROM
BRAZIL-FIRST KNIGHT-TOTAL RECALL-POWDER-MacARTHUR-
PATTON-TWILIGHT ZONE-STAR TREK-STAR TREK: VOYAGER-
STAR TREK: FIRST CONTACT- THE OMEN

116. **GOODWIN Ron** British Light Music - New Zealand Symph
MARCO POLO (Select): 8.223518 (CD) | Orchestra 1996
633 SQUADRON Main Theme-DRAKE 400 Suite-PUPPET SERE
NADE-NEW ZEALAND SUITE Premier-ARABIAN CELEBRATION-
THE VENUS WALTZ-PRISONERS OF WAR MARCH: The Kriegle
MINUET IN BLUE-THE TRAP Main Theme (London Marathon
Theme)-LANCELOT & GUINEVERE Main Theme-GIRL WITH A
DREAM (all composed and conducted by Ron Goodwin)

117. **GOODWIN Ron** - Conducts Film and TV Themes
FLYBACK (Chandos): FBCD 2004 (CD) 1997
LONDON MARATHON (Theme from 'The TRAP')-HERE WHERE
YOU ARE-*MEDLEY:* KOJAK/HILL STREET BLUES/STAR TREK/
DYNASTY/DALLAS-HERE'S THAT RAINY DAY- *TRIBUTE TO
MIKLOS ROZSA:* BEN HUR main theme/PARADE OF THE CHAR
IOTEERS/LOVE THEME/THE RED HOUSE/THE FOUR FEATHERS
TROLLEY SONG- *DISNEYTIME SELECT:* ZIP A DEE DOO DAH/
SOMEDAY MY PRINCE WILL COME/I WANNA BE LIKE YOU/
LITTLE APRIL SHOWERS/WHEN YOU WISH UPON A STAR-
CARAVAN-GIRL FROM CORSICA- *STEPHEN FOSTER SUITE:*
OH SUSANNAH/SWANEE RIVER/BEAUTIFUL DREAMER/CAMPTOWN
RACES-BEAUTY AND THE BEAST-FESTIVAL TIME-CANDLESHOE
FORCE TEN FROM NAVARONE-MINUET IN BLUE-SPACEMAN AND
KING ARTHUR-GIRL WITH THE MISTY EYES-AMAZING GRACE
see also 'BRITISH LIGHT MUSIC'

--- **GRAINER Ron** - *see* A-Z OF BRITISH TV THEMES

118.GRAY Barry - No Strings Attached   *1981*
CINEPHILE (Pinn): CINCD 011 (CD) reissued 1999
The original themes from the ATV 1960's TV series
THUNDERBIRDS-CAPTAIN SCARLETT-STINGRAY-AQUA MARINA
WELL DONE PARKER-JOE 90-MYSTERONS Theme / *see also*
(TV Section) THUNDERBIRDS-STINGRAY-CAPTAIN SCARLETT

119.GREAT BRITISH EXPERIENCE The - Various Artists
HMV CLASSICS: HMV 573 550-2 (2CDs)   *re-issued 1999*
EMI CLASSICS: CDGB 50 (2CD) TCGB 50 (2MC)   *1997*
1.DEVIL'S GALLOP *(DICK BARTON)* Charles Williams
2.CALLING ALL WORKERS *(MUSIC WHILE YOU WORK)* Eric
Coates 3.WESTMINSTER WALTZ Robert Farnon 4.PUFFIN'
BILLY *(CHILDREN'S FAV.)* Edward White 5.HORSE GUARDS
WHITEHALL *DOWN YOUR WAY* Haydn Wood 6.IN PARTY MOOD
(HOUSEWIVES CHOICE) Jack Strachey 7.BY THE SLEEPY
LAGOON *(DESERT ISLAND DISCS)* Eric Coates 8.GIRLS IN
GREY *(BBC TV NEWSREEL)* Charles Williams 9.SILKS AND
SATINS *(EMERGENCY WARD 10 Closing mus)* Peter Yorke
10.MARCH FROM A LITTLE SUITE *(DR.FINLAY'S CASEBOOK)*
Trevor Duncan 11.BARWICK GREEN *(THE ARCHERS)* Arthur
Wood 12.THE RUNAWAY ROCKING HORSE Edward White 13.
GIRL FROM CORSICA Trevor Duncan 14.NON STOP *(ITN
NEWS 60's-70's)* John Malcolm 15.SKYSCARAPER FANTASY
Donald Phillips 16.HEADLESS HORSEMAN Ron Goodwin 17
ON A SPRING NOTE Sidney Torch 18.SEA SONGS *(BILLY
BUNTER OF GREYFRIARS SCHOOL)* Vaughan Williams 19.
CHANGING MOODS *(PC 49 THEME 'ADVENTURES OF PC 49)*
Ronald Hanmer20.A CANADIAN IN MAYFAIR Angela Morley
21.DANCER AT THE FAIR John Fortis 22.LAS VEGAS
ANIMAL MAGIC Laurie Johnson 23.STARLIGHT ROOF WALTZ
George Melachrino 24.EVENSONG Easthope Martin 25.
KNIGHTSBRIDGE MARCH *(IN TOWN TONIGHT)* Eric Coates
CD2: MARCHING STRINGS *(TOP OF TGHE FORM)* Ray Martin
2.CORONATION SCOTT *(PAUL TEMPLE)* Vivian Ellis 3.
JUMPING BEAN *SEND FOR SHINER* Robert Farnon 4.SOUND
AND VISION *(ATV OPENING MARCH)* Eric Coates 5.YOUNG
BALLERINA *(TV INTERLUDE:THE POTTER'S WHEEL)* Charles
Williams 6.PARISIAN MODE *(WHAT'S MY LINE)* Wolfe
Phillips 7.HORSE FEATHERS *(MEET THE HUGGETS)* Philip
Green 8.PORTRAIT OF A FLIRT *(IN TOWN TONIGHT. LINK)*
Robert Farnon 9.CAVALCADE OF YOUTH *(THE BARLOWS OF
BEDDINGTON)* Jack Beaver 10.RUNNING OFF THE RAIL
Clive Richardson 11.SAILING BY *(RADIO 4 LATE NIGHT
SHIPPING FORECAST)* Ronald Binge 12.WINTER SUNSHINE
George Melachrino 13.PARAKEETS AND PEACOCKS Jack
Coles 14.MELODY ON THE MOVE Clive Richardson 15.
HIGH HEELS Trevor Duncan 16.THE HAUNTED BALLROOM
Geoffrey Toye 17.ALL STRINGS AND FANCY FREE Sidney
Torch 18.SAPPHIRES AND SABLES Peter Yorke 19.DANCE
OF AN OSTRACISED IMP Frederic Curzon 20.SMILE OF A
LATIN Trevor Duncan 21.BEACHCOMBER Clive Richardson
22.DREAMING Archibald Joyce 23.CONCERT JIG Ernest
Tomlinson 24.A QUIET STROLL *(TV FARMING)* Charles
Williams 25.MARCH FROM LITTLE SUITE Malcolm Arnold

120.GREAT BRITISH FILM MUSIC ALBUM - Various Artists
SILVA SCREEN (Koch): FILMXCD 309 (2CD)   *1999*
inc: FRENZY-OLIVER TWIST-HENRY V-HAMLET-BATTLE OF
THE BULGE-FAR FROM THE MADDING CROWD-SOUND BARRIER
SINK THE BISMARCK-THE LADY VANISHES-EMMA-DUELLISTS
CURSE OF THE WEREWOLF-DAMBUSTERS-STAGE FRIGHT-THE
HAUNTING-COASTAL COMMAND-UNDER CAPRICORN-NIGHT TO
REMEMBER-CRIMSON PIRATE-RED SHOES complete score

121.GREAT MOVIE SCORES FROM FILMS OF STEVEN SPIELBERG
ERICH KUNZEL & THE CINCINNATI POPS
TELARC (BMG): CD 80495   *1999*
SUGARLAND EXPRESS-JAWS-CLOSE ENCOUNTERS OF THE
THIRD KIND-1941-RAIDERS OF THE LOST ARK-POLTERGEIST
E.T.-TWILIGHT ZONE THE MOVIE-INDIANA JONES AND THE
TEMPLE OF DOOM-COLOR PURPLE-EMPIRE OF THE SUN-
INDIANA JONES AND THE LAST CRUSADE-ALWAYS-HOOK-
JURASSIC PARK-SCHINDLER'S LIST-THE LOST WORLD-
AMISTAD-SAVING PRIVATE RYAN

122.GREAT SPORTING EXPERIENCE - Various Artists
EMI Classics: CDGOAL 1 (CD) TCGOAL 12 (MC)   *1998*
30 GREAT RADIO & TV SPORTS THEMES FROM 40'S-1990'S
1.GRANDSTAND current theme *(composer: K.MANSFIELD)*
2.GRANDSTAND orig theme 'News Scoop' *(L.STEVENS)* 3.
LONDON MARATHON 'The Trap' *(R.GOODWIN)* 4.SKI SUNDAY
'Pop Looks Bach' *(S.FONTEYN)* 5.TEST CRICKET 'Soul
Limbo' *(BOOKER T.& MG's)* 6.SNOOKER 'Drag Racer' *(D.
WOOD)* 7.MATCH OF THE DAY 'Offside' *(B.STOLLER)* 8.
MATCH OF THE DAY (orig)'Drum Majorette'*(A.STECK)* 9.
SPORTSNIGHT *(T.HATCH)* 10.ALLSPORTS MARCH *(R.FARNON)*
11.WIMBLEDON (opening theme) 'Light and Tuneful'
(K.MANSFIELD) 12.WIMBLEDON (closing mus.) 'Sporting
Occasion'*(A.STECK)* 13.RUGBY SPECIAL 'Holy Mackerel'
(B.BENNETT) 14.DARTS 'Cranes' *(D.WOOD)* 15.DERBY DAY
(R.FARNON) 16.BBC SPORTS PERSONALITY OF THE YEAR
'The Challenge' *(C.WILLIAMS)* 17.WORLD SERIES (1)
(R.FARNON) 18.SPORTSVIEW 'Saturday Sports'*(W.BURNS)*
19.CROWN GREEN BOWLS 'Soul Riff' *(Douglas WOOD)* 20.
INTERNATIONAL SPORTS MARCH *(S.TORCH)* 21.WORLD OF
SPORT 'World Of Sport March'*(D.HARPER)* 22.ATHLETICS
'World Series'(2) *(K.MANSFIELD)* 23.GRANDSTAND radio
(R.FARNON) 24.SPORTS REPORT 'Out Of The Blue' *(H.
BATH)* 25.GOODWOOD GALOP *(R.FARNON)* 26.SPORTSMASTER
(R.BUSBY) 27.SUPERSTARS 'Heavy Action' *(J.PEARSON)*
28.THE BIG MATCH *(K.MANSFIELD)* 29.TOUR DE FRANCE
(radio) *(E.WHITE)* 30.FOOTBALL FANFARE *(R.BURNETT)*

123.GREAT WAR THEMES - Various Artists
E2-MCI (DISC-THE): ETDCD 038 (CD)   *1999*
BATTLE OF BRITAIN-A BRIDGE TOO FAR-THE DAM BUSTERS-
LAWRENCE OF ARABIA-SPITFIRE PRELUDE *(BATTLE OF
BRITAIN)* RIDE OF THE VALKYRIE *(APOCALYPSE NOW)*-MASH
CAVATINA *(DEERHUNTER)* COLDITZ-COCKLESHELL HEROES-
COLONEL BOGIE *(BRIDGE ON THE RIVER KWAI)*-VICTORY AT
SEA-633 SQUADRON-LONGEST DAY-ACES HIGH *(BATTLE OF
BRITAIN)*-GUNS OF NAVARONE-THE GREAT ESCAPE

124.GREGORY John - SIX MILLION DOLLAR TV THEMES
SPECTRUM (UNIV): 544 258-2 (CD) *2000*
1.MISSION IMPOSSIBLE 2.THE ROCKFORD FILES 3.CANNON
4.SOFTLY SOFTLY 5.COLUMBO 6.M SQUAD 7.IRONSIDE 8.
GRIFF 9.THE UNTOUCHABLES 10.MANNIX 11.ROUTE 66 12.
MacMILLAN AND WIFE 13.HARRY O 14.STREETS OF SAN
FRANCISCO 15.SIX MILLION DOLLAR MAN 16.HAWAII 5-0
17.IT TAKES A THIEF 18.THEME FROM SWAT 19.I SPY 20.
McCLOUD 21.PERRY MASON 22.THE NAME OF THE GAME 23.
BANACEK 24.JOHNNY STACCATO 25.POLICEWOMAN 26.THE
SWEENEY 27.THE AVENGERS 28.KOJAK

125.HAMMER COMEDY FILM MUSIC COLLECTION - Var.Artists
GDI (ABM): GDICD 004 (CD) *1999*
Themes and music cues from ON THE BUSES-MUTINY ON
THE BUSES-HOLIDAY ON THE BUSES-LOVE THY NEIGHBOUR-
UP THE CREEK-MAN ABOUT THE HOUSE-GEORGE AND MILDRED
FURTHER UP THE CREEK-NEAREST & DEAREST-RISING DAMP-
I ONLY ARSKED!-THAT'S YOUR FUNERAL

126.HAMMER FILM MUSIC COLLECTION VOLUME 1 - Var.Artists
GDI (ABM): GDICD 002 (CD) *1998*
1.THE DEVIL RIDES OUT *(comp: JAMES BERNARD)* 2.TWINS
OF EVIL *(HARRY ROBINSON)* 3.THE MUMMY *(FRANZ REIZENS
TEIN)* 4.CAPTAIN KRONOS VAMPIRE HUNTER *(LAURIE JOHNS
ON)* 5.DRACULA *(J.BERNARD)* 6.MOON ZERO TWO *DON ELLIS*
7.FRANKENSTEIN MUST BE DESTROYED *(JAMES BERNARD)* 8.
WHEN DINOSAURS RULED THE EARTH *(MARIO NASCIMBENE)*
9.KISS OF THE VAMPIRE *(J.BERNARD)* 10.GORGON *(J.BERN
ARD)*11.SCARS OF DRACULA *(J.BERNARD)* 12.HANDS OF THE
RIPPER*(CHRISTOPHER GUNNING)* 13.CURSE OF THE MUMMY'S
TOMB *(CARLO MARTELLI)* 14.VAMPIRE LOVERS *H.ROBINSON*
15.CREATURES THR WORLD FORGOT *(M.NASCIMBENE)* 16.THE
CURSE OF FRANKENSTEIN *(J.BERNARD)* 17.DOCTOR JEKYLL
AND SISTER HYDE *(DAVID WHITAKER)* 18.LUST FOR A VAMP
IRE *(H.ROBINSON)* 19.QUATERMASS AND THE PIT *TRISTRAM
CARY)* 20.COUNTESS DRACULA*(H.ROBINSON)* 21.SHE *(JAMES
BERNARD)* 22.BRIDES OF DRACULA *(MALCOLM WILLIAMSON)*
23.BLOOD FROM THE MUMMY'S TOMB *(TRISTRAM CARY)* 24.
LEGEND OF THE 7 GOLDEN VAMPIRES *(JAMES BERNARD)* 25.
TASTE THE BLOOD OF DRACULA *(JAMES BERNARD)*

127.HAMMER FILM MUSIC COLLECTION VOLUME 2 - Var.Artists
GDI (ABM): GDICD 005 (CD) *1999*
1.PLAGUE OF THE ZOMBIES *(JAMES BERNARD)* 2.TO THE
DEVIL A DAUGHTER *(PAUL GLASS)* 3.DRACULA HAS RISEN
FROM THE GRAVE *(JAMES BERNARD)* 4.QUATERMASS II
(JAMES BERNARD) 5.ABOMINABLE SNOWMAN *(HUMPHREY
SEARLE)* 6.SATANIC RITES OF DRACULA *(JOHN CACAVAS)*
7.WITCHES *(RICHARD RODNEY BENNETT)* 8.FEAR IN THE
NIGHT *(JOHN McCABE)* 9.THE PIRATES OF BLOOD RIVER
(J.HOLLINGSWORTH) 10.DRACULA AD.1972 *(MIKE VICKERS)*
11.PHANTOM OF THE OPERA *(EDWIN ASTLEY)* 12.RASPUTIN
THE MAD MONK *(DON BANKS)* 13.FRANKENSTEIN AND THE
MONSTER FROM HELL *(JAMES BERNARD)* 14.MUMMY'S SHROUD
(DON BANKS) 15.LOST CONTINENT *(GERARD SCHURMANN)* 16
VENGEANCE OF SHE *(MARIO NASCIMBENE)* 17.HOUND OF THE

BASKERVILLES *(JAMES BERNARD)* 18.VAMPIRE CIRCUS
(DAVID WHITAKER) 19.DEMONS OF THE MIND *(HARRY
ROBINSON)* 20.EVIL OF FRANKENSTEIN *(DON BANKS)* 21.
FRANKENSTEIN CREATED WOMAN *(JAMES BERNARD)* 22.CURSE
OF THE WEREWOLF *(BENJAMIN FRANKEL)* 23.SLAVE GIRLS
(CARLO MARTELLI) 24.CRESCENDO *(MALCOLM WILLIAMSON)*
25.ONE MILLION YEARS BC *(MARIO NASCIMBENE)*

128.HAMMERSTEIN II Oscar - **Legacy Volume 1: Operettas**
PEARL (Pavilion): GEM 0131 *(CD)* 2001
Music and songs from: MUSIC IS IN THE AIR-NEW MOON-
ROSE MARIE-THE DESERT SONG-GIVE US THE NIGHT-THE
THREE SISTERS-THE NIGHT IS YOUNG-THE GREAT WALTZ
Artists: JEANNETE McDONALD-NELSON EDDY-JAN KIEPURA
*EVELYN LAYE-STANLEY HOLLOWAY-LAWRENCE TIBBETT-HARRY
WELCHMAN & EDITH DAY-MARY ELLIS and RICHARD TAUBER*

129.HAMMERSTEIN II Oscar - **Legacy Volume 2: Musicals**
PEARL (Pavilion): GEM 0132 *(CD)* 2001
Music and songs from: STATE FAIR-SHOW BOAT-HIGH AND
WIDE-CAROUSEL-CENTENNIAL SUMMER-SOUTH PACIFIC-
OKLAHOMA-ROBERTA-VERY WARM FOR MAY-SWEET ADELINE
Artists: DICK HAYMES-TONY MARTIN-FRANCES LANGFORD-
*ELLA FITZGERALD-FRANK SINATRA-ELIZABETH WELCH-PAUL
ROBESON-MARY MARTIN-BING CROSBY-HELEN FORREST-TOMMY
DORSEY-VIC DAMONE-JUDY GARLAND*

--- **HANNA-BARBERA** - see **TUNES FROM THE TOONS**

130.HARLE John - **SILENCIUM: SONGS OF THE SPIRIT**
ARGO-DECCA (UNIV): 458 356-2 *(CD)* 1997
1.MORNING PRAYER 2.SPIRITU *(BABY IT'S YOU,C4)* 3.AIR
AND ANGELS 4.FAMILY OF LOVE 5.LACRIMOSAM *(BUTTERFLY
KISS)* 6.ASTREA *(NISSAN AD)* 7.SCHOOL OF MYSTERIES
(DEFENCE OF THE REALM,BBC1) 8.LIGHT *(HMS BRILLIANT,
BBC1)* 9.HYMN TO THE SUN 10.VICES & VIRTUES 11.NIGHT
FLIGHT 12.SILENCIUM *(SILENT WITNESS theme, BBC1)*
John Harle composer/solo saxoph. Silencium Ensemble
Catherine Bott-Sarah Leonard-Nicole Tibbels (sop's)
Alexander Balanescu (viola) Paul Clarvis (perc) and
Choristers Worcester Cathedral,Academy of St.Martin
in The Fields, Children from New Brighton PS.Wirral

131.HATCH Tony - **The Best of Tony Hatch**
SEQUEL-CASTLE (Pinn): NEMCD 920 *(CD)* 1996
1.NAKED CITY THEME *(May)* 2.JOANNA *(Hatch-Trent)* 3.
DICK POWELL THEATRE THEME *(Gilbert)* 4.SOUL COAXING
Polnareff) 5.MONDO KANE THEME (MORE) *(Ortolani-Oliv
iero-Newell)* 6.MUSIC TO WATCH GIRLS BY *Velona-Ramin*
7.CROSSROADS THEME *(Hatch)* 8.DOWNTOWN *(Hatch)* 9.MAN
ALIVE THEME *(Hatch)* 10.THE DOCTORS THEME *(Hatch)* 11
SPORTSNIGHT THEME *(Hatch)*12.SOUNDS OF THE SEVENTIES
(Hatch) 13.MEMORIES OF SUMMER (LOVE STORY THEME-TV)
(Hatch) 14.AN OCCASIONAL MAN *(Martin-Blane)* 15.THE
CHAMPIONS THEME *(Hatch)* 16.CALL ME *(Hatch)* 17.EMMER
DALE THEME *(Hatch)* 18.BIRDS *(Hatch)* 19.HADLEIGH *(Ha
tch)* 20.MAORI *(Hatch)* 21.MR.& MRS. (BE NICE TO EACH
OTHER) *(Hatch-Trent)* Jackie Trent 22.WHILE THE CITY

SLEEPS *(Hatch-Trent)* 23.WILLOW WALTZ (TIM FRAZER'S
THEME) *(Watters)* 24.BEST IN FOOTBALL *(Hatch)* 25.
DEVIL'S HERD Anthony *(Hatch)* 26.THE SURREY WITH THE
FRINGE ON THE TOP*(Rodgers-Hammerstein)* 27.LA PALOMA
Yradier*(Hatch)* 28.THE WORLD AT WAR *(Davis)* 29.A MAN
AND A WOMAN*(Lai-Barouh)* 30.OUT OF THIS WORLD*(Siday)*
132.HELLO CHILDREN EVERYWHERE: TOP BBC CHILDREN'S TUNES
BBC Worldwide (Koch UK): 33636-2 (CD) -4 (MC) 1997
1.POSTMAN PAT Ken Barrie 2.BLUE PETER *BARNACLE BILL*
orig theme Sydney Torch Orch 3.BERTHA Ken Barrie 4.
4.FIREMAN SAM Maldwyn Pope 5.HEADS AND TAILS Derek
Griffith 6.CHIGLEY Freddie Phillips & Brian Cant 7.
HENRY'S CAT Peter Shade 8.JIM'LL FIX ITDavid Mindel
9.MOP & SMIFF Mike Amatt 10.PLAY AWAY Lionel Morton
11.RAGTIME Fred Harris-Maggie Henderson 12.TRUMPTON
13.RUBOVIA 14.CAMBERWICK GREEN Freddie Phillips 15.
SUPERTED 16.RECORD BREAKERS Roy Castle 17.TOYTOWN
18.SWAP SHOP B.A.Robertson 19.WILLOW THE WISP 20._
20.ROOBARB 21.MAGIC ROUNDABOUT
133.HERRMANN Bernard - At FOX Volume 1
VARESE (Pinn): VSD 6052 (CD)   *1999*
Suites from: TENDER IS THE NIGHT (1961); A HATFUL
OF RAIN (1957); MAN IN THE GREY FLANNEL SUIT (1956)
134.HERRMANN Bernard - At FOX Volume 2
VARESE (Pinn): VSD 6053 (CD)   *1999*
Complete Suites from: GARDEN OF EVIL (1954);
PRINCE OF PLAYERS (1955); MAN IN THE GREY FLANNEL
SUIT (1956); KING OF THE KHYBER RIFLES (1953)
135.HERRMANN Bernard - CITIZEN KANE: The Essential
Bernard Herrmann Film Collection - Various Artists
SILVA SCREEN (Koch): FILMXCD 308 (2CD)   *1999*
SYMPHONIC THEMES AND SUITES FROM:- CAPE FEAR-PSYCHO
NAKED AND THE DEAD-THE TROUBLE WITH HARRY-JASON AND
T.ARGONAUTS-TWILIGHT ZONE-SEVENTH VOYAGE OF SINBAD-
CITIZEN KANE-DAY THE EARTH STOOD STILL-GHOST AND
MRS.MUIR-OBSESSION-SNOWS OF KILLIMANJARO-VERTIGO-
THE MAN WHO KNEW TOO MUCH-THREE WORLDS OF GULLIVER-
NORTH BY NORTHWEST-ON DANGEROUS GROUND-TAXI DRIVER-
MYSTERIOUS ISLAND + rejected score for TORN CURTAIN
136.HERRMANN Bernard - PARTNERSHIP IN TERROR: HITCHCOCK
City Of Prague Philharmonic conduct: Paul Bateman
SILVA SCREEN (Koch): SILVAD 3010 (CD)   *1996*
PSYCHO-NORTH BY NORTHWEST-MARNIE-MAN WHO KNEW TOO
MUCH-TROUBLE WITH HARRY-VERTIGO-TORN CURTAIN (rej)
137.HESS Nigel - TV Themes with LONDON FILM ORCHESTRA
plus CHAMELEON and Royal Shakespeare Comp.Ensemble
CHANDOS (Chandos): CHAN 9750 (CD)   *1999*
1.HETTY WAINTHROP INVESTIGATES 2.BADGER 3.THE
ONE GAME "Saylon Dola" Chameleon 4.WYCLIFFE 5.WOMAN
OF SUBSTANCE 6.SUMMER'S LEASE "Carmina Valles"
Chameleon 7.DANGERFIELD 8.JUST WILLIAM 9.
EVERY WOMAN KNOWS A SECRET 10.PERFECT SCOUNDRELS
11.ANNA OF THE FIVE TOWNS 12.CAMPION 13.MAIGRET
(1992) 14.VIDAL IN VENICE 15.CLASSIC ADVENTURE 16.

ALL PASSION SPENT 17.CHIMERA "Rosheen Du" Chameleon
18.TESTAMENT 19.VANITY FAIR 20.AFFAIR IN MIND 21.
LONDON EMBASSY 22.ATLANTIS 23.A HUNDRED ACRES 24.
GROWING PAINS 25.US GIRLS 26.TITMUSS REGAINED 27.
AN IDEAL HUSBAND

*138.*HISTORY OF HORROR from NOSFERATU to the SIXTH SENSE
SILVA CLASSICS (Koch): FILMXCD 331 (2CD) *2000*
1.NOSFERATU 2.PHANTOM OF THE OPERA 3.THE BRIDE OF
FRANKENSTEIN 4.THE THING 5.GODZILLA 6.DRACULA 7.THE
HORRORS OF THE BLACK MUSEUM 8.THE HAUNTING 9.THE
DEVIL RIDES OUT 10.TASTE THE BLOOD OF DRACULA 11.
EXORCIST 12.YOUNG FRANKENSTEIN 13.OMEN 14.SUSPIRIA
15.HALLOWEEN 15.ALIEN 16.THE SHINING 17.DRESSED TO
KILL 18.POLTERGEIST 19.NIGHTMARE ON ELM STREET 20.
HELLRAISER 21.BRAM STOKER'S DRACULA 22.THE HAUNTING
23.NINTH GATE 24.SIXTH SENSE 25.THE LIGHTHOUSE 26.
FRANKENSTEIN UNBOUND 27.PEEPING TOM

*139.*HIT TV - Television's Top Themes - Various Artists
VARESE (Pinn): VSD 5957 (CD) *1999*
tracks include X-FILES, E.R., FRASIER, ALLY McBEAL,
SOUTH PARK, FRIENDS

*140.*HITCHCOCK Alfred - ALFRED HITCHCOCK 100 YEARS
Royal Philharmonic Orchestra cond: Elmer BERNSTEIN
RCA (BMG IMPT): 74321 71000-2 (CD) *2000*
1.PSYCHO *Suite* 2.VERTIGO *Sce d'amour* 3.MAN WHO KNEW
TOO MUCH *CANTATA/STORM CLOUDS* 4.NORTH BY NORTHWEST
PRELUDE 6.THE WRONG MAN *PRELUDE* 7.PSYCHO *THE MURDER
1999 Remix* 8.THE BRIDE WORE BLACK *MUSICAL SCENARIO*
9.FAHRENHEIT *FINALE (THE BOOK PEOPLE)* 10.BERNARD
HERMANN (Interview) *(on a composer's responsibilty)*

*141.*HITCHCOCK Alfred - DIAL M FOR MURDER
Czech Symphony Orchestra conducted by Paul Bateman
SILVA SCREEN (Koch): FILMCD 137 (CD) *1993*
New Digital Recordings Of Suites From A.H.Films
DIAL M FOR MURDER *(composed by DIMITRI TIOMKIN)*
UNDER CAPRICORN *(RICHARD ADDINSELL)* TOPAZ *(MAURICE
JARRE)* REBECCA and SUSPICION *(FRANZ WAXMAN)* SPELLB
OUND *(MIKLOS ROZSA)* VERTIGO-NORTH BY NORTHWEST-MAR
NIE-PSYCHO *(BERNARD HERRMANN)* FRENZY *(RON GOODWIN)*

*142.*HITCHCOCK Alfred - MASTER OF MAYHEM
San Diego Symphony Orch.conducted by Lalo Schifrin
SION (Direct): SION 18170 (CD) *1997*
1.INVISIBLE THIRD:Overture 2.ALFRED HITCHCOCK THEME
3.VERTIGO:Suite 4.MARNIE:Suite 5.PSYCHO:Intro/The
Murder/City) 6.REBECCA:Suite 7.REAR WINDOW:Intro/
Rhumba/The Ballet/The Finale 8.ROLLERCOASTER:Theme
9.BULLITT 10.MANNIX:Theme 11.DIRTY HARRY:Suite 12.
MISSION IMPOSSIBLE: Plot/Theme * cond Lalo Schifrin

*143.*HITCHCOCK Alfred - MOVIE THRILLERS
London Philharmonic Orchestra cond.Bernard Herrmann
DECCA PHASE 4 (UNIV): 443 895-2 (CD) reissued 1996
Suites from: PSYCHO / MARNIE / NORTH BY NORTHWEST
VERTIGO / 'A Portrait Of Hitch' : NIGHTMARE / THE
TROUBLE WITH HARRY * conducted by Bernard Herrmann

**144.HITCHCOCK Alfred - PSYCHO: THE ESSENTIAL ALFRED H.
City Of Prague Philharmonic cond. by Paul Bateman**
SILVA SCREEN: FILMXCD 320 (2CDs) *1999*
THE THIRTY NINE STEPS-THE LADY VANISHES-REBECCA-
SUSPICION-LIFEBOAT-SPELLBOUND-ROPE-UNDER CAPRICORN-
STAGE FRIGHT-STRANGERS ON A TRAIN-DIAL M FOR MURDER
REAR WINDOW-TO CATCH A THIEF-THE TROUBLE WITH HARRY
T.MAN WHO KNEW TOO MUCH-VERTIGO-NORTH BY NORTHWEST-
PSYCHO-MARNIE-TORN CURTAIN-TOPAZ-FRENZY-FAMILY PLOT
HITCHCOCK TV THEME (Funeral March Of A Marionette)

**145.HOLDRIDGE Lee - The Film Music Of Lee Holdridge
London Symphony Orchestra conduct: Charles Gerhardt**
CITADEL (Hot): STC 77103 (CD) *1992*
WIZARDS AND WARRIORS (Overture)-SPLASH (Love Theme)
GREAT WHALES (Introduction & Theme)-HEMINGWAY PLAY
(Parisian Sketch)-GOING HOME(The Journey)-THE BEAST
MASTER (Suite) JONATHAN LIVINGSTON SEAGULL (Music
For Strings) - EAST OF EDEN (Suite)

146.HOLLYWOOD HEROES - City Of Prague Philharmonic Orch
(Paul Bateman/Nic Raine/Kenn.Alwyn/Derek Wadsworth)
SILVA SCREEN Treasury (Koch): SILVAD 3501 (CD) 1997
1:GREAT ESCAPE *(E.BERNSTEIN)* 2:DANCES WITH WOLVES
(J.BARRY) 3:RAIDERS OF THE LOST ARK *(J.WILLIAMS)* 4:
HIGH ROAD TO CHINA *(J.BARRY)* 5:MAD MAX III BEYOND
THUNDERDOME *(M.JARRE)* 6:THE ALAMO *(D.TIOMKIN)* 7:
BORN ON THE 4TH OF JULY *(J.WILLIAMS)* 8:EL CID *(M.
ROZSA)* 9:ZULU *(J.BARRY)* 10:OUT OF AFRICA *(J.BARRY)*
11:OUTLAW JOSEY WALES *(J.FIELDING)* 12:TORN CURTAIN
(J.ADDISON) 13:ROBIN AND MARIAN *(JOHN BARRY)* 14:
CLIFFHANGER *(T.JONES)*

147.HOLLYWOOD GOES TO WAR City Of Prague Philharmonic
SILVA SCREEN (Koch): FILMXCD 333 (2CD) *2000*
BUCCANEER-GETTYSBURG-FRIENDLY PERSUASION-GLORY-SGT.
YORK-PATHS OF GLORY-BLUE MAX-NAKED AND THE DEAD-IN
HARMS WAY-MIDWAY-MACARTHUR-PATTON-LONGEST DAY-GREAT
ESCAPE-SAVING PRIVATE RYAN-BATTLE OF THE BULGE-THE
BRIDGE AT REMAGEN-SCHINDLER'S LIST-EMPIRE OF T.SUN-
SHARKFIGHTERS-MOUNTAIN ROAD-CAINE MUTINY-M*A*S*H*-
BORN ON T.FOURTH OF JULY-CASUALTIES OF WAR-PLATOON-
DR.STRANGELOVE-RAMBO 1-RAMBO 2-HUNT FOR RED OCTOBER

148.HORNER James Essential James Horner Film Music Coll
SILVA SCREEN (Koch): FILMXCD 197 (2CD) *1998*
GLORY-STAR TREK 2-RANSOM-LEGENDS OF THE FALL-THE
ROCKETEER-BRAVEHEART-RED HEAT-APOLLO 13-COCOON-THE
LAND BEFORE TIME-WILLOW-PATRIOT GAMES-NAME OF THE
ROSE-COMMANDO-FIELD OF DREAMS-DEEP IMPACT-TITANIC

149.HORNER James - Titanic and Other Film Scores
VARESE (Pinn): VSD 5943 (CD) 1998 TITANIC-APOLLO 13
CASPER-COURAGE UNDER FIRE-ONCE AROUND-COCOON: THE
RETURN-STAR TREK II-ALIENS-BRAINSTORM-BRAVEHEART

150.HORROR! - Monsters Witches and Vampires / Var.Orch
SILVA SCREEN Treasury (Koch): SILVAD 3507 (CD) 1997
1:OMEN *(J.GOLDSMITH)* 2:BRIDE OF FRANKENSTEIN *(Franz
WAXMAN)* 3:DRACULA *(J.BERNARD)* 4:TASTE THE BLOOD OF

DRACULA *(J.BERNARD)* 5:DRACULA HAS RISEN FROM THE
GRAVE *(J.BERNARD)* 6:HORRORS OF THE BLACK MUSEUM *(G.
SCHURMANN)* 7:HALLOWEEN *(J.CARPENTER)* 8:PRINCE OF DA
RKNESS *(J.CARPENTER)* 9:THEY LIVE *(CARPENTER-HOWARTH)*
10:WITCHFINDER GENERAL *(P.FERRIS)* 11:DEVIL RIDES
OUT *(J.BERNARD)* 12:HUNGER (Flower Duet from Lakme)
(DELIBES, sung by Lesley Garrett*)* 13:CURSE OF THE
WEREWOLF *(B.FRANKEL)* 14:VAMPIRE CIRCUS *(D.WHITAKER)*

151.HORROR! - Westminster Philharm.Orch (Kenneth Alwyn)
SILVA SCREEN (Koch): FILMCD 175 (CD)   *1996*
HORRORS OF THE BLACK MUSEUM *(GERARD SCHURMANN 1959)*
THE HAUNTING *HUMPHREY SEARLE 63)* CORRIDORS OF BLOOD
(BUXTON ORR 62) NIGHT OF THE DEMON *(CLIFTON PARKER
1957)* ABOMINABLE SNOWMAN *(HUMPHREY SEARLE 1957)* THE
WITCHFINDER GENERAL *(PAUL FERRIS 1968)* CURSE OF THE
MUMMY'S TOMB *(CARLO MARTELLI 64)* KONGA *(GERARD SCHU
RMANN 1961)* FIEND WITHOUT A FACE *(BUXTON ORR 1957)*
THE DEVIL RIDES OUT *(JAMES BERNARD 1968)* THE CURSE
OF THE WEREWOLF *(BENJAMIN FRANKEL 1961)*

152.IN SESSION: A FILM MUSIC CELEBRATION Var.Orchestras
VARESE (Pinn): VSD 6225-2 (2CD)   *2001*
New recordings by Royal Scottish National Orchestra
2001 A SPACE ODYSSEY-REBECCA-CITIZEN KANE-ANNA AND
THE KING-THAT HAMILTON WOMAN-CAPTAIN FROM CASTILLE-
STREETCAR NAMED DESIRE-VIVA ZAPATA-THE TROUBLE WITH
HARRY-PEYTON PLACE-VERTIGO-7TH VOYAGE OF SINBAD-THE
TWILIGHT ZONE-PSYCHO-THE DUEL-TO KILL A MOCKINGBIRD
BREAKFAST AT TIFFANY'S-MARNIE-HAMLET-AGONY AND THE
ECSTACY-SAND PEBBLES-WHO'S AFRAID OF VIRGINIA WOOLF
BORN FREE-FAHRENHEIT 451-PATTON-TORA TORA TORA-JAWS
MIDWAY-SUPERMAN THE MOVIE-STAR TREK THE MOTION PICT
URE-SOMEWHERE IN TIME-BODY HEAT-OUT OF AFRICA-STAR
WARS-PLATOON-TARAS BULBA

--- **JAMES BOND** - *see* BOND James

153.JARRE Maurice: Essential Maurice Jarre Film Music
Collection / City Of Prague Philharmonic
SILVA SCREEN (Koch): FILMXCD 324 (2CD)   *2000*
FATAL ATTRACTION-NO WAY OUT-JESUS OF NAZARETH-GHOST
VILLA RIDES-MAD MAX 3-TOPAZ-YEAR OF LIVING DANGEROU
SLY-IS PARIS BURNING-EL CONDOR-PROFESSIONALS-ENEMY
MINE-NIGHT OF THE GENERALS-MAN WHO WOULD BE KING-
TIN DRUM-DOCTOR ZHIVAGO-LAWRENCE OF ARABIA-RYAN'S
DAUGHTER-A PASSAGE TO INDIA-WITNESS-MOSQUITO COAST

154.JARRE Maurice - DOCTOR ZHIVAGO: Classic Film Music
City Of Prague Philharmon.Orchestra (Paul Bateman)
SILVA SCREEN (Koch): FILMCD 158 (CD)   *1995*
DOCTOR ZHIVAGO-A PASSAGE TO INDIA-RYAN'S DAUGHTER-
LAWRENCE OF ARABIA-GHOST-WITNESS-IS PARIS BURNING-
THE NIGHT OF THE GENERALS-THE MAN WHO WOULD BE KING
FATAL ATTRACTION-VILLA RIDES-THE FIXER-EL CONDOR-
suite from JESUS OF NAZARETH

155.JAZZ CLUB The Very Best Of - Various Artists
GLOBAL TV (BMG): RADCD 87 (2CD) RADMC 87 (MC   2000
1.GREEN ONIONS *(SHELL)* Booker T.& MGs 2.COMPARED TO

155.JAZZ CLUB The Very Best Of - Various Artists
GLOBAL TV (BMG): RADCD 87 (2CD) RADMC 87 (MC 2000
1.GREEN ONIONS *(SHELL)* Booker T.& MGs 2.COMPARED TO
WHAT *(CASINO/BOOGIE NIGHTS/ICE STORM)* Eddie Haris &
Les McCann 3.WHAT'D I SAY *(HEATWAVE/TOMMY BOY)* Ray
Charles 4.COMIN' HOME *(IRON GIANT)* Mel Torme 5.WADE
IN THE WATER Ramsay Lewis 6.HARD AT WORK John Hanby
7.IN-CROWD *(FIAT UNO)* Ramsay Lewis 8.YEH YEH *(FUNNY
BONES)* John Hendricks 9.GOT MY MOJO WORKING Jimmy
Smith 10.SOUL BOSSA NOVA *NIKE* Quincy Jones 11.
SHULIE A BOP Sarah Vaughan 12.TAKE THE A TRAIN
(RADIO DAYS/EUROPA) Ella Fitzgerald 13.MACK THE
KNIFE *SWING/BUTCHER BOY)* Ella Fitzgerald 14.SO WHAT
(PLEASANTVILLE) Miles Davis 15.TAKE 5 *FORD/CADBURY)*
Dave Brubeck 16.MOANIN' *(TETLEY BITTER)* Art Blakey
17.SIDEWINDER Lee Morgan 18.HIT THE ROAD JACK *(THE
FISHER KING/SPEECHLESS)* Wild Bill Davies 19.CERVEZA
(BOX OF MOONLIGHT) Boots Browm & His Blockbusters
20.PINK PANTHER THEME Henry Mancini 21.WATERMELON
MAN *(OUT OF SIGHT)* Mongo Santamaria 22.JIVE SAMBA
(BACARDI) Cannonball Adderley 23.FEVER *(CADBURY/
IMPULSE)* Peggy Lee 24.CHITLINS CON CARNE *(I WENT
DOWN)* Kenny Burrell 25.MY BABY JUST CARES FOR ME
(CHANEL NO.5/OVALTINE) Nina Simone

156.JOHNSON Laurie The Professional (Best Of L.Johnson)
REDIAL (UNIVERS.): 557 210-2 (CD) 1998
THE AVENGERS-DOCTOR STRANGELOVE-THIS IS YOUR LIFE-
WHEN THE KISSING HAD TO STOP-TIGER BAY-SHIRLEY'S
WORLD-CAESAR SMITH-HOT MILLIONS-THE PROFESSIONALS-
JASON KING-NEW AVENGERS-AVENGERS TAG SCENE-LADY AND
THE HIGHWAYMAN-HAZARD OF HEARTS-A DUEL OF HEARTS-
GHOST IN MONTE CARLO-FOUR MUSKETEERS-THE FIRST MEN
IN THE MOON-ROMANCE-I AIM AT THE STARS-ANIMAL MAGIC
FREEWHEELERS-BOLERO-AVENGERS (Re-mix)

157.JOHNSON, Laurie...With A Vengeance
SEQUEL-CASTLE (Pinn): NEMCD 935(CD) 1997 1.AVENGERS
2.TOP SECRET 3.DR.STRANGELOVE 4.NO HIDING PLACE 5.
BEAUTY JUNGLE 6.DOIN'THE RACOON 7.ECHO FOUR-TWO 8.
M1 (M-ONE) 9.SOLO 10.CITY 11.LIMEHOUSE 12.WEST END
13.LATIN QUARTER 14.GRAND CENTRAL 15.TIMES SQUARE
16.SOUTH BEACH 17.SEVENTH AVANUE 18.STICK OR TWIST
19.DRUM CRAZY 20.MINOR BOSSA NOVA 21.DEAR FRIEND 22
HEATWAVE 23.TWANGO 24.WINTER WONDERLAND 25.HOE DOWN
26.THE DEPUTY 27.DONKEY SERENADE-28.SPRING SPRING
SPRING 29.CHAKA 30.SABRE DANCE *see also COLLECT 294*

158.JOHNSON Laurie - **THE ROSE AND THE GUN** - Music Of LJ
FLY-U.Kanch (H.Mundi-FLY Dir): FLYCD 103 1992
LADY AND THE HIGHWAYMAN (TVM 89)-A HAZARD OF HEARTS
(TVM 87)-A DUEL OF HEARTS (TVM 88)-A GHOST IN MONTE
CARLO (TVM 90)-THE AVENGERS (Theme/Tag)-THE NEW AVE
NGERS-TIGER BAY THEME-WHEN THE KISSING HAD TO STOP
CAESAR SMITH/THERE IS ANOTHER SONG/THIS TIME (from:
Hot Millions)-SHIRLEY'S THEME/RICKSHAW RIDE (from:
Shirley's World)-I AIM AT THE STARS Theme-THIS IS

YOUR LIFE (Gala Performance)-JASON KING theme-ROMAN
CE (The First Men In The Moon)-THE PROFESSIONALS
LONDON STUDIO SYMPHONY ORCHESTRA (Laurie Johnson)

159.**KAMEN Michael** - The Michael Kamen SOUNDTRACK Album
DECCA-POLYGRAM: 458 912-2 (CD) -4 (MC)   1998
extracts: ROBIN HOOD PRINCE OF THIEVES-MR.HOLLAND'S
OPUS-DON JUAN DE MARCO AND THE CENTREFOLD-CIRCLE OF
FRIENDS-CRUSOE-HIGHLANDER-NEXT MAN-WINTER GUEST-DIE
HARD-EDGE OF DARKNESS-BRAZIL *feat:* Kate Bush (voc)
Seattle Symphony Orch and London Metropolitan Orch

160.**KORNGOLD Erich Wolfgang** - The Warner Bros Years
EMI ODEON: CDODEON 13   1996
CAPTAIN BLOOD-GREEN PASTURES-ANTHONY ADVERSE-PRINCE
AND THE PAUPER-ADVENTURES OF ROBIN HOOD-JAUREZ-THE
PRIVATE LIVES OF ELIZABETH & ESSEX-SEA HAWK-THE SEA
WOLF-KINGS ROW-CONSTANT NYMPH-DEVOTION-BETWEEN TWO
WORLDS-OF HUMAN BONDAGE-ESCAPE ME NEVER-DECEPTION

--- **KUBRICK Stanley** - *see* DR.STRANGELOVE

161.**LADYKILLERS The** - Music From Glorious EALING Films
Royal Ballet Sinfonia conducted by Kenneth Alwyn
SILVA SCREEN (Koch): FILMCD 177 (CD)   1997
THE MAN IN THE WHITE SUIT *(1951-BENJAMIN FRANKEL)*
PASSPORT TO PIMLICO *(1949-GEORGES AURIC)*
THE TITFIELD THUNDERBOLT *(1952-GEORGES AURIC)*
THE LAVENDER HILL MOB *(1951-GEORGES AURIC)* THE
CRUEL SEA *(1953-ALAN RAWSTHORNE)* THE CAPTIVE HEART
(1946-ALAN RAWSTHORNE) SARABAND FOR DEAD LOVERS
(1948-ALAN RAWSTHORNE) WHISKY GALORE *(1949-ERNEST
IRVING)* KIND HEARTS AND CORONETS *(1949-MOZART)*
THE MAN IN THE SKY *(1956-GERARD SCHURMANN)* THE
LADYKILLERS *(1955-TRISTRAM CARY)* THE OVERLANDERS
(1946-JOHN IRELAND)

162.**LAI Francis** - Great Film Themes
PRESTIGE (Pinn):CDPC 5001 (CD)   o.1990 reiss 2001
BILITIS-LOVE STORY-THE BLUE ROSE-EMOTION-HAPPY NEW
YEAR-LOVE IN THE RAIN-SEDUCTION-IMTIMATE MOMENTS-
PAR LE SANG DES AUTRES-A MAN AND A WOMAN-LIVE FOR
LIFE-AFRICAN SUMMER-SUR NOTRE ETOILE-LA RONDE-LES
UNES ET LES AUTRES-SMIC SMAC-SOLITUDE-WHITECHAPEL

163.**LANZA Mario** - MY ROMANCE
RCA VICTOR (BMG): 09026 63751-2 (CD)   2001
1.ALL THE THINGS YOU ARE *VERY WARM FOR MAY* 2.A KISS
/THE SONG IS YOU *MUSIC IN THE AIR* 3.WHERE OR WHEN
BABES IN ARMS 4.LOVE IS THE SWEETEST THING *SAY IT
WITH MUSIC* 5.I'LL SEE YOU AGAIN *BITTER SWEET* 6.
NIGHT AND DAY *GAY DIVORCE* 7.YOUR EYES HAVE TOLD ME
SO 8.THEY DIDN'T BELIEVE ME *GIRL FROM UTAH* 9.IF I
LOVED YOU *CAROUSEL* 10.ONLY A ROSE *VAGABOND KING* 11.
YOU AND THE NIGHT AND THE MUSIC *REVENGE WITH MUSIC*
12.SYLVIA 13.ON THE STREET WHERE YOU LIVE *MY FAIR
LADY* 14.FOOLS RUSH IN 15.BEAUTIFUL LOVE 16.I'VE GOT
YOU UNDER MY SKIN *BORN TO DANCE* 17.LONG AGO AND FAR
AWAY 18.YOU ARE LOVE *SHOWBOAT* 19.I'LL BE SEEING YOU
ROYAL PALM REVUE 20.MY ROMANCE

164.LANZA Mario - THE ULTIMATE COLLECTION
RCA VICTOR (BMG): 74321 18574-2 (CD) -4 (MC)   1994
BE MY LOVE-DRINK DRINK DRINK-LA DONNA E MOBILE-AVE
MARIA-DANNY BOY-GRENADA-BECAUSE YOU'RE MINE-THE LOV
ELIEST NIGHT OF THE YEAR-VALENCIA-SONG OF INDIA-THE
DONKEY SERENADE-BECAUSE-O SOLE MIO-VESTI LA GIUBBA-
SERENADE-FUNICULI FUNICULA-GOLDEN DAYS-ARRIVERDERCI
ROMA-YOU'LL NEVER WALK ALONE-BELOVED-COME PRIMA-E
LUCEVAN LE STELLE-SANTA LUCIA-I'LL WALK WITH GOD

165.LAUREL & HARDY - LEGENDS OF THE 20TH CENTURY
EMI: 522 816-2 (CD) Orig Dialogue and Music   *1999*
1.LAUREL & HARDY Theme music "DANCE OF THE CUCKOOS"
(Marvin T.Hatley) 2.FRESH FISH *from TOWED IN A HOLE*
3.FURNITURE PAYMENT *(THICKER THAN WATER)* 4.THE GAY
CAVIARS *(SWISS MISS)* 5.WHAT FLAVOURS HAVE YOU *(COME
CLEAN)* 6.HIGHER ENDEAVORS *(THEIR FIRST MISTAKE)* 7.
MISTAKEN IDENTITY *(PARDON US)* 8.THE TRAIL OF THE
LONESOME PINE *(WAY OUT WEST)* 9.LONG DISTANCE *(FIXER
UPPERS)* 10.WHEN THE MICE ARE AWAY *(HELPMATES)* 11.
DANGER BY CLOCKWORK *THICKER THAN WATER* 12.LAZY MOON
(PARDON US) 13.BIG SUCKER *(BEAU HUNKS)* 14.THERE'S A
DOLLAR *(BELOW ZERO)* 15.HARD BOILED EGGS AND NUTS
(COUNTY HOSPITAL) 16.WHERE WERE YOU BORN *(LAUREL &
HARDY MURDER CASE)* 17.OH GASTON *(BELOW ZERO)* 18.
STAGECOACH MANNERS *(WAY OUT WEST)* 19.AT THE BALL
THAT'S ALL *(WAY OUT WEST)* 20.TURN ON THE RADIO
(BUSY BODIES) 21.A CLEAN SWEEP *(DIRTY WORK)* 22.DUAL
DECEIT *(SONS OF THE DESERT)* 23.EVEN AS YOU AND I
(FIXER UPPERS) 24.COURT AGAIN *(SCRAM)* 25.WAY DOWN
SOUTH *(WAY OUT WEST)* 26.HAL ROACH-MGM PRESENTS
LAUREL & HARDY PARTS 1 & 2

166.LEGRAND Michel - Paris Was Made For Lovers
PRESTIGE (Pinn): CDPC 5001 (CD)   o.1990 reiss 2001
WINDMILLS OF YOUR MIND-SUMMER OF 42-I STILL SEE YOU
(GO-BETWEEN)-SEA AND SKY *sung by DUSTY SPRINGFIELD*-
CONCERTO FOR CABS-THE STREET WHERE THEY LIVED
WHERE LOVE BEGINS-IN LOVE IN NORMANDY-A PLACE IN PA
RIS *sung by MATT MONRO*-OLD LOVERS NEVER DIE-ON THE
ROAD (LADY IN THE CAR)-DO YOU COME HERE OFTEN-THEY
SIMPLY FADE AWAY-WHERE LOVE ENDS-PAVANNE FOR PEOPLE
PARIS WAS MADE FOR LOVERS *see also Coll 228 (1998)*

167.LLOYD WEBBER Andrew - PREMIERE COLLECTION - Encore
POLYDOR: 517 336-2 (CD) -4 (MC) -5 (DCC)   1988
MEMORY *(Barbra Streisand)* LOVE CHANGES EVERYTHING
(Michael Ball) AMIGOS PARA SIEMPRE *(Jose Carreras-
Sarah Brightman)* ANY DREAM WILL DO *(Jason Donovan)*
CLOSE EVERY DOOR *Phillip Schofield)* OH WHAT A CIRC
US *(David Essex)* POINT OF NO RETURN *(Sarah Brightm
an-Michael Crawford)* + I AM THE STARLIGHT-WISHING
YOU WERE SOMEHOW HERE AGAIN-ARGENTINE MELODY-SEEING
IS BELIEVING-JELLICLE BALL- EVERYTHING'S ALRIGHT-
FIRST MAN YOU REMEMBER-ANYTHING BUT LONELY-HOSANNA

168.LLOYD WEBBER Andrew - VERY BEST OF
REALLY USEFUL-POLY (Univ): 523 860-2 (CD)

1.MEMORY Elaine Paige 2.MUSIC OF THE NIGHT Michael
Crawford 3.TAKE THAT LOOK OFF YOUR FACE Marti Webb
4.ANY DREAM WILL DO Jason Donovan 5.DON'T CRY FOR
ME ARGENTINA Sarah Brightman 6.LOVE CHANGES EVERY
THING Michael Ball 7.I DON'T KNOW HOW TO LOVE HIM
Sarah Brightman 8.PERFECT YEAR Dina Carroll 9.THE
PHANTOM OF THE OPERA Steve Harley-Sarah Brightman
10.OH WHAT A CIRCUS David Essex 11.TELL ME ON A
SUNDAY Marti Webb 12.CLOSE EVERY DOOR Philip
Schofield 13.WITH ONE LOOK Barbra Streisand 14.
ALL I ASK OF YOU Cliff Richard-Sarah Brightman 15.
SUNSET BOULEVARD Michael Ball 16.AS IF WE NEVER
SAID GOODBYE Glenn Close 17.NEXT TIME YOU FALL IN
LOVE Riva Rice-Greg Ellis 18.AMIGOS PARA SIEMPRA
Jose Carreras-Sarah Brightman

169.LUGOSI: HOLLYWOOD'S DRACULA - Various
McWHORTER-GREENSHAW/LUGOSI (Nervous) LUG 001 (CD)
ORGAN PRELUDE from MYSTERY HOUSE-OCSKAY BRIGADEROS
SUITE-SWAN LAKE-BLACK AND TAN FANTASY-VARIATION ON
GERSHWIN'S PRELUDE-LON CHANEY'S GONNA GET YOU IF
YOU DON'T WATCH OUT-SWAN LAKE OVERTURE-BROTHER CAN
YOU SPARE A DIME-LISTEN TO THE LAMBS-WHITE ZOMBIE-
TEXACO STAR THEATRE-VARIATION ON HUNGARIAN RHAPSODY
NO.1-MAIL CALL-CHILD OF THE NIGHT-WE'RE HORRIBLE
HORRIBLE MEN-ADAPTATION OF CHOPIN'S NOCTURNE IN E.
FLAT-HUNCHBACK NAMED YGOR-DEVIL BAT-RUDY VALLEE
SHOW-SWAN LAKE ROCK-CANDID MICROPHONE-CZARDAS-THERE
ARE SUCH THINGS-LUGOSI HOLLYWOOD'S DRACULA-REPRISE

170.MANCINI Henry - IN THE PINK:- Ultimate Collection
RCA VICTOR (BMG): 74321 24283-2 (CD) -4 (MC) 1995
PINK PANTHER-MOON RIVER-DAYS OF WINE & ROSES-PETER
GUNN-CHARADE-TWO FOR T.ROAD-THORN BIRDS-LOVE STORY-
MR.LUCKY-EXPERIMENT IN TERROR-SHOT IN THE DARK-BLUE
SATIN-BABY ELEPHANT WALK-HATARI-PENNYWHISTLE JIG-
PIE IN THE FACE POLKA-MOMENT TO MOMENT-MOONLIGHT
SONATA-DEAR HEART-SHADOW OF YOUR SMILE-THE MOLLY
MAGUIRE'S THEME-SUMMER OF 42-ROMEO & JULIET-AS TIME
GOES BY-MISTY-TENDER IS THE NIGHT-EVERYTHING I DO-
MOMMIE DEAREST-RAINDROPS KEEP FALLING ON MY HEAD-
CRAZY WORLD-MONA LISA-UNCHAINED MELODY-WINDMILLS OF
YOUR MIND-TILL THERE WAS YOU-SPEEDY GONZALES-DREAM
A LITTLE DREAM OF ME-THE SWEETHEART TREE-LONESOME-
LOVE IS A MANY SPLENDORED THING-BY THE TIME I GET
TO PHOENIX-ONE FOR MY BABY-BREAKFAST AT TIFFANY'S-
-THAT OLD BLACK MAGIC-EVERGREEN-MIDNIGHT COWBOY

171.MARVIN Hank- Marvin At The Movies
UNIVERSAL MUSIC: 157 057-2 (CD) -4 (MC) 2000
1.A HARD DAY'S NIGHT 2.THE SOUND OF SILENCE 3.THE
GOOD THE BAD AND THE UGLY 4.A KISS FROM A ROSE 5.
HOW DEEP IS YOUR LOVE 6.WINDMILLS OF YOUR MIND 7.
WHEN YOU SAY NOTHING AT ALL 8.SON OF A PREACHER MAN
9.GOLDFINGER 10.A GROOVY KIND OF LOVE 11.LA BAMBA
12.THEME FROM STAR WARS 13.MY HEART WILL GO ON 14.
AIN'T NO SUNSHINE 15.LOVE IS ALL AROUND 16.JAMES

BOND MEDLEY: James Bond Theme/From Russia With Love
You Only Live Twice/We Have All The Time In The
World 17.WILL YOU REMEMBER ME
172.**MEDICS: GREAT TV DRAMA THEMES** - Various Artists
HALLMARK (ABM): 30868-2 (CD) -4 (MC)   1998
1.CASUALTY 2.ANGELS 3.M*A*S*H* 4.MARCUS WELBY MD 5.
A COUNTRY PRACTICE 6.GENERAL HOSPITAL 7.DR.FINLAY'S
CASEBOOK 8.OWEN MD 9.CHICAGO HOPE 10.E.R. 11.SAINT
ELSEWHERE 12.SHORTLAND STREET 13.WHERE THE HEART IS
14.QUINCY 15.DOCTOR KILDARE 16.CHILDREN'S HOSPITAL
17.DANGERFIELD 18.PEAK PRACTICE
--- **MISSION The** - *see* MORRICONE Ennio
173.**MONROE Marilyn** KISS + Jane Russell-Frankie Vaughan
CAMEO-TARGET (BMG): CD 3555 (CD)   1995
YOU'D BE SURPRISED-THE RIVER OF NO RETURN *(RIVER OF
NO RETURN)* I WANNA BE LOVED BY YOU-WHEN IF FALL IN
LOVE *(ONE MINUTE TO ZERO)* BYE BYE BABY-DIAMONDS ARE
A GIRL'S BEST FRIEND *(GENTLEMEN PREFER BLONDES)* ONE
SILVERDOLLAR-I'M GONNA FILE MY CLAIM-WHEN LOVE GOES
WRONG NOTHING GOES RIGHT *(GENTLEMEN PREFER BLONDES)*
AFTER YOU GET WHAT YOU WANT YOU DON'T WANT IT-MY
HEART BELONGS TO DADDY-SPECIALISATION-RUNNIN' WILD-
TWO LITTLE GIRLS FROM LITTLE ROCK-HEATWAVE *(THERE'S
NO BUSINESS LIKE SHOW BUSINESS)* KISS *(NIAGARA)*
174.**MONSTER MOVIE MUSIC ALBUM** - 'GODZILLA vs KING KONG'
City Of Prague Philharmonic Orchestra with The
Crouch End Festival Chorus (cond: NIC RAINE)
SILVA SCREEN (Koch-S.Screen): FILMCD 196 (CD) 1998
GODZILLA KING OF THE MONSTERS-DESTROY ALL MONSTERS-
GODZILLA VS MONSTER ZERO-KING KONG (3 SUITES by *MAX
STEINER,JOHN BARRY,JOHN SCOTT)*-MYSTERIOUS ISLAND-
THE LAND BEFORE TIME-WE'RE BACK: A DINOSAUR'S STORY
FLINSTONES-ONE MILLION YEARS BC-WHEN DINOSAURS
RULED THE EARTH-CREATURES THE WORLD FORGOT-THEODORE
REX-BABY: SECRET OF A LOST LEGEND
---.**MONSTER MOVIE THEMES** - *see* CREATURE FEATURES
175.**MONTENEGRO Hugo** - Best Of
RCA VICTOR (BMG): 74321 72713-2 (CD)   2000
1.COME SPY WITH ME 2.SECRET AGENT MAN 3.I-SPY
4.THUNDERBALL 5.MAN FROM UNCLE 6.JAMES BOND THEME
7.SILENCERS 8.GET SMART 9.FBI 10.MAN FROM THRUSH
11.SPY WHO CAME IN FROM THE COLD 12.GOLDFINGER 13.
OUR MAN FLINT 14.ILYA 15.GOOD THE BAD AND THE UGLY
16.HANG 'EM HIGH-17.FOR A FEW DOLLARS MORE 18.A
FISTFUL OF DOLLARS 19.THEME FOR THREE 20.GODFATHER
--- **MORE MUSIC TO WATCH GIRLS BY** *see* MUSIC TO WATCH 2
176.**MORRICONE Ennio** - CINEMA CONCERTO
Orchestra and Chorus of Accademia Nazionale De
Santo Cecilia Rome (conducted by Ennio Morricone)
SONY CLASSICS (TEN): SK 61672 (CD)   2000
1.CINEMA PARADISO 2.INVESTIGATION OF A CITIZEN
ABOVE SUSPICION 3.PURE FORMALITY 4.BUGSY 5.H2S 6.
GOOD THE BAD AND THE UGLY 7.ONCE UPON A TIME IN
THE WEST 8.GUI LA TESTA 9.METTI UNA SERA A CENA

10.SOSTIENE PERIERA 11.LAS CLASS OPERAIA VA IN PARA
DISO 12.CASUALTIES OF WAR 13.QUEMADA 14.THE MISSION

177.MORRICONE Ennio - FILM MUSIC OF ENNIO MORRICONE
VIRGIN VIP (EMI): CDVIP 123 (CD) TCVIP 123 (MC)
THE GOOD THE BAD AND THE UGLY-THE SICILIAN CLAN-CHI
MAI (Life And Times Of David Lloyd George)-THE MAN
WITH THE HARMONICA (Once Upon A Time In The West)-
LA CALIFFA (Lady Caliph)-GABRIEL'S OBOE (Mission)-
A FISTFUL OF DYNAMITE-ONCE UPON A TIME IN THE WEST-
COCKEYE'S THEME (Once Upon A Time In America)-THE
MISSION remix-COME MADDELENA (Madelena)-MOSES THEME
(Moses The Lawgiver)-THE FALLS (Mission)-MY NAME IS
NOBODY-LE VENT LE CRI(Professional) DEBORAH'S THEME

178.MORRICONE Ennio - THE MISSION: Classic Film Music
City Of Prague Philharmonic Orchestra conducted by
Paul Bateman and Derek Wadsworth
SILVA SCREEN (Koch): FILMCD 171 (CD) 1996
THE MISSION (Suite for Orch & Choir): *The Mission/
Gabriel's Oboe/Ave Maria (Guarini)/On Earth As It
Is In Heaven/Epilogue: The Falls)* -THE UNTOUCHABLES
(Theme)-ONCE UPON A TIME IN AMERICA *Deborah's Theme*
1900 (Romanza)-CASUALTIES OF WAR *(Elegy For Brown)*-
TWO MULES FOR SISTER SARA-IN THE LINE OF FIRE-THE
THING-CHI MAI-MARCO POLO-ONCE UPON A TIME IN THE
WEST *(Man With The Harmonica)*-GOOD THE BAD AND THE
UGLY-A FISTFUL OF DOLLARS-FOR A FEW DOLLARS MORE-
ONCE UPON A TIME IN THE WEST-THE GOOD THE BAD AND
THE UGLY *(Ecstasy Of Gold)*-CINEMA PARADISO

179.MOVIE BRASS - Grimethorpe Colliery UK Coal Band
RCA VICTOR (BMG): 74321 88393-2 (CD) -4 (MC) 2001
GREAT ESCAPE-BRAVEHEART-INDIANA JONES & THE TEMPLE
OF DOOM-JAMES BOND MEDLEY-SUPERMAN-BRIDGE OVER THE
RIVER KWAI-FORREST GUMP-STAR WARS-DAM BUSTERS-ROCKY
JURASSIC PARK-BEN HUR-CHICKEN RUN-GLADIATOR

180.MOVIE HIT LIST - Killer Tracks from the Flicks
EMI GOLD: 523 775-2 (CD) 2001
1.YOU SEXY THING *(FULL MONTY)* Hot Chocolate 2.MORE
THAN A WOMAN *(SATURDAY NIGHT FEVER)* Tavares 3.MAKE
ME SMILE *(VELVET GOLDMINE)* Steve Harley & Cockney
Rebel 4.CALL ME *(AMERICAN GIGOLO)* Blondie 5.WHITE
WEDDING *(WEDDING SINGER)* Billy Idol 6.DAY BEFORE
YESTERDAY'S MAN *(SHOOTING FISH)* Supernaturals 7.
CRYING GAME *(CRYING GAME)* Boy George 8.TEMPTATION
(TRAINSPOTTING) Heaven 17 9.MARY'S PRAYER *(THERE'S
SOMETHING ABOUT MARY)* Danny Wilson 10.DO YOU REALLY
WANT TO HURT ME *(WEDDING SINGER)* Culture Club 11.
GOD ONLY KNOWS *BOOGIE NIGHTS* Beach Boys 12.RUNAWAY
(AMERICAN GRAFFITI) Del Shannon 13.BLUEBERRY HILL
12 MONKEYS Fats Domino 14.BIG SPENDER *(LITTLE VOICE
/SWEET CHARITY)* Shirley Bassey 15.I GOT IT BAD *(BIG
LEBOWSKI)* Nina Simone 16.AC-CENT-CHU-ATE THE
POSITIVE *(LA CONFIDENTIAL)* Johnny Mercer 17.DON'T
WORRY BE HAPPY *WELCOME TO SARAJEVO* Bobby McFerrin
18.BAKER STREET *(GOOD WILL HUNTING)* Gerry Rafferty

181.MOVIE MEMORIES Nuremberg Symphony Orchestra
VARESE (Pinn): VSD 5939 (CD) *2001*
new recordings of themes and suites including:
GONE WITH THE WIND-SPARTACUS-DR.ZHIVAGO-CASABLANCA-
GHOST-THE MAGNIFICENT 7-HIGH NOON-MURDER ON THE
ORIENT EXPRESS-POLTERGEIST-OUT OF AFRICA-PAPILLON-
RAIDERS OF THE LOST ARK

182.MOVIE MUSIC - THE DEFINITIVE PERFORMANCES / V.Arts
SONY MUSIC: J2K 65813 (2CD) *1999*
MUSIC FOR SILENT MOVIES Charlie Young 1.SINGIN' IN
THE RAIN *HOLLYWOOD REVUE 1929* Cliff Edwards 2.YOU
ARE TOO BEAUTIFUL *HALLELUJAH I'M A BUM* Al Jolson 3.
GUY WHAT TAKES HIS TIME *SHE DONE HIM WRONG* Mae West
4.TEMPTATION *GOING HOLLYWOOD* Bing Crosby 5.INKA DIN
KA DOO *JOE PALOOKA* Jimmy Durante 6.ROCK AND ROLL
TRANSATLANTIC MERRYGOUND Boswell Sisters 7.LULLABY
OF BROADWAY *GOLD DIGGERS OF 1935* Dick Powell 8.
WAY YOU LOOK TONIGHT *SWING TIME* Fred Astaire 9.
LOVELY WAY TO SPEND AN EVENING *HIGHER AND HIGHER*
Frank Sinatra10.SECRET LOVE *CALAMITY JANE* Doris Day
11.MAN THAT GOT AWAY *A STAR IS BORN* Judy Garland
12.GIANT *GIANT* WB Orch & Chorus 13.MARCH FROM THE
RIVER KWAI/COLONEL BOGIE *BRIDGE ON THE RIVER KWAI*
Mitch Miller Or 14.AN AFFAIR TO REMEMBER Vic Damone
15.CERTAIN SMILE Johnny Mathis 16.MY HEART BELONGS
TO DADDY *LET'S MAKE LOVE* Marilyn Monroe 17.OVERTURE
WEST SIDE STORY Johnny Green Orch 18.WITH A LITTLE
BIT OF LUCK *MY FAIR LADY* Stanley Holloway 19.TO SIR
WITH LOVE Lulu 20.MRS.ROBINSON *THE GRADUATE* Simon &
Garfunkel 21.BALLAD OF THE EASY RIDER Byrds 22.BE
JONATHAN LIVINGSTON SEAGULL Neil Diamond 23.WAY WE
WERE Barbra Streisand 24. CD2:1.SUICIDE IS PAINLESS
M.A.S.H. The MASH 2.KNOCKIN' ON HEAVEN'S DOOR *PAT
GARRETT AND BILLY THE KID* Bob Dylan 3.EVERGREEN
A STAR IS BORN Barbra Streisand 4.ON THE ROAD AGAIN
HONEYSUCKLE ROSE Willie Nelson 5.TENDER YEARS *EDDIE
& THE CRUISERS* John Cafferty & Beaver Brown Band 6.
FOOTLOOSE Kenny Loggins 7.TAKE MY BREATH AWAY *TOP
GUN* Berlin 8.IT HAD TO BE YOU *WHEN HARRY MET SALLY*
Harry Connick Jnr 9.JOHN DUNBAR THEME *DANCES WITH
WOLVES* John Barry Orch 10.STATE OF LOVE AND TRUST
SINGLES Pearl Jam 11.WHEN I FALL IN LOVE *SLEEPLESS
IN SEATTLE* Celine Dion & Clive Griffin 12.STREETS
OF PHILADEPHIA *PHILADELPHIA* B.Springsteen 13.I'M
FORREST *FORREST GUMP* Alan Silvestri 14.CHILDHOOD
FREE WILLY2 Michael Jackson 15.SWEETEST THING *LOVE
JONES* Refugee Camp AllStars-Lauryn Hill 16.MEN IN
BLACK Will Smith 17.I SAY A LITTLE PRAYER *MY BEST
FRIENDS WEDDING* Diana King 18.SOUTHAMPTON *TITANIC*
J.H. 19.MY HEART WILL GO ON *TITANIC* Celine Dion 20
I DON'T WANT TO MISS A THING *ARMAGEDDON* Aerosmith

183.MUNDO LATINO! - Various Artists
SONY MUSIC: SONYTV2CD (CD) SONYTVMC 2(MC) reis 1998
1.GUAGLIONE Perez Prado 2.LA CUMPARSITA (The Masked

One) Xavier Cugat 3.OYE MI CANTO Gloria Estefan 4.
SOUL LIMBO (Latino Summer Mix) **Mr.Bongo** 5.SOMETHING
IN MY EYE Corduroy 6.LA BAMBA Los Lobos 7.BAMBOLEO
Gypsy Kings 8.OYE COMA VA Santana 9.LIBERTANGO
Astor Piazzolla 10.SOUL SOUCE Cal Tjader 11.SOUL
BOSSA NOVA Quincy Jones 12.MAS QUE NADA Sergio
Mendes Brasil 66 13.WATERMELON MAN Mongo Santamaria
14.ESO BESO Nancy Ames 15.MORE MORE MORE Carmel 16.
HOT HOT HOT Arrow 17.CUBA The Gibson Bothers 18.
GOT MYSELF A GOOD MAN Pucho 19.CERVEZA Boots Brown
and His Blockbusters 20.TEQUILA The Champs

184.<u>**MUSIC FROM THE MOVIES**</u> - Classical Music Selections
DG UNIVERSAL: 469 256-2 (2CD)   *2001*
LAST ACTION HERO-UNTOUCHABLES-GODFATHER III-HOWARDS
END-PHILADELPHIA-APOCALYPSE NOW-AMADEUS-HANNAH AND
HER SISTERS-THE LADYKILLERS-ROOM WITH A VIEW-SWAN
LAKE-ANNA KARENINA-CASINO-DEATH IN VENICE-ELVIRA
MADIGAN-PUNCHLINE-THE WITCHES OF EASTWICK-2001 A
SPACE ODYSSEY-A CLOCKWORK ORANGE-FATAL ATTRACTION-
KOLYA-WALL STREET-DIVA-SHINE-OUT OF AFRICA-PLATOON-
BOLERO-JURASSIC PARK-DANCES WITH WOLVES-BRAVEHEART-
THE ENGLISH PATIENT-TITANIC

185.<u>**MUSIC TO WATCH GIRLS BY**</u> - Various Artists
SONYMUSIC: SONYTV 67(CD)(MC) (2CDs/Mc)   *1999*
CD1:1.MUSIC TO WATCH GIRLS BY Andy Williams 2.UP UP
AND AWAY Fifth Dimension 3.GOOD LIFE Tony Bennett 4
SPANISH EYES Al Martino 5.THEME FROM A SUMMER PLACE
Percy Faith 6.ON THE STREET WHERE YOU LIVE V.Damone
7.LA MER (BEYOND THE SEA) Bobby Darin 8.A CERTAIN
SMILE Johnny Mathis 9.VALLEY OF THE DOLLS Dionne
Warwick 10.JOANNA Scott Walker 11.WISHIN' & HOPIN'
Dusty Springfield 12.WICHITA LINEMAN Glen Campbell
13.MOON RIVER Danny Williams 14.GIRL WITH THE SUN
IN HER HAIR John Barry 15.MAGIC MOMENTS Perry Como
16.FLY ME TO T.MOON Julie London 17.PERHAPS PERHAPS
PERHAPS Doris Day 18.ALMOST LIKE BEING IN LOVE Vic
Damone 19.DON'T SLEEP IN THE SUBWAY Petula Clark
CD2: 1.THAT'S AMORE Dean Martin 2.DOWNTOWN Petula
Clark 3.MOVE OVER DARLING Doris Day 4.LOVE LETTERS
IN THE SAND Pat Boone 5.A SWINGIN' SAFARI Bert
Kaempfert 6.THESE BOOTS ARE MADE FOR WALKING Nancy
Sinatra 7.BLUE VELVET Bobby Vinton 8.IT HAD TO BE
YOU Vic Damone 9.MACK THE KNIFE Louis Armstrong 10
BLUE MOON Mel Torme 11.LADY IS A TRAMP Buddy Greco
12.MAMBO ITALIANO Rosemary Clooney 13.DO YOU MIND
Anthony Newley 14.SHE Peter Skellern 15.NO ONE BUT
YOU Billy Eckstine 16.FOOLS RUSH IN Brook Benton
17.SUGAR TOWN Nancy Sinatra 18.LET THERE BE LOVE
Nat King Cole & George Shearing 19.CAN'T TAKE MY
EYES OFF YOU Andy Williams

186.<u>**MUSIC TO WATCH GIRLS BY**</u> 2: MORE MUSIC TO WATCH.....
SONYMUSIC: SONYTV 75(CD)(MC) (2CDs/Mc)   *1999*
1.CAN'T HELP FALLING IN LOVE Andy Williams 2.THE
BEST IS YET TO COME Tony Bennett 3.S'WONDERFUL Ray

Conniff 4.SOMETHIN'STUPID Frank & Nancy Sinatra 5.
THE LOOK OF LOVE Dusty Springfield 6.BORN FREE Matt
Monro 7.ALFIE Cilla Black 8.CAST YOUR FATE TO THE
WIND Sounds Orchestral 9.RAINDROPS KEEP FALLING ON
MY HEAD B.J.Thomas 10.MEMORIES ARE MADE OF THIS
Dean Martin 11.BY THE TIME I GET TO PHOENIX Glen
Campbell 12.ANYONE WHO HAD A HEART Dionne Warwick
13.WIVES AND LOVERS Jack Jones 14.I COULDN'T LIVE
WITHOUT YOUR LOVE Petula Clark 15.ON THE REBOUND
Floyd Cramer 16.QUE SEA SERA Doris Day 17.PEACEFUL
Georgie Fame 18.WHERE ARE YOU NOW Jackie Trent 19.
WONDERFUL WONDERFUL Johnny Mathis 20.ALMOST THERE
Andy Williams CD2: 1.SWAY Perez Prado feat Rosemary
Clooney 2.COME SEPTEMBER Bobby Darin Orchestra 3.
MORE I SEE YOU Chris Montez 4.IN CROWD Dobie Gray
5.COMIN'HOME BABY Mel Torme 6.CASINO ROYALE Jet Set
7.OUR DAY WILL COME Doris Day 8.IF YOU GO AWAY
Scott Walker 9.FEVER Peggy Lee 10.I LEFT MY HEART
IN SAN FRANCISCO Tony Bennett 11.WHAT A DIFFERENCE
Dinah Washington 12.CATCH A FALLING STAR Perry Como
13.WINDMILLS OF YOUR MIND Noel Harrison 14.WHAT A
WONDERFUL WORLD Louis Armstrong 15.GUAGLIANO Perez
Prado 16.59TH ST.BRIDGE SONG FEELIN' GROOVY Harpers
Bizarre 17.WINDY Association 18.STONED SOUL PICNIC
5th Dimension 19.FROM RUSSIA WITH LOVE John Barry
20.MacARTHUR PARK Richard Harris

187.**<u>MUSIC TO WATCH GIRLS BY</u> 3: VARIOUS ORIG ARTISTS....**
SONYMUSIC: SONYTV 96(CD)(MC) (2CDs/Mc)   *2000*
1.WHAT'S NEW PUSSYCAT Tom Jones2.VOLARE Dean Martin
3.CHERRY PINK & APPLE BLOSSOM WHITE Perez Prado 4.
JUST A GIGOLO Louis Prima 5.MACK THE KNIFE Bobby
Darin 6.STRANGER IN PARADISE Tony Bennett 7.WINDOWS
OF THE WORLD Scott Walker 8.GUANTAMANERA Sandpipers
9.MOON RIVER Henry Mancini 10.UNFORGETTABLE Dinah
Washington 11.I'LL TRY ANYTHING Dusty Springfield
12.SPOOKY Andy Williams 13.TWELFTH OF NEVER Johnny
Mathis 14.I SAY A LITTLE PRAYER Aretha Franklin 15
SMILE Nat King Cole 16.ALWAYS SOMETHING THERE TO
REMIND ME Dusty Springfield 17.MY LOVE Petula Clark
18.BECAUSE THEY'RE YOUNG Duane Eddy 19.MAD ABOUT
THE BOY Dinah Washington 20.LAST DATE Floyd Cramer
21.GOD ONLY KNOWS Beach Boys 22.IT'S IMPOSSIBLE
Perry Como 23.BONNIE AND CLYDE Georgie Fame 24.A
WALK IN THE BLACK FOREST Horst Jankowski 25.HOUSE
OF BAMBOO Andy Williams 26.I'LL NEVER FALL IN LOVE
AGAIN Dionne Warwick 27.YOU'RE MY WORLD Cilla Black
28.JE T'AIME Jane Birkin-Serge Gainsbourg 29.TRAINS
AND BOATS AND PLANES Burt Bacharach 30.SHADOW OF
YOUR SMILE Tony Bennett 31.SECRET LOVE Doris Day 32
SPEAK SOFTLY LOVE Andy Williams 33.SMOKE GETS IN
YOUR EYES Vic Damone 34.MISTY Johnny Mathis 35.
EXCERPT FROM A TEENAGE OPERA Keith West 36.NEVER MY
LOVE Association 37.ANYTHING GOES Harpers Bizzarre
38.DREAM A LITTLE DREAM OF ME Mama Cass Elliot 39.

LOVE IS BLUE Paul Mauriat 40.WHAT KIND OF FOOL AM I
Anthony Newley 41.HEY THERE Rosemary Clooney 42.
LIGHT MY FIRE Jose Feliciano 43.THIS IS MY SONG
Petula Clark 44.HELP YOURSELF Tom Jones

188.NEW PURE MOODS - Various Artists
VIRGIN (EMI): VTDCD 158 (2CD)   1997
1.CACHARPAYA Incantation 2.WILD MOUNTIN THYME
(SCOTTISH TOURIST BOARD) Silencers 3.LILY WAS HERE
David A.Stewart feat Candy Dulfer 4.CHILDREN Robert
Miles 5.HARRY'S GAME Clannad 6.CAVATINA DEER HUNTER
John Williams 7.BRIDESHEAD REVISTED (KELLOGG'S CORN
FLAKES/VW GOLF) Geoffrey Burgon 8.DON'T CRY FOR ME
ARGENTINA Shadows 9.THEME FROM SCHINDLER'S LIST
Tamsin Little 10.RIVERDANCE John Anderson Concert
11.MERRY CHRISTMAS MR.LAWRENCE Ryuichi Sakamoto 12.
LITTLE FLUFFY CLOUDS The Orb 13.PLAY DEAD (VAUXHALL
VECTRA) Bjork w.David Arnold 14.SONG FOR GUY Elton
John 15.SWEET LULLABY Deep Forest 16.ONLY YOU (FIAT
TEMPRA)Praise 17.ALBATROSS Fleetwood Mac 18.OXYGENE
IV Jean Michel Jarre 19.CROCKETT'S THEME Jan Hammer
20.YEHA NOHA Sacred Spirit. CD2: ADIEMUS (DELTA AIR
WAYS) Adiemus 2.CANTUS SONG OF TEARS (CHELTENHAM &
GLOUCESTER B.SOC) Adiemus 3.TUBULAR BELLS PART ONE
Mike Oldfield 4.INSPECTOR MORSE Barrington Pheloung
5.ANOTHER GREEN WORLD (ARENA) Brian Eno 6.ANCIENT
PERSON OF MY HEART Divine Works 7.PROTECTION(MAZDA)
Massive Attack feat Tracy 8.THE MISSION E.Morricone
9.HEART ASK PLEASURE FIRST/THE PROMISE (THE PIANO)
Michael Nyman 10.ARIA ON AIR (B.AIRWAYS) Malcolm
McLaren 11.RETURN TO INNOCENCE Enigma 12.SADNESS
Enigma 13.CHI MAI (LIFE AND TIMES OF DAVID LLOYD
GEORGE) Ennio Morricone 14.BLOW THE WIND/PIE JESU
(ORANGE) Jocelyn Pook 15.WOODBROOK Micheal O'Suill
eabhain 16.LAST EMPEROR David Byrne 17.PRELUDE
(B.AIRWAYS) Yanni 18.TWIN PEAKS-FIRE WALK WITH ME
Angelo Badalamenti 19.SUN RISING (ALPEN) Beloved
20.THEME FROM THE X-FILES DJ Dado

189.NEWMAN Alfred - Essential Alfred Newman Collection
Man Of Galilee + other film music excerpts & suites
City Of Prague Philharmonic Orch (Raine/Bateman)
SILVA SCREEN (Koch): FILMXCD 352 (2CD)   2001
1.20th CENTURY FOX FANFARE 2.HOW TO MARRY A MILLION
AIRE 3.DIARY OF ANNE FRANCK 4.MARK OF ZORRO 5.
ANASTASIA 6.THE SONG OF BERNADETTE 7.HOW THE WEST
WAS WON 8.THE CAPTAIN FROM CASTILLE 9.KEYS OF THE
KINGDOM 10.NEVADA SMITH 11.RAZOR'S EDGE 12.
WUTHERING HEIGHTS 13.MAN OF GALILEE 14.THE ROBE
15.THE GREATEST STORY EVER TOLD

190.NEWMAN Alfred - WUTHERING HEIGHTS: A Tribute
New Zealand Symphony Orch cond: Richard Kaufman
KOCH INT.CLASSICS: 37376-2 (CD)   1997
WUTHERING HEIGHTS (1939) - PRINCE OF FOXES (1949)
DAVID AND BATHSHEBA (1951) - DRAGONWYCK (1946)
PRISONER OF ZENDA (1937) - BRIGHAM YOUNG (1940)

--- <u>NO STRINGS ATTACHED</u> - *see* GRAY Barry
191.<u>NORTH Alex</u> - NORTH BY NORTH
   CITADEL (Hot): STC 77114 (2CD)   *1999*
   UNCHAINED (55)/GHOST (90)-VIVA ZAPATA-THE BAD SEED
   A STREETCAR NAMED DESIRE-THE ROSE TATTOO-DESIREE-
   THE BACHELOR PARTY-13TH LETTER-I'LL CRY TOMORROW-
   LES MISERABLES-THE RACERS-STAGE STRUCK plus the
   complete score of JOURNEY INTO FEAR (1975)
192.<u>NYMAN Michael</u> - Film Music 1980 - 2001
   VIRGIN VENTURE (EMI): CDVED 957 (2CD)   *2001*
   1.BIRD LIST (live) 2.CHASING SHEEP BEST IS LEFT TO
   SHEPHERDS 3.EYE FOR OPTICAL THEORY 4.HOMAGE TO
   MAURICE 5.ANGELFISH DECAY 6.TIME LAPSE 7.TRYSTING
   FIELDS 8.WHEELBARROW WALK 9.KNOWING THE ROPES 10.
   MEMORIAL 11.SKATING 12.PEEKING 13.ABANDONING 14.
   SKIRTING 15.LE THEATRE D'HOMBRES CHINOISES 16.HERE
   TO THERE 17.HEART ASKS PLEASURE FIRST 18.PROMISE
   19.ALL IMPERFECT THINGS 20.DREAMS OF A JOURNEY 21.
   ESCAPE 22.FLY DRIVE 23.INFINITE COMPLEXITIES OF
   CHRISTMAS 24.IF 25.ABEL CARRIES EPHRAIM 26.GATTACA
   (radio edit) 27.MORROW 28.OTHER SIDE 29.DEPARTURE
   30.COVENING THE COVEN 31.STRANGER AT THE WINDOW
   32.CANNIBAL FANTASY 33.MOLLY 34.EDDIE 35.DAN 36.
   EILEEN 37.SARAH DIES 38.END OF THE AFFAIR 39.SHOOT
   OUT 40.BURNING
193.<u>NYMAN Michael</u> - Music From Peter GREENAWAY Films
   Michael Nyman and Essential Michael Nyman Band
   ARGO/DECCA (Polyg): 436 820-2 (CD) -4 (MC)   *1992*
   CHASING SHEEP IS BEST LEFT TO SHEPHERDS/AN EYE FOR
   OPTICAL THEORY/THE GARDEN IS BECOMING A ROBE ROOM
   (all: The Draughtsman's Contract) PRAWN WATCHING/TI
   ME LAPSE *(Zed & Two Noughts)* FISH BEACH/WHEELBARROW
   WALK/KNOWING THE ROPES *(Drowning By Numbers)*
   MISERERE PARAPHRASE/MEMORIAL*(The Cook The Thief His
   Wife And Her Lover)* STROKING/SYNCHRONISING *(Water
   Dances)* MIRANDA *(Prospero's Books)*
--- <u>NYPD BLUE - The BEST OF MIKE POST</u> - *see* POST Mike
---.<u>OFF YER BOX: MUSIC TO WATCH TV BY</u> - (TV ADS MUSIC)
   WRASSE (UNIVERSAL MUSIC): WRASS 039 (CD)   *2001*
   see page 50 and 338 for full track details
--- <u>OMEN The</u> - *see* GOLDSMITH Jerry
194.<u>ONLY CHORAL ALBUM YOU'LL EVER NEED The</u> Var.Artists
   RCA CLASSIC (BMG): 75605 51360-2 (2CD) -4 (MC) 1998
   1.AGNUS DEI: Adagio For Strings *(BARBER)* 2.THE BELL
   CHORUS: I Pagliacci *(LEONCAVALLO)* 3.JERUSALEM *PARRY*
   4.MARCH OF THE TOREADORS: Carmen *(BIZET)* 5.REQUIEM
   (In Paradisium) *(FAURE)* 6.REQUIEM AETERNAM (Kyrie)
   (MOZART) 7.MISERERE *(ALLEGRI)* 8.POLOTSVIAN DANCES:
   Prince Igor *(BORODIN)* 9.SAILOR'S CHORUS: The Flying
   Dutchman *(WAGNER)*10.HUMMING CHORUS: Madam Butterfly
   (PUCCINI) 11.ALLES VERGANGLICHE: 8th Symph.*(MAHLER)*
   12.GRAND MARCH: Aida *(VERDI)* 13.CRUCIFIXUS *(LOTTI)*
   14.DEUS IN ADIUTORIUM: Vespro Della Beata Vergine
   (MONTEVERDI) 15.HALLELUJAH CHORUS: Messiah *(HANDEL)*

CD2 1.ANVIL CHORUS: Il Trovatore *VERDI* 2.HOW LOVELY
ARE THY DWELLING PLACES: German Requiem *(BRAHMS)* 3.
AVE VERUM CORPUS *(MOZART)* 4.ENTR'ACTE AND WALTZ:
EUGENE ONEGIN *TCHAIKOVSKY* 5.ZADOK THE PRIEST *HANDEL*
6.THE LAMB *(TAVENER)*7.QUI TOLLIS PECCATA MUNDI *BACH*
8.EASTER HYMN: Cavalleria Rusticana *(MASCAGNI)* 9.
ODE TO JOY: Symph.9 *BEETHOVEN* 10.AVE MARIA: Vespers
(RACHMANINOV) 11.HEAR MY PRAYER *PURCELL* 12.BRIDAL
CHORUS: Lohengrin *(WAGNER)* 13.CHAMPAGNE CHORUS:Die
Fledermaus *(J.STRAUSS II)* 14.SHEPERDS FAREWELL:
L'enfance du Christ *(BERLIOZ)* 15.CHORUS OF T.HEBREW
SLAVES: Nabucco *(VERDI)* 16.SOLDIERS CHORUS: Faust
(GOUNOD) 17.O FORTUNA: Carmina Burana *(ORFF)*

195.**ONLY CLASSICAL ALBUM YOU'LL EVER NEED The** Var.Arts
RCA-CONIFER (BMG): 75605 51332-2 (2CD) -4 (MC) 1998
1.CARMINA BURANA:O Fortuna *(ORFF)* Old Spice 2.LAKME
Flower Duet *(DELIBES)* B.Airways 3.SYMPH.NO.9: New
World *(DVORAK)* Hovis 4.PEER GYNT: Morning *(GRIEG)*
Nescafe 5.LA BOHEME: Che Gelida Manina *(PUCCINI)*
Moonstruck 6.RHAPSODY ON A THEME BY PAGANINI: No.18
RACHMANINOV) Groundhog Day 7.CLAIRE DE LUNE *DUBUSSY*
Frankie & Johnny 8.IL TROVATORE: Anvil Chorus *VERDI*
Wranglers 9.CANON IN D.*(PACHELBEL)* Ordinary People
10.EXSULTATE JUBILATE: Alleluia *(MOZART)* Royal Wedd
ing 11.PAVANE *(FAURE)* BBC World Cup 1998 12.CARMEN:
Flower Song *(BIZET)* 13.ADAGIO IN G.MINOR *(ALBINONI)*
Galipoli 14.ROMEO & JULIET: Dance Of The Knights
(PROKOFIEV) L'Egoiste 15.ENIGMA VARIATIONS: Nimrod
(ELGAR) 16.1812 OVERTURE: Finale *(TCHAIKOVSKY)* CD2:
1.POMP AND CIRCUMSTANCE MARCH NO.1 *(ELGAR)* 2.THE
PEARLFISHERS: Au Fond Du Temple Saint (Duet)*(BIZET)*
Galipoli3.CAVALLAERIA RUSTICANA:Intermezzo *MASCAGNI*
Raging Bull 4.MESSIAH: Why Do The Nations *(HANDEL)*
5.MESSIAH: Hallelujah Chorus*(HANDEL)* 6.FOUR SEASONS
Spring *(VIVALDI)* 7.REQUIEM: Pie Jesu *(FAURE)* 8.
SPARTACUS: Adagio *(KHACHATURIAN)* Onedin Line theme
9.GYMNOPEDIE NO.1 *(SATIE)* 10.AIR ON A G.STRING *BACH*
Hamlet 11.GIANNI SCHICCHI: Oh My Beloved Daddy *(PUC
CINI)* A Room With A View 12.PASTORAL SYMPH: 5TH m/m
(ext)*(BEETHOVEN)* Fantasia 13.JERUSALEM *(PARRY)* 14.
CLARINET CONCERTO: 2nd m/m *(MOZART)* Out Of Africa
15.AGNUS DEI: Adagio *(BARBER)* 16.TURANDOT: Nessun
Dorma *(PUCCINI)* World Cup 1990. *Artists include
LESLEY GARRETT-LUCIANO PAVAROTTI-JAMES GALWAY-BRYN
TERFEL-PLACIDO DOMINGO-ANGELA GHEORGHIU-JANICE
WATSON-JUSSI BJORLING-ROBERT MERRILL-CAMILLA OTAKI*

196.**ONLY MUSICALS ALBUM YOU'LL EVER NEED The** Var.Arts
RCA (BMG): 74321 60825-2 (2CD) -4 (MC)   1999
1.SECRET LOVE *(CALAMITY JANE)* Doris Day 2.SOUND OF
MUSIC Julie Andrews 3.SOME ENCHANTED EVENING *(SOUTH
PACIFIC)* 4.ALL THAT JAZZ *(CHICAGO)* 5.LUCK BE A LADY
(GUYS & DOLLS) 6.IF I WERE A RICH MAN *(FIDDLER ON
THE ROOF)* 7.THERE'S NO BUSINESS LIKE SHOW BUSINESS
(ANNIE GET YOUR GUN) 8.SEND IN THE CLOWNS *(A LITTLE*

NIGHT MUSIC) Glenn Close 9.I KNOW HIM SO WELL *CHESS*
Elaine Paige-Barbara Dickson 10.HELLO DOLLY Carol
Channing 11.SINGIN' IN THE RAIN Gene Kelly 12.SHALL
WE DANCE *(KING & I)* Yul Brynner 13.STRANGER IN
PARADISE *(KISMET)* 14.BROTHERHOOD OF MAN *(HOW TO
SUCEED IN BUSINESS)* 15.BRING HIM HOME *(LES MISERA.)*
Colm Wilkinson 16.MUSIC OF THE NIGHT *(PHANTOM OF..)*
Michael Crawford 17.MEMORY *(CATS)* Elaine Paige 18.
OH WHAT A BEAUTIFUL MORNIN' *(OKLAHOMA)* 19.CABARET
Natasha Richardson 20.CLIMB EVERY MOUNTAIN *(SOUND
OF MUSIC)* Leslie Garrett
CD2: 1.CONSIDER YOURSELF *(OLIVER)* 2.YOU'RE THE TOP
(ANYTHING GOES) 3.LOSING MY MIND *(FOLLIES)* Barbara
Cook 4.EVERYTHING'S COMING UP ROSES *(GYPSY)* Angela
Lansbury 5.OL'MAN RIVER *(SHOW BOAT)* 6.LOVE CHANGES
EVERYTHING *(ASPECTS OF LOVE)* Michael Ball 7.AMERICA
(WEST SIDE STORY) 8.IMPOSSIBLE DREAM *(MAN OF LA MAN
CHA)* 9.OVER THE RAINBOW *(WIZARD OF OZ)* Judy Garland
10.I GOT RHYTHM *(CRAZY FOR YOU)* Ruthie Henshall 11.
IF I LOVED YOU *(CAROUSEL)* 12.AQUARIUS *(HAIR)* 13.A
COUPLE OF SWELLS *(EASTER PARADE)* Fred Astaire-Judy
Garland 14.I TALK TO THE TREES *(PAINT YOUR WAGON)*
15.BIG SPENDER *(FOSSE THE MUSICAL/SWEET CHARITY)*
16.I WANNA BE LOVED BY YOU *(SOME LIKE IT HOT)*
Marilyn Monroe 17.LULLABY OF BROADWAY *(42ND STREET)*
18.WITH ONE LOOK *(SUNSET BOULEVARD)* Michael Ball 19
MAMMY *(JOLSON)* Brian Conley 20.I COULD HAVE DANCED
ALL NIGHT *(MY FAIR LADY)* Lesley Garrett
197.ONLY OPERA ALBUM YOU'LL EVER NEED The Var.Artists
RCA-CONIFER (BMG): 75605 51356-2 (2CD) -4 (MC) 1999
1.BRINDISI *(LA TRAVIATA)* Lesley Garrett 2.UN BEL DI
*(MADAME BUTTERFLY/FATAL ATTRACTION)*Angela Gheorghiu
3.OMBRA MAI FU *(SERSE/DANGEROUS LIAISONS)* Judith
Malafronte 4.TOREADOR'S SONG*(CARMEN)* Robert Merrill
5.EBBEN NE ANDRO LONTANA *(LA WALLY/DIVA)* Eva Marton
6.SUMMERTIME*(PORGY & BESS)* Leontyne Price 7.O SOAVE
FANCIULLA *(LA BOHEME/MOONSTRUCK)* Luciano Pavarotti
8.SONG TO THE MOON *(RUSALKA/DRIVING MISS DAISY)*
Leontyne Price 9.UNA FURTIVA LAGRIMA *(L'ELISIR D'
AMORE/PRIZZI'S HONOR)* Placido Domingo 10.HABANERA
*(CARMEN)*Leontyne Price 11.LARGO AL FACTOTEM *(BARBER
OF SEVILLE/MRS.DOUBTFIRE)* Robert Merrill 12.FLOWER
DUET *(LAKME/BRITISH AIRWAYS AD)* Janice Watson-Ruby
Philogene 13.WHEN I A LAID IN EARTH *(DIDO & AENEAS)*
Leontyne Price 14.GRAND MARCH *(AIDA)* Kings Division
Normandy Band 15.SOAVE SIA IL VENTO *(COSI FAN TUTTE
SUNDAY BLOODY SUNDAY)* Lynne Dawson-Della Jones-
Francois Le Roux) 16.NESSUN DORMA Johan Botha
CD2: 1.WILLIAM TELL OVERTURE *(LONE RANGER)* Yehudi
Menuhin & Sinfonia Varsovia 2.SEGUEDILLE *(CARMEN)*
Lesley Garrett 3.E LUCEVAN LE STELLE *(TOSCA)* Johan
Botha 4.BARCAROLLE *(TALES OF HOFFMAN/BAILEY'S IRISH
CREAM)* Janice Watson-Ruby Philogene 5.CHORUS OF THE
HEBREW SLAVE *(NABUCCO)* Robert Shaw Chorale 6.VOI

CHE SAPETTE *(THE MARRIAGE OF FIGARO)* Della Jones 7.
VESTO LA GIUBBA *(I PAGLIACCI/MOONRAKER)* Placido
Domingo) 8.CASTA DIVA *(NORMA/FORD MONDEO)* Monserrat
Caballe 9.DER HOLLE RACHE *(MAGIC FLUTE)* Sylvia
Geszty 10.LA DONNE E MOBILE *(RIGOLETTO)* Placido Dom
ingo 11.CHE FARO SENZA EURIDICE *(ORFEO ET EURIDICE)*
Vesselina Kasarova 12.AU FOND DU TEMPLE SAINT *PEARL*
FISHERS/GALLIPOLI) Robert Merrill-Jussi Bjoerling
13.RIDE OF THE VALKYRIES *(DIE WALKURE/APOCALYPSE*
NOW) Netherlands Radio Philharmonic 14.NON PIU
ANDRAI *(MARRIAGE OF FIGARO)* Francois Le Rue 15.
CELESTE AIDA *(AIDA)* Placido Domingo 16.ENTR'ACTE &
WALTZ *(EUGENE ONEGINO)* Royal Opera House Chor/Orch

198.ORFF Carl - The Best Of CARL ORFF
RCA (BMG): 75605 51537-2 (CD) *1999*
CARMINA BURANA - Highlights (15 trks) inc O FORTUNA
(OLD SPICE AD). feat LUCIA POPP-JOHN VAN KESTEREN-
HERNIAM PREY & MUNICH RADIO ORCH cond: KURT EICHORN
SCHULWERK (School Work) - (19 tracks) including
RUNDADINELLA *(BBC LEARNING ZONE AD)* GASSENHAUER
(VW GOLF AD) TOLZER BOYS CHOIR-GERHARDT SCHMIDT
GADEN-CHAMBER CHOIR OF THE MUNICH NATIONAL COLLEGE
STUTTGART CHORUS-HEINZ MENDA-INSTRUMENTAL ENSEMBLE
DER KLUGE (Wise Woman) DER MOND (The Moon) *extracts*

199.PAIGE Elaine - PERFORMANCE
RCA CAMDEN (BMG): 74321 44680-2(CD) -4(MC) re: 1997
1.I HAVE DREAMED *KING AND I* 2.ANYTHING GOES 3.HEART
DON'T CHANGE MY MIND 4.ANOTHER SUITCASE IN ANOTHER
HALL *EVITA* 5.THE ROSE 6.LOVE HURTS 7.WHAT'LL I DO /
WHO 8.I ONLY HAVE EYES FOR YOU 9.HE'S OUT OF MY LIF
LIFE 10.I KNOW HIM SO WELL *CHESS* 11.DON'T CRY FOR
ME ARGENTINA *EVITA* 12.MEMORY *CATS* 13. MEMORY Repr.

200.PERSUADERS AND OTHER TOP 70'S TV THEMES - V.Artists
SEQUEL-CASTLE (Pinn): NEMCD 424 (2CD) *1999*
CD1: 1.PERSUADERS Cyril Stapleton Orch 2.HAWAII 5-0
Victor Silvester Or 3.RETURN OF THE SAINT Saint Orc
4.INCREDIBLE HULK Acker Bilk 5.M*A*S*H*Tony Hatch O
6.PINK PANTHER Alan Tew Or 7.KOJAK Victor Silvester
8.IRONSIDE Alan Tew Orch 9.VAN DER VALK "Eye Level"
Tony Hatch Orch 10.TAXI "Angela" Bob James 11.THE
GOODIES The Goodies 12.MORECAMBE & WISE "Positive
Thinking" Jackie Trent & Tony Hatch 13. LOVE THY
NEIGHBOUR Nina Baden-Semper 14.THE ODD COUPLE Tony
Hatch Orch 15.THE FUZZ Button Down Brass 16.AGONY
Babs Fletcher 17.BACKS TO THE LAND Anne Shelton 18.
EMMERDALE FARM Tony Hatch Or 19.UPSTAIRS DOWNSTAIRS
Victor Silvester Orch 20.MR.AND MRS.Jackie Trent &
Tony Hatch 21.SOAP Acker Bilk 22.GENERAL HOSPITAL
"Girl In.The White Dress" Derek Scott Orch. 23.
BACKS TO THE LAND Anne Shelton 24.OWEN MD "Sleepy
Shores" Cyril Stapleton O 25.BUDGIE "Nobody's Fool"
Cold Turkey
CD2: 1.MATCH OF THE DAY Offside 2.SPORTSNIGHT Tony
Hatch Orch 3.BEST IN FOOTBALL Tony Hatch Orch 4.

ITV EUROPEAN FOOTBALL "World At Their Feet" John Shakespeare Orch 5.WORLD CUP ARGENTINA 1978 Ennio Morricone Orch 6.GAME OF THE CENTURY "Argentina Heroes (We're On Our Way)" Moon Williams 7.MISTER MEN Acker Bilk 8.RUPERT Jackie Lee 9.SESAME STREET Street Kids 10.CLOPPA CASTLE Rainbow Cottage 11. HADLEIGH Tony Hatch Orch 12.ONEDIN LINE "Love Theme from Spartacus" (Khachaturian) Cyril Stapleton Orch 13.DUCHESS OF DUKE STREET Royal Doulton Band 14. BOUQUET OF BARBED WIRE Acker Bilk 15.SEVEN FACES OF WOMAN "She" Russ Conway 16.CLAYHANGER Royal Doulton Band 17.WHO PAYS THE FERRYMAN Royal Doulton Band 18 LOTUS EATERS "Ta Trena Pou Fyghan" Manos Tacticos & His Bouzoukis 19.MACKINNON COUNTRY Iain Sutherland Orch 20.SAILOR "Sailing" Acker Bilk 21.NEW FACES "You're A Star" Carl Wayne 22.COLDITZ Colditz March Alyn Ainsworth Orch 23.WORLD AT WAR Tony Hatch Orch 24.FILM 72 etc."I Wish I Knew How It Would Feel To Be Free" Alan Tew Orc 25.CROSSROADS "Benny's Theme" Paul Henry and Mayson Glen Orchestra

201.PHANTOM MENACE AND OTHER FILM HITS - Var.Artists
VARESE (Pinn): VSD 6086 (CD)   *2000*
1.PHANTOM MENACE *(MEDLEY)* 2.MUMMY *(SAND VOLCANO)* 3. SIXTH SENSE *(DR.PROFUNDIS)* 4.INSTINCT 5.WILD WILD WEST 6.13TH WARRIOR *(OLD BAGHDAD)* 7.SAVING PRIVATE RYAN *HYMN TO THE FALLEN* 8.DEEP BLUE SEA *(AFTERMATH)* 9.IRON GIANT *(EVE OF THE STORM)* 10.THE HAUNTING *(HOME SAFE)* 11.MATRIX *MAIN TITLE/TRINITY INFINITY* 12.PAYBACK *(MAIN T.)* 13.SHAKESPEARE IN LOVE *(SUITE)* 14.BOWFINGER *(FINALE/FED-EX DELIVERS)*

202.PORTMAN Rachel - SOUNDTRACKS
REDIAL UNIVERSAL: 465 920-2 (CD)   *2000*
1.RATCATCHER Main title 2.BELOVED 3.CLOSER YOU GET Main Title 4.CIDER HOUSE RULES (Main title) 5.EMMA (Frank Churchill Arrives) 6.EMMA (End titles) 7. MARVIN'S ROOM (Main title) 8.MARVIN'S ROOM (Tell Tales) 9.PALOOKAVILLE 10.BENNY AND JOON 11.ADDICTED TO LOVE (Painting the wall) 12.WHERE ANGELS FEAR TO TREAD 13.JOY LUCK CLUB (Story Of The Swan) 14.ETHAN FROME (main title) 15.SMOKE (Augie's photos) 16. ONLY YOU Venice 17.DO YOU LOVE HIM 18.LIFE IS SWEET (main title) 19.ORANGES ARE NOT THE ONLY FRUIT main title 20.GREAT MOMENTS IN AVIATION (main title) 21. WAR OF THE BUTTONS (Chasing the fox) 22.WAR OF THE BUTTONS (end title)

203.POST Mike - NYPD BLUE (The Best Of Mike Post)
SILVA SCREEN (Koch): SILVAD 3511 (CD)
22 themes including: NYPD BLUE-DOOGIE HOWSER, MD-HILL STREET BLUES-L.A.LAW-HUNTER-LAW AND ORDER-HARDCASTLE & McCORMACK-MAGNUM, PI-QUANTUM LEAP-THE ROCKFORD FILES-WISEGUY-TOP OF THE HILL

204.PREMIERE - Classic Soundtracks
RCA CAMDEN (Univ): 74321 66106-2 (CD)   *1999*
1.SCHINDLER'S LIST *JOHN WILLIAMS* 2.THE UNFORGIVEN

CLINT EASTWOOD 3.DANCES WITH WOLVES *JOHN BARRY* 4.
A ROOM WITH A VIEW *PUCCINI* 'O Mio Babbino Caro' 5.
THE ENGLISH PATIENT *GABRIEL YARED* 6.GODFATHER III
MASCAGNI 'Intermezzo Cavaleria Rusticana' 7.TAXI
DRIVER *BERNARD HERRMANN* 8.YOU ONLY LIVE TWICE *JOHN
BARRY* 9.THE LIVING DAYLIGHTS *BARRY/WAAKTAR/HYNDE* 10
PLATOON *SAMUEL BARBER* 'Adagio For Strings' 11.DEATH
IN VENICE *MAHLER* '5th Symphony in C.Sharp Minor' 12
FRANKIE & JOHNNY *DEBUSSY* 'Claire De Lune' 13.THE
PINK PANTHER *HENRY MANCINI* 'The Lonely Princess' 14
BRASSED OFF *RODRIGUEZ* 'En Aranjuez Con Tu Amor' 15.
A FISTFUL OF DOLLARS *ENNIO MORRICONE* 16.DEER HUNTER
STANLEY MYERS 'Cavatina' arr.JOHN WILLIAMS

205.PRESLEY Elvis - **Elvis Movies (re-mastered tracks)**
RCA (BMG): 74321 68241-2 (CD)   *1999*
1.GOT A LOT 'O LIVIN' TO DO 2.LOVE ME TENDER 3.
(YOU'RE SO SQUARE) BABY I DON'T CARE 4.CRAWFISH 5.
I SLIPPED I STUMBLED I FELL 6.DOIN' THE BEST I CAN
7.FLAMING STAR 8.RETURN TO SENDER 9.LOVING YOU 10.
G.I.BLUES 11.GIRLS GIRLS GIRLS 12.I NEED SOMEBODY
TO LEAN ON 13.A LITTLE LESS CONVERSATION 14.FOLLOW
THAT DREAM 15.VIVA LAS VEGAS 16.TROUBLE 17.SWING
SWING DOWN SWEET CHARIOT 18.BOSSA NOVA BABY 19.
RUBBERNECKIN 20.THEY REMIND ME TOO MUCH OF YOU

206.PRESLEY Elvis - **Can't Help Falling In Love: The
Hollywood Hits** *RCA (BMG): 0786 367873-2 (CD)* *1999*
JAILHOUSE ROCK-LOVING YOU-HARD HEADED WOMAN-TEDDY
BEAR-KING CREOLE-TREAT ME NICE-LOVE ME TENDER-
ROUSTABOUT-WOODEN HEART- ROCK-A-HULA BABY -FOLLOW
THAT DREAM-KING OF T.WHOLE WIDE WORLD-SUCH AN EASY
QUESTION-RETURN TO SENDER-ONE BROKEN HEART FOR SALE
BOSSA NOVA BABY-VIVA LAS VEGAS-KISSIN'COUSINS-CLEAN
UP YOUR OWN BACK YARD-PUPPET ON A STRING-SHOPPIN'
AROUND-CAN'T HELP FALLING IN LOVE

---.**PRESLEY Elvis** - *see also ELVIS PRESLEY INDEX p.342*
--- **PSYCHO: ESSENTIAL ALFRED HITCHCOCK** *see* **HITCHCOCK**

207.QUATERMASS FILM MUSIC COLLECTION
GDI (ABK): GDICD 008 (CD)   *1999*
QUATERMASS EXPERIMENT (1955)   music: JAMES BERNARD
QUATERMASS II (1957)   music: JAMES BERNARD
QUATERMASS AND THE PIT (1967)   music: TRISTRAM CARY

208 RAWSTHORNE Alan - **FILM MUSIC OF ALAN RAWSTHORNE**
BBC Philharmonic Orchestra conducted by RUMON GAMBA
CHANDOS RECORDS: CHAN 9749 (CD)   *2000*
1.Suite (7 extracts) from THE CAPTIVE HEART (1946)
2.WEST OF ZANIBAR (1954) 3.THE CRUEL SEA (1953)
4.WHERE NO VULTURES FLY (1951) 5.UNCLE SILAS (1947)
6.LEASE OF LIFE (1954) 7.The DANCING FLEECE 8.BURMA
VICTORY 9.SARABAND FOR DEAD LOVERS (1948)

--- **RELAX...** - *see* **COLLECTIONS** *72 and 73 (Classic FM)*

209.REPRISE MUSICALS Frank Sinatra-D.Martin-B.Crosby-S.
Davis Jr-Dinah Shore-Pete Lawford *inc:*SOUTH PACIFIC
KISS ME KATE / GUYS & DOLLS / FINIAN'S RAINBOW'
REPRISE (TEN): 9362 47775-2 (4CDs issued 11/2000)

210.RICHARD Cliff - AT THE MOVIES 1959-1974
EMI UK: CDEMD 1096 (2CD) *1996*
Serious Charge (1959): NO TURNING BACK-LIVING DOLL-
MAD ABOUT YOU Expresso Bongo (1959):LOVE-A VOICE IN
THE WILDERNESS *(EP ver)*-SHRINE ON THE SECOND FLOOR
The Young Ones (1961): FRIDAY NIGHT-GOT A FUN
NY FEELING *(alternate take)*-NOTHING IS IMPOSSIBLE-
THE YOUNG ONES*(original undubbed master)*-LESSONS IN
LOVE-WHEN THE GIRL IN YOUR ARMS-WE SAY YEAH-IT'S
WONDERFUL TO BE YOUNG *(alternate take 24)*-OUTSIDER
Summer Holiday(1963) SEVEN DAYS TO A HOLIDAY-SUMMER
HOLIDAY-LET US TAKE YOU FOR A RIDE-STRANGER IN TOWN
BACHELOR BOY-A SWINGIN' AFFAIR-DANCIN' SHOES-THE
NEXT TIME-BIG NEWS Wonderful Life (1964): WONDERFUL
LIFE-A GIRL IN EVERY PORT-A LITTLE IMAGINATION *(edi
ted vers.)*-ON THE BEACH-DO YOU REMEMBER-LOOK DON'T
TOUCH *(prev.unreleased)*-IN THE STARS-WHAT'VE I GOT
TO DO-A MATTER OF MOMENTS-WONDERFUL LIFE *(alternate
take 18)* Thunderbirds Are Go (1967): SHOOTING STAR
Finders Keepers (1966): FINDERS KEEPERS-TIME DRAGS
BY-WASHERWOMAN-LA LA LA SONG-OH SENORITA *(ext.vers)*
THIS DAY-PAELLA Two A Penny (1967): TWO A PENNY-
TWIST & SHOUT-I'LL LOVE YOU FOREVER TODAY-QUESTIONS
(film version) Take Me High (1973): IT'S ONLY MONEY
MIDNIGHT BLUE-THE GAME-BRUMBURGER DUET-TAKE ME HIGH
THE ANTI BROTHERHOOD OF MAN-WINNING bonus tracks:-
YOUNG ONES *(film vers)*-LESSONS IN LOVE *ed.film vers*
BACHELOR BOY *(film v)*-SUMMER HOLIDAY *end title film*
--- **ROSE AND THE GUN** - *see* **JOHNSON Laurie**

211.ROTA Nino - FILM MUSIC
CHANDOS: CHAN 9771 (CD) *2000*
8½ / DEATH ON THE NILE / LUXURY GIRLS / FANTASMI A
ROMA / LEOPARD / GLASS MOUNTAIN / JULIET OF THE
SPIRITS / THE GODFATHER / OBSESSION / HER FAVOURITE
HUSBAND / ROMEO & JULIET / TAMING OF THE SHREW
212.ROTA Nino - SYMPHONIC FELLINI City Of Prague Phil *
SILVA SCREEN (Koch): FILMCD 720 (CD) 1991 reis:2000
Music Of NINO ROTA For The FEDERICO FELLINI Films
LA DOLCE VITA-LA STRADA-IL BIDONE-THE WHITE SHEIKH
ROMA-SATYRICON-CASANOVA-ORCHESTRA REHEARSAL-NIGHTS
OF CABIRIA-THE CLOWNS-I VITELLONI-AMARCORD-BOCCACC
IO 70-JULIET OF THE SPIRITS * Derek Wadsworth cond
213.ROZSA Miklos - EPIC FILM MUSIC - City Of Prague
Philharmonic Orchestra conducted by Kenneth Alwyn
SILVA SCREEN (Koch): FILMCD 170 (CD) *1996*
Symphonic Suites and Themes from Original Scores:
GOLDEN VOYAGE OF SINBAD *Prelude/Sinbad Battles Kali
/Finale)*-KING OF KINGS *(Prelude)*-EL CID *(Overture/
Love Scene)*-SODOM AND GOMORRAH *Overture*-QUO VADIS
(Prelude/Arabesque/Romanza/Ave Caesar-KING OF KINGS
(The Lord's Prayer)-BEAU BRUMMELL *Prelude/King's Vi
sit and Farewell)*-BEN HUR *Prelude/Love Theme/Parade
Of The Charioteers)*-ALL THE BROTHERS WERE VALIANT

(Main Title/Finale)-MADAME BOVARY *(Waltz/Bonus trk)*
KING OF KINGS *(Orchestral theme version)*

214.ROZSA Miklos - ESSENTIAL MIKLOS ROSZA COLLECTION
City Of Prague Philharmonic Orch.conducted by
Kenneth Alwyn-Paul Bateman-Nic Raine
SILVA SCREEN (Koch): FILMXCD 334 (2CD) 2000
1-3.BEN HUR 4.PROVIDENCE VALSE...5.JULIUS CAESAR
6-7.EL CID 8.SODOM AND GOMORRAH 9.BEAU BRUMMELL 10.
SPELLBOUND 11-14.THIEF OF BAGDAD 15-16.KING OF
KINGS 17.ALL THE BROTHERS WERE VALIANT 18.MADAME
BOVARY 19.GOLDEN VOYAGE OF SINBAD 20-23.QUO VADIS

215.ROSZA Miklos - LEGENDARY HOLLYWOOD
CITADEL (Hot): STC 77111 (CD) 2000
themes and suites from MIKLOS ROZSA film scores
THE WORLD THE FLESH AND THE DEVIL-BECAUSE OF HIM-EL
CID-YOUNG BESS-JULIUS CAESAR-SODOM AND GOMORRAH-
KING OF KINGS-BEN HUR-THE STORY OF THREE LOVES

216.SAKAMOTO Ryuichi - CINEMAGE
SONY CLASSICS: SK 60780 (CD) SM 60780 (MC) 1999
includes music from: MERRY CHRISTMAS MR.LAWRENCE-
THE LAST EMPEROR-LITTLE BUDDAH-WUTHERING HEIGHTS-
REPLICA-EL MAR MEDITERRANI SUITE (1992 OLYMP.GAMES)

217.SCHWARZENEGGER Arnold - GREATEST FILM THEMES
SILVA SCREEN (Koch): FILMCD 721 (CD) reissue 2000
CONAN THE BARBARIAN/THE DESTROYER-TOTAL RECALL-THE
TERMINATOR-TERMINATOR 2-RED HEAT-RAW DEAL-COMMANDO-
JUNIOR-TWINS-KINDERGARTEN COP-PREDATOR-TRUE LIES

218.SCI-FI's GREATEST HITS Vol.1 - 'Final Frontiers'
EDEL/TVT/SCI-FI CHANN (Vital) 004426-2ERE (CD) 1999
1.2001 A SPACE ODYSSEY 2.STAR WARS 3.EMPIRE STRIKES
BACK 4.RETURN OF THE JEDI 5.STAR TREK 6.STAR TREK
THE NEXT GENERATION 7.LOST IN SPACE (1965 TV) 8.
LOST IN SPACE (1967 TV) 9.LOST IN SPACE (film) 10.
BATTLESTAR GALACTICA 11.SPACE 1999 12.BUCK ROGERS
IN THE 25TH CENTURY 13.BABYLON 5 14.THE BLACK HOLE
15.ALIEN 16.THE ABYSS 17.VOYAGE TO THE BOTTOM OF
THE SEA 18.JOURNEY TO THE CENTRE OF THE EARTH 19.
LAND OF THE GIANTS 20.PLANET OF THE APES 21.TIME
TUNNEL 22.FIREBALL XL-5 23.DOCTOR WHO 24.STARGATE
25.TOTAL RECALL 26.BLADE RUNNER 27.TRON 28.STRANGE
DAYS 29.VR-5 30.SPACE ABOVE AND BEYOND 31.INSIDE
SPACE 32.WELCOME TO PARADOX 33.MISSION: GENESIS

219.SCI-FI's GREATEST HITS Vol.2 - 'The Dark Side'
EDEL/TVT/SCI-FI CHANN (Vital) 004427-2ERE (CD) 1999
1.OUTER LIMITS 2.TWILIGHT ZONE 3.ALFRED HITCHCOCK
PRESENTS 4.DARK SHADOWS 5.NIGHT GALLERY 6.KOLCHAK:
THE NIGHT STALKER 7.RIPLEY'S BELIEVE IT OR NOT 8.
CREEPSHOW 9.TALES FROM THE DARKSIDE 10.TALES FROM
THE CRYPT 11.INCREDIBLE SHRINKING MAN 12.SCANNERS
13.THE FLY 14.VIDEODROME 15.A CLOCKWORK ORANGE 16.
THE OMEN 17.HALLOWEEN 18.HELLRAISER 19.SUSPIRIA 20.
POLTERGEIST 21.DRACULA THE SERIES 22.FOREVER KNIGHT
23.THE HUNGER 24.12 MONKEYS 25.THE PRISONER 26.
NOWHERE MAN 27.FRIDAY THE 13TH THE SERIES 28.BEYOND

REALITY 29.THE ODYSSEY 30.OUTER LIMITS (film) 31.
DARK CITY 32.BEETLEJUICE 33.EDWARD SCISSORHANDS 34.
LABYRINTH 35.MYSTERY SCIENCE THEATER3000 36.X-FILES

220.SCI-FI's GREATEST HITS Vol.3 - 'The Uninvited'
EDEL/TVT/SCI-FI CHANN (Vital) 004428-2ERE (CD) 1999
1.WAR OF THE WORLDS (radio-intro) 2.DAY THE EARTH
STOOD STILL 3.IT CAME FROM OUTER SPACEE 4.WAR OF
THE WORLDS (disturbance) 5.THE INVADERS 6.WAR OF
THE WORLDS (first attack) 7.WAR OF THE WORLDS (TV)
8.V: THE SERIES 9.MARS ATTACKS! 10.INDEPENDENCE DAY
11.WAR OF THE WORLDS (gravity of the situation) 12.
CLOSE ENCOUNTERS OF THE THIRD KIND 13.E.T.THE EXTRA
TERRESTRIAL 14.STARMAN 15.ALIEN NATION (Film) 16.
ALIEN NATION (TV) 17.THE BEAST FROM 20,000 FATHOMS
18.PREDATOR 19.JAWS 20.THE CREATURE FROM THE BLACK
LAGOON 21.THEM! 22.TARANTULA 23.JURASSIC PARK 24.
GREMLINS 25.UFO 26.WAR OF THE WORLDS (end is near)
27.KILLER KLOWNS FROM OUTER SPACE 28.ATTACK OF THE
KILLER TOMATOES!

221.SCI-FI's GREATEST HITS Vol.4 - Defenders Of Justice
EDEL/TVT/SCI-FI CHANN (Vital) 004429-2ERE (CD) 1999
1.ASTRO BOY 2.GIGANTOR 3.SPEED RACER 4.THUNDERBIRDS
5.CAPTAIN SCARLET & THE MYSTERONS 6.CAPTAIN VIDEO &
HIS VIDEO RANGERS 7.TOM CORBETT, SPACE CADETT 8.
SPACE PATROL 9.UNDERDOG 10.ATOM ANT 11.BATMAN (TV)
12.BATMAN: THE ANIMATED SERIES 13.BATMAN (Film) 14.
BATMAN RETURNS 15.SUPERMAN (Film) 16.LOIS AND CLARK
THE NEW ADVENTURES OF SUPERMAN 17.THE GREEN HORNET
18.THE AMAZING SPIDER-MAN 19.SPIDER-WOMAN 20.WONDER
WOMAN 21.THE FLASH 22.TEENAGE MUTANT NINJA TURTLES
23.MIGHTY MORPHIN POWER RANGERS 24.THE TICK 25.THE
X-MEN 26.SIX MILLION DOLLAR MAN 27.BIONIC WOMAN 28.
INCREDIBLE HULK 29.KNIGHT RIDER 30.MAX HEADROOM 31.
THE TERMINATOR 32.ROBOCOP 33.ROBOCOP:THE SERIES 34.
QUANTUM LEAP 35.ESCAPE FROM NEW YORK 36.THE ROAD
WARRIOR (MAX MAD 2) 37.MORTAL KOMBAT

222.SHAKEN AND STIRRED: A JAMES BOND Film Songs Collect
produced and masterminded by DAVID ARNOLD   1997
EAST WEST (TEN): 3984 20738-2 (CD) -4 (MC)
1.DIAMONDS ARE FOREVER *DIAMONDS ARE FOREVER* David
McAlmont 2.JAMES BOND THEME *(M.Norman)* LTJ Buckem 3
NOBODY DOES IT BETTER *SPY WHO LOVED ME* Aimee Mann 4
ALL TIME HIGH *OCTOPUSSY* Pulp 5.SPACE MARCH *YOU ONLY
LIVE TWICE* Leftfield 6.LIVE AND LET DIE Chryssie
Hynde 7.MOONRAKER Shara Nelson 8.THUNDERBALL ABC 9.
FROM RUSSIA WITH LOVE Natasha Atlas 10.YOU ONLY
LIVE TWICE Candi Staton 11.ON HER MAJESTY'S SECRET
SERVICE Propellorheads 12.WE HAVE ALL THE TIME IN
THE WORLD *ON HER MAJESTY'S SECRET SERVICE* Iggy Pop

223.SHAKEN NOT STIRRED - Original Artists Film Music
SONY TV (TEN): STVCD 107 (2CD)   2001
1.JAMES BOND John Barry 2.MISSION IMPOSSIBLE Lalo
Schifrin 3.GOLDFINGER Shirley Bassey 4.THE AVENGERS
Laurie Johnson 5.SAINT Cyril Stapleton Eliminators

6.PERSUADERS John Barry 7.BULLIT Lalo Schifrin 8.
PETER GUNN Henry Mancini 9.IPCRESS FILE John Barry
10.THUNDERBALL Tom Jones 11.SEARCH FOR VULCAN Leroy
Holmes 12.FROM RUSSIA W.LOVE Matt Monro 13.YOU ONLY
LIVE TWICE Nancy Sinatra 14.COME SPY WITH ME Hugo
Montenegro 15.ON HER MAJESTY'S SECRET SERVICE John
Barry 16.GOODBYE CARTER Roy Budd 17.PROFESSIONALS
London Studio Symphony Orch 18.SWEENEY Harry South
19.DIAL M FOR MURDER Ian Rich 20.MAN IN A SUITCASE
Ron Grainer 21.STEPPING STONES Johnny Harris 22.
FEAR IS THE KEY Roy Budd 23.SHAKEN NOT STIRRED M15
24.SHAFT Isaac Hayes 25.IRONSIDE Quincy Jones 26.
TROUBLE MAN Marvin Gaye 27.GREEN ONIONS Booker T. &
MG's 28.WALK ON THE WILD SIDE Jimmy Smith 29.
MANNISH BOY Muddy Waters 30.FEELIN'GOOD Nina Simone
31.BOSS James Brown 32.SON OF A PREACHER MAN Dusty
Springfield 33.BLUE VELVET Bobby Vinton 34.SEA OF
LOVE Phil Phillips 35.FBI Spectres 36.THE MAN FROM
UNCLE Ray Fischer 37.OUR MAN FLINT Hugo Montenegro
38.LITTLE GREEN BAG George Baker 39.DIRTY HARRY
Lalo Schifrin 40.STARSKY & HUTCH Tom Scott 41.
CHARLIE'S ANGELS H.Mancini 42.HILL ST.BLUES Mike
Post-P.Carpenter 43.MIAMI VICE Jan Hammer 44.TWIN
PEAKS A.Badalamenti 45.CHINATOWN Terence Blanchard

224.SHAKESPEARE AT THE MOVIES City Of Prague Phil.Orch-
Crouch End Festival Chorus (Paul Bateman-Nic Raine)
conducted by Kenneth Alwyn
SILVA CLASSICS (Koch): SILKD 6024 (2CD)   *2001*
music & dialogue TWELFTH NIGHT-HAMLET-JULIUS CAESAR
TAMING OF THE SHREW-ROMEO AND JULIET-RICHARD III-A
MIDSUMMER NIGHT'S DREAM-SHAKESPEARE IN LOVE-HENRY V

225.SHOSTAKOVICH Dimitri - The Film Album *
DECCA (UNIV): 460 792-2 (CD)   *1999*
THE COUNTERPLAN SUITE-ALONE-TALE OF THE SILLY
LITTLE MOUSE (Op.56)-HAMLET SUITE (Op.116a)-THE
GREAT CITIZEN-SOFIA PETROVSKAYA (Op.132)-PIROGOV-
THE GADFLY SUITE (Op.97a)
* Concertgebouw Orch.of Amsterdam (Richard Chailly)

---.SILENCIUM: SONGS OF THE SPIRIT - *see* HARLE John
---.SILENTS The - *see under* DAVIS Carl
226.SILVESTRI Alan - CAST AWAY
VARESE (Pinn): VSD 6213 (CD)   *2001*
ROMANCING THE STONE-BACK TO THE FUTURE-WHO FRAMED
ROGER RABBIT-DEATH BECOMES HER-FORREST GUMP-CONTACT
WHAT LIES BENEATH-CAST AWAY

227.SINATRA Frank - SCREEN SINATRA
EMI GOLD: 493 982-2 (CD)   *1998*
FROM HERE TO ETERNITY-THREE COINS IN THE FOUNTAIN-
YOUNG AT HEART-JUST ONE OF THOSE THINGS-SOMEONE TO
WATCH OVER ME-NOT AS A STRANGER-(LOVE IS)THE TENDER
TRAP-JOHNNY CONCHO THEME (WAIT FOR ME)-ALL THE WAY-
CHICAGO-MONIQUE (KINGS GO FORTH)-THEY CAME TO CONDU
RA-TO LOVE AND BE LOVED-HIGH HOPES-ALL MY TOMORROWS
IT'S ALRIGHT WITH ME-C'EST MAGNIFIQUE-DREAM

228.**SINATRA Frank** - REMEMBERS THE MOVIES 1943-1946
GREAT MOVIE THEMES (Target-BMG): CD 60016 (CD) 1997
THREE LITTLE WORDS-WHERE OR WHEN-THAT OLD BLACK
MAGIC-IF I HAD MY WAY-MY IDEAL-TILL THE END OF TIME
MAKE BELIEVE-I ONLY HAVE EYES FOR YOU-EMPTY SADDLES
SOMEBODY LOVES ME-THAT'S FOR ME-IT'S BEEN A LONG LO
NG TIME-WHITE CHRISTMAS-YOU'LL NEVER KNOW-AS TIME
GOES BY-EASY TO LOVE-I'VE GOT YOU UNDER MY SKIN-
ON THE ATCHINSON TOPEKA & SANTA FE-PEOPLE WILL SAY
WE'RE IN LOVE-DON'T FENCE ME IN-WITH A SONG IN MY
HEART-A HOT TIME IN THE OLD TOWN OF BERLIN-
I'LL REMEMBER APRIL-THERE GOES THAT SONG AGAIN

229.**SNOW Mark** - **The Snow Files**
SONIC IMAGES: 78282 78902-2 (SID 8902) (CD) 1999
LA FEMME NIKITA-X.FILES-20,2000 LEAGUES UNDER THE
SEA-OLDEST LIVING CONFEDERATE WIDOW TELLS ALL-WOMAN
SCORNED-CONUNDRUM-MAX HEADROOM-DISTURBING BEHAVIOUR

230.**SONDHEIM Stephen**: **SONDHEIM TONIGHT**
TER (Koch): CDTER2 1250 (2CD)   *1999*
A Live Recording Of The Complete London Barbican
Centre Concert, with The London Philharmonic Orch.
conducted by David Firman and Charles Prince
<u>Artists included</u>: MICHAEL BALL-LEN CARIOU-DAME EDNA
EVERAGE (BARRY HUMPHRIES)-MARIA FRIEDMAN-CLEO LAINE
MILLICENT MARTIN-JULIA McKENZIE-JULIA MIGENES-CLIVE
ROWE-NED SHERRIN-ELAINE STRITCH-DAVID KERNAN etc.
<u>Songs included</u>: COMEDY TONIGHT-NOT WHILE I'M AROUND
MORE-COMPANY-BEING ALIVE-THE BALLAD OF SWEENEY TODD
BROADWAY BABY-LOVING YOU-BEAUTIFUL GIRLS-LADIES WHO
LUNCH-SEND IN THE CLOWNS-LOSING MY MIND-I NEVER DO
ANYTHING TWICE-BARCELONA-NIGHT WALTZ-SUNDAY IN THE
PARK WITH GEORGE-ANOTHER 100 PEOPLE

231.**SOUND GALLERY** - Various Artists
EMI STUDIO 2: CDTWO 2001 / 7243 832280-2 (CD) 1995
OH CALCUTTA:Dave Pell Singers BLACK RITE:Mandingo-
PUNCH BOWL:Alan Parker NIGHT RIDER *(Cadbury's Milk
Tray)*:Alan Hawkshaw RIVIERA AFFAIR:Neil Richardson
JET STREAM:John Gregory HALF FORGOTTEN DAYDREAMS
John Cameron JAGUAR:John Gregory LIFE OF LEISURE
Keith Mansfield GIRL IN A SPORTSCAR:Alan Hawkshaw-
YOUNG SCENE *(ITV BIG MATCH)*:Keith Mansfield
IT'S ALL AT THE CO-OP NOW *(Co-op ad)*:Alan Hawkshaw
FUNKY FEVER:Alan Moorehouse & Bond Street Parade
SHOUT ABOUT PEPSI *(Pepsi)*:Denny Wright & Hustlers
THE HEADHUNTER:Mandingo BLARNEY'S STONED *Dave Allen
Theme)*: Alan Hawkshaw THE EARTHMEN:Paddy Kingsland
I FEEL THE EARTH MOVE:John Keating THE PENTHOUSE
SUITE:Syd Dale THE SNAKE PIT:Mandingo BOOGIE JUICE
Brian Bennett THE DETECTIVES *(Two Ronnies 'Charlie
Farley & Piggy Malone'theme)*:Alan Tew JESUS CHRIST
SUPERSTAR:John Keating MUSIC TO DRIVE BY:Joe Loss

232.**SPACE AND BEYOND** City Of Prague Philh.Orc.Nic Raine
SILVA SCREEN (Koch): FILMXCD 185 (2CD)   *1997*
2001:A SPACE ODYSSEY *(68-RICHARD STRAUSS)*-SPECIES

(94-CHRISTOPHER YOUNG)-CAPRICORN ONE *(78-JERRY GOLD
SMITH)*-APOLLO 13 *(94-JAMES HORNER)*-THE RIGHT STUFF
(83-BILL CONTI)-ALIEN*(79-JERRY GOLDSMITH)*-THE BLACK
HOLE *(79-JOHN BARRY)*-COCOON *(85-JAMES HORNER)*-THE
EMPIRE STRIKES BACK *(80)* STAR WARS *(77-J.WILLIAMS)*
ENEMY MINE *(85-MAURICE JARRE)*-LIFEFORCE *(85-HENRY
MANCINI)*-CLOSE ENCOUNTERS OF THE THIRD KIND *(77-JW)*
STAR TREK I/II/IV/V/VI/DEEPSPACE NINE/NEXT GENERATI
ON/VOYAGER/GENERATIONS/HEAVY METAL *(ALEX.COURAGE/
JERRY GOLDSMITH/DENNIS McCARTHY/J.HORNER/LEONARD
ROSENMAN/CLIFF EIDELMAN)*

233.SPACE AND BEYOND 2: ALIEN INVASION
City Of Prague Philharmonic Orchestra (Nic Raine) &
Crouch End Festival Chorus (David Temple)
SILVA SCREEN (Koch): FILMXCD 190 (2CD) 1999
CD1 1.MARS ATTACKS-2.THE DAY THE EARTH STOOD STILL
3.DUNE 4.STAR TREK: Klingon Attack 5.STAR TREK:DEEP
SPACE NINE 6.STAR TREK: FIRST CONTACT 7.WHEN WORLDS
COLLIDE 8.BATTLE BEYOND THE STARS 9.THE THING FROM
ANOTHER WORLD 10.TWILIGHT ZONE: THE MOVIE Suite 11.
BATTLESTAR GALACTICA 12.STARGATE CD2 1.FORBIDDEN
PLANET 2.MARS (PLANETS) 3.CONTACT 4.STARSHIP TROOPE
RS 5.PREDATOR 6.WAR OF THE WORLDS 7.EMPIRE STRIKES
BACK: Imperial March 8.SPACE: ABOVE AND BEYOND
Suite 9.V 10.STARMAN 11.INDEPENDENCE DAY

234.SPACE AND BEYOND VOL.3: BEYOND THE FINAL FRONTIER
City Of Prague Philharmonic Orchestra
SILVA SCREEN (Koch): FILMXCD 332 (2CD) 2000
27 tracks inc ALIENS-ROBOCOP-THE MATRIX-BACK TO THE
FUTURE-LOST IN SPACE-SILENT RUNNING-ARMAGEDDON-
JOURNEY TO THE FAR SIDE OF THE SUN-STAR WARS: THE
PHANTOM MENACE-GALAXY QUEST-STRANGE INVADERS etc..

235.SPELLBOUND - Great Film Themes / Various Artists
MEMOIR CLASSICS (Target-BMG): CDMOIR 451 (CD) 2000
1.WAY TO THE STARS Two Cities Symphony Orchestra
2.FIRST OF THE FEW (Spitfire Prelude/Fugue) Halle O
3.DANGEROUS MOONLIGHT (Warsaw Concerto) London S.O.
4.LEGEND OF THE GLASS MOUNTAIN George Melachrino Or
5.LEGEND OF THE GLASS MOUNTAIN (Song Of The Mountai
n) Sidney Torch Orch 6.OBSESSION Sidney Torch Orch.
7.WHILE I LIVE (Dream Of Olwen) Charles Williams Or
8.BLITHE SPIRIT (The Waltz) London SO. 9.SPELLBOUND
(Concerto) Queens Hall Light Orch. 10.LOVE STORY
(Cornish Rhapsody) London S.O. 11.THE THIRD MAN
(Harry Lime Theme) Anton Karas 12.HENRY V (Death of
Falstaff/Touch Her Soft Lips) Philharmonia String O
13.MATTER OF LIFE AND DEATH Queens Hall Light Orch
---.**SPIRITS OF NATURE** - *see pages 50 and 338*

236.STAR TREK: Best Of Star Trek Original Film scores
RCA CAMDEN (BMG): 74321 77383-2 (CD) 2000
MUSIC FROM THE STAR TREK MOVIES (1-5) COMPOSED BY
JERRY GOLDSMITH-JAMES HORNER and LEONARD ROSENMAN

237.STAR WARS / CLOSE ENCOUNTERS - Geoff Love Orchestra
MFP (EMI): CD(TC)MFP 6395 (CD/MC) or 7243 857687-2
(70's albums reissued now on 1 CD first time 1997)
STAR WARS-U.F.O.-STAR TREK-BARBARELLA-SPACE 1999-
2001 A SPACE ODYSSEY-MARCH FROM THINGS TO COME-PRIN
CESS LEIA'S THEME FROM STAR WARS-DOCTOR WHO-MARS
BRINGER OF WAR FROM PLANETS SUITE-CLOSE ENCOUNTERS
LOGAN'S RUN-THE TIME MACHINE-MAIN TITLE & 'CANTINA
BAND' FROM STAR WARS-BLAKE'S 7-THE OMEGA MAN

238.STAR WARS TRILOGY Orig Soundtrack Anthology   *1994*
ARISTA (BMG): 07822 11012-2 (4CD box set) FEATURING
'Star Wars'/'The Empire Strikes Back' + previously
unavailable expanded score 'Return Of The Jedi' and
special outtakes + unreleased mus + 50 page booklet

239.STEINER Max - Essential Max Steiner Film Music Coll
City Of Prague P.O.cond.by Nic Raine & Paul Bateman
SILVA SCREEN (Koch/BMG): FILMXCD 351 (2CD)   *2001*
Overtures & Suites from:
KING KONG-DISTANT TRUMPET-ADVENTURES OF DON JUAN-
PARRISH-FLAME AND THE ARROW-CAINE MUTINY-ICE PALACE
NOW VOYAGER-LIFE WITH FATHER-HANGING TREE-TREASURE
OF THE SIERRA MADRE-CASABLANCA-CHARGE OF THE LIGHT
BRIGADE-ADVENTURES OF MARK TWAIN-SPENCER'S MOUNTAIN
THE SEARCHERS-MILDRED PIERCE-SERGEANT YORK-A SUMMER
PLACE-DARK AT THE TOP OF THE STAIRS-FBI STORY-
JOHNNY BELINDA-GONE WITH THE WIND

--- **SUNSET BOULEVARD** - *see* **WAXMAN** Franz

240.SWASHBUCKLERS - City Of Prague Philhar.Paul Bateman
SILVA SCREEN (Koch): FILMXCD 188 (2CD)   *1997*
CD1 Suites & themes 1.CAPTAIN BLOOD 2.PRIVATE LIVES
OF ELIZABETH & ESSEX 3.HOOK 4.THE CRIMSON PIRATE 5.
WILLOW 6.ROBIN HOOD 7.ROBIN HOOD PRINCE OF THIEVES
8.ROBIN AND MARIAN 9/10.ADVENTURES OF ROBIN HOOD
CD2: 1.SEA HAWK 2.MARK OF ZORRO 3/4/5/6.DUELLISTS
7.THE BUCCANEER 8.ADV.OF DON JUAN 9.MONTY PYTHON'S
THE MEANING OF LIFE 10.SEVENTH VOYAGE OF SINBAD 11.
GOLDEN VOYAGE OF SINBAD 12.SWORDSMAN OF SIENNA 13.
CUTTHROAT ISLAND

--- .**SWITCHED ON: THE COOL SOUND OF TV ADVERTISING**
FOR COMPLETE TRACK LISTING see pages 50 and 338
--- .**TAKE A BREAK!** *FOR TRACK LISTING see pages 51 & 339*

241.TASTE OF MUSIC, A - Music from BBC TV Programmes:-
Rick Stein's Taste Of The Sea / Antonio Carlucci's
Italian Feast / Far Flung Floyd / Floyd On Italy /
Floyd on Africa. performed by CROCODILE MUSIC 1997
BBC-VOYAGER (Pinn): V.1021 (CD) V/1022 (MC)

242.TELEVISION'S GREATEST HITS 1 - 65 Orig TV Themes
TVT-EDEL/CINERAMA (Vital) 0022702CIN (CD)   *reiss 96*
CAPTAIN KANGAROO-LITTLE RASCALS-FLINSTONES-WOODY WO
ODPECKER SHOW-BUGS BUNNY-CASPER THE FRIENDLY GHOST-
FELIX THE CAT-POPEYE-YOGI BEAR-MAGILLA GORILLA-TOP
CAT-JETSONS-FIREBALL XL5-HOWDY DOODY-BEVERLY HILLBI

LLIES-PETTICOAT JUNCTION-GREEN ACRES-MR.ED-MUNSTERS
ADDAMS FAMILY-MY THREE SONS-DONNA REEDSHOW-LEAVE IT
TO BEAVER-DENNIS THE MENACE-DOBIE GILLIS-PATTY DUKE
SHOW-DICK VAN DYKE SHOW-GILLIGAN'S ISLAND-McHALE'S
NAVY-I DREAM OF JEANNIE-I LOVE LUCY-ANDY GRIFFITH
SHOW-STAR TREK-LOST IN SPACE-TWILIGHT ZONE-SUPERMAN
ALFRED HITCHCOCK PRESENTS-BATMAN-FLIPPER-RIFLEMAN-
COMBAT-BONANZA-BRANDED-F.TROOP-RIN TIN TIN-WILDWILD
WEST-DANIEL BOONE-LONE RANGER-HAPPY TRAILS-MISSION
IMPOSSIBLE-MAN FROM UNCLE-GET SMART-SECRET AGENTMAN
DRAGNET-PERRY MASON-ADAM 12-FBI-HAWAII 50-77 SUNSET
STRIP-SURFSIDE 6-IRONSIDE-MANNIX-MOD SQUAD-TONIGHT

243.TELEVISION'S GREATEST HITS 2 - 65 Orig TV Themes
TVT-EDEL/CINERAMA (Vital) 0022712CIN (CD)   *reiss 96*
3 STOOGES-MERRIE MELODIES-ROCKY & BULLWINKLE-HUCKLE
BERRY HOUND-MIGHTY MOUSE-COURAGEOUS CAT & MINUTE MO
USE-PINK PANTHER-ROAD RUNNER-GEORGE OF THE JUNGLE-
JONNY QUEST-SPIDERMAN-UNDERDOG-LOONEY TUNES-PEANUTS
THEME-MISTER ROGER'S NEIGHBOURHOOD-ODD COUPLE-COURT
SHIP OF EDDIE'S FATHER-MARY TYLER MOORE-GIDGET-THAT
GIRL-BEWITCHED-LOVE AMERICAN STYLE-HONEYMOONERS-THE
MONKEES-I MARRIED JOAN-BRADY BUNCH-PARTRIDGE FAMILY
MY MOTHER THE CAR-CAR 54 WHERE ARE YOU-IT'S ABOUT
TIME-MY FAVOURITE MARTIAN-JEOPARDY-HOGAN'S HEROES-
GOMER PYLE-RAT PATROL-TWELVE O'CLOCK HIGH-TIME TUNN
EL-VOYAGE TO THE BOTTOM OF THE SEA-SEA HUNT-DAKTARI
TARZAN-ADVENTURES OF ROBIN HOOD-RAWHIDE-BAT MASTERS
ON-MAVERICK-WAGON TRAIN-HAVE GUN WILL TRAVEL-REBEL-
THE VIRGINIAN-PETER GUNN-ROUTE 66-ISPY-THE AVENGERS
THE SAINT-HAWAIIAN EYE-GREEN HORNET-OUTER LIMITS-
DARK SHADOWS-BEN CASEY-MEDICAL CENTER-MYSTERY MOVIE
ABC'S WIDE WORLD OF SPORTS-JACKIE GLEASON-SMOTHERS
BROTHERS COMEDY HOUR-MONTY PYTHON'S FLYING CIRCUS

244.TELEVISION'S GREATEST HITS 3 - 70's and 80's
TVT-EDEL/CINERAMA (Vital) 0022722CIN (CD)   *reiss 97*
SESAME STREET-MUPPET SHOW-ALVIN SHOW-SPEED RACER-MR
MAGOO-INSPECTOR GADGET-THE SMURFS-DASTARDLY& MUTLEY
SCOOBY DOO-FAT ALBERT & CROSBY KIDS-ARCHIES-JOSIE &
PUSSYCATS-DUDLEY DORIGHT-FRACTURED FAIRY TALES-BOB
NEWHART SHOW-CHEERS-GREATEST AMERICAN HERO-WELCOME
BACK KOTTER-ROOM 222-WKRP IN CINCINNATI-TAXI-BARNEY
MILLER-THREE'S COMPANY-HAPPY DAYS-LAVERNE & SHIRLEY
FACTS OF LIFE-GOOD TIMES-ONE DAY AT A TIME-GIMME A
BREAK-MAUDE-JEFFERSONS-ALL INTHE FAMILY-SANFORD AND
SON-DALLAS-DYNASTY-KNOTS LANDING-L.A.LAW-MARCUS WEL
BY MD-ST.ELSEWHERE-MASH-WALTONS-LITTLE HOUSE ON THE
PRAIRIE-HART TO HART-CHARLIE'S ANGELS-WONDER WOMAN-
LOVE BOAT-AMERICAN BANDSTAND-SOLID GOLD-ENTERTAINME
NT TONIGHT-MIAMI VICE-SWAT-BARETTA-STREETS OF SAN
FRANCISCO-BARNABY JONES-STARSKY & HUTCH-ROOKIES-KOJ
AK-A.TEAM-NAME O.T.GAME-QUINCY-HILL ST.BLUES-SIMON
& SIMON-MAGNUM-ROCKFORD FILES-SATURDAY NIGHT LIVE

245.TELEVISION'S GREATEST HITS 4 Black & White Classics
TVT-EDEL/CINERAMA (Vital) 0022732CIN (CD) *1997*
ASTRO BOY-ROGER RAMJET-MIGHTY HERCULES-GUMBY SHOW-
BEANY AND CECIL SHOW-TENNESSEE TUXEDO-QUICK DRAW
McGRAW-WALLY GATOR-KING LEONARDO AND SHORT SUBJECTS
BIG WORLD OF LITTLE ADAM-KUKLA FRAN AND OLLIE-SOUPY
SALES SHOW-CAPTAIN MIDNIGHT-MAKE ROOM FOR DADDY-
FATHER KNOWS BEST-MY LITTLE MARGIE-ADVENTURES OF
OZZIE AND HARRIET-HAZEL-OUR MISS BROOKS-KAREN-THE
REAL McCOYS-LASSIE-LIFE AND LEGEND OF WYATT EARP-
GUNSMOKE-THE LAWMAN-26 MEN-COLT 45-CHEYENNE-BRONCO
LEGEND OF JESSE JAMES-HOPALONG CASSIDY-EVERGLADES-
ADVENTURES IN PARADISE-DR.KILDARE-MEDIC-BURKE'S LAW
HIGHWAY PATROL-M.SQUAD-DETECTIVES-UNTOUCHABLES-THE
FUGITIVE-CHECKMATE-TIGHTROPE-BOURBON STREET BEAT-
PETE KELLY'S BLUES-ASPHALT JUNGLE-MR.BROADWAY-NAKED
CITY-TWENTY FIRST CENTURY-FRENCH CHEF-CANDID CAMERA
YOU BET YOUR LIFE-AMOS 'N' ANDY-ABBOTT & COSTELLO-
LAUREL & HARDY-LAWRENCE WELK SHOW-TED MACK'S ORIG.
AM.HOUR-MISS AMERICA-RED SKELTON SHOW-BOB HOPE SHOW
246.TELEVISION'S GREATEST HITS 5 - In Living Color
TVT-EDEL/CINERAMA (Vital) 0022742CIN (CD) *1997*
STINGRAY-THUNDERBIRDS-GIGANTOR-COOL McCOOL-GO GO
GOPHERS-WORLD OF COMMANDER McBRAGG-SECRET SQUIRREL-
THE ATOM ANT SHOW-WACKY RACES-HONG KONG PHOOEY-
SUPERCHICKEN-TOM SLICK RACER-H.R.PUFNSTUF-LAND OF
THE LOST-SIGMUND AND THE SEA MONSTERS-BANANA SPLITS
PLEASE DON'T EAT THE DAISIES-THE GHOST AND MRS.MUIR
NANNY AND THE PROFESSOR-HERE COME THE BRIDES-THE
FLYING NUN-FAMILY AFFAIR-DATING GAME-NEWLYWED GAME-
LET'S MAKE A DEAL-ALL MY CHILDREN-GENERAL HOSPITAL-
PEYTON PLACE-MARY HARTMAN MARY HARTMAN-GENTLE BEN-
SKIPPY THE BUSH KANGAROO-LIFE AND TIMES OF GRIZZLY
ADAMS-HIGH CHAPARRAL-THE BIG VALLEY-CIMARRON STRIP
LAREDO-THE MEN FROM SHILOH-IT TAKES A THIEF-THE
MAGICIAN-SWITCH-THE FELONY SQUAD-POLICE WOMAN-MEN-
CANNON-JUDD FOR THE DEFENSE-EMERGENCY!-POLICE STORY
SIX MILLION DOLLAR MAN-BIONIC WOMAN-THE GIRL FROM
U.N.C.L.E.-NIGHT GALLERY-KOLCHAK: THE NIGHT STALKER
INVADERS-LAND OF T.GIANTS-LOST IN SPACE-MASTERPIECE
THEATRE-WHERE THE ACTION IS-ROWAN & MARTIN'S LAUGH
IN-THE DEAN MARTIN SHOW-THE CAROL BURNETT SHOW
247.TELEVISION'S GREATEST HITS 6 - Remote Control
TVT-EDEL/CINERAMA (Vital) 0022752CIN (CD) *1997*
FISH-NIGHT COURT-WHAT'S HAPPENING-DIFFERENT STROKES
MR.BELVEDERE-GROWING PAINS-CHARLES IN CHARGE-SILVER
SPOONS-WEBSTER-TOO CLOSE FOR COMFORT-WHO'S THE BOSS
PERFECT STRANGERS-ALICE-IT'S A LIVING-ANGIE-227-THE
GOLDEN GIRLS-ALF-MORK AND MINDY-POLICE SQUAD-BENSON
MOONLIGHTING-SOAP-BENNY HILL SHOW-THE YOUNG ONES-
THE PEOPLE'S COURT-FAMILY FEUD-THE PRICE IS RIGHT-
SISKEL & EBERT-MONDAY NIGHT FOOTBALL-LIFESTYLES OF
THE RICH & FAMOUS-FAME-PAPER CHASE-FANTASY ISLAND-
FALCON CREST-THE COLBY'S-HIGHWAY TO HEAVEN-DUKES OF

HAZZARD-B.J.& THE BEAR-THE FALL GUY-JAMES AT 15-
EIGHT IS ENOUGH-BAA BAA BLACK SHEEP-TRAPPER JOHN MD
CHIPS-VEGAS-MATT HOUSTON-CAGNEY & LACEY-T.J.HOOKER-
HARDCASTLE & McCORMICK-HUNTER-MACGYVER-KNIGHT RIDER
AIRWOLF-THE INCREDIBLE HULK-V THE SERIES-THE NEW
TWILIGHT ZONE-DOCTOR WHO-MYSTERY-HARDY BOYS & NANCY
DREW MYSTERIES-ROOTS-VIETNAM A TELEVISION HISTORY

248.TELEVISION'S GREATEST HITS 7 Cable Ready 80s & 90s
TVT-EDEL/CINERAMA (Vital) 0022762CIN (CD) 1997
THE SIMPSONS-REN AND STIMPY-BROTHERS GRUNT-DUCKMAN-
ADVENTURES OF PETE AND PETE-SPACE GHOST COAST TO
COAST-CLARISSA EXPLAINS IT ALL-BARNEY AND FRIENDS-
WHERE IN THE WORLD IS CARMEN SANDIEGO-SAVED BY THE
BELL-MAJOR DAD-MY TWO DADS-BLOSSOM-FULL HOUSE-EMPTY
NEST-FAMILY MATTERS-COSBY SHOW-DIFFERENT WORLD-ROC-
FRESH PRINCE OF BEL AIR-HOME IMPROVEMENT-ROSEANNE-
SEINFELD-MAD ABOUT YOU-IT'S GARRY SHANDLING'S SHOW-
JOHN LARROQUETTE SHOW-HUDSON STREET-THE SINGLE GUY-
DAVIS RULES-MURPHY BROWN-THE NANNY-DESIGNING WOMEN-
DOOGIE HOWSER MD-WINGS-ANYTHING BUT LOVE-SISTERS-
EVENING SHADE-THE DAYS AND NIGHTS OF MOLLY DODD-
I'LL FLY AWAY-THIRTYSOMETHING-MY SO CALLED LIFE-
BEVERLY HILLS 90210-MELROSE PLACE-HEIGHTS-21 JUMP
STREET-IN THE HEAT OF THE NIGHT-MIDNIGHT CALLER-
AMERICA'S MOST WANTED-UNSOLVED MYSTERIES-SLEDGE
HAMMER-THE EQUALIZER-NYPD BLUE-LAW AND ORDER-TWIN
PEAKS-STAR TREK NEXT GENERATION-LOIS AND CLARK NEW
ADV.OF SUPERMAN-ALIEN NATION-TALES FROM THE CRYPT-
QUANTUM LEAP-MAX HEADROOM-LIQUID TV-TRACEY ULLMAN
SHOW-KIDS IN T.HALL-LATE SHOW WITH DAVID LETTERMAN

249.THEMES FROM CLASSIC SCIENCE FICTION FILMS - V.Arts
VARESE (Pinn): VSD 5407 (CD) 1993
THE MOLE PEOPLE-THE CREATURE FROM THE BLACK LAGOON-
THIS ISLAND EARTH-THE INCREDIBLE SHRINKING MAN-IT
CAME FROM OUTER SPACE-THE CREATURE WALKS AMONG US-
HOUSE OF FRANKENSTEIN-HORROR OF DRACULA-TARANTULA-
SON OF DRACULA-REVENGE OF THECREATURE-DEADLY MANTIS

250.THIS IS CULT FICTION ROYALE - Various Artists
VIRGIN (EMI): VTDCD 151 (2CD) VTDMC 151 (MC) 1997
1.BULLITT MAIN TITLE Lalo Schifrin 2.THE PERSUADERS
John Barry 3.EVA Jean Jacques Perrey 4.THE PRISONER
Ron Grainer 5.SPACE 1999 Barry Gray 6.DIRTY HARRY
Lalo Schifrin 7.THE SWEENEY Harry South (perform.by
Wallace & Brint) 8.MAN IN A SUITCASE Ron Grainer 9.
JAMES BOND THEMEMonty Norman 10.GET CARTER Roy Budd
11.WHODUNNIT (PRECINCT) S.Haseley 12.THE CHAMPIONS
Tony Hatch 13.JOE 90 Barry Gray 14.PROTECTORS (THE
AVENUES AND ALLEYWAYS) Mitch Murray-Peter Callander
(performed by Tony Christie) 15.RANDALL AND HOPKIRK
DECEASED Edwin Astley 16.VAN DER VALK (EYE LEVEL)
Jack Trombey 17.AVENGERS Laurie Johnson 18.SAINT
Edwin Astley (perf: Les Reed Brass) 19.DEMPSEY AND
MAKEPEACE Alan Parker (perf: South Bank Orch) 20.
JASON KING Laurie Johnson 21.SAPPHIRE AND STEEL

Cyril Ornadel 22.UFO **Barry Gray** 23.THE BARON Edwin
Astley 24.THE PROFESSIONALS Laurie Johnson (special
12" Blueboy mix) CD2: MISSION IMPOSSIBLE L.Schifrin
2.DEPARTMENT S.Edwin Astley 3.MAN FROM U.N.C.L.E.
Jerry Goldsmith (perf: Hugo Montenegro) 4.RETURN OF
THE SAINT Martin-Dee (Saint Orch) 5.PROFESSIONALS
Laurie Johnson (perf: London Studio SO) 6.STINGRAY
Barry Gray 7.DANGER MAN (HIGH WIRE) Edwin Astley
(perf: Bob Leaper Orch) 8.007 John Barry 9.ON THE
WAY TO SAN MATEO (from BULLITT) Lalo Schifrin 10.
FIREBALL XL5 **Barry Gray** (vocal: Don Spencer) 11.
THUNDERBIRDS **Barry Gray** 12.STRANGE REPORT Roger
Webb (perf: Geoff Love) 13.NEW AVENGERS Laurie
Johnson 14.CAPTAIN SCARLET **Barry Gray** 15.SUPERCAR
Barry Gray 16.TISWAS Jack Parnell-David Lindup 17.
MAGIC ROUNDABOUT Alain LeGrand 18.TALES OF THE UN
EXPECTED Ron Grainer 19.AQUA MARINA **Barry Gray** (v:
Gary Miller) 20.CROWN COURT (DISTANT HILLS) Reno-
Haseley 21.HILL ST.BLUES Mike Post 22.TWIN PEAKS
Angelo Badalamenti 23.BLADE RUNNER BLUES Vangelis
251.THRILLER MEMORANDUM The - **Various Artists**
RPM (Pinn): RPM 173 (CD) 1996   reissued 1999
2.MEXICAN FLYER Ken Woodman & Piccadilly Brass 2.
THE MAIN CHANCE John Schroeder Orc 3.YES AND NO Des
Champ 4.THE PARTY Nico Mamangakis 5.FLY BY NIGHT
Briab Marshall Orch 6.GHOST SQUAD Tony Hatch OrC 7.
SILENCERS Patti Seymour 8.FADE OUT John Shakespeare
9.LE TRAIN FOU Jacques Denjean 10.LIVE AND LET DIE
David Lloyd & His London Or. 11.KISSY SUZUKI Sounds
Orchestral 12.TWELVE BY TWO Ken Woodman Piccadilly
Brass 13.A NIGHT WITH NUKI Brian Marshall Orch 14.
THE SAINT Edwin Astley Or. 15.SHARP SHARKS Ingfried
Hoffman 16.MISSION IMPOSSIBLE Mike Hurst Orches 17.
ADVENTURE Mark Wirtz Orch 18.WEDNESDAY'S CHILD Mike
Hurst Orch 19.THE HUSTLE Basil Kirchen 20.BIG M Des
Champ 21.INTERCEPTION David Whittaker Orch 22.
PENTHOUSE (MAIN TITLOE)/DANCE Johnny Hawsworth 23.
DANGER MAN Edwin Astley Orch 24.MAN IN A SUITCASE
Alexander Stone
252.THRILLERS! - City Of Prague Philharm.(Paul Bateman/
Nic Raine/Derek Wadsworth) / London Screen Orchest
Royal Philharmonic Concert Orch (Mike Townend) and
Lesley Garrett w.Chamber Orch of London (Nic Raine)
SILVA SCREEN Treasury (Koch): SILVAD 3504 (CD) 1997
1:NORTH BY NORTHWEST *(B.HERRMANN)* 2:PATRIOT GAMES
(J.HORNER) 3:UNTOUCHABLES *(E.MORRICONE)* 4:FUGITIVE
(J.NEWTON HOWARD) 5:QUILLER MEMORANDUM *(J.BARRY)*
6:NIGHTHAWKS *(K.EMERSON)* 7:IN THE LINE OF FIRE *(E.
MORRICONE)* 8:THE FIRM *(D.GRUSIN)* 9:IPCRESS FILE
(J.BARRY) 10:MAGNUM FORCE / 11:MISSION IMPOSSIBLE
(L.SCHIFRIN) 12:PRESUMED INNOCENT *(J.WILLIAMS)* 13:
INNOCENT SLEEP *(M.AYRES, sung by* Lesley Garrett*)*
14:WITNESS *(M.JARRE)*   *tpt: 50.18*

253.THUNDERBIRDS & OTHER TOP 60s TV THEMES VOL.2 V.Arts
SEQUEL-CASTLE (Pinn): NEBCD 425 (CD) *1999*
1.THUNDERBIRDS Cyril Stapleton & The Eliminators 2.
AVENGERS "The Shake" (orig version) Laurie Johnson
3.STEPTOE & SON Eagles 4.Z-CARS "Z-Cars Cha Cha"
John Warren Orch 5.PEYTON PLACE/CORONATION STREET
Bruce Forsyth 6.IT'S DARK OUTSIDE "Where Are You
Now" Jackie Trent 7.FRONT PAGE STORY "The Big Beat"
Eric Delaney Orch 8.MAVERICK Terry Young 9.WAGON
TRAIN "Roll Along Wagon Train" Robert Horton 10.
COMEDY PLAYHOUSE "Happy Joe" Eagles 11.DICK POWELL
SHOW Tony Hatch Orch 12.EUROFASHION "Birds" Tony
Hatch Orch 13.AT LAST THE 1948 SHOW "Ferret Song"
John Cleese & 1948 Show Choir 14.STINGRAY "Aqua
Marina" Gary Miller 15.CAPTAIN SCARLET "Mysterons"
Barry Gray 16.JOE 90 "Hi-jacked" Barry Gray 17.
THUNDERBIRDS "Parker Well Done" B.G.18.THIRD MAN
"Harry Lime" Big Ben Banjo Band 19.DESPERATE PEOPLE
"Desperados" Eagles 20.STRANGER ON THE SHORE Eagles
21.CROSSROADS "Where Will You Be" Sue Nicholls 22.
LUNCH BOX" Lunch Boxer" Jerry Allen Trio 23.OLYMPIC
"Mexico" Long J.Baldry 24.HANCOCK "Spying Tonight"
Derek Scott Music 25.ANDORRA Ron Grainer Orch 26.
STEPTOE & SON "Junk Shop" Harry H.Corbett 27.SAINT
Les Reed Brass 28.ROBIN HOOD Gary Miller 29.DARK
ISLAND Alexander Brothers 30.BATMAN Kinks

254.TIOMKIN Dimitri - LEGENDARY HOLLYWOOD
CITADEL (Hot): STC 77128 (CD) *2000*
themes and suites from DIMITRI TIOMKIN film scores
THE GUNS OF NAVARONE / THE PRESIDENT'S COUNTRY /
RHAPSODY OF STEEL / WILD IS THE WIND / THE FALL OF
THE ROMAN EMPIRE

255.TIOMKIN Dimitri Western Film World London Studio SO
Laurie Johnson,John McCarthy Sing. *UNICORN KANCHANA
(H.Mundi): UKCD 2011 (CD)* Suites: GIANT-RED RIVER-
DUEL IN THE SUN-HIGH NOON-NIGHT PASSAGE-RIO BRAVO
Suites and Film score themes from Classic Westerns

256.TOTALLY MOVIES: The Essential Soundtrack Album
EMI GOLD: 531 987-2 (CD) *2001*
1.PUMPING ON YOUR STEREO Supergrass *(ROAD TRIP)* 2.
EVERY DAY SHOULD BE A HOLIDAY Dandy Warhols *THERE'S
SOMETHING ABOUT MARY* 3.DAY BEFORE YESTERDAY'S MAN
Supernaturals *(SHOOTING FISH)* 4.GET IT ON T.Rex
(BILLY ELLIOT) 5.GOLDEN BROWN Stranglers *(SNATCH)*
6.MONY MONY Billy Idol *(STRIPTEASE)* 7.POWER OF LOVE
Huey Lewis & News *(BACK TO THE FUTURE)* 8.CALL ME
Blondie *(AMERICAN GIGOLO)* 9.WALKING ON SUNSHINE
Katrina & Waves *(HIGH FIDELITY)* 10.ON A CAROUSEL
Hollies *EAST IS EAST* 11.MARY'S PRAYER Danny Wilson
THERE'S SOMETHING ABOUT MARY 12.TENDER TRAP Robert
Palmer *(TRUE ROMANCE)* 13.KING OF WISHFUL THINKING
Go West *PRETTY WOMAN* 14.DO YOU REALLY WANT TO HURT
ME Culture Club *WEDDING SINGER* 15.TEMPTATION Heaven
17 *TRAINSPOTTING* 16.BOOGIE SHOES KC & Sunshine Band

BOOGIE NIGHTS 17.HEAVEN MUST BE MISSING AN ANGEL
Tavares *(CHARLIE'S ANGELS)* 18.YOU SEXY THING Hot
Chocolate *(THE FULLL MONTY)*

257.**TOWERING INFERNO: Great Disaster Movies** - V.Artists
VARESE (Pinn): VSD 5807 (CD)   *1999*
Royal Scottish Nat.Orch. TOWERING INFERNO-TWISTER-
EARTHQUAKE-SWARM-POISEIDON ADVENTURE-DANTE'S PEAK-
VOLCANO-OUTBREAK-INDEPENDENCE DAY-TITANIC

258.**TRUE GRIT: Music from classic films of JOHN WAYNE**
City Of Prague Philharmonic cond: by Paul Bateman
SILVA SCREEN (Koch): FILMCD 725 (CD)   *2000*
1.STAGECOACH SUITE 2/3/4.THE QUIET MAN SUITE 5.THE
HIGH AND THE MIGHTY 6.HOW THE WEST WAS WON 7.THE
LONGEST DAY 8.SEARCHERS 9.HATARI 10/11.THE ALAMO
12.SONS OF KATIE ELDER 13/14.IN HARM'S WAY 15.SHE
WORE A YELLOW RIBBON 16.TRUE GRIT 17.THE COWBOYS

259.**TUNES FROM THE TOONS** - The Best Of HANNA-BARBERA
MCI (MCI-THE): MCCD(MCTC) 279 (CD/MC)   *1996*
1-2 DASTARDLY & MUTTLEY 3-5 TOP CAT 6-8 YOGI BEAR 9
-12FLINTSTONES 13-14 HUCKLEBERRY HOUND 15-16 PERILS
OF PENELOPE PITSTOP 17-18 SNOOPER & BLABBER 19-21
JETSONS 22-23 HAIR BEAR BUNCH 24.SECRET SQUIRREL 25
HONG KONG PHOOEY 26-27 JOSIE & THE PUSSYCATS 28-29
SCOOBY DOO WHERE ARE YOU 30.NEW SCOOBY DOO 31-32
TOUCHE TURTLE 33-34 WALLY GATOR 35-37 PIXIE & DIXIE
38-40 QUICK DRAW McGRAW 41-42 SNAGGLEPUSS 43.HONEY
WOLF 44.AUGIE DOGGIE 45.YANKY DOODLE 46.LIPPY LION
& HARDY HA HA 47.WACKY RACES 48.BANANA SPLITS THEME

---.**TURN ON! TUNE IN!** - Various Artists   *1999*
FOR COMPLETE TRACK LISTING see pages 52 and 339

260.**TV 2000** Themes* & tracks from TV Shows / Var.Arts
SONY TV (TEN): SONYTV82CD (CD)   *2000*
DAWSONS CREEK*-FRIENDS*-ALLY McBEAL*-ROYLE FAMILY*-
BUFFY T.VAMPIRE SLAYER-TRIGGER HAPPY TV-COLD FEET*
SABRINA THE TEENAGE WITCH-PARTY OF 5-FATHER TED-MEN
BEHAVING BADLY-ABSOLUTELY FABULOUS*-SHIPWRECKED*THE
SOPRANOS*-SOUTH PARK-NORTH HOLLYWOOD HIGH-X-FILES

261.**TV THEMES OF THE SIXTIES** - Various Artists
CASTLE PIE (Pinn): PIESD 025 (CD)   *1999*
1.THUNDERBIRDS Barry Gray Orch 2.AVENGERS Laurie
Johnson Orch 3.THE SAINT Les Reed Brass 4.DANGERMAN
Bob Leaper Orch 5.FUGITIVE John Schroeder Orch 6.
THANK YOUR LUCKY STARS Peter Knight Or 7.TOP SECRET
Laurie Johnson Orch 8.NAKED CITY Tony Hatch Orch
9.SPIES Cyril Stapleton Orch 10.ODD COUPLE Button
Down Brass 11.IRONSIDE Alan Tew Orch 12.WHICKER'S
WORLD Laurie Johnson 13.MAN ALIVE Tony Hatch 14.
CAPTAIN SCARLET Barry Gray Orch 15.MAIGRET Eagles
16.Z-CARS Johnny Keating & Z Men 17.STEPTOE AND SON
Ron Grainer 18.PERRY MASON Tony Hatch Orch

262.**ULTIMATE MOVIE ALBUM The** - Various Artists
UNIVERSAL MUSIC TV: 585 712-2 (2CD)   *2001*
1.OUT OF REACH *(BRIDGET JONES DIARY)* 2.NOW WE ARE
FREE *(GLADIATOR)* 3.DEAD ALREADY *(AMERICAN BEAUTY)*

4.DOWN TO THE RIVER TO PRAY *(O BROTHER WHERE ART THOU)* 5.WHEN YOU SAY NOTHING AT ALL *(NOTTING HILL)* 6.18 WITH A BULLET *(LOCK STOCK AND 2 SMOKING BARR.)* 7.FOR THE LOVE OF A PRINCESS *(BRAVEHEART)* 8.VIDE COR MEUM *(HANNIBAL)* 9.SCHINDLER'S LIST MAIN THEME 10.MISSION IMPOSSIBLE 11.ADAGIO *(PLATOON/ELEPHANT MAN)* 12.JURASSIC PARK End Credits/Main Theme 13. HYMN TO THE FALLEN *(SAVING PRIVATE RYAN)* 14.JAWS Main theme and first victim theme 15.JUST DROPPED IN *(BIG LEBOWSKI)* 16.LA MAMMA MORTA Maria Callas *(PHILADELPHIA)* 17.HERNANDO'S HIDEAWAY *(SNATCH)* 18. MUSTANG SALLY *(COMMITMENTS)* 19.COSMIC DANCER *BILLY ELLIOT* 20.PELAGIA'S SONG *(CAPTAIN CORELLI'S MANDOLIN)* 21.LOVE IS ALL AROUND *(FOUR WEDDINGS & A FUNERAL)* 22.STAR WARS MAIN THEME 23.JOHN DUNBAR *(DANCES WITH WOLVES)* 24.SHE *(NOTTING HILL)* 25.LET THE DRAW BEGIN *(WAKING NED)* 26.OUT OF AFRICA LOVE THEME 27.BATTLE excerpt from *GLADIATOR* 28.GOLDBERG VARIATIONS *(SILENCE OF THE LAMBS)* 29.PIANO CONCERTO NO.3 IN D.MINOR (RACHMANINOV) *(SHINE)* 30.INTERMEZZO FROM CAVALLERIA RUSTICANA (MASCAGNI) (GODFATHER 3) 31.DEATH CAMP *(X-MEN)* 32.O MIO BABBINO CARO (PUCCINI) *(ROOM WITH A VIEW)* 33.ADAGIO FROM CELLO SONATA BWV 1029 (BACH) *(TRULY MADLY DEEPLY)* 34. YOU'RE THE FIRST THE LAST MY EVERYTHING *(FOUR WEDDINGS AND A FUNERAL)*35.SON OF A PREACHER MAN *(PULP FICTION)*

---.UTOPIA - Chilled Classics - *see COLL.286*

263.VANGELIS - GENIUS: The Music Of VANGELIS
N2 (Sound and Media): NEW 213 (CD) 1999
1492...-ANTARCTICA-CHUNH KUO-L'EFANT-MUTINY ON THE BOUNDARY-BLADERUNNER-HYMN-CHARIOTS OF FIRE-LOVE THEME FROM BLADERUNNER-TO AN UNKNOWN MAN-MISSING-PULSTAR-CIRCLES-WILL OF THE WORLD-DAWN-VOICES

264.VANGELIS - REPRISE 1990 to 1999
EAST WEST (Ten): 3984 29828-2 (CD) 1999
BLADERUNNER-1492 CONQUEST OF PARADISE-ANTARCTICA-DREAMS OF SURF-OPENING-MONASTERY AT LA RABIDA-COME TO ME-LIGHT AND SHADOW-FIELDS OF CORAL-EL GRECO (m/m 5)-EL GRECO (m/m 6)-WEST ACROSS THE OCEAN SEA THEME FROM BITTER MOON-RACHEL'S SONG-EL GRECO (m/m 4)-THEME FROM THE PLAGUE-DAWN-PRELUDE

265.WAR! - City Of Prague Philharmonic (Paul Bateman)
SILVA SCREEN Treasury (Koch): SILVAD 3502 (CD) 1997
1:WHERE EAGLES DARE *(RON GOODWIN)* 2:BATTLE OF THE BULGE *(B.FRANKEL)* 3:CASUALTIES OF WAR *(E.MORRICONE)* 4: 633 SQUADRON *(R.GOODWIN)* 5:SINK THE BISMARCK! *(C.PARKER)* 6:BRIDGE AT REMAGEN *(E.BERNSTEIN)* 7: MACARTHUR / PATTON *(J.GOLDSMITH)* 8:DAS BOOT (BOAT) *(K.DOLDINGER)* 9:NIGHT OF THE GENERALS *(M.JARRE)* 10: GUNS OF NAVARONE *(D.TIOMKIN)* 11:LONGEST DAY*(P.ANKA)* 12:BATTLE OF MIDWAY *(J.WILLIAMS)* 13:IN HARM'S WAY *(GOLDSMITH)* 14:IS PARIS BURNING *(M.JARRE)* tpt 54.19

266.WARRIORS OF THE SILVER SCREEN City Of Prague Phil.*
SILVA SCREEN (Koch): FILMXCD 187 (2CD)   *1997*
Symphonic Suites: BRAVEHEART-THE THIEF OF BAGDAD-
TARAS BULBA-ANTHONY AND CLEOPATRA-FIRST KNIGHT-
HENRY V-EL CID-PRINCE VALIANT-BEN HUR-THE VIKINGS
Themes: ROB ROY-SPARTACUS-THE 300 SPARTANS-WAR LORD
LAST VALLEY-CONAN T.BARBARIAN-JASON AND T.ARGONAUTS
City Of Prague P.O. and Crouch End Festival Chorus

--- **WARSAW CONCERTO** - *see also under* ADDINSELL Richard

267.WARSAW CONCERTO & OTHER FILM THEMES Bournemouth SO*
CFP (EMI): CDCFP 9020 (CD) CFP 41 4493-4 (MC)   *1988*
WARSAW CONCERTO from 'Dangerous Moonlight'(Film 41)
(Richard Addinsell)- THE DREAM OF OLWEN from 'While
I Live' (Film 47) (Charles Williams)-SPELLBOUND CON
CERTO from 'Spellbound' (Film 45)(Miklos Rozsa)-THE
CORNISH RHAPSODY from 'Love Story' (Film 44)(Hubert
Bath) -RHAPSODY IN BLUE (Film 45) (George Gershwin)
(K.Alwyn) feat Daniel Adni (Piano) 1980 reiss 1988

268.WARSAW CONCERTO + OTHER PIANO CONCERTOS FROM MOVIES
NAXOS (Select): 8.554323 (CD)   *1998*
1.WARSAW CONCERTO *(R.ADDINSELL)* 2.PORTRAIT OF ISLA
(J.BEAVER) 3.SPELLBOUND *(M.ROSZA)* 4.LEGEND OF THE
GLASS MOUNTAIN *(NINO ROTA)* 5.MURDER ON THE ORIENT
EXPRESS *(R.R.BENNETT)* 6.CORNISH RHAPSODY *(H.BATH)*
7.HANGOVER SQUARE *(B.HERRMANN)* 8.THE DREAM OF OLWEN
(C.WILLIAMS) 9.JULIE *(L.STEVENS, arr.PENNARIO)* feat
RTE CONCERT ORCH (P.O'Duinn, cond) PHILIP FOWKE pno

269.WARSAW CONCERTO - Jean Yves Thibudet (piano) with*
Romantic Piano Classics From The Silver Screen
DECCA CLASSICS (UNIV): 460 503-2 (CD)   *1998*
1.WARSAW CONCERTO *(R.ADDINSELL)* Dangerous Moonlight
2.PIANO CONCERTO NO.2 *(RACHMANINOV)* Brief Encounter
/ Seven Year Itch 3.RHAPSODY ON A THEME OF PAGANINI
(RACHMANINOV) Story Of Three Loves / Groundhog Day
4.RHAPSODY IN BLUE *(GERSHWIN)* 5.PIANO CONCERTO NO.2
*(SHOSTAKOVICH) *Cleveland Orch.& BBC Symphony Orch.*

270.WAXMAN Franz - LEGENDS OF HOLLYWOOD
VARESE (Pinn): VSD 5242 (CD) New Recordings   *1990*
TASK FORCE-OBJECTIVE BURMA-PEYTON PLACE-SORRY WRONG
NUMBER-THE PARADINE CASE-DEMETRIUS & THE GLADIATORS

271.WAXMAN Franz - LEGENDS OF HOLLYWOOD - Volume 2
VARESE (Pinn): VSD 5257 (CD)   *1991*
BRIDE OF FRANKENSTEIN-MR.ROBERTS-POSSESSED-CAPTAINS
COURAGEOUS-THE NUN'S STORY-HUCKLEBERRY FINN etc.

272.WAXMAN Franz - LEGENDS OF HOLLYWOOD - Volume 3
VARESE (Pinn): VSD 5480 (CD)   *1994*
ELEPHANT WALK (6 tracks)-THE FURIES (5)-DESTINATION
TOKYO (5)-THE SILVER CHALICE (6)-NIGHT AND THE CITY
NIGHT UNTO NIGHT-HOTEL BERLIN-MR.SKEFFINGTON (2)

273.WAXMAN Franz - LEGENDS OF HOLLYWOOD - Volume 4
VARESE (Pinn): VSD 5713 (CD)   *1996*
New recordings of Suites from Franz Waxman's scores
Queensland Symphony Orch.conducted by Richard Mills
1.UNTAMED (1955) 2/3/4.ON BORROWED TIME (39) 5/6/7.

MY GEISHA (62) 8.DEVIL DOLL (36) 9.MY COUSIN RACHEL
(52) 10/11/12.STORY OF RUTH (60) 13/14/15.DARK CITY
(1950) 16/17/18/19/20.A CHRISTMAS CAROL (1938)

---.**WAYNE John** - see under **'TRUE GRIT'**

274.**WEBB Marti** PERFORMANCE with Philharmonia Orch.*1989*
FIRST NIGHT (Pinn): OCRCD 6033 (CD)   reissued 1995
Introduction: I DREAMED A DREAM *Les Miserables* /
ALMOST LIKE BEING IN LOVE *Brigadoon* / MUSIC OF THE
NIGHT *Phantom* /LOSING MY MIND *Follies* /ANYTHING BUT
LONELY *Aspects Of Love* / ONLY HE *Starlight Express*
MEMORY *Cats* / LOVE CHANGES EVERYTHING *Aspects*/ ONCE
YOU LOSE YOUR HEART *Me and My Girl* /LAST MAN IN MY
Life *Tell Me On A Sunday*/BLOW GABRIEL *Anything Goes*

275.**WEBB Roy** - Film Music / Slovak Radio Symphony Orch.
MARCO POLO (Select): 8.225125 (CD)   2000
Music from CAT PEOPLE (1942); THE SEVENTH VICTIM
(1943); BEDLAM (1946); THE BODY SNATCHER (1945);
I WALKED WITH A ZOMBIE (1943)

276.**WESTERN MOVIE THEMES** - Various Artists
LASERLIGHT-Target (BMG): 24608 (2CD)   2001
RIO BRAVO-HANG 'EM HIGH-MAN WITH THE HARMONICA-A
FISTFUL OF DOLLARS-MAGNIFICENT 7-ONCE UPON A TIME
IN THE WEST-MY NAME IS NOBODY-HIGH NOON-BALLAD OF
THE ALAMO-HOW THE WEST WAS WON-JOHNNY GUITAR-GOOD
LUCK JACK-COMANCHEROS-WANDRIN'STAR-GOOD THE BAD AND
THE UGLY-FOR A FEW DOLLARS MORE-CLAUDIA'S THEME-RIO
BRAVO-SHANE-BLAZE OF GLORY-VERA CRUZ-THE VIRGINIAN-
PREFESSIONAL GUN-HIGH PLAINS DRIFTER-BONANZA-MAN
FROM LARAMIE-TARA'S THEME-RAINDROPS KEEP FALLING ON
MY HEAD-KNOCKIN'ON HEAVEN'S DOOR-WINNETOU MELODIE-
DER MIT DERM WOLF TANZT-RIDERS IN THE SKY

277.**WESTERNS!** - City Of Prague Philharm. (Paul Bateman/
Nic Raine/Derek Wadsworth) Philharmonia Orch. (Tony
Bremner) / Westminster Philh.Orch (Kenneth Alwyn)
SILVA SCREEN Treasury (Koch): SILVAD 3503 (CD) 1997
1:BIG COUNTRY *(J.MOROSS)* 2:WILD ROVERS*(J.GOLDSMITH)*
3:UNFORGIVEN *(C.EASTWOOD)* 4: A DISTANT TRUMPET *(MAX
STEINER)* 5: and 6:ONCE UPON A TIME IN THE WEST *(E.
MORRICONE)* 7:HOW THE WEST WAS WON *(ALFRED NEWMAN)*
8:DANCES WITH WOLVES *(J.BARRY)* 9: MAGNIFICENT SEVEN
(E.BERNSTEIN) 10:FISTFUL OF DOLLARS *(E.MORRICONE)*
11:STAGECOACH *(arr,TOWNEND)* 12:TRUE GRIT *(ELMER
BERNSTEIN)* 13:TWO MULES FOR SISTER SARA *(MORRICONE)*
14:SONS OF KATIE ELDER *(ELMER BERNSTEIN)*

278.**W.G.SNUFFY WALDEN** - Music By...
BMG IMPORTS: 01934 11424-2 (CD)   2001
WEST WING-ANGELA SMILED-FELICITY-ONCE AND AGAIN-
LOVE UNSPOKEN-THIRTYSOMETHING-SKETCHES OF TOPANGA-
EUGENE'S RAGTOP-BIG CITY ALONE-TURTLE BAY

279.**WILD WEST The** - Essential Western Film Music Coll.
SILVA SCREEN (Koch): FILMXCD 315 (2CDs)   1999
tracks: THE ALAMO-BIG COUNTRY-BUFFALO GIRLS-
THE COWBOYS-DANCES WITH WOLVES-DISTANT TRUMPET-
EL CONDOR-A FISTFUL OF DOLLARS-GETTYSBURG-GLORY-

HEAVEN'S GATE-HIGH PLAINS DRIFTER-HOW THE WEST WAS
WON-LAST OF THE MOHICANS-LONESOME DOVE-MAGNIFICENT
SEVEN-MAVERICK-MONTE WALSH-ONCE UPON A TIME IN THE
WEST-PROFESSIONALS-OUTLAW JOSEY WALES-PROUD REBEL-
RARE BREED-RED SUN-THE SEARCHERS-STAGECOACH-
SILVERADO-SHE WORE A YELLOW RIBBON-SONS OF KATIE
ELDER-TRUE GRIT-TWO MULES FOR SISTER SARA-THE
UNFORGIVEN-VILLA RIDES-WAGON TRAIN (TV)-THE WILD
BUNCH-WILD ROVERS-WYATT EARP-WILD WILD WEST (TV)

280.**WILLIAMS** John - **CLOSE ENCOUNTERS: The Essential
JOHN WILLIAMS Film Music Album** *featuring the*
City Of Prague Philharmonic and Crouch End Festival
Chorus conducted by Paul Bateman and Nic Raine
SILVA SCREEN (Koch): FILMXCD 314 (2CD)   *1999*
SAVING PRIVATE RYAN-HOOK-COWBOYS-BORN ON THE 4TH OF
JULY-FAMILY PLOT-JFK-EMPIRE OF THE SUN-AMISTAD-THE
TOWERING INFERNO-SUPERMAN-THE RIVER-JAWS-STAR WARS-
EMPIRE STRIKES BACK-PRESUMED INNOCENT-INDIAN JONES
& THE TEMPLE OF DOOM-SCHINDLER'S LIST-BLACK SUNDAY-
CLOSE ENCOUNTERS OF THE THIRD KIND-INDIANA JONES &
THE LAST CRUSADE-RARE BREED

281.**WILLIAMS** John - **John Williams Greatest Hits 1969-99**
SONY CLASSICS: 2SK(S2T)(S2M) 51333 (2CD/MC/md) 1999
London Symph.Orch/Boston Pops Orch (John Williams)
themes & music: STAR WARS-E.T.-SUPERMAN-JAWS-SAVING
PRIVATE RYAN-STAR WARS: THE PHANTOM MENACE-INDIANA
JONES AND THE LAST CRUSADE-SUGARLAND EXPRESS-JFK-
RAIDERS OF TH LOST ARK-RETURN OF THE JEDI-REIVERS-
OLYMPIC THEME and FANFARE-EMPIRE IF THE SUN-CLOSE
ENCOUNTERS OF THE THIRD KIND-EMPIRE STRIKES BACK-
JURASSIC PARK-SCHINDLER'S LIST-HOOK-1941-STEPMOM-
ROSEWOOD-SEVEN YEARS IN TIBET-FAR AND AWAY-SUMMON
THE HEROES-HOME ALONE-BORN ON THE FOURTH OFJULY-

282.**WITH A SMILE AND A SONG: Best Of Film Cartoon Songs**
FLAPPER-Pavilion (Pinn): PASTCD 7842 (CD)   *2000*
ORIGINAL CAST VOICE RECORDINGS
Dumbo: LOOK OUT FOR MR.STORK/CASEY JONES/MR.STORK/
BABY MINE/PARADE OF THE PINK ELEPHANTS/WHEN I SEE
AN ELEPHANT FLY/SONG OF THE ROUSTABOUTS-FARMYARD
SYMPHONY (Parts 1/2) Pinocchio: WHEN YOU WISH UPON
A STAR/GIVE A LITTLE WHISTLE/HI DIDDLE DE DEE (AN
ACTORS LIFE FOR ME)/I'VE GOT NO STRINGS-THREE
LITTLE PIGS.Snow White & The 7 Dwarfs: WITH A SMILE
AND A SONG/DIG DIG DIG..HEIGH HO/I'M WISHING/ONE
SONG/WHISTLE WHILE YOU WORK/DWARF'S YODEL SONG/SOME
DAY MY PRINCE WILL COME.MICKEY'S GRAND OPERA Bambi:
LOVE IS A SONG/LITTLE APRIL SHOWER.3 LITTLE WOLVES

283.**WORLD OF SOUND: FAVOURITE THEMES FROM BBCTV & RADIO**
BBC Worldwide (Koch UK): 33635-2 (CD) -4 (MC) 1997
1.999/999 INTERNATIONAL Roger Bolton 2.CASUALTY Ken
Freeman 3.CHILDREN'S HOSPITAL Debbie Wiseman 4.BY
THE SLEEPY LAGOON *(DESERT ISLAND DISCS)* Eric Coates
5.HETTY WAINTHROP INVESTIGATES Nigel Hess 6.FAWLTY
TOWERS Dennis Wilson Quartet 7.HOWARDS' WAY Simon

May Or.8.HAVE I GOT NEWS FOR YOU Big George Webley
9.DOCTOR WHO Ron Grainer 10.RHODES MAIN THEME Alan
Parker Orchestra 11.BRING ME SUNSHINE *(MORECAMBE &
WISE SHOW)* Morecambe & Wise 12.EASTENDERS Simon May
13.MICHAEL'S THEME *(PARKINSON)* Harry Stoneham Five
14.I WISH I KNEW HOW IT WOULD FEEL TO BE FREE *(FILM
98)*Billy Taylor Trio 15.AT THE SIGN OF THE SWINGIN'
CYMBAL *(PICK OF THE POPS)* Brian Fahey Orchestra 16.
GOING STRAIGHT Ronnie Barker17.ON A MOUNTAIN STANDS
A LADY *(LIVER BIRDS)* Scaffold 18.MARCHING STRINGS
(TOP OF THE FORM) Ray Martin Orchestra 19.THAT WAS
THE WEEK THAT WAS Millicent Martin 20.HIT AND MISS
(JUKE BOX JURY) John Barry 21.SAILING BY *(RADIO 4
SHIPPING FORECAST)*John Scott 22.CALLING ALL WORKERS
(MUSIC WHILE YOU WORK) Eric Coates Orchestra 23.
IMPERIAL ECHOES *(RADIO NEWSREEL)* Band Of The R.A.F.
24.IN PARTY MOOD *(HOUSEWIVE'S CHOICE)* Jack Strachey
25.SOMEBODY STOLE MY GAL *(BILLY COTTON BAND SHOW)*
Billy Cotton Band 26.MUCH BINDING IN THE MARSH Kenn
eth Horne-Richard Murdoch BBC Radio Orch (S.Black)
284.YOUNG Victor - SHANE: A TRIBUTE TO VICTOR YOUNG
New Zealand Symphony Orch, conduct: Richard Kaufman
KOCH INTernational (Koch): 3-7365-2H1 (CD)   1996
SHANE *(1952)* FOR WHOM THE BELL TOLLS *(1943)* AROUND
THE WORLD IN EIGHTY DAYS *(1956)* THE QUIET MAN*(1952)*
SAMSON AND DELILAH *(1949)* *cond.by Richard Kaufman
285.CHILDREN'S FAVOURITE TV THEMES - **Various Artists**
UNIVERSAL MUSIC: 585 571-2 (CD)   2001
1.BOB THE BUILDER CAN WE FIX IT 2.TWEENIES READY TO
PLAY 3.POSTMAN PAT 4.TELETUBBIES SAY EH OH 5.THE
JELLYKINS 6.MAISY MOUSE 7.POOH BEAR LITTLE BLACK
RAIN CLOUD 8.BILL AND BEN 9.BARNEY THE DINOSAUR I
LOVE YOU 10.FIREMAN SAM 11.TWEENIES NUMBER ONE 12.
THUNDERBIRDS 13.BANANAS IN PYJAMAS 14.FETCH THE VET
15.KIPPER THE DOG 16.LETTERLAND 17.ROSIE & JIM 18.
NODDY IN TOYLAND 19.TWEENIES DO THE LOLLYPOP 20.
NELLIE THE ELEPHANT 21.WOMBLES WOMBLING SONG 22.
RUPERT THE BEAR 23.TOY STORY 2: WOODY'S ROUND UP
24.LITTLE GREY RABBIT 25.SOOTY 26.PUFF THE MAGIC
DRAGON 27.THE SNOWMAN: WALKING IN THE AIR 28.
PICOCCHIO: WHEN YOU WISH UPON A STAR
286.UTOPIA Chilled Classics - **Various Artists**
UNIVERSAL MUSIC TV: 472 064-2 (2CD)   2001
inc.music from GLADIATOR / BLUE PLANET / PLATOON /
SILENT WITNESS / DEER HUNTER / AMERICAN BEAUTY /
ONE GAME / CAPTAIN CORELLI'S MANDOLIN / THE PIANO
BLADERUNNER / SCHINDLER'S LIST/ DANCES WITH WOLVES
BRAVEHEART / IF / MY DINNER WITH ANDRE / TITANIC /
NOSTRADAMUS and various classical works including
works by *MOZART-SISSEL-MASSENET-FAURE-BIZET-SATIE*
Artists include RUSSELL WATSON-NIGEL KENNEDY-NEW
COLLEGE CHOIR-VANGELIS

BEST TV ADS...EVER - Various Artists
VIRGIN (EMI): VTDCDX 306 (2CD) VTDMC 306 (MC) 2000
C1 1.INKANYEZI NEZAZI Ladysmith Black Mambazo *HEINZ*
2.I HEARD IT THROUGH THE GRAPEVINE Marvin Gaye *LEVI*
3.YOU GOTTA BE Des'ree *FORD FOCUS* 4.SERACH FOR THE
HERO M People *PEUGEOT 406* 5.I JUST WANNA MAKE LOVE
TO YOU Etta James *DIET COKE* 6.LET'S FACE THE MUSIC
& DANCE Nat King Cole *ALLIED DUNBAR* 7.MEMORIES ARE
MADE OF THIS Dean Martin *PEUG.306* 8.MUSIC TO WATCH
GIRLS BY Andy Williams *FIAT PUNTO* 9.GUAGLIONE Perez
Prado *GUINNESS* 10.BULLITT Lalo Schifrin *FORD PUMA*
11.BLOW UP A-GO-GO James Clark *GAP* 12.MAS QUE NADA
Sergio Mendes *NIKE* 13.FLY ME TO THE MOON Julie
London *FORD PROBE* 14.WONDROUS PLACE Billy Fury *TOY.*
YARIS 15.MELLOW YELLOW Donovan *GAP* 16.I CAN'T LET
MAGGIE GO Honeybus *NIMBLE* 17.GOOD VIBRATIONS Beach
Boys *BT* 18.PART OF THE UNION Strawbs *NORWICH UNION*
19.WILD THING Troggs *B.KING* 20.WE GOTTA GET OUT OF
THIS PLACE Animals *HONDA* 21.HE AIN'T HEAVY Hollies
MILLER LITE 22.YOUR CHEATIN' HEART Glen Campbell
CASTLEMAINE XXXX 23.THAT'S AMORE Dean Martin *PIZZA
HUT* 24.STAND BY ME Ben E.King *LEVI* 25.WHEN A MAN
LOVES A WOMAN Percy Sledge *LEVI* 26.MERCEDES BENZ
Janis Joplin *MERCEDES BENZ* CD2 1.FIND MY BABY Moby
NISSAN ALMERA 2.THE UNIVERSAL Blur *BRITISH GAS* 3.
SHE'S THE ONE Robbie Williams *SEGA DREACAST* 4.SMILE
Supernaturals *SMILE INTERNET* 5.PASSENGER Iggy Pop
TOYOTA AVENSIS 6.HEROES David Bowie *CGU* 7.INSIDE
Stiltskin *LEVI* 8.DO YOU WANT ME Felix *TANGO* 9.FLAT
BEAT Mr.Oizo *LEVI* 10.DRINKING IN L.A.Bran Van 3000
ROLLING ROCK 11.TURN ON TUNE IN COPOUT Freakpower
LEVI 12.SPACEMAN Babylon Zoo *LEVI* 13.BOOMBASTIC
Shaggy *LEVI* 14.JUMP AROUND House Of Pain *CAFFREYS*
15.OOH LA LA Wiseguys *BUDWEISER* 16.CARS Gary Numan
CARLING 17.ONE WAY OR ANOTHER Blondie *CAFFREYS* 18.
THAT'S THE WAY I LIKE IT KC & Sunshine Band *KFC* 19.
IN THESE SHOES? Kirsty MacColl *ADIDAS SPORTWEAR* 20.
MAYBE TOMORROW (LITTLEST HOBO THEME) Scooch *(not
the orginal Terry Bush version)* NAT.WEST
COMMERCIAL BREAK: Old Tunes from The New Ads - Var
ASV (Select): AJA 5281 (CD) 1998
1.JEEPERS CREEPERS *(SURE SENSIVE)* Louis Armstong 2.
HAPPY FEET *(CLARK'S SHOES)* Jack Hylton Orchestra 3.
BOTTLENECK BLUES 4.JUNGLE JAMBOREE Duke Ellington
4.SWEET AND LOVELY *(CADBURY HIGH LIGHTS)* Al Bowlly
5.WON'T YOU GET OFF IT PLEASE *(TATE & LYLE)* Fats
Waller 6.EGYPTIAN ELLA *(TERRY'S PYRAMINTS)*Ted Lewis
7.SUN HAS GOT HIS HAT ON *(BRITISH GAS)* Sam Browne 8
LOVE IS THE SWEETEST THING *(BLACK MAGIC)* Al Bowlly
9.TEDDY BEAR'S PICNIC *(PERSIL/SONY CAMCORDER)* Henry
Hall Orch 10.LET'S FACE THE MUSIC AND DANCE *(ALLIED
DUNBAR)* Fred Astaire 11.STOMPIN'AT THE SAVOY *(P.& O
FERRIES)* Benny Goodman Orch 12.VERY THOUGHT OF YOU
PRETTY POLLY) Al Bowlly 13.PENNIES FROM HEAVEN*(BT)*

Frances Langford, Bing Crosby & Louis Armstrong 14. ORIENTAL SHUFFLE *(RADIO TIMES)* Stephane Grappelli & Django Reinhardt 15.BOUM *(PPP HEALTHCARE)* Charles Trenet 16.IN THE MOOD *(RADION/ANCHOR BUTT/DORITOS)* Glenn Miller Or 17.LA CUMPARSITA *(No.7)* Dinah Shore 18.WHEN YHOU WISH UPON A STAR *(DISNEYLAND)* Cliff Edwards 19.GRASSHOPPERS DANCE *(MILK)*Alfredo Campoli 20.YES SIR THAT'S MY BABY *(JOHNSON'S BABY)* Eddie Cantor 21.TICO TICO *(WHISKAS)* Andrews Sisters 22. SENTIMENTAL JOURNEY *(CADBURY'S INSPIRATIONS)* Doris Day 23.ZIP-A-DEE-DOO-DAH *(MITSUBISHI CARISMA)* 24. AS TIME GOES BY *(NPI PENSIONS)* Dooley Wilson

COMMERCIAL BREAKS COLLECTION - Various Artists

EMI HMV: 533 842-2 (CD)   *2001*
1.YOUR CHEATIN' HEART Glen Campbell *CASTLMAINE XXXX* 2.YOU WERE MADE FOR ME Freddie & Dreamers *DAIRYLEA* 3.ROADRUNNER Animals *FORD FIESTA* 4.AIR THAT I BREATHE Hollies *COMFORT CONDITIONER* 5.I'LL PUT YOU TOGETHER AGAIN Hot Chocolate *CADBURY'S HIGHLIGHTS* 6 MELLOW YELLOW Donovan *KRAFT MELLO* 7.TEACH ME TIGER April Stevens *WHISKAS* 8.WHEN YOU'RE SMILING Louis Prima *FINCHES ORANGE* 9.WILD IS THE WIND Nuna Simone *LINDT CHOCOLATE* 10.NIGHT RIDER Alan Hawkshaw *MILK TRAY orig* 11.THOSE MAGNIFICENT MEN IN THEIR FLYING MACHINES Ron Goodwin *RED BULL* 12.IN THE MOOD Joe Loss *ANCHOR BUTTER* 13.I'M SITTING ON TOP OF T.WORLD Bobby Darin *LEVI DOCKERS* 14.ANGELENA Louis Prima *MASTERCARD* 15.STOMPIN' AT THE SAVOY Benny Goodman *P.& O.Ferries* 16.GOPHER TANGO Perez Prado *ADDICTION* 17.PUT A LITTLE LOVE IN YOUR HEART Jackie DeShannon *MICHELOB* 18.CALL ME IRRESPONSIBLE Dinah Washington *VW* 19.I LOVE YOU PORGY Nina Simone *ORANGE* 20.FLY ME TO THE MOON Julie London *FORD PROBE* 21.STORY OF MY LIFE Michael Holliday *GUINNESS* 22.CRAZY Willie Nelson *ELIZABETH SHAW CHOCOLATES*

COMMERCIAL BREAKS: COOLER SIDE OF TV ADVERTISING

COMMERCIAL BREAKS: COMBCD 001 (2CD)   *2001*
1.WOMAN IN BLUE Pepe De Luxe *LEVI* 2.ORIGINAL Leftfield *GUINNESS* 3.UNDERWATER LOVE SmokeCity *LEVI* 4.ITCHY & SCRATCHY Boss Hogg *LEVIS* 5.SLIP INTO SOMETHING MORE COMFORTABLE Kinobe *KRONENBERG* 6. DEATH IN VEGAS Dirge *LEVI* 7.RUN ON Moby *RENAULT* 8. THE CHILD *ALEX GOPHER* 9.NOVELTY WAVES Biosphere *LEVI* 10.HISTORY REPEATING ITSELF Propellerheads *JAGUAR* 11.CLUBBED TO DEATH Rob D *CAFFREYS* 12.SIX UNDERGROUND Sneaker Pimps *CARLING* 13.BLINDFOLD Mocheeba 14.IF EVERYBODY LOOKED THE SAME Groove Armada *MERCEDES* 15.EVA Jean Jacques Perrey *LUCOZADE* 16.CARS Gary Numan *A.EXPRESS* 17.SECOND LINE Clinic *LEVI* 18.HEATMISER/ANGEL Massive Attack *MORGAN STANLEY* 19.LIFE IN MONO Mono *ROVER 25* 20.ADAGIO FOR STRINGS William Orbit *TIMES* 21.PURE MORNING Placebo *LEXUS* 22.IN THE MEANTIME Spacehog *MERCURY ONE-2-ONE* 23.SUNBURN Muse *IMAC* 24.PLAY DEAD Bjork *VAUXHALL*

OFF YER BOX - Various Original Artists (TV ADS MUSIC)
WRASSE (UNIV): WRASS 039 (CD)   *2001*
1.GUAGLIONE Perez Prado 2.CHEWY CHEWY Ohio Express
3.GIMME DAT DING Pipkins 4.HOT DIGGITY Perry Como
5.ISRAELITES Desmond Dekker 6.WIPEOUT Surfaris
7.MINISKIRT Esquivel Orc.8.BABY ELEPHANT WALK Henry
Mancini 9.BARBARABATIRI Benny More 10.BOUM Charles
Trenet 11.INCIDENTALLY ROBERT Tot Taylor 12.VA BA
BOOM Edmundo Ross 13.SOUL BOSSA NOVA Quincy Jones
14.FOX Hugo Montenegro 15.DICK TRACY Dean Fraser
16.GREEN BOSSA Tot Taylor 17.SURFIN' Ernest Ranglin
18.DA DA DA Trio 19.HOOTS MON Lord Rockingham's XI
20.RUBBER BISCUIT Chips 21.BANANA BOAT SONG (DAY-O)
Harry Belafonte 22.FOLLOW THE YELLOW BRICK ROAD
Victor Young Orchestra

SPIRITS OF NATURE - Various Original Artists
VIRGIN (EMI): VTCD 87 (CD) VTMC 87 (MC)   *1996*
1.YE-HA NO-HA (WISHES OF HAPPINESS AND PROSPERITY)
Sacred Spirit 2.SWEET LULLABY Deep Forest 3.LITTLE
FLUFFY CLOUDS The Orb 4.THE SUN RISING The Beloved
5.X-FILES (DJ DADO PARANORMAL ACTIVITY MIX) DJ Dado
6.RETURN TO INNOCENCE Enigma 7.STARS (MOTHER DUB)
Dubstar 8.THE WAY IT IS Chameleon 9.PLAY DEAD Bjork
& David Arnold 10.ARIA ON AIR *BRITISH AIRWAYS AD*
Malcolm McLaren 11.ADIEMUS *DELTA AIRWAYS AD* Adiemus
12.ONLY YOU *FIAT TEMPRA* Praise 13.FALLING*TWIN PEAKS*
Julee Cruise 14.MAD ALICE LANE: A GHOST STORY *LAND
ROVER DISCOVERY* Peter Lawlor 15.SENTINEL Mike Oldfi
eld 16.THEME FROM THE MISSION Ennio Morricone 17.
THE HEART ASKS PLEASURE FIRST/THE PROMISE from THE
PIANO Michael Nyman 18.FASHION SHOW II from THREE
COLOURS RED Zbigbniew Preisner 19.CHARIOTS OF FIRE

SWITCHED ON: THE COOL SOUND OF TV ADVERTISING *2000*
TELSTAR RECORDS: TTVCD 3086 (2CD) TTVMC 3086 (2MC)
CD1 1.SMILE Supernaturals *SMILE* 2.WHAT I LIKE ABOUT
YOU Loop Da Loop *MILLER* 3.DRIFTING AWAY Faithless
ROLLING ROCK 4.DRINKING IN LA Bran Van 3000 *R.ROCK*
5.ORIGINAL Leftfield *VAUXHALL* 6.AND THE BEAT GOES
ON All Seeing Eye *BT CELLNET* 7.RIGHT HERE RIGHT NOW
Fatboy Slim *ADIDAS* 8.PURPLE Crustation with Bronagh
Slevin *DAEWOO* 9.LOOSE FIT Happy Mondays *ORANGE* 10.
RUDE BOY ROCK Lion Rock *SONY MD* 11.MUCHO MAMBO SWAY
Shaft *KISS* 12.SOUND OF DA POLICE KRS One *PHYSIO
SPORTS* 13.SUGAR IS SWEETER CJ Bolland *IMPULSE* 14.
ORGAN GRINDER'S SWING Jimmy Smith *RENAULT CLIO* 15.
JUMP AROUND House Of Pain *CAFFREYS* 16.ENTER THE
MONK Monk & Canatella *DAEWOO* 17.CAN'T TAKE MY EYES
OFF YOU Andy Williams *PEUGEOT 306* 18.HISTORY REPEAT
ING Propellerheads-Shirley Bassey *JAGUAR* 19.BULLITT
Lalo Shifrin *-S/T- BULLITT* 20.6 UNDERGROUND Sneaker
Pimps *CARLING* 21.FLAT BEAT Mr.Oizo *LEVI* CD2: 1.DIVE
Propellerheads *ADIDAS* 2.CLUBBED TO DEATH Rob D *THE
MATRIX/CAFFREYS* 3.EASY LEASING SUPERSTAR Le Hammond
Inferno *NIKE* 4.BACK BY DOPE DEMAND King Bee *BODDING*

TONS 5.CONNECTED Stereo MCs *CARPHONE WAREHOUSE* 6.
RUN ON Moby *RENAULT KANGOO* 7.BLUE MONDAY '88 New
Order *AMERICAN EXPRESS* 8.RODNEY YATES David Holmes
NAT.WEST 9.BENTLEY'S GONNA SORT YOU OUT Bentley
Rhythm Ace *LYNX* 10.TURN ON TUNE IN COP...Freakpower
LEVI 11.BLOW UP A GO-GO James Clarke *GAP* 12.DON'T
YOU WANT ME Felix *TANGO* 13.ENCORE UNE FOIS Sash!
L'OREAL 14.GOING OUT OF MY HEAD Fatboy Slim *ROVER45*
15.BRIMFUL OF ASHA Cornershop *CAFFREYS* 16.HAVE A GO
HERO Urban DK *MASTERCARD* 17.JACQUES YOUR BODY (MAKE
ME SWEAT) Les Rhythmes Digitales *SUNNY DELIGHT* 18.
TAME Pixies *SMIRNOFF RED LAB.* 19.SHE SELLS SANCTUARY
Cult *KENCO* 20.ONE WAY OR ANOTHER Blondie *BAILEYS*
21.OOH LA LA Wiseguys *BUDWEISER* 22.FUN LOVIN'
CRIMINAL Fun Lovin' Criminals *MERCEDES*

TAKE A BREAK! - **Various Artists**
COLUMBIA (Ten): 494 464-2 (CD) -4 (MC)   1999
1.MUSIC TO WATCH GIRLS BY Andy Williams *FIAT PUNTO*
2.PUT YOU TOGETHER AGAIN Hot Chocolate *CADBURY'S HC*
3.DOWNTOWN Petula Clark *ROVER* 4.ON THE STREET WHERE
YOU LIVE Nat King Cole *QUALITY STREET* 5.WHAT A DIFF
ERENCE A DAY MADE Dinah Washington *CROWN PAINTS* 6.
PERHAPS PERHAPS PERHAPS Doris Day *CANDEREL* 7.I CAN
HELP Billy Swan *BT* 8.CALL ME Chris Montez *BT* 9.IF I
HAD A HAMMER Trini Lopez*BARCLAYCARD* 10.SHE'S A LADY
Tom Jones *WEETABIX* 11.JUMP JIVE & WAIL Louis Prima
GAP 12.DON'T FENCE ME IN Bing Crosby & Andrews Sist
ers *CENTERPARCS* 13.YOU DO SOMETHING TO MEAlma Cogan
GALAXY 14.CAN'T SMILE WITHOUT YOU Lena Fiagbe *BT* 15
SHE'S NOT THERESantana *KFC* 16.WALK LIKE AN EGYPTIAN
Bangles *KINDER EGGS* 17.WALKING ON SUNSHINE Katrina
& The Waves *SHREDDED WHEAT* 18.THAT LADY Isley Bros.
KFC 19.LOLA Kinks *WEETABIX* 20.DON'T STOP MOVIN'
Livin' Joy *TAKE A BREAK*

TURN ON! TUNE IN! - **Various Artists**
JAZZ FM/BEECHWOOD (BMG): JAZZFMCD 15 (2CD)   1999
1.ON THE STREET WHERE YOU LIVE Nat King Cole *TV AD:
QUALITY STREET* 2.WE HAVE ALL THE TIME IN THE WORLD
Louis Armstrong *GUINNESS* 3.I JUST WANNA MAKE LOVE
TO YOU Etta James *DIET COKE* 4.FEELING GOOD Nina
Simone *VW GOLF/COMFORT* 5.MAD ABOUT THE BOY Dinah
Washington *LEVI* 6.SPEAKING OF HAPPINESS Gloria Lynn
FORD MONDEO 7.LEFT BANK2 Noveltones*VW GOLF/AMBROSIA*
8.LET'S FACE THE MUSIC & DANCE Nat King Cole *ALLIED
DUNBAR* 9.MY SHIP HAS SAILED Sarah Vaughan *GALAXY* 10
I PUT A SPELL ON YOU Nina Simone *DIET COKE/PERRIER*
11.I WANT TWO LIPS April Stevens *PEUGEOT 306* 12.
WHEN A A MAN LOVES A WOMAN Percy Sledge *LEVI* 13.I'M
SITTING ON TOP OF THE WORLD Al Jolson *GUINNESS/RENN
IES* 14.STAND BY ME Ben E.King *LEVI* 15.MY BABY JUST
CARES FOR ME Nina Simone *CHANEL NO.5* 16.SMOKESTACK
LIGHTNING John Lee Hooker *BUDWEISER* 17.CAN'T SMILE
WITHOUT YOU Lena Fiagby *BT* 18.OCEAN DRIVE The
Lighthouse Family *ALPEN* 19.FLY ME TO THE MOON Julie

London *FORD PROBE* 20.DREAM A LITTLE DREAM Mamas and Papas *PEUGEOT 406* 21.CALL ME Chris Montez *BT* 22. TURN ON TUNE IN COP OUT Freakpower *LEVI* 23. CANTELOUPE ISLAND Us 3 *KFC* 24.SOUL BOSSA NOVA Quincy Jones *NIKE* 25.MAS QUE NADA Tamba Trio *NIKE* 26.GUAGLIONE Perez Prado *GUINNESS* 27.BIG BAMBOOZLE Barry Adamson *BAILEY'S IRISH CREAM* 28.JUMP JIVE AND WAIL Brian Setzer *GAP JEANS* 29.EVA Jean Jacques Perrey *LUCOZADE* 30.MOVE ON UP Curtis Mayfield *CITROEN XSARA* 31.GET DOWN TONIGHT KC & Sunshine Band *BUDWEISER* 32.PATRICIA Perez Prado *ROYAL MAIL*

SOUNDTRACKS-DVD-VHS VIDEOS

ALADDIN (1993) Mus: ALAN MENKEN-HOWARD ASHMAN-TIM RICE
 CD -S/T- *Disney: 014 260-2DNY (CD)*
 VHS   *Disney: D.216622*
ALICE IN WONDERLAND (1951) Music score: OLIVER WALLACE
 CD -S/T- *Disney USA: 609607*
 DVD   *Disney: DO 34530 /* VHS *Disney: D.200362*
AN EXTREMELY GOOFY MOVIE (2000)
 VHS   *Disney: D.610624*
 DVD   *Disney: DO 610624*
ARISTOCATS The (1970) Songs: RICHARD and ROBERT SHERMAN
 CD -S/T- *Disney: 014 250-2DNY /* VHS *Disn: D.241902*
ATLANTIS THE LOST EMPIRE (2001)
 CD *Disney: 60713-7 (CD)*
BAMBI (1943) Songs: FRANK CHURCHILL-E.PLUMB-LARRY MOREY
 CD -S/T- *Disney USA: AVCW 12073 (CD)*
 VHS   *Disney: D.209422*
BASIL THE GREAT MOUSE DETECTIVE 1986 Mus: HENRY MANCINI
 VHS   *Disney: D.213602*
BEAUTY AND THE BEAST (1992) Songs: ALAN MENKEN-H.ASHMAN
 CD -S/T- *Disney: 011 360-2DNY (CD)*
 VHS   *Disney: D.213252*
BEDKNOBS AND BROOMSTICKS (1971) Songs by R.& R.SHERMAN
 VHS   *Disney: D.200162 / D.300165 (special ed.)*
BLACK HOLE The (1979) Music score by JOHN BARRY
 VHS   *Disney: D.200112*
BLACKBEARD'S GHOST (1967) Music score: ROBERT BRUNNER
 VHS   *Disney: D.200622*
BUG'S LIFE, A (1998) Music & songs: RANDY NEWMAN
 CD -S/T- *Disney: 010634-2DNY (CD)*
 DVD   *Disney: DO 34631*
 VHS   *Disney: 610214 / 910214 (widescreen)*
CINDERELLA (1950) M: OLIVER WALLACE-PAUL J.SMITH & oth.
 VHS   *Disney: D.204102*
DUCKTAILS THE MOVIE (1991) Music score: DAVID NEWMAN
 VHS   *Disney: D.210822*
DUMBO (1941) Music: F.CHURCHILL-O.WALLACE-N.WASHINGTON
 CD -S/T- *Disney USA: AVCW 12076*
 DVD   *Disney: DO 34539 /* VHS *Disney: D.202472*
FANTASIA (1940) -S/T- (dig.remastered in 1990)
 CD -S/T- *Disney: DSTCD 452D (2CD)*
 DVD   *Disney: D.888085*
FANTASIA 2000 (1999) *details see page 107*
 CD -S/T- *Disney: 010 558-2DNY (CD)*
 DVD   *Disney: D.888100*
FLUBBER (1997) Music score: DANNY ELFMAN
 CD -S/T- *Disney: WD 77566-2 (CD)*
 DVD   *Disney: DO 34521 /* VHS: *D.610486/D.610867*
FOX AND THE HOUND The (1981) Songs: RICHARD & R.SHERMAN
 VHS VID *Disney: D.220412*

GEORGE OF THE JUNGLE (1997)
CD -S/T-   *Disney: 010 444-2DNY (CD)*
DVD   *Disney: DO.34511 / VHS   Disney: D.610108*
GOOFY MOVIE The (1995) Music: DON DAVIS + V.Artsists
CD -S/T-   *Disney: WD 76400-2 (CD)*
DVD   *Disney: DO 34598 / VHS   Disney: D.274512*
HERCULES (1997) Music score: ALAN MENKEN
CD -S/T-   *Disney: WD 60864-2 (CD)*
DVD   *Disney: DO 34687 / VHS   Disney D.270832*
HUNCHBACK OF NOTRE DAME The (1996) Music: ALAN MENKEN
CD -S/T-   *Disney: WD 77190-2 (CD)*
VHS   *Disney: D.610058*
JAMES AND THE GIANT PEACH (1995) M/Songs: RANDY NEWMAN
CD -S/T-   *Disney: WD 68120-2 (CD)*
DVD   *Guild: P8870DVD /   VHS   Guild: G8870S*
JUNGLE BOOK (1967) Songs: RICHARD and ROBERT SHERMAN
CD -S/T-   *Disney: WD 70400-2 (CD)*
DVD   *Disney: DO 34689 / VHS Disney: D.211222*
LADY AND THE TRAMP The (1956) Songs: PEGGY LEE-J.BURKE
CD -S/T-   *Disney: WD 6021328 (CD)*
DVD   *Disney: DO 34688 / VHS Disney: D.205822*
LION KING The (1994) M: HANS ZIMMER-ELTON JOHN-TIM RICE
CD -S/T-   *Disney: WD 60802-2 (CD) ROCKET: 522 690-2*
VHS   *Disney: D.229772 deleted*
LION KING 2 - *see* 'SIMBA'S PRIDE'
CD -S/T-   *Disney: 010 150-2DNY (CD)*
DVD   *Disney: DO 34549*
VHS   *Disney: 270892 / 970892 (VHS widescreen)*
LITTLE MERMAID (1990) Songs: ALAN MENKEN-HOWARD ASHMAN
CD -S/T-   *Disney: WD 60628-2 (CD) WD 60946-2 (CD)*
DVD   *Disney: DO 34690 / VHS Disney: D.209132*
MARY POPPINS (1964) Songs by RICHARD and ROBERT SHERMAN
CD -S/T-   *Disney: WD 77572-2 (CD)*
DVD   *Disney: DO 34550 / VHS Disney: D.200232*
MONSTERS INC. (2001)   Music by RANDY NEWMAN
CD   *Disney: D.60712*
MULAN (1998) Music score by JERRY GOLDSMITH
CD -S/T-   *Disney (USA): 60631 (CD)*
DVD   *Disney: DO 34686 delet / VHS : D.270852*
OLIVER AND COMPANY (1989) Music score by J.A.C.REDFORD
CD -S/T-   *Disney: WD 608902 (CD)*
VHS   *Disney: D.240302*
101 DALMATIONS (1961) Songs: MEL LEVIN m: BRUNS/DUNHAM
DVD   *Disney: DO34691 / VHS Disn: D.212632 del.*
101 DALMATIONS (1996) Music score: MICHAEL KAMEN
CD -S/T-   *Disney: WD 69940-2 (CD)*
VHS   *Disney: D.271262*
102 DALMATIONS (2000) Music Score by DAVID NEWMAN
CD -S/T-   *Disney: 012 219-2DNY (CD)*
PETER PAN (FILM 1953) Music: OLIVER WALLACE-PAUL SMITH
CD -S/T-   *Disney: WD 77583-2 (CD)*
VHS   *Disney: D.202452 deleted*
PETE'S DRAGON (1977) Mus.dir: IRWIN KOSTAL with V.Arts
DVD   *Disney: DO 34557 / VHS Disney: D.200102*

PINOCCHIO (1939) M: LEIGH HARLINE-P.SMITH-N.WASHINGTON
CD -S/T-   Disney: WD 75430-2 (CD)
DVD   Disney: DO 34692 / VHS Disney: D.202392
POCAHONTAS (1995) Music ALAN MENKEN-STEPHEN SCHWARTZ
CD -S/T-   Disney: WDR 75462-2 (CD)
VHS   Disney: Vista D.274522
RELUCTANT DRAGON The (1941)
VHS   Disney: D.205332
RESCUERS The (1976) 'Story Of The Rescuers'
VHS   Disney: D.240642
RESCUERS DOWN UNDER The (1990) Mus sco: BRUCE BROUGHTON
CD -S/T-   Disney (USA): 60613-2 (CD)
VHS   Disney: D.211422
RETURN OF JAFAR (1994)
VHS   Disney: D.222372
ROBIN HOOD (1973) ROGER MILLER-PHIL HARRIS-TERRY THOMAS
VHS   Disney: D.202282
SLEEPING BEAUTY (1959) Mus: GEORGE BRUNS
CD -S/T-   Disney: WDR 75622-2 (CD)
VHS   Disney: D.204762
SNOW WHITE & THE SEVEN DWARFS 1937 ADRIANA CASELOTTI
CD -S/T-   Disney: WD 74540-2 (CD)
VHS   Disney: / VHS : D.215242 limited
DVD   Disney: D.888340 (Oct.2001) limited
SONG OF THE SOUTH (1946) Music by: DANIEL AMFITHEATROF
VHS   Disney: D.201022
SUMMER MAGIC (1963)   Songs: RICHARD and ROBERT SHERMAN
VHS   Disney: deleted
SWORD IN THE STONE (1963) Songs: RICHARD/ROBERT SHERMAN
DVD   Disney: DO 34575 / VHS Disney: D.202292
TARZAN (1999) Music: MARK MANCINA Songs by PHIL COLLINS
CD -S/T-   Disney: 010247-2DNY (CD) + 010248-2DNY
DVD   Disney: DO 888083 / DO 888084 (coll edit)
VHS   Disney: D.670862
THREE CABALLEROS The (1945) Mus: CHARLES WOLCOTT & oth.
VHS   Disney: D.200912
TIGGER MOVIE The (2000) - see page 243
CD -S/T-   Disney: 010 874-2DNY (CD)
DVD   Disney: DO 888087 / VHS Disney: D.610197
TOY STORY (1996) Music and songs by RANDY NEWMAN
CD -S/T-   Disney: WD 77130-2(CD)
DVD   Disney: DO 888125 / VHS D.272142 deleted
TOY STORY 2 (1999) Music & Songs by RANDY NEWMAN
CD -S/T-   Disney (USA): 60647 (CD)
DVD   Disney: DO 888108 wide / VHS Disn: 610213
WIND IN THE WILLOWS The (1949)
VHS   Disney: D.204272 deleted
WINNIE THE POOH Many Adventures Of Winnie The Pooh 1977
VHS   Disney: D.200252
WINNIE THE POOH 'The Many Songs of WINNIE THE POOH'
CD AUDIO   Disney: WD 11564-2 (CD)
WINNIE THE POOH AND A DAY FOR EEYORE 1983 SHERMAN BROS.
VHS   Disney: D.205322

WINNIE THE POOH AND CHRISTMAS TOO 1991 M: SHERMAN BROS.
VHS   *Disney: D.241232*
WINNIE THE POOH AND T.BLUSTERY DAY (1968) SHERMAN BROS.
VHS   *Disney: D.200632*
WINNIE THE POOH AND THE HONEY TREE (1966) SHERMAN BROS.
VHS   *Disney: D.200492*
WINNIE THE POOH AND TIGGER TOO (1974) Mus:SHERMAN BROS.
VHS   *Disney: D.200642*
WINNIE THE POOH: GREAT RIVER RESCUE (New Adventures Of)
VHS   *Disney: D.241032*

DISNEY'S GREATEST HITS - Various Artists   2000
TELSTAR (BMG): TTVCD 3151 (2CD) TTVMC 3151 (2MC)
1.YOU'LL BE IN MY HEART *(TARZAN)* Phil Collins 2.EGG
TRAVELS *DINOSAUR* 3.WHOLE NEW WORLD *ALADDIN* Peabo
Bryson-Regina Belle 4.WHEN SHE LOVED ME *TOY STORY 2*
Sarah McLachlan 5.BARE NECESSITIES *JUNGLE BOOK* Phil
Harris 6.REFLECTION *MULAN* Christina Aguilera 7.
SOMEDAY *HUNCHBACK OF NOTRE DAME* Eternal 8.HEIGH HO!
SNOW WHITE& 7DWARFS 9.CAN YOU FEEL THE LOVE TONIGHT
LION KING 10.COLOURS OF THE WIND *POCAHONTAS* Vanessa
Williams 11.CRUELLA DE VILLE *101 DALMATIONS* Dr.John
12.STAR IS BORN *HERCULES* Jocelyn Brown 13.BIBBIDY
BOBBIDY BOO *CINDERELLA* Louis Armstrong 14.HE'S A
TRAMP *LADY AND THE TRAMP* Peggy Lee 15.WHEN I SEE AN
ELEPHANT FLY *DUMBO* 16.KISS THE GIRL *LITTLE MERMAID*
Peter Andre 17.TIME OF YOUR LIFE *A BUG'S LIFE* Randy
Newman 18.SORCERER'S APPRENTICE (Dukas) *FANTASIA
2000* Philharmonic Orch 19.SHOOTING STAR *HERCULES*
Boyzone 20.HAKUNA MATATA *LION KING* 21.I WILL GO
SAILING NO MORE *TOY STORY* Randy Newman 22.GO THE
DISTANCE *HERCULES* Michael Bolton 23.I WANNA BE LIKE
YOU *JUNGLE BOOK* 24.TRUE TO YOUR HEART *MULAN* 25.98
DEGREES *BEAUTY AND THE BEAST* Angela Lansbury 26.
SOMEDAY *HERCULES* Donna Summer 27.ZIP A DEE DOO DAH
SONG OF THE SOUTH James Baskett 28.REFLECTION *MULAN*
Vanessa Mae 29.LITTLE APRIL SHOWER *BAMBI* 30.SUPERCA
LIFRAGILISTICEXPIALIDOCIOUS *MARY POPPINS* 31.MONKEYS
UNCLE Annette Funicello-Beach Boys 32.GOSPEL TRUTH
HERCULES Jocelyn Brown 33.SOMEDAY MY PRINCE WILL
COME *SNOW WHITE* Adriana Caselotti 34.ZERO TO HERO
HERCULES Sounds Of Blackness 35.TOCCATA AND FUGUE
(Bach)/NUTCRACKER SUITE (Tchaikovsky) *FANTASIA* 36.
WHEN YOU WISH UPON A STAR *Pinocchio* Louis Armstrong

DISNEY'S HIT SINGLES & MORE - Various Artists   1998
WALT DISNEY-EDEL (Vital) 010 054-2DNY (CD) -4 (MC)
1.CIRCLE OF LIFE *(LION KING)* Elton John 2.SHOOTING
STAR *(HERCULES)* Boyzone 3.SOMEDAY *(HUNCHBACK OF NOT
RE DAME)* Eternal 4.BEAUTY AND THE BEAST Celine Dion
& Peabo Bryson 5.COLOURS OF THE WIND *(POCAHONTAS)*

Vanessa Williams 6.YOU'VE GOT A FRIEND IN ME *(TOY STORY)* Randy Newman 7.CRUELLA DE VILLE *(101 DALMAT IONS)* Dr.John 8.HE'S A TRAMP *(LADY AND THE TRAMP)* Peggy Lee 9.BIBBIDI BOBBIDI BOO *(CINDERELLA)* Louis Armstrong 10.EVERYBODY WANTS TO BE A CAT *ARISTOCATS* O.Cast 11.ZIP A DEE DOO DAH *(SONG OF THE SOUTH)* Or. Cast 12.CHIM CHIM CHEREE *(MARY POPPINS)* O.Cast 13. JUNGLE BOOK GROOVE: I WANNA BE LIKE YOU + BARE NECE SSITIES Master Upbeat Mix 14.WHISTLE WHILE YOU WORK *(SNOW WHITE)* O.Cast 15.HAKUNA MATATA *(LION KING)* OC 16.A STAR IS BORN *HERCULES* Jocelyn Brown 17.PART OF YOUR WORLD *LITTLE MERMAID* Olivia Newton John 18.A WHOLE NEW WORLD *(ALADDIN)* P.Bryson-Regina Belle 19. CAN YOU FEEL THE LOVE TONIGHT *LION KING* Elton John 20.WHEN YOU WISH UPON A STAR *PINOCCHIO* L.Armstrong

DISNEY IMMORTALS - Tilsley Orchestra
SPECTRUM UNIVERSAL: 544 668-2 (CD)   *2001*
ZIP A DEE DOO DAH-SOMEDAY MY PRINCE WILL COME-WHO'S AFRAID OF THE BIG BAD WOLF-LAVENDER BLUE-CHIM CHIM CHEREE-DREAM IS A WISH YOUR HEART MAKES-WHISTLE WHILE YOU WORK-SEOND STAR TO THE RIGHT-WHEN I SEE AN ELEPHANT FLY-BALLAD OF DAVY CROCKETT-BELLE NOTE-SPOONFUL OF SUGAR-ONCE UPON A DREAM-BIBBIDY BOBBIDY BOO-LITTLE APRIL SHOWER-HEIGH HO-THAT DARN CAT-GIVE A LITTLE WHISTLE-I'M LATE-WHEN YOU WISH UPON A STAR

DISNEY MOVIE FAVOURITES - BBC Concert Orchestra
DELTA-TARGET (BMG): CD 11022 (CD)   *1999*
I WANNA BE LIKE YOU-CAN YOU FEEL THE LOVE TONIGHT-WHOLE NEW WORLD-SOME DAY-CRUELLA DE VILLE-COLOURS OF THE WIND-BEAUTY AND THE BEAST-CIRCLE OF LIFE-WHEN I SEE AN ELEPHANT FLY-DREAM IS A WISH YOUR HEART MAKES-EVERYBODY WANTS TO BE A CAT-BIBBIDI BOBBIDI BOO-ALICE IN WONDERLAND-YOU CAN FLY-UNDER THE SEA-WHEN YOU WISH UPON A STAR

MICHAEL CRAWFORD - The Disney Album
WEA (TEN): 0927 42406-2 (CD) -4 (MC)   *2001*
1.COLOURS OF THE WIND *POCAHONTAS* 2.WHEN SHE LOVED ME *TOY STORY2* 3.YOUR HEART WILL LEAD YOU HOME *THE TIGGER MOVIE* 4.YOU'LL BE IN MY HEART *TARZAN* 5.IF YOU NEVER KNEW YOU w Sherie Rene Scott *POCAHONTAS* 6.REFLECTION *MULAN* 7.BABY MINE *DUMBO* 8.*LION KING MEDLEY*: CAN YOU FEEL THE LOVE TONIGHT/CIRCLE OF LIFE/HE LIVES IN YOU/SHADOWLAND 9.I KNOW THE TRUTH *AIDA* 10.WILL GO SAILING NO MORE *TOY STORY*

S O U N D T R A C K S – D V D – V H S   V I D E O S

1) **DOCTOR NO** 1962 / *Sean Connery* / *Ursula Andress*
   Title theme 'The James Bond Theme' (MONTY NORMAN)
   -S/T- *EMI Premier: CZ 558 (CD)*
   DVD: *16160DVD*   VHS: *16160s* VHS widescreen: *16160w*

2) **FROM RUSSIA WITH LOVE** 1963 / *Sean Connery*
   "From Russia With Love" (Lionel Bart) MATT MONRO
   -S/T- *reissue: EMI Premier: CZ 550 (CD)*
   DVD: *16175DVD*   VHS: *16175s* VHS widescreen: *16175w*

3) **GOLDFINGER** 1964 / *Sean Connery* / *Honor Blackman*
   Title song "Goldfinger"(John Barry-Leslie Bricusse
   Anthony Newley) sung by SHIRLEY BASSEY
   -S/T- *reissue: EMI Premier: CZ 557 (CD)*
   DVD: *16178DVD*   VHS: *16178s* VHS widescreen: *16178w*

4) **THUNDERBALL** 1965 / *Sean Connery* / *Claudine Auger*
   T.song "Thunderball" (J.Barry-Don Black) TOM JONES
   -S/T- *reissue: EMI Premier: CZ 556 (CD)*
   DVD: *16228DVD*   VHS: *16228s* VHS widescreen: *16228w*

5) **YOU ONLY LIVE TWICE** 1967 / *Sean Connery*
   Title song (J.Barry-Leslie Bricusse) NANCY SINATRA
   -S/T- *reissue: EMI Premier: CZ 559 (CD)*
   DVD: *16138DVD*   VHS: *16138s* VHS widescreen: *16138w*

6) **ON HER MAJESTY'S SECRET SERVICE** 1969 *George Lazenby*
   Title song "We Have All The Time In The World"
   (Hal David-John Barry) sung by LOUIS ARMSTRONG
   -S/T- *reissue: EMI Premier: CZ 549 (CD)*
   DVD: *16206DVD*   VHS: *16206s* VHS widescreen: 16206w

7) **DIAMONDS ARE FOREVER** 1971 / *Sean Connery*
   Title song (John Barry-Don Black) by SHIRLEY BASSEY
   -S/T- *reissue: EMI Premier: CZ 554 (CD)*
   DVD: *16349DVD*   VHS: *16349s* VHS widescreen: *16349w*

8) **LIVE AND LET DIE** 1973 / *Roger Moore* / *Jane Seymour*
   Title song (Paul & Linda McCartney) PAUL McCARTNEY
   -S/T- *reissue: EMI Premier: CZ 553 (CD)*
   DVD: *16192DVD*   VHS: *16192s* VHS widescreen: *16192w*

9) **THE MAN WITH THE GOLDEN GUN** 1974 *Roger Moore*
   Title song (Don Black-John Barry) sung by LULU
   -S/T- *reissue: EMI Premier: CZ 552 (CD)*
   DVD: *16197DVD*   VHS: *16197s* VHS widescreen: *16197w*

10) **THE SPY WHO LOVED ME** 1977 / *Roger Moore*
    Title song "Nobody Does It Better" (Carol Bayer
    Sager-Marvin Hamlisch) sung by CARLY SIMON
    -S/T- *reissue: EMI Premier: CZ 555 (CD)*
    DVD: *16222DVD*   VHS: *16222s* VHS widescreen: *16222w*

11) **MOONRAKER** 1979 / *Roger Moore* / *Lois Chiles*
    "Moonraker" (John Barry-Hal David) SHIRLEY BASSEY
    -S/T- *reissue: EMI Premier: CZ 551 (CD)*
    DVD: *16203DVD*   VHS: *16203s*   VHS widescreen: *16203w*

12) **FOR YOUR EYES ONLY** 1981 *Roger Moore-Carole Bouquet*
    "For Your Eyes Only" (Michael Leeson-Bill Conti)
    SHEENA EASTON -S/T- *RYKODISC (Vit) RCD 10751 (CD)*
    DVD: *16172DVD*   VHS: *16172s*   VHS widescreen: *16172w*

13) **OCTOPUSSY** 1983 / *Roger Moore* / *Maud Adams*
Title song "All Time High" (John Barry-Tim Rice)
RITA COOLIDGE -S/T- *RYKODISC (Vit): RCD 10705 (CD)*
DVD: *16205DVD* VHS: *16205s* VHS widescreen: *16205w*

13a) **NEVER SAY NEVER AGAIN** 1983 *Sean Connery*
Title song "Never Say Never Again" (Michel Legrand
-Alan and Marilyn Bergman) and sung by LANI HALL
-S/T- *Silva Screen (Koch): FILMCD 145 (CD)*
VHS: *19882S (unavailable in the UK)*

14) **A VIEW TO A KILL** 1985 / *Roger Moore   Tanya Roberts*
Title song "A View To A Kill" (That Fatal Kiss) by
DURAN DURAN -S/T- *EMI: TOCP 8813 (CD)*
DVD: *16234DVD* VHS: *16234s* VHS widescreen: *16234w*

15) **THE LIVING DAYLIGHTS** 1987 *Timothy Dalton*
Title song "The Living Daylights"(John Barry-A.HA)
-S/T- *RYKODISC (Vital): RCD 10725 (CD)*
DVD: *available 2001* VHS: *16193s* VHS wides: *16193w*

16) **LICENCE TO KILL** 1989 *Timothy Dalton / Carey Lowell*
"Licence To Kill" (Walden-Cohen-Afansieff) GLADYS
KNIGHT / M: MICHAEL KAMEN -S/T- *MCA: MCAD 6307 CD*
DVD: *available 2001* VHS: *15847D* VHS wides: *15847s*

17) **GOLDENEYE** 1995 *Pierce Brosnan / Samantha Bond*
Music score by ERIC SERRA / Title song "Goldeneye"
(Bono-The Edge) by TINA TURNER *Parlophone (EMI):*
-S/T- *Virgin US (EMI): CDVUSX 100 (CD)*
DVD: *16177D* VHS: *16177s* VHS widescreen: *16177w*

18) **TOMORROW NEVER DIES** 1997 *Pierce Brosnan*
Music score by DAVID ARNOLD / Title song by
SHERYL CROW / closing song vocal by k.d.lang
-S/T- *A.& M.(Poly): 540 830-2 (CD) -4 (MC)*
DVD: *15919D* VHS: *15919s* VHS widescreen: *15919w*

19) **WORLD IS NOT ENOUGH The** 1999 *Pierce Brosnan*
Music score by DAVID ARNOLD / Title song by David
Arnold-Don Black and performed by GARBAGE
-S/T- *UNIVERSAL: 112 161-2 (CD) -4 (MC*
DVD: *15767D* VHS: *15767s* VHS widescreen: *15767w*

20) *TO BE CONTINUED...*   *(2002)*

JAMES BOND MUSIC COLLECTIONS

BOND James: BACK IN ACTION!   - see COLL.44 *page 274*
  SILVA SCREEN (Koch): FILMCD 317 (CD) 1999

BOND James: BACK IN ACTION! VOL.2 see COLL.45 *page 274*
  SILVA SCREEN (Koch): FILMCD 340 (CD) 2001

BOND James: BEST OF JAMES BOND - see COLL.46 *page 274*
  EMI (EMI): 523 294-2 (CD) -4 (MC) 1999

BOND James: THE ESSENTIAL   - see COLL.47 *page 274*
  SILVA SCREEN (Koch): FILMCD 007 (CD) revised 1998

```
 1)  LOVE ME TENDER        vid: FOX 1172C       5 songs-1956
 2)  LOVING YOU            vid: MEDUS.deleted   7 songs-1957
 3)  JAILHOUSE ROCK        vid: WHV PES 50011   7 songs-1957
 4)  KING CREOLE           vid: POLYG deleted  12 songs-1958
 5)  G.I.BLUES             vid: POLYG 6343583  10 songs-1960
 6)  FLAMING STAR          vid: FOX 1173        6 songs-1961
 7)  WILD IN THE COUNTRY   vid: FOX 1174        6 songs-1961
 8)  BLUE HAWAII           vid: POLYG deleted  16 songs-1961
 9)  FOLLOW THAT DREAM   vid: WHV    deleted    6 songs-1962
10)  KID GALAHAD         vid: WHV    deleted    6 songs-1962
11)  GIRLS GIRLS GIRLS  vid: POLYG deleted    14 songs-1962
12)  IT HAPPENED AT THE WORLD'S FAIR delet    10 songs-1963
13)  FUN IN ACAPULCO       vid: POLYG deleted  11 songs-1963
14)  KISSIN' COUSINS       vid: WHV PES 51488   9 songs-1964
15)  VIVA LAS VEGAS        vid: WHV  SO 50116   9 songs-1964
16)  ROUSTABOUT            vid: POLYG deleted  11 songs-1964
17)  TICKLE ME             vid: POLYG deleted   9 songs-1965
18)  GIRL HAPPY            vid: WHV PES 51487  11 songs-1965
19)  HARUM SCARUM Holiday v: WHV PES 50486     9 songs-1965
20)  PARADISE HAWAIIAN STYLE v:POL deleted    10 songs-1965
21)  FRANKIE AND JOHNNY vid: WHV    deleted   13 songs-1966
22)  SPINOUT California Holiday v:PES51489     9 songs-1966
23)  EASY COME EASY GO   vid: POLYG deleted    7 songs-1966
24)  DOUBLE TROUBLE        vid: WHV PES 50485   8 songs-1967
25)  CLAMBAKE              vid: WHV PES 99667   7 songs-1967
26)  STAY AWAY JOE         vid: WHV PES 50525   5 songs-1968
27)  SPEEDWAY              vid: WHV PES 50476   9 songs-1968
28)  LIVE A LITTLE LOVE...WHV SO 35767 +26     4 songs-1968
29)  CHARRO!               vid: WHV    deleted  2 songs-1969
30)  CHANGE OF HABIT       vid: POLYG deleted   5 songs-1969
31)  TROUBLE WITH GIRLS v: WHV SO 35629 +3     7 songs-1969
32)  ELVIS - NBC TV SPECIAL v: BMG 74321 106623    -1968
33)  ELVIS - THAT'S THE WAY IT IS WHV PES 50373    -1970
34)  ELVIS - ON TOUR     video: WHV PES 50153      -1972
35)  THIS IS ELVIS Compil. video: WHV  SO 11173    -1981
------------------      SOUNDTRACKS      ------------------
BLUE HAWAII                        07863 66959-2 (CD)
CHANGE OF HABIT     + 28 & 29 & 31 07863 66559-2 (CD)
CHARRO!             + 28 & 30 & 31 07863 66559-2 (CD)
CLAMBAKE                 + 14 & 26 07863 66362-2 (CD)
DOUBLE TROUBLE               + 22  07863 66361-2 (CD)
EASY COME EASY GO            + 27  07863 6655-8  (CD)
ELVIS-NBC TV SPECIAL 1968              ND 83894  (CD)
FLAMING STAR             + 7 & 9   07863 66557-2 (CD)
FOLLOW THAT DREAM        + 6 & 7   07863 66557-2 (CD)
FRANKIE & JOHNNY             + 20  07863 66360-2 (CD)
FUN IN ACAPULCO              + 12  74321 13431-2 (CD)
G.I.BLUES                          07863 66960-2 (CD)
GIRL HAPPY                   + 19  74321 13433-2 (CD)
GIRLS GIRLS GIRLS            + 10  74321 13430-2 (CD)
HARUM SCARUM                 + 18  74321 13433-2 (CD)
IT HAPPENED AT THE WORLD'S.. + 13  74321 13431-2 (CD)
JAILHOUSE ROCK                     07863 67453-2 (CD)
KID GALAHAD                  + 11  74321 13430-2 (CD)
```

```
KING CREOLE                              07863 67454-2 (CD)
KISSIN'COUSINS           + 25 & 26       07863 66362-2 (CD)
LIVE A LITTLE LOVE..+ 29 & 30 & 31       07863 66559-2 (CD)
LOVE ME TENDER        4 songs on Coll 'Essential Elvis'
LOVING YOU                               07863 67452-2 (CD)
PARADISE HAWAIIAN STYLE        + 21      07863 66360-2 (CD)
ROUSTABOUT                     + 15      74321 13432-2 (CD)
SPEEDWAY                       + 23      07863 66558-2 (CD)
SPINOUT                        + 24      07863 66361-2 (CD)
STAY AWAY JOE             + 14 & 25      07863 66362-2 (CD)
THAT'S THE WAY IT IS                     74321 14690-2 (CD)
TROUBLE WITH GIRLS  + 28 & 29 & 30       07863 66558-2 (CD)
VIVA LAS VEGAS                 + 16      74321 13432-2 (CD)
WILD IN THE COUNTRY          + 6 & 9     07863 66557-2 (CD)
```

ELVIS COMMAND PERFORMANCES: Essential 60's Masters II
   RCA (BMG): 07863 66601-2 (2CD) (Elvis Movies) 1995
   G.I.BLUES-WOODEN HEART-SHOPPIN'AROUND-DOIN'THE BEST
   I CAN-FLAMING STAR-WILD IN THE COUNTRY-LONELY MAN-
   BLUE HAWAII-ROCK A HULA BABY-CAN'T HELF FALLING IN
   LOVE-BEACH BOY BLUES-HAWAIIAN WEDDING SONG-FOLLOW
   THAT DREAM-ANGEL-KING OF THE WHOLE WIDE WORLD-I GOT
   LUCKY-GIRLS GIRLS GIRLS-BECAUSE OF LOVE-RETURN TO
   SENDER-ONE BROKEN HEART FOR SALE-I'M FALLING IN
   LOVE TONIGHT-THEY REMIND ME TOO MUCH OF YOU-FUN IN
   ACAPULCO-BOSSA NOVA BABY-MARGUERITA-MEXICO-KISSIN'
   COUSINS-ONE BOY TWO LTTLE GIRLS-ONCE IS ENOUGH-VIVA
   LAS VEGAS-WHAT'D I SAY disc two: ROUSTABOUT-POISON
   IVY LEAGUE-LITTLE EGYPT-THERE'S A BRAND NEW DAY ON
   THE HORIZON-GIRL HAPPY-PUPPET ON A STRING-DO THE CL
   AM-HAREM HOLIDAY-SO CLOSE YET SO FAR-FRANKIE & JOHN
   NY-PLEASE DON'T STOP LOVING ME-PARADISE HAWAIAAN ST
   YLE-THIS IS MY HEAVEN-SPINOUT-ALL THAT I AM-I'LL BE
   BACK-EASY COME EASY GO-DOUBLE TROUBLE-LONG LEGGED
   GIRL-CLAMBAKE-YOU DON'T KNOW ME-STAY AWAY JOE-SPEED
   WAY-YOUR TIME HASN'T COME YET BABY-LET YOURSELF GO-
   ALMOST IN LOVE-A LITTLE LESS CONVERSATION-EDGE OF
   REALITY-CHARRO!-CLEAN UP YOU OWN BACKYARD

ESSENTIAL ELVIS (Film S/Tracks) RCA: 74321 57347-2 (CD)
   LOVE ME TENDER (2)-LET ME-POOR BOY-WE'RE GONNA MOVE
   LOVING YOU (3)-PARTY-HOT DOG-TEDDY BEAR-MEAN WOMAN
   BLUES-GOT A LOT O'LIVIN' TO DO (2)-LONESOME COWBOY
   JAILHOUSE ROCK (2)-TREAT ME NICE-YOUNG & BEAUTIFUL
   DON'T LEAVE ME NOW-I WANT TO BE FREE-BABY I DON'T
   CARE-MEAN WOMAN BLUES-LOVING YOU-TREAT ME NICE

COLLECTOR'S GOLD - RCA (BMG): PD(PK) 90574 (3CD/3MC)
   (1) Hollywood Album: GI BLUES-POCKETFUL OF RAINBOWS
   BIG BOOTS-BLACK STAR-SUMER KISSES WINTER TEARS-I SL
   IPPED I STUMBLED I FELL-LONELY MAN-WHAT A WONDERFUL
   LIFE-AWHISTLING TUNE-BEYOND THE BEND-ONE BROKEN HEA
   RT FORSALE-YOU'RE THE BOSS-ROUSTABOUT-GIRL HAPPY-SO
   CLOSE YET SO FAR-STOP LOOK & LISTEN-AM I READY-HOW
   CAN YOU LOSE WHATYOU NEVER HAD (2) Nashville Album
   (15 Tracks) (3) Live In Las Vegas 1969 (20 Tracks)
*** SEE ALSO COLLECTIONS 205 and 206 on page 317 ***

* CURRENT   WEST   END   THEATRE   MUSICAL   SHOWS *

*BLOOD BROTHERS - *PHOENIX Theatre from 28 JULY 1988*
LYN PAUL-MARK HUTCHINSON-DEBBIE PAUL-ANDY SNOWDEN
recording 1995 First Night (Pinn): CASTCD 49 (CD)
see also page 74

*BUDDY - *STRAND Theatre (or.Palace Theatre.19 OCT 1989)*
ANGUS MacGREGOR-MILES GUERRINI-SIMON RAWLINGS & Co.
1995 'Live' Rec: First Night (Pinn): CASTCD 55 (CD)
1989 Orig London Cast: First Night: QUEUECD 1 (CD)
see also page 80

*CATS - *NEW LONDON Theatre from 11 MAY 1981*
NEW LONDON THEATRE CAST
1981 Orig London Cast: Polydor: 817 810-2 (2CD)
Highlights Recording: Polydor: 839 415-2 (CD)
see also page 85

*CHICAGO - *ADELPHI Theatre from 18 NOVEMBER 1997*
ANITA LOUISE COMBE-LEIGH ZIMMERMAN-CLARKE PETERS &
BARRY JAMES-MICHAEL SIMKINS-PAUL RYDER & Company
recording (1998) RCA (BMG): 09026 63155-2 (CD)
see also page 87

*CHITTY CHITTY BANG BANG *LONDON PALLADIUM 19 MARCH 2002*
MICHAEL BALL-EMMA WILLIAMS-ANTON RODGERS-NICHOLA
McAULIFFE-BRIAN BLESSED-RICHARD O'BRIEN
recording to be confirmed / see also FILM page 88

*FAME - *VICTORIA PALACE from 28 SEPTEMBER 2000 and*
        CAMBRIDGE THEATRE from 20 SEPTEMBER 2001
2000/2001 LONDON CAST COMPANY
recording to be confirmed / see also page 113

*KING AND I, The - *LONDON PALLADIUM from 03 MAY 2000*
JOSIE LAWRENCE-KEO WOOLFORD-CLAIRE MOORE-SAAED
JAFFREY *prev:* ELAINE PAIGE-JASON SCOTT LEE-PAUL
PAUL NAKAUCHI
rec: (Elaine Paige & Comp) **WEA: 8573 84389-2 (CD)**
see also page 153

*KISS ME KATE - *VICTORIA PALACE from 16 OCTOBER 2001*
REVIVAL MUSICAL - DETAILS TO BE CONFIRMED
see also page 154

*LADY SALSA - *TALK OF LONDON from APRIL 2001- JAN2002*
THE CUBAN DANCE SPECTACULAR

*LES MISERABLES - *PALACE Theatre from 4 DECEMBER 1985*
SIMON BOWMAN-PETER CORRY-REBECCA THORNHILL & Comp.
1985 Orig London Cast - First Night: ENCORECD 1

* CURRENT WEST END THEATRE MUSICAL SHOWS *

---

*LION KING The - *LYCEUM from 19 OCTOBER 1999*
   inc.music by ELTON JOHN-TIM RICE and others
   O.Broadway Cast: DISNEY-EDEL (Pinn): 010 455-2DNY
   O.London Cast: CURRENTLY UNAVAILABLE
   see also page 162

*MAMMA MIA! *PRINCE EDWARD Theatre from 23 MARCH 1999*
   MUSICAL BASED ON THE SONGS OF ABBA
   recording: POLYDOR (Univ): 543 115-2 (CD) -4 (MC)
   see also page 169

*MY FAIR LADY *DRURY LANE from 21 JULY 2001 (previously*
   at The NATIONAL from 15 MARCH 2001)
   MARTINE McCUTCHEON-(ALEXANDRA JAY)-JONATHAN PRYCE-
   NICHOLAS LE PREVOST-DENNIS WATERMAN-MARK UMBERS-
   PATSY ROWLANDS
   rec: (Martine McCutcheon) *FIRST NIGHT: CASTCD 83*
   see also page 180

*PHANTOM OF THE OPERA *HER MAJESTY'S from 9 OCTOBER 1986*
   SCOTT DAVIS-CHARLOTTE PAGE-MATTHEW CAMMELLE & Comp
   1986 Orig London Cast - Polydor: 831 273-2 (CD)
   see also page 195

*STARLIGHT EXPRESS *APOLLO VICTORIA 27MAR1984-12JAN2002*
   New Re-Vamped 1993 Show - LON SATTON-RAY SHELL & Co
   1984 Orig London Cast - Polydor: 519 041-2 (CD)
   see also page 229

CHECK WITH THE THEATRE BOX OFFICE FOR LATEST DETAILS

E U R O V I S I O N   S O N G   C O N T E S T
2 0 0 1

BRITISH SONG CONTEST (SONG FOR EUROPE) 2001

BBC TV Centre 11 March 2001
Winning Order / Song Title / Performing Artist / Points
```
-------------------------------------------------
1 - NO DREAM IMPOSSIBLE     - LINDSAY DRACASS   45464
2 - MEN                              - NANNE    -----
3 - THAT'S MY LOVE            - TONY MOORE      -----
4 - JUST ANOTHER RAINBOW    - LUCY RANDELL      -----
```

"NO DREAM IMPOSSIBLE" (Russ Ballard-Chris Winter)
then went on to represent the UK in The 46th...

EUROVISION SONG CONTEST 2001

*From the Parken Stadium, Copenhagen, 12th May 2001
and Transmitted By BBC1 TV and BBC Radio 2*

Country	Song	Artist	Points
1.ESTONIA	"Everybody"	TANEL PADAR-DAVE BENTON -	198
2.DENMARK	"Never Ever Let You Go"	ROLLO & KING -	177
3.GREECE	"Die For You"	ANTIQUE -	147
4.FRANCE	"Je N'ai Que Mon Ami"	NATASHA ST.PIER -	142
5.SWEDEN	"Listen To Your Heartbeat"	FRIENDS -	100
6.SPAIN	"Dile Que La Quiero"	DAVID CIVERA -	76
7.SLOVENIA	"Energy"	NUSA DERENDA -	70
8.GERMANY	"Wer Liebe Lebt"	MICHELLE -	66
9.MALTA	"Another Summer Night"	FABRIZIO FANIELLO -	48
10.CROATIA	"Strings Of My Heart"	VANNA -	42
11.TURKEY	"Sevgiliye Son"	SEDAT YUCE -	41
12.RUSSIA	"Lady Alpine Blue"	MUMIY TROLL -	37
13.LITHUANIA	"You Got Style"	SKAMP -	40
14.BOSNIA H.	"Hano"	NINO -	29
15.U.K.	"No Dream Impossible"	LINDSAY DRACASS -	28
16.ISRAEL	"Ein Davar"	TAL SONDAK -	25
17.PORTUGAL	"So Sei Ser Feliz Assim"	MTM -	17
18.HOLLAND	"Out Here On My Own"	MICHELLE -	16
18.LATVIA	"Too Much"	ARNIS MEDNIS -	16
20.POLAND	"2 Long"	PIASEK -	11
21.IRELAND	"Without Yout Love"	GARY O'SHAUGHNESSY -	6
22.ICELAND	"Angel"	TWO TRICKY -	3
24.NORWAY	"On My Own"	HALDOR LAEGREID -	3

ALL SONGS AVAILABLE ON BMG IMP CD: 74321 84292-2 (CD)

previous EUROVISION SONG CONTESTS see pages 109-111